P9-CKB-246

MATHPOWER™ Nine

Western Edition

Authors

George Knill, B.Sc., M.S.Ed.
Hamilton, Ontario

Dino Dottori, B.Sc., M.S.Ed.
North Bay, Ontario

Enzo Timoteo, B.A., B.Ed.
Edmonton, Alberta

Rene Baxter, B.A., B.Ed., M.Ed.
Saskatoon, Saskatchewan

George Fawcett, B.A.
Hamilton, Ontario

Mary Lou Forest, B.Ed.
Edmonton, Alberta

David Kennedy, B.Sc., Ph.D.
Langley, British Columbia

Stan Pasko, B.A., B.Ed., M.Ed.,
Ph.D.
North Bay, Ontario

Harry Traini, B.Sc.
Hamilton, Ontario

Consultants

Laurie Birnie
Green Timbers Elementary School
Surrey, British Columbia

Bruce Christie
Garden City Collegiate
Winnipeg, Manitoba

Sylvia Coverdale
Colonel Irvine Junior High School
Calgary, Alberta

Katie Donnachie
Father Whelihan Elementary School
Calgary, Alberta

Carol Jaap Klass
Louis St. Laurent School
Edmonton, Alberta

Richard Kopan
R. T. Alderman Junior High School
Calgary, Alberta

Peter Luongo
Glenwood Elementary School
Langley, British Columbia

Diane Malecki
Cardinal Leger Junior High School
Edmonton, Alberta

John Macnab
Grandview Heights School
Edmonton, Alberta

Betty Morris
Consultant, Edmonton Catholic
School District
Edmonton, Alberta

Susan Schroeder
Windsor Park Collegiate
Winnipeg, Manitoba

Harold Wardrop
Princess Margaret School
Surrey, British Columbia

McGraw-Hill Ryerson Limited

Toronto   Montreal   New York   Auckland   Bogotá   Caracas
Lisbon   London   Madrid   Mexico   Milan   New Delhi
San Juan   Singapore   Sydney   Tokyo

COPIES OF THIS BOOK
MAY BE OBTAINED BY
CONTACTING:

McGraw-Hill Ryerson Ltd.

WEBSITE:
http://www.mcgrawhill.ca

E-MAIL:
Orders@mcgrawhill.ca

TOLL FREE FAX:
1-800-463-5885

TOLL FREE CALL:
1-800-565-5758

OR BY MAILING
YOUR ORDER TO:
McGraw-Hill Ryerson
Order Department,
300 Water Street
Whitby, ON L1N 9B6

Please quote the ISBN and
title when placing your
order.

MATHPOWER™ 9
Western Edition

ISBN-13: 978-0-07-552653-7
ISBN-10: 0-07-552653-0

14 15 TRI 7

Printed and bound in Canada

Care has been taken to trace ownership of copyright
material contained in this text. The publishers will gladly
accept any information that will enable them to rectify any
reference of credit in subsequent editions.

Canadian Cataloguing in Publication Data

Main entry under title:

Mathpower nine

Western ed.
Includes index.
ISBN 0-07-552653-0

1. Mathematics. 2. Mathematics – Problems,
exercises, etc.   I. Knill, George, date.

QA107.M37642 1996   510   C95-932900-5

Publisher: Andrea Crozier
Editorial Consulting: Michael J. Webb Consulting Inc.
Associate Editors: Sheila Bassett, Mary Agnes Challoner, Jean Ford
Senior Supervising Editor: Carol Altilia
Copy Editors: Dianne Brassolotto, Debbie Davies
Permissions Editor: Tina Dell
Production Coordinator: Yolanda Pigden
Cover and Interior Design: Pronk&Associates
Electronic Assembly: Pronk&Associates
Art Direction: Pronk&Associates/Joe Lepiano
Production: Pronk&Associates/ Technical Art and Page Assembly,
      Linda Stephenson, Chris Trubela; Production Coordinator, Nelly Toomey;
      Production Assistant, Nancy Cook; Art Assistant, Caren Thomas;
      Typesetting, Stanley Tran, Craig Swistun
Cover Illustration: Doug Martin
Photo Researcher: Lois Browne/In a word communications Services

This book was manufactured in Canada using
acid-free and recycled paper.

CONTENTS

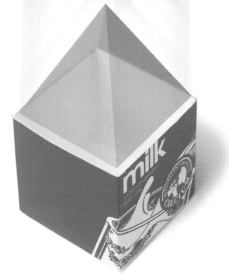

USING MATHPOWER™ 9

Each chapter contains a number of sections.
In a typical section, you find the following features.

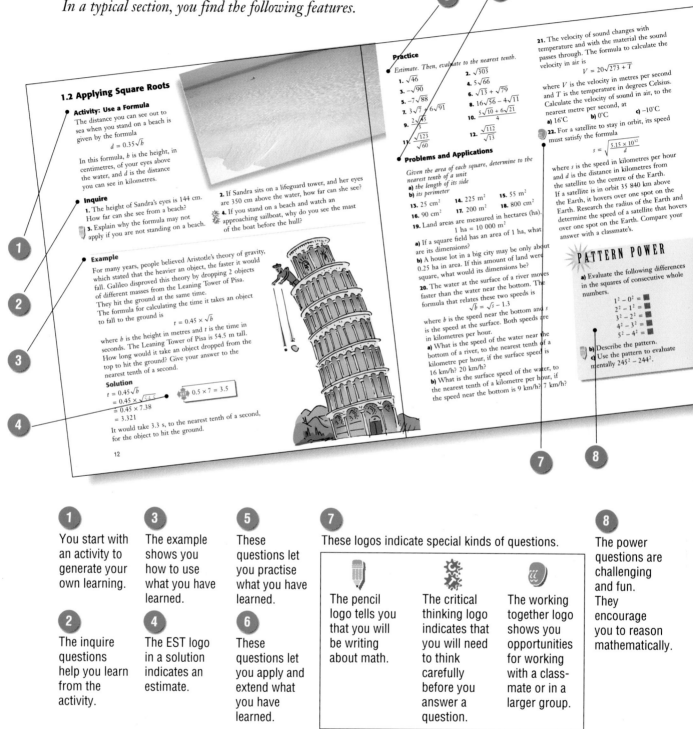

1.2 Applying Square Roots

Activity: Use a Formula

The distance you can see out to sea when you stand on a beach is given by the formula

$$d = 0.35\sqrt{h}$$

In this formula, h is the height, in centimetres, of your eyes above the water, and d is the distance you can see in kilometres.

Inquire

1. The height of Sandra's eyes is 144 cm. How far can she see from a beach?

2. If Sandra sits on a lifeguard tower, and her eyes are 350 cm above the water, how far can she see?

3. Explain why the formula may not apply if you are not standing on a beach.

4. If you stand on a beach and watch an approaching sailboat, why do you see the mast of the boat before the hull?

Example

For many years, people believed Aristotle's theory of gravity, which stated that the heavier an object, the faster it would fall. Galileo disproved this theory by dropping 2 objects of different masses from the Leaning Tower of Pisa. They hit the ground at the same time. The formula for calculating the time it takes an object to fall to the ground is

$$t = 0.45 \times \sqrt{h}$$

where h is the height in metres and t is the time in seconds. The Leaning Tower of Pisa is 54.5 m tall. How long would it take an object dropped from the top to hit the ground? Give your answer to the nearest tenth of a second.

Solution

$t = 0.45\sqrt{h}$
$= 0.45 \times \sqrt{54.5}$ $0.5 \times 7 = 3.5$
$\doteq 0.45 \times 7.38$
$\doteq 3.321$

It would take 3.3 s, to the nearest tenth of a second, for the object to hit the ground.

12

Practice

Estimate. Then, evaluate to the nearest tenth.

1. $\sqrt{46}$
2. $\sqrt{303}$
3. $-\sqrt{90}$
4. $5\sqrt{66}$
5. $-7\sqrt{88}$
6. $\sqrt{13} + \sqrt{79}$
7. $3\sqrt{7} + 6\sqrt{91}$
8. $16\sqrt{56} - 4\sqrt{11}$
9. $\frac{2\sqrt{5}}{3}$
10. $\frac{5\sqrt{10} + 6\sqrt{21}}{4}$
11. $\frac{\sqrt{123}}{\sqrt{60}}$
12. $\frac{\sqrt{112}}{\sqrt{13}}$

Problems and Applications

Given the area of each square, determine to the nearest tenth of a unit
a) *the length of its side*
b) *its perimeter*

13. 25 cm²
14. 225 m²
15. 55 m²
16. 90 cm²
17. 200 m²
18. 800 cm²

19. Land areas are measured in hectares (ha).

$$1 \text{ ha} = 10\ 000 \text{ m}^2$$

a) If a square field has an area of 1 ha, what are its dimensions?
b) A house lot in a big city may be only about 0.25 ha in area. If this amount of land were square, what would its dimensions be?

20. The water at the surface of a river moves faster than the water near the bottom. The formula that relates these two speeds is

$$\sqrt{b} = \sqrt{s} - 1.3$$

where b is the speed near the bottom and s is the speed at the surface. Both speeds are in kilometres per hour.
a) What is the speed of the water near the bottom of a river, to the nearest tenth of a kilometre per hour, if the surface speed is 16 km/h? 20 km/h?
b) What is the surface speed of the water, to the nearest tenth of a kilometre per hour, if the speed near the bottom is 9 km/h? 7 km/h?

21. The velocity of sound changes with temperature and with the material the sound passes through. The formula to calculate the velocity in air is

$$V = 20\sqrt{273 + T}$$

where V is the velocity in metres per second and T is the temperature in degrees Celsius. Calculate the velocity of sound in air, to the nearest metre per second, at
a) 16°C
b) 0°C
c) –10°C

22. For a satellite to stay in orbit, its speed must satisfy the formula

$$s = \sqrt{\frac{5.15 \times 10^{12}}{d}}$$

where s is the speed in kilometres per hour and d is the distance in kilometres from the satellite to the centre of the Earth. If a satellite is in orbit 35 840 km above the Earth, it hovers over one spot on the Earth. Research the radius of the Earth and determine the speed of a satellite that hovers over one spot on the Earth. Compare your answer with a classmate's.

PATTERN POWER

a) Evaluate the following differences in the squares of consecutive whole numbers.

$1^2 - 0^2 = $ ▓
$2^2 - 1^2 = $ ▓
$3^2 - 2^2 = $ ▓
$4^2 - 3^2 = $ ▓
$5^2 - 4^2 = $ ▓

b) Describe the pattern.
c) Use the pattern to evaluate mentally $245^2 - 244^2$.

---

1 You start with an activity to generate your own learning.

2 The inquire questions help you learn from the activity.

3 The example shows you how to use what you have learned.

4 The EST logo in a solution indicates an estimate.

5 These questions let you practise what you have learned.

6 These questions let you apply and extend what you have learned.

7 These logos indicate special kinds of questions.

The pencil logo tells you that you will be writing about math.

The critical thinking logo indicates that you will need to think carefully before you answer a question.

The working together logo shows you opportunities for working with a class-mate or in a larger group.

8 The power questions are challenging and fun. They encourage you to reason mathematically.

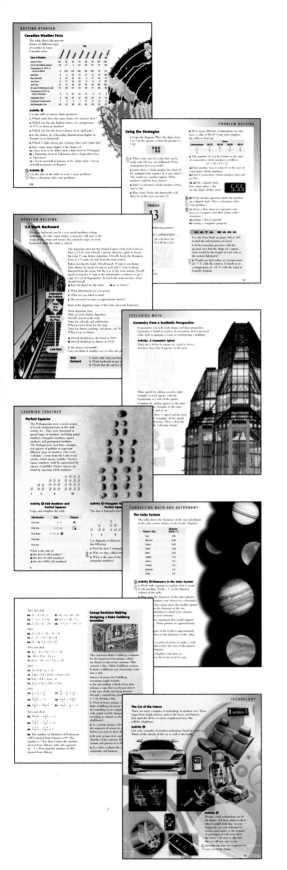

In the first 4 chapters of the book, there are 12 PROBLEM SOLVING sections that help you to use different problem solving strategies.

At or near the end of each chapter is a page headed PROBLEM SOLVING: Using the Strategies. To solve the problems on this page, you use the strategies you have studied. In all chapters, this page ends with DATA BANK questions. To solve them, you need to look up information in the Data Bank on pages 364 to 369.

There are 14 EXPLORING MATH pages before chapter 1. The activities on these pages let you explore 14 mathematical standards that will be essential for citizens of the twenty-first century.

A GETTING STARTED section begins each chapter. This section reviews, in a fun way, what you should know before you work on the chapter. Each GETTING STARTED section includes a set of Mental Math questions.

In LEARNING TOGETHER sections, you learn by completing activities with your classmates.

The TECHNOLOGY sections show you some uses of technology and how you can apply technology to solve problems.

Some sections are headed CONNECTING MATH AND.... In these sections, you apply math to other subject areas, such as art, language, science, and the environment.

Each chapter includes sets of questions called REVIEW and CHAPTER CHECK, so that you can test your progress.

At the end of each review is a column headed GROUP DECISION MAKING. Here, you work with your classmates to research careers and do other projects.

Chapters 4 and 8 end with sets of questions headed CUMULATIVE REVIEW. These reviews cover the work you did in chapters 1–4 and 5–8. A CUMULATIVE REVIEW that covers chapters 1–9 follows chapter 9.

The GLOSSARY on pages 390 to 395 helps you to understand mathematical terms.

On pages 370 to 389 there are ANSWERS to most of the problems in this book.

A Problem Solving Model

The world is full of mathematical problems. A problem exists when you are presented with a situation and are unable to make sense of it. To solve any problem, you must make decisions.

MATHPOWER™ *9* will help you to become actively involved in problem solving by providing the experiences and strategies you need.

George Polya was one of the world's best problem solvers. The problem solving model used in this book has been adapted from a model developed by George Polya.

The problem solving model includes the following 4 stages.

Understand the Problem

First, read the problem and make sure that you understand it. Ask yourself these questions.
- Do I understand all the words?
- What information am I given?
- What am I asked to find?
- Can I state the problem in my own words?
- Am I given enough information?
- Am I given too much information?
- Have I solved a similar problem?

Think of a Plan

Organize the information you need. Decide whether you need an exact or approximate answer. Plan how to use the information. The following list includes some of the problem solving strategies that may help.
- Act out the problem.
- Manipulate materials.
- Work backward.
- Account for all possibilities.
- Change your point of view.
- Draw a diagram.
- Look for a pattern.
- Make a table.
- Use a formula.
- Guess and check.
- Solve a simpler problem.
- Use logical reasoning.

Carry Out the Plan

Choose the calculation method you will use to carry out your plan. Estimate the answer to the problem.
Carry out your plan, using paper and pencil, a calculator, a computer, or manipulatives.
Write a final statement that gives the solution to the problem.

Look Back

Check all your calculations.
Check your answer against the original problem. Is your answer reasonable? Does it agree with your estimate?
Look for an easier way to solve the problem.

The following 14 pages of activities will let you explore 14 mathematical standards that will be essential for citizens of the twenty-first century.

Problem Solving

Being a good problem solver is an important life skill. *MATHPOWER*™ *9* will help you develop this skill.

Activity

Solve these problems.
In each case, describe the method you used.

1. How many different, even 4-digit house numbers can you make with the digits 2, 3, 4, and 5?

2. A basketball team is standing in a circle. The team members are evenly spaced and numbered in order, clockwise, from 1 up. Player number 5 is directly opposite player number 12. How many players are in the circle?

3. The diagram shows how to shade 4 of the 9 squares to give just 1 line of symmetry. In how many other ways can you shade 4 of the 9 squares to give 1 line of symmetry?

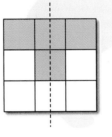

4. The number that represents the area of a square is twice the number that represents the sum of its sides. What is the side length of the square?

5. Take 6 dominoes, the 0/0, 0/1, 0/2, 1/1, 1/2, and 2/2. Arrange them in a square so that each side of the square contains the same number of dots.

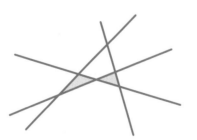

6. The diagram shows how to make 2 non-overlapping triangles with 4 straight lines. How many non-overlapping triangles can you make with 5 straight lines?

Mathematics as Communication

As you develop new ideas in any field, it is important to be able to communicate these ideas to others.

Activity ❶

There are 2 research camps located in the desert at A and B. Each camp has a jeep. A water station is to be located so that the total distance the 2 jeeps must travel to the water and back is as short as possible.

1. What is the total distance the jeeps travel if the water station is placed at position 3? at position 4? at position 1? at A? at B?

1 km	1 km	1 km	1 km	1 km	1 km
A	1	2	3	4	5	B

2. Where should the water station be placed so that the total distance travelled by the jeeps is the shortest?

Activity ❷

There are now 3 research camps, A, B, and C, in the desert. Each camp has a jeep.

1. What is the total distance travelled by the jeeps to get water if the water station is placed at position 3? at position 2? at A? at B? at C?

1 km	1 km	1 km	1 km	1 km	1 km
A	1	B	2	3	4	C

2. Where should the water station be placed so that the total distance travelled by the jeeps is the shortest?

Activity ❸

Where should the water station be placed so that the total distance travelled by the jeeps is the shortest in each diagram?

1.

1 km	1 km	1 km	1 km	1 km	1 km
A	1	B	2	3	C	D

2.

1 km	1 km	1 km	1 km	1 km	1 km
A	1	B	2	C	D	E

Activity ❹

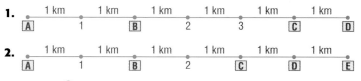

1. Write a rule for finding where the station should be placed if there is an even number of camps.

2. Write a rule for finding where the station should be placed if there is an odd number of camps.

3. Test your rules for 6 camps and 7 camps.

Mathematics as Reasoning

The ability to reason logically, to think your way through a problem, is a skill you can develop.

Activity ❶

For each card, use all the numbers only once. Use as many of the operations +, −, ×, ÷, and brackets ( ) as you wish. Write a number sentence with the value 24 for each card.

1.
8
4   2
5

2.
7
4   4
4

3.
7
4   4
4

Activity ❷

There are three books on the counter. The books are blue, green, and black. The titles of the books are *MATHPOWER*™ , *SCIENCEPOWER*, and *COMPUTERPOWER*. The books belong to Sari, Terri, and Dmitri. Use the clues to reason who owns which book.

1. Sari's book is not about computers.

2. Dmitri's book is not blue or green.

3. *SCIENCEPOWER* is not green.

4. *MATHPOWER*™ is a blue book.

Copy and complete these tables to sort out the owners, colours, and book titles.

	Colour of Book		
	Blue	Green	Black
Sari			
Terri			
Dmitri			

	Colour of Book		
	Blue	Green	Black
MATHPOWER™			
SCIENCEPOWER			
COMPUTERPOWER			

	Colour of Book	Title of Book
Sari		
Terri		
Dmitri		

Activity ❸

Use the table to make up the clues to a problem that can be solved by reasoning.

	Bicycles	
Jim	green	3–speed
Ali	blue	5–speed
Sue	red	10–speed

Mathematical Connections

Mathematics can be found in many places.
The following activities explore some of them.

Activity ❶

Work with a classmate to plan a 2-week vacation.

You will be travelling by car. Decide where you want to go and the route you are going to take to get there. You will need some maps. Assume that you can travel for a maximum of 8 h/day and that you will sleep in motels or hotels. You will want to spend at least 7 days at your vacation spot.

Keep a list of what you will spend every day for gas, food, lodging, and entertainment. Determine the total cost of the vacation.

Activity ❷

1. Select a sport and list 5 ways in which mathematics is used in this sport.

2. Describe how the sport would be different if it did not include any mathematics.

Activity ❸

The people responsible for playing the music you listen to on the radio use mathematics every day. List some of the ways in which mathematics is used at a radio station.

Activity ❹

There are many geometric shapes that you see and use every day.

1. List 5 geometric shapes found in your classroom.

2. List 5 geometric shapes you see on your way to school.

Activity ❺

There are many examples of mathematics in nature.

The chambers in a nautilus shell form a spiral.

Animals and plants have lines of symmetry.

Use your research skills to make a poster that shows how mathematics is found in nature.

Algebra

Algebra is the language of mathematics.

Activity ❶

The concept of a variable is one of the most important in algebra. A variable can represent different numbers at different times.

In the following equation there are two variables, a triangle and a square.

$$\blacktriangle + \blacktriangle + \blacksquare = \blacksquare + \blacksquare$$

If you replace the ▲ with 1 and the ■ with 2, you get

$$1 + 1 + 2 = 2 + 2$$

This is a true statement.

If you replace the ▲ with 2 and the ■ with 3, you get

$$2 + 2 + 3 = 3 + 3$$

This is not a true statement.

1. a) Find 3 other pairs of whole numbers that can replace the ▲ and the ■ to make a true statement. Put the pairs in a table.

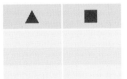

b) Describe the pattern.

2. Repeat the activity for the following equations. If you cannot find 3 pairs of whole numbers that make true statements, explain why.

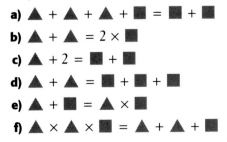

a) $\blacktriangle + \blacktriangle + \blacktriangle + \blacksquare = \blacksquare + \blacksquare$

b) $\blacktriangle + \blacktriangle = 2 \times \blacksquare$

c) $\blacktriangle + 2 = \blacksquare + \blacksquare$

d) $\blacktriangle + \blacktriangle = \blacksquare + \blacksquare + \blacksquare$

e) $\blacktriangle + \blacksquare = \blacktriangle \times \blacksquare$

f) $\blacktriangle \times \blacktriangle \times \blacksquare = \blacktriangle + \blacktriangle + \blacksquare$

Activity ❷

Find the value of the letter to make each equation true.

1. $m + 8 = 15$ **2.** $x - 5 = 7$

3. $6 - t = 4$ **4.** $x + x + 5 = 17$

5. $n \div 2 = 10$ **6.** $2 \times t + 7 = 11$

Activity ❸

1. $s + u = 15$
$r + s + t = 15$
If $r = 6$ and $t = 4$, find u.

2. $y + z = 5$
$w + x = 7$
$x + y = 6$
If $w = 3$, find z.

3. $a = b$
$x = a + b + c + d$
$c = d$
If $x = 10$ and $b = 2$, find d.

4. $w = y$
$x = w + z$
$z = y + m$
If $w = 3$ and $x = 10$, find m.

5. $y + w = u$
$x = y - z$
If $x = 8$, $z = 3$, and $u = 11$, find w.

Functions

In much of the mathematics you do, you study patterns. There are many patterns in nature.

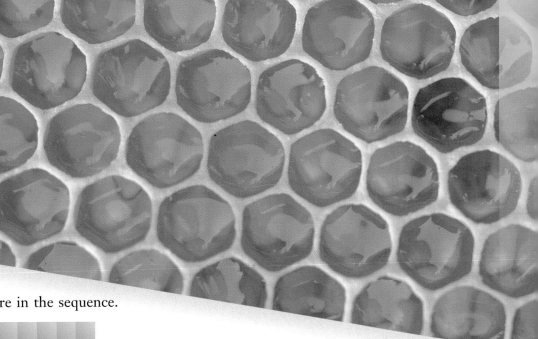

Activity ❶

1. a) Draw the next figure in the sequence.

1   2   3

b) Copy and complete the table for the sequence.

Figure	Perimeter
1	4
2	8
3	12
4	
5	
10	
100	

c) Describe the pattern in words.

2. Repeat question 1 for these sequences.

a)

b)

c)

Activity ❷

Copy each table.

Describe the rule that lets you find *y* if you know *x* or find *x* if you know *y*.

Use the rule to complete each table.

1.

x	*y*
9	1
15	7
22	
8.1	
	11
	3.3

2.

x	*y*
8	4
36	18
40	
6.4	
	8.1
	9.7

3.

x	*y*
3	17
9	11
13	7
4	
18	
	6.2
	15.5

4.

x	*y*
1	3
5	11
9	19
6	
12	
2.5	
	9

Geometry from a Synthetic Perspective

In geometry, you will study shapes and their properties. Geometry is found in science, in recreation, and in practical tasks, such as painting a room or constructing a building.

Activity: A Geometric Spiral

Mark out a 16-by-16 square on a grid as shown and draw four 4-by-4 squares on the grid.

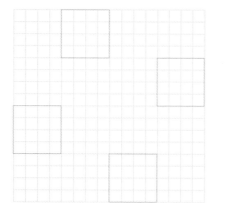

Make spirals by adding isosceles right triangles to each square, with the hypotenuse as a side of the square.

Continue by adding squares to the sides of the triangles, triangles to the sides of the squares, and so on.

The diagram shows 1 spiral and the start of the other 3. Complete all the spirals in your own drawing. Then, colour the figures to make a pleasing design.

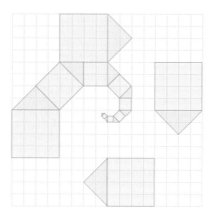

Geometry from an Algebraic Perspective

The study of geometry through the use of transformations has changed geometry from static to dynamic. For example, geometry can now be used to make moving images on film or videotape.

Activity ❶ Patterns

Copy each pattern onto a grid and continue it.

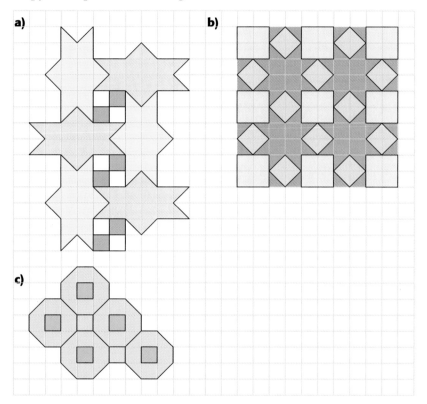

a)

b)

c)

Activity ❷ Reflections

Copy each diagram onto grid paper and draw its reflection in the reflection line.

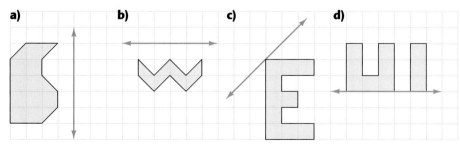

a)   b)   c)   d)

Trigonometry

Trigonometry is the study of the measures of triangles.
Trigonometry has many uses, including surveying and navigation.

Activity

1. In each of these right triangles, ∠B is 27° and ∠A is 63°.
Measure sides BC and AC of each triangle.

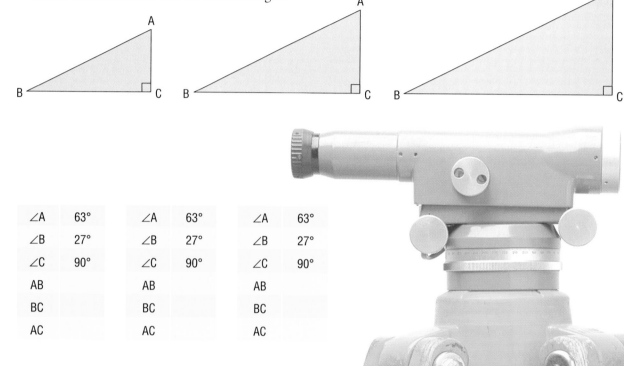

∠A	63°		∠A	63°		∠A	63°
∠B	27°		∠B	27°		∠B	27°
∠C	90°		∠C	90°		∠C	90°
AB			AB			AB	
BC			BC			BC	
AC			AC			AC	

2. a) Calculate the quotient $\frac{BC}{AC}$ to the nearest
hundredth for each triangle.
b) What do you notice about the values of
the quotient?

3. Use your result from question 2 and the
information in the diagram to find the
height of the flagpole.

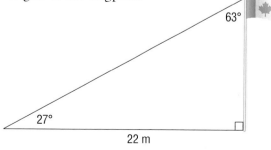

63°

27°

22 m

Statistics

Statistics play a very important part in our lives. They are found everywhere, even in the machines we use and the games we play.

Activity ❶ The QWERTY Keyboard

The picture shows a manual typewriter first manufactured in 1872. The keys were arranged in this way to avoid the locking of the type bars of the most frequently used letters. This keyboard is often called the QWERTY keyboard.

The table gives the average number of times a letter appears in 100 letters of written material.

A	8.2	H	5.3	O	8	V	0.9
B	1.4	I	6.5	P	2	W	1.5
C	2.8	J	0.1	Q	0.1	X	0.2
D	3.8	K	0.4	R	6.8	Y	2
E	13	L	3.4	S	6	Z	0.05
F	3	M	2.5	T	10.5		
G	2	N	7	U	2.5		

1. Draw a QWERTY keyboard.

2. On each key, write the number of times that letter will appear in 100 letters of written material.

3. Explain the arrangement of the letters on the keyboard.

4. How might you have placed the letters differently?

5. Why is the QWERTY keyboard still used today?

Activity ❷ Breaking Codes

Codes or puzzles are constructed by letting one letter stand for another.

1. How could the table in Activity 1 be used to help decipher codes or puzzles?

2. Make up a coded message and have a classmate decipher it.

Activity ❸ SCRABBLE®

1. List the letters of the alphabet. Beside each letter, write how many tiles of that letter are found in a SCRABBLE® game and the point value of that letter.

2. Explain why you think the makers of the game used these numbers of tiles and this point system.

3. Choose any 7 tiles to make the word that will give you the most points. Compare your word with your classmates'.

Probability

Probability has been called the mathematics of chance. Knowing about probability will help you make informed decisions about the likelihood of events.

Activity ❶

Suppose there are 2 blue marbles, 3 red marbles, and 5 white marbles in a bag. You select 1 marble, look at the colour, and return it to the bag.

1. a) The probability of picking a red marble is $\frac{3}{10}$. Why?

b) What is the probability of picking a blue marble? a white marble?

2. What percent of the time should you pick a white marble?

3. If you selected a marble 100 times, how many times should you pick a white marble?

Activity ❷

1. Estimate the number of times a baseball cap will land right side up if you toss it 10 times.

2. Toss a baseball cap 10 times and compare the result with your estimate.

3. What is the probability that a baseball cap will land right side up?

Activity ❸

Some homes have automatic garage doors that are operated by a garage-door opener. An opener has 8 switches. Each switch can be set in 2 positions, on and off.

What is the chance that 2 people have the same code for their garage-door openers? To find out, start with simple cases. What if there is only 1 switch that can be set to on or off? In this case, there are only 2 possibilities. This means that there is 1 chance out of 2 that both people will have the same code.

What if there are 2 switches?

When switch 1 is on, switch 2 can be on or off. When switch 1 is off, switch 2 can be on or off. This means that there are 4 possibilities in total, so the chance is now 1 in 4. What if there are 3 switches? 4 switches? 8 switches?

SWITCH 1	SWITCH 2
on	on
	off
off	on
	off

Mathematics and Counting (Discrete Mathematics)

Discrete mathematics is the study of things that can be counted.

Activity ❶

1. If you follow the arrows, how many different paths spell COUGAR?

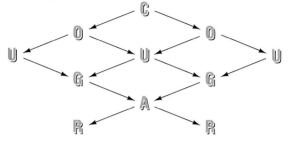

2. Make up your own path puzzle using the name of a rock group. Ask a classmate to solve your puzzle.

Activity ❷

There are 2 roads from Hart to Adams.
There are 4 roads from Adams to Young.
How many different routes are there from Hart to Young?

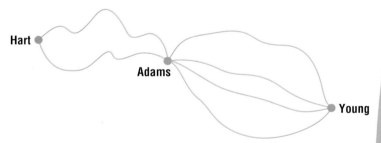

Activity ❸

Four people, Lisa, Ben, Ona, and Dino, are going on a trip in a car. The car will seat 2 in the front and 2 in the back. Only Lisa and Dino can drive. In how many different ways can the 4 people sit in the car?

Activity ❹

Copy each sequence and predict the next 3 terms.

1. 2, 6, 10, 14, ▪, ▪, ▪

2. 3, 7, 15, 31, ▪, ▪, ▪

3. 486, 162, 54, 18, ▪, ▪, ▪

4. 3, 4, 7, 11, 18, ▪, ▪, ▪

Investigating Limits

A very important branch of mathematics is known as calculus. It is applied in many fields, including the sciences, the social sciences, and business. The study of limits plays an essential part in understanding calculus.

Activity ❶

Consider this series.

$$\frac{1}{2} + \frac{1}{4} + \frac{1}{8} + \frac{1}{16} + \frac{1}{32} + \cdots$$

The series can be summed in parts as shown.

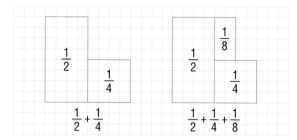

1. Draw a 16-by-16 grid and continue the pattern.

2. What number does the sum of the series approach? Check your answer with a calculator.

Activity ❷

1. Draw a circle with radius 5 cm.

2. Divide the circle into 10 rectangles, each 1 cm wide.

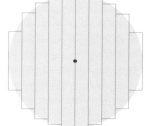

3. Measure the length of each rectangle and find the area of each rectangle.

4. Find the sum of the areas of the rectangles.

5. Find the area of the circle using the formula $A = \pi r^2$. You can assume that π is about 3.14.

6. Compare your answers from steps 4 and 5.

7. If you made the rectangles narrower, would the sum of their areas be closer to the area found using the formula? Explain.

Mathematical Structure

When is 10 + 4 = 2?
When is 10 + 10 = 8?
When you are telling time.
If it is now 10 o'clock, it will be
2 o'clock in 4 h, and 8 o'clock in 10 h.
Clock arithmetic is an example
of modular arithmetic.

Activity ❶

A scientist is doing an experiment that takes 41 h to complete. The experiment was started at 12 noon.

1. At what time will the experiment be completed?

2. How long had the experiment been running at 8 a.m. on the second day?

3. Complete the following calculations using the arithmetic of the 12-h clock.

a) 3 + 5   **b)** 9 + 9
c) 13 + 15   **d)** 15 + 22
e) 3 × 6   **f)** 4 × 7
g) 5 − 7   **h)** 3 − 8

Activity ❷

On the 4-h clock shown, the hours are 1, 2, 3, and 0.
Use the 4-h clock for the following.

1. State whether the expressions in each pair are equal.
a) 2 + 3 and 3 + 2
b) 3 − 2 and 2 − 3
c) 2 + 2 and 2 − 2
d) 3 + 3 and 3 − 3

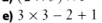

2. Simplify.
a) 2 × (3 + 2)
b) (2 + 3) × 3
c) (2 × 3) × 2
d) (2 × 3) × 3
e) 3 × 3 − 2 + 1

3. State whether the expressions in each pair are equal.
a) 3 × (3 + 2) and 3 × 3 + 3 × 2
b) (3 + 1) × (2 + 3) and
3 × 1 + 3 × 2 + 1 × 2 + 1 × 3

CHAPTER 1

Numbers

A square engraving has sides of length 4 cm.

The sides of a photographic enlargement of the engraving are 3 times as long as the sides of the engraving. How do the areas of the photograph and the engraving compare?

A reduced image of the engraving is used on a postage stamp. The area of the image on the stamp is 4 times smaller than the area of the engraving. What is the length of a side of the image on the stamp?

1

Activity ❶ Prime Numbers

The number 10 has 4 **factors**, 1, 2, 5, and 10. Each factor divides 10 evenly. A **prime number** is a whole number with exactly 2 factors, itself and 1. The number 1 is not considered to be prime. The first 4 prime numbers are 2, 3, 5, and 7.

1. The numbers 5 and 7 are called **twin primes**. They are consecutive odd numbers that are also prime. Find all the twin primes less than 100.

2. Prime triplets are 3 consecutive odd numbers that are also prime. What is the only set of prime triplets?

3. In 1742, the mathematician Goldbach stated that every even number, except 2, can be written as the sum of 2 prime numbers.

$$8 = 3 + 5$$
$$18 = 7 + 11 \text{ or } 18 = 5 + 13$$

Write each of the following as the sum of 2 prime numbers.

a) 24   **b)** 30   **c)** 42   **d)** 100

4. Until 1903, it was thought that $2^{67} - 1$ was a prime number. That year, a mathematician named Cole received a standing ovation at a meeting of the American Mathematical Association. He multiplied out 2^{67} and subtracted 1, then moved to another chalkboard and multiplied the following numbers.

$$\begin{array}{r} 761\ 838\ 257\ 287 \\ \times\ 193\ 707\ 721 \\ \hline \end{array}$$

He got the same result from both calculations. Cole had factored a number previously thought to be prime.

a) Estimate $2^{67} - 1$. Compare your method with your classmates'.

b) Investigate why mathematicians find prime numbers so interesting.

Activity ❷ Squares, Cubes, and Factors

Study the following steps.

- List the factors of 6.

    1, 2, 3, 6

- Find the number of factors each factor of 6 has.

Factor of 6	1	2	3	6
Number of Factors	1	2	2	4

- Find the sum of the cubes of the numbers of factors.

Number of Factors	1	2	2	4
Number of Factors Cubed	1	8	8	64

$$1 + 8 + 8 + 64 = 81$$

- Find the square of the sum of the numbers of factors.

$$1 + 2 + 2 + 4 = 9 \text{ and } 9^2 = 81$$

1. Write a statement about the relationship between "the sum of the cubes of the numbers of factors" and "the square of the sum of the numbers of factors" for the factors of a number.

2. Test your statement, starting with these numbers.

a) 12   **b)** 20

Activity ❸ Amazing Square

Copy the square onto grid paper.

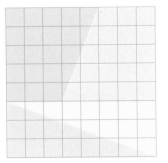

Cut out the 4 pieces and rearrange them to form a rectangle.

1. What was the area of the original square?

2. What is the area of the rectangle?

3. Can you explain the difference in the areas, or is there some magic in squares?

Mental Math

Calculate.

1. 5×23	**2.** 16×9
3. 7^2	**4.** 11^2
5. 66×5	**6.** $5 \times 2 \times 8$
7. 19×7	**8.** 103×4
9. 100×16	**10.** 2323×3

Calculate.

11. $85 \div 5$	**12.** $123 \div 10$
13. $217 \div 7$	**14.** $366 \div 6$
15. $6684 \div 2$	**16.** $5000 \div 100$
17. $950 \div 1000$	**18.** $1200 \div 20$
19. $1500 \div 50$	**20.** $800 \div 25$

Calculate.

21. $356 + 222$	**22.** $140 + 555$
23. $199 + 299$	**24.** $234 + 587$
25. $435 - 225$	**26.** $810 - 105$
27. $367 - 202$	**28.** $287 - 369$
29. $450 + (-301)$	**30.** $-215 - 680$

Calculate.

31. $17 + 23 - 8$	**32.** $9 - 8 - 3$
33. $27 + 14 + 38$	**34.** $15 - 16 + 20$
35. $3 + 22 - 16$	**36.** $-4 + 15 - 18$
37. $22 + (-15) + 13$	**38.** $-10 + 35 + 12$
39. $42 + 16 + (-10)$	**40.** $-17 + 26 - 35$

Calculate.

41. 2×5^2	**42.** $100 \div (6 + 4)$
43. $5 \times 2 \times 8$	**44.** $73 - 7 \times 5$
45. 4×7^2	**46.** $5^2 + 3^2$
47. $(17 - 11)^2$	**48.** $(11 - 17)^2$
49. $15 \times (65 - 55)$	**50.** $10 \times 5 - 70$

The Rational Numbers

Most numbers belong to several different sets of numbers at the same time.

Activity ❶ Natural Numbers, Whole Numbers, and Integers

1. Which of these sets of numbers is the set of counting numbers or **natural numbers**?
a) 2, 4, 6, 8, 10, 12, 14, 16, 18, 20
b) 0, 1, 2, 3, 4, 5, 6, 7, 8, 9, 10
c) 1, 2, 3, 4, 5, 6, 7, 8, 9, 10

2. a) Is the set of numbers you chose in question 1 also made up of whole numbers?
b) Are these numbers also integers? Explain.

3. The 3 nested boxes show how the natural numbers, the whole numbers, and the integers are related. Explain the meaning of the diagram.

Integers
Whole Numbers
Natural Numbers

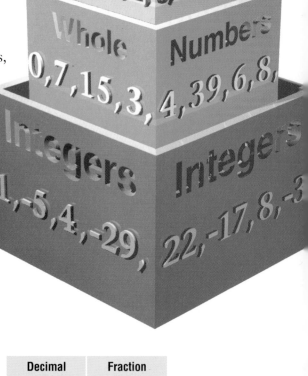

Activity ❷ Terminating Decimals

1. Complete this table of rational numbers. Write the fraction in lowest terms.

2. What is meant by a terminating decimal?

3. a) When a rational number is written as a fraction, is it the quotient of 2 integers? Explain.
b) Examine the decimal forms of the rational numbers in the table. Are they integers? Why?
c) Can the decimal form of a rational number ever be an integer? If so, give an example.

Decimal Form	Fraction Form
0.5	
0.25	
0.625	
−0.2	
−0.75	
−0.85	

Activity ❸ Repeating Decimals

1. Copy and complete this table of rational numbers.

Fraction Form	Decimal Form
$\frac{2}{3}$	
$-\frac{7}{11}$	
$\frac{1}{6}$	
$-\frac{5}{9}$	

2. a) Does the repeating part of each decimal ever terminate?
b) What special mark can be written over the first digit or first set of digits that repeat?

3. Rewrite each decimal using the special mark.

4. Draw 4 boxes that nest inside one another. Label each box with the label "natural numbers," "whole numbers," "integers," or "rational numbers" to show how these sets of numbers are related. Compare your diagram with a classmate's.

5. Write a definition of the rational numbers.

Activity ❹ Classify the Numbers

1. Which of the following statements are true? Explain.
a) The rational number $-\frac{3}{8}$ is made up of two integers, one positive and one negative.
b) The decimal form of $\frac{1}{4}$ is an integer.
c) The number -5 is a natural number.
d) The number $0.232\ 425\ 262$ is a repeating decimal.
e) The square root of 4, $\sqrt{4}$, is a rational number.
f) The square root of 2, $\sqrt{2}$, is a rational number.

2. Explain why 2 is a natural number, a whole number, an integer, and a rational number.

3. Explain why -10 is a rational but not a whole number.

4. Write one example of a number that is an integer but not a whole number.

5. The ratio of the circumference of a circle to its diameter is π. Is π a rational number? Explain.

Activity ❺ Numbers and Variables

1. State the rational number that multiplies each variable.
a) $\frac{1}{3}a^2$ **b)** $\frac{1}{8}y^3$
c) $-\frac{1}{10}w^5$ **d)** $-\frac{1}{7}x^2$

2. State the rational number that multiplies each variable.
a) $\frac{q^2}{2}$ **b)** $\frac{x^4}{3}$
c) $-\frac{b^7}{5}$ **d)** $-\frac{x^9}{8}$

Perfect Squares

The Pythagoreans were a secret society of Greek mathematicians in the sixth century B.C. They were interested in special types of numbers, including prime numbers, triangular numbers, square numbers, and pentagonal numbers. The Pythagoreans used lines, triangles, and squares of pebbles to represent different types of numbers. Our word "calculate" comes from the Latin word *calculus*, which means "pebble." Perfect square numbers could be represented by squares of pebbles. Perfect squares are found by squaring whole numbers.

Activity ❶ Odd Numbers and Perfect Squares

Copy and complete the table.

Odd Numbers	Sum	Diagram
First one	1 = 1	■
First two	1 + 3 = 4	⊡
First three	1 + 3 + 5 = ▦	
First four		
First five		

What is the sum of
a) the first 8 odd numbers?
b) the first 10 odd numbers?
c) the first 1000 odd numbers?

Activity ❷ Triangular Numbers and Perfect Squares

The first 4 triangular numbers are shown.

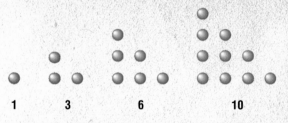

Use diagrams to illustrate your solutions to the following.

1. Find the next 3 triangular numbers.

2. Why are they called triangular numbers?

3. What is the sum of any 2 consecutive triangular numbers?

Activity ❸ The Locker Problem

Southridge School has a very long hallway, with 1000 lockers along one side. They are numbered from 1 to 1000.

On April Fool's Day, each of Southridge's 1000 students walks down the hallway to leave the school. Every student walks in the same direction, past locker 1 first and locker 1000 last.

The first student closes every locker door. The second student opens every second locker door. The third student changes the state of every third locker door. This means that, if the locker door is open, the student closes it. If it is closed, the student opens it. The fourth student changes the state of every fourth locker door.

This pattern continues until the thousandth student leaves and changes the state of the thousandth locker door.

What are the numbers of the locker doors that are closed after the last student leaves?

Hint: Solve a simpler problem. You may want to make a table to show the states of some locker doors after the first few students walk down the hall. Use the table to predict which of the 1000 doors are closed after 1000 students leave. Another way is to use cards or counters as lockers and act out the problem.

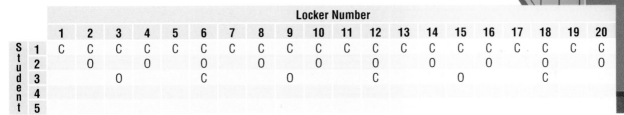

		Locker Number																			
		1	2	3	4	5	6	7	8	9	10	11	12	13	14	15	16	17	18	19	20
S t u d e n t	1	C	C	C	C	C	C	C	C	C	C	C	C	C	C	C	C	C	C	C	C
	2		O		O		O		O		O		O		O		O		O		O
	3			O			C			O			C			O			C		
	4																				
	5																				

Activity ❹ Fermat and Perfect Squares

French mathematician Pierre de Fermat (1601–1675) stated that any whole number can be written as the sum of, at most, 4 perfect squares.

$21 = 4^2 + 2^2 + 1^2$ or $21 = 3^2 + 2^2 + 2^2 + 2^2$
$39 = 5^2 + 3^2 + 2^2 + 1^2$ or $39 = 6^2 + 1^2 + 1^2 + 1^2$

1. Write each of the following as the sum of, at most, 4 perfect squares.

a) 33   b) 42   c) 77   d) 88
e) 153   f) 212   g) 208   h) 903

2. Compare your answers with a classmate's.

7

1.1 Estimating and Calculating Square Roots

The world's top chess players are called Grandmasters. Thirteen-year-old Alexandre Lesiège of Quebec beat a Russian Grandmaster at the World Open in 1989.

A chess board is a square. It is covered by 64 smaller squares that are equal in area. There are 8 squares along each side of the board. We can say that 64 is the square of 8, but how can we describe 8 in relation to 64?

Activity: Use the Diagrams

Draw figures A, B, C, and D on 1-cm grid paper or construct them with elastics on a geoboard. Determine the area of each square.

Inquire

1. The length of each side of a square is the **square root** of its area. What is the square root of area A? area B? area C?

2. Count squares to determine the area of square D. Measure the side of square D. What is the approximate square root of area D?

3. Write your definition of the square root of a number.

4. a) What is the square root of 64?
b) Is any other integer also the square root of 64? Explain.

5. A Snakes and Ladders game board is a square with 100 smaller squares marked on it.
a) How many smaller squares lie along each side of the board?
b) What are the square roots of 100?
c) Which of the square roots of 100 could not be used to describe the number of squares along each side of the board or the length of a side of a square?

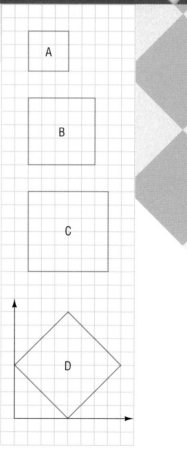

Since $5 \times 5 = 25$ and $(-5) \times (-5) = 25$, then 5 and -5 are the square roots of 25.
Since $1.2 \times 1.2 = 1.44$ and $(-1.2) \times (-1.2) = 1.44$, then 1.2 and -1.2 are the square roots of 1.44.

The **radical sign**, $\sqrt{}$, is used to represent the positive square root of a number. Thus, $\sqrt{25} = 5$, and $\sqrt{1.44} = 1.2$.

The positive square root is also called the **principal square root**. To avoid confusion, mathematicians do not use the radical sign for negative square roots.

Example 1	**Solution**		
Evaluate.	**a)** $9 \times 9 = 81$	**b)** $0.6 \times 0.6 = 0.36$	**c)** $80 \times 80 = 6400$
a) $\sqrt{81}$	so $\sqrt{81} = 9$	so $\sqrt{0.36} = 0.6$	so $-\sqrt{6400} = -80$
b) $\sqrt{0.36}$			
c) $-\sqrt{6400}$			

Many numbers, such as $\sqrt{2}$ and $\sqrt{3}$, cannot be written as a fraction or a terminating decimal. These square roots are non-terminating, non-repeating decimals, or **irrational numbers**. Together with the natural numbers, whole numbers, integers, and rational numbers, the irrational numbers form the set of **real numbers**. To determine the approximate values of such square roots as $\sqrt{2}$ and $\sqrt{3}$, we estimate or use a calculator.

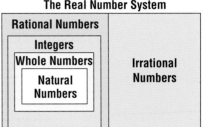

The Real Number System

Example 2	**Solution**
Estimate $\sqrt{356}$.	Start with numbers whose squares you know.
	$30 \times 30 = 900$ (too high), $20 \times 20 = 400$ (too high),
	$10 \times 10 = 100$ (too low)
	Since 356 is between 100 and 400, and is closer to 400,
	a good estimate for $\sqrt{356}$ is $\sqrt{400}$ or 20.

Another way to estimate the square root of a number is to divide the number into groups of 2 digits, starting at the decimal point. Then, for numbers greater than 1, estimate the square root of the group furthest from the decimal point and add 1 zero for each other group. Thus, for $\sqrt{1535}$, we consider the two groups 15 and 35.
$\sqrt{15} \doteq 4 \leftarrow$ square root of the group furthest from the decimal point.
There is one other group of digits, so we add one zero.
So, $\sqrt{1535} \doteq 40$.

$\doteq$ means "approximately equals"

For numbers less than 1, estimate the square root of the non-zero group closest to the decimal point. Thus, for $\sqrt{0.086}$, we consider the two groups of 08 and 60. $\sqrt{08} \doteq 3$, so $\sqrt{0.086} \doteq 0.3$.

Example 3	**Solution**			
Estimate the square roots.	**a)** $\sqrt{567}$	**b)** $\sqrt{12\ 300}$	**c)** $\sqrt{0.45}$	**d)** $\sqrt{0.0067}$
a) $\sqrt{567}$	$\sqrt{5}\ \ 67$	$\sqrt{1}\ \ 23\ \ 00$	$0\ .\ \sqrt{45}$	$0\ .\ 00\ \ \sqrt{67}$
b) $\sqrt{12\ 300}$	$\downarrow\ \ \ \downarrow$	$\downarrow\ \ \ \downarrow\ \ \ \downarrow$	$\downarrow\ \ \ \ \downarrow$	$\downarrow\ \ \ \ \downarrow\ \ \ \ \downarrow$
c) $\sqrt{0.45}$	$2\ \ \ \ \ 0$	$1\ \ \ \ 0\ \ \ \ 0$	$0\ .\ \ \ 7$	$0\ .\ \ 0\ \ \ \ 8$
d) $\sqrt{0.0067}$	$\sqrt{567} \doteq 20$	$\sqrt{12\ 300} \doteq 100$	$\sqrt{0.45} \doteq 0.7$	$\sqrt{0.0067} \doteq 0.08$

The square root key on your calculator may appear as ⬚ or ⬚.

To find the square root of a number, enter the number, then press the square root key.

CONTINUED ▶

Example 4

Evaluate to the nearest tenth.

a) $\sqrt{42}$

b) $-\sqrt{164}$

Solution

a) Press 42 $\boxed{\surd}$

Display 42 6.4807407

So, $\sqrt{42}$ is 6.5 to the nearest tenth.

> **EST** $6 \times 6 = 36$, so $\sqrt{42} \doteq 6$

b) Press 164 $\boxed{\surd}$

Display 164 12.806248

So, $-\sqrt{164}$ is -12.8 to the nearest tenth.

> **EST** $13 \times 13 = 169$, so $-\sqrt{164} \doteq -13$

Example 5

Evaluate to the nearest tenth.

a) $5\sqrt{3} + 7\sqrt{2}$

b) $\dfrac{6\sqrt{11}}{7}$

Solution

a) $5\sqrt{3}$ means $5 \times \sqrt{3}$ and $7\sqrt{2}$ means $7 \times \sqrt{2}$

$\boxed{C}$ 5 $\boxed{\times}$ 3 $\boxed{\surd}$ $\boxed{+}$ 7 $\boxed{\times}$ 2 $\boxed{\surd}$ $\boxed{=}$ $\boxed{18.559749}$

So, $5\sqrt{3} + 7\sqrt{2} = 18.6$ to the nearest tenth.

> **EST** $5\sqrt{3} + 7\sqrt{2}$
> $\doteq 5 \times 2 + 7 \times 1$
> $= 17$

b) $\boxed{C}$ 6 $\boxed{\times}$ 11 $\boxed{\surd}$ $\boxed{\div}$ 7 $\boxed{=}$ $\boxed{2.8428212}$

So, $\dfrac{6\sqrt{11}}{7} = 2.8$ to the nearest tenth.

> **EST** $\dfrac{6\sqrt{11}}{7} \doteq \dfrac{6 \times 3}{6}$
> $= 3$

Practice

Find the square roots of each number.

1. 49   **2.** 81   **3.** 121   **4.** 625

5. 0.64   **6.** 0.01   **7.** 1.96   **8.** 0.25

Evaluate.

9. $\sqrt{25}$ **10.** $\sqrt{100}$ **11.** $\sqrt{225}$

12. $\sqrt{256}$ **13.** $\sqrt{169}$ **14.** $\sqrt{0.36}$

15. $\sqrt{0.04}$ **16.** $\sqrt{1.21}$ **17.** $\sqrt{0.81}$

Estimate.

18. $\sqrt{30}$ **19.** $\sqrt{66}$ **20.** $\sqrt{92}$

21. $\sqrt{765}$ **22.** $\sqrt{989}$ **23.** $\sqrt{3245}$

24. $\sqrt{7800}$ **25.** $\sqrt{56\,000}$ **26.** $\sqrt{880\,000}$

Estimate.

27. $\sqrt{0.8}$ **28.** $\sqrt{0.77}$

29. $\sqrt{0.05}$ **30.** $\sqrt{0.067}$

31. $\sqrt{0.0382}$ **32.** $\sqrt{0.0023}$

33. $\sqrt{0.009}$ **34.** $\sqrt{0.0006}$

35. $\sqrt{0.000\,22}$ **36.** $\sqrt{0.000\,34}$

Estimate. Then, calculate to the nearest tenth.

37. $\sqrt{31}$ **38.** $\sqrt{44}$

39. $\sqrt{62}$ **40.** $\sqrt{79}$

41. $\sqrt{101}$ **42.** $\sqrt{206}$

43. $\sqrt{1123}$ **44.** $\sqrt{20\,183}$

45. $\sqrt{86\,003}$ **46.** $\sqrt{202\,183}$

Evaluate to the nearest tenth.

47. $\sqrt{3} + \sqrt{7}$ **48.** $\sqrt{10} - \sqrt{5}$

49. $3\sqrt{11}$ **50.** $6\sqrt{23}$

51. $(\sqrt{3})(\sqrt{2})$ **52.** $7\sqrt{12} - 6$

53. $\sqrt{14} \div \sqrt{5}$ **54.** $\dfrac{\sqrt{20} - \sqrt{10}}{\sqrt{31}}$

Problems and Applications

55. Evaluate for $a = 5$ and $b = -2$.

a) $\sqrt{4a + 2b}$

b) $\sqrt{\dfrac{125}{a}}$

c) $\sqrt{-18b}$

d) $\sqrt{a^2 - 12b}$

e) $-\sqrt{(ab)^2}$

f) $\sqrt{10a - 5b + 4}$

g) $\sqrt{-10ab^3}$

h) $-3\sqrt{a^2 + 2ab + b^2}$

i) $7.3\sqrt{a^2 - 2ab + b^2}$

56. Calculate the perimeter of each figure to the nearest tenth of a unit.

a)   **b)**

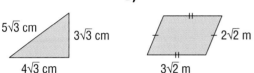

57. The Greek mathematician Heron found the following formula for the area of a triangle.

$$A = \sqrt{s(s - a)(s - b)(s - c)}$$

where a, b, and c are the side lengths, and s is half the perimeter.

$$s = \frac{a + b + c}{2}$$

Use Heron's formula to calculate the area of each triangle.

a)   **b)**

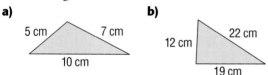

58. The area, a, of an equilateral triangle is given by the formula $a \doteq 0.43s^2$, where s is the side length.
For each area, find the side length to the nearest tenth of a unit.

a) 15.6 cm²

b) 44 m²

c) 346.9 mm²

d) 876.4 cm²

59. The world's largest city square is Tiananmen Square in Beijing, China. It has an area of 0.396 km². What is the length of a side of the square to the nearest metre?

60. a) Evaluate $2\sqrt{2}$.   **b)** Evaluate $\sqrt{8}$.
c) Compare your answers and explain your findings.

61. How are the square roots of a perfect square related?

62. A square has an area of 169 cm². What is the radius of the largest circle you can fit inside it? Explain.

63. Try to evaluate $\sqrt{-9}$ on your calculator. What is the result? Why?

64. One corner of a square is at (0, 0). It has an area of 49 square units. Find the possible coordinates of the other vertices.

65. To find the square root of a perfect square by subtraction, subtract the odd numbers in increasing order until the result is 0.

25 − 1 = 24
24 − 3 = 21
21 − 5 = 16
16 − 7 = 9
9 − 9 = 0

We need 5 subtractions to reach 0 from 25, so $\sqrt{25} = 5$.

a) Use this method to find the following.

$\sqrt{289}$ $\sqrt{576}$ $\sqrt{784}$ $\sqrt{1089}$

b) Explain why this method works. Compare your explanation with your classmates'.

LOGIC POWER

There are 14 cubes in the structure, which sits on a table. The face of each cube has an area of 1 m². If you paint the exposed surface, how many square metres do you paint?

11

1.2 Applying Square Roots

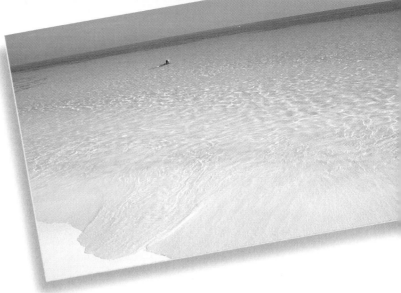

Activity: Use a Formula

The distance you can see out to sea when you stand on a beach is given by the formula

$$d = 0.35\sqrt{h}$$

In this formula, h is the height, in centimetres, of your eyes above the water, and d is the distance you can see in kilometres.

Inquire

1. The height of Sandra's eyes is 144 cm. How far can she see from a beach?

2. If Sandra sits on a lifeguard tower, and her eyes are 350 cm above the water, how far can she see?

3. Explain why the formula may not apply if you are not standing on a beach.

4. If you stand on a beach and watch an approaching sailboat, why do you see the mast of the boat before the hull?

Example

For many years, people believed Aristotle's theory of gravity, which stated that the heavier an object, the faster it would fall. Galileo disproved this theory by dropping 2 objects of different masses from the Leaning Tower of Pisa. They hit the ground at the same time.
The formula for calculating the time it takes an object to fall to the ground is

$$t = 0.45 \times \sqrt{h}$$

where h is the height in metres and t is the time in seconds. The Leaning Tower of Pisa is 54.5 m tall. How long would it take an object dropped from the top to hit the ground? Give your answer to the nearest tenth of a second.

Solution

$t = 0.45\sqrt{h}$
$= 0.45 \times \sqrt{54.5}$ **EST** $\boxed{0.5 \times 7 = 3.5}$
$\doteq 0.45 \times 7.38$
$= 3.321$

It would take 3.3 s, to the nearest tenth of a second, for the object to hit the ground.

Practice

Estimate. Then, evaluate to the nearest tenth.

1. $\sqrt{46}$ **2.** $\sqrt{303}$

3. $-\sqrt{90}$ **4.** $5\sqrt{66}$

5. $-7\sqrt{88}$ **6.** $\sqrt{13} + \sqrt{79}$

7. $3\sqrt{7} + 6\sqrt{91}$ **8.** $16\sqrt{56} - 4\sqrt{11}$

9. $\dfrac{2\sqrt{45}}{3}$ **10.** $\dfrac{5\sqrt{10} + 6\sqrt{21}}{4}$

11. $\dfrac{\sqrt{123}}{\sqrt{60}}$ **12.** $\dfrac{\sqrt{112}}{\sqrt{13}}$

Problems and Applications

Given the area of each square, determine to the nearest tenth of a unit
a) *the length of its side*
b) *its perimeter*

13. 25 cm²   **14.** 225 m²   **15.** 55 m²

16. 90 cm²   **17.** 200 m²   **18.** 800 cm²

19. Land areas are measured in hectares (ha).
$$1 \text{ ha} = 10\ 000 \text{ m}^2$$
a) If a square field has an area of 1 ha, what are its dimensions?
b) A house lot in a big city may be only about 0.25 ha in area. If this amount of land were square, what would its dimensions be?

20. The water at the surface of a river moves faster than the water near the bottom. The formula that relates these two speeds is
$$\sqrt{b} = \sqrt{s} - 1.3$$
where b is the speed near the bottom and s is the speed at the surface. Both speeds are in kilometres per hour.
a) What is the speed of the water near the bottom of a river, to the nearest tenth of a kilometre per hour, if the surface speed is 16 km/h? 20 km/h?
b) What is the surface speed of the water, to the nearest tenth of a kilometre per hour, if the speed near the bottom is 9 km/h? 7 km/h?

21. The velocity of sound changes with temperature and with the material the sound passes through. The formula to calculate the velocity in air is
$$V = 20\sqrt{273 + T}$$
where V is the velocity in metres per second and T is the temperature in degrees Celsius. Calculate the velocity of sound in air, to the nearest metre per second, at
a) 16°C   **b)** 0°C   **c)** −10°C

22. For a satellite to stay in orbit, its speed must satisfy the formula
$$s = \sqrt{\frac{5.15 \times 10^{12}}{d}}$$
where s is the speed in kilometres per hour and d is the distance in kilometres from the satellite to the centre of the Earth. If a satellite is in orbit 35 840 km above the Earth, it hovers over one spot on the Earth. Research the radius of the Earth and determine the speed of a satellite that hovers over one spot on the Earth. Compare your answer with a classmate's.

PATTERN POWER

a) Evaluate the following differences in the squares of consecutive whole numbers.

$$1^2 - 0^2 = \blacksquare$$
$$2^2 - 1^2 = \blacksquare$$
$$3^2 - 2^2 = \blacksquare$$
$$4^2 - 3^2 = \blacksquare$$
$$5^2 - 4^2 = \blacksquare$$

b) Describe the pattern.
c) Use the pattern to evaluate mentally $245^2 - 244^2$.

1.3 Guess And Check

You can solve many problems by guessing the answer and then testing it to see if it is correct. If it is wrong, you can keep guessing until you get the right answer.

Understand the Problem

Think of a Plan

Carry Out the Plan

Look Back

Jeannine wanted to raise $10 000 for charity by holding a massed bands concert in a 400-seat auditorium. She decided to sell reserved seats for $40 each and general admission seats for $16 each. How many of each type of ticket did she have printed?

1. What information are you given?

2. What are you asked to find?

Guess at the number of reserved tickets to be printed. This number will give the number of general admission tickets. Then, calculate the total receipts to see if they equal $10 000. If not, try another guess.

GUESS			CHECK
Number of Reserved Tickets	Number of General Admission Tickets	Total Revenue ($)	Is the total $10 000?
100	300	$100 \times 40 + 300 \times 16$ $= 8800$	Too low
200	200	$200 \times 40 + 200 \times 16$ $= 11\ 200$	Too high
150	250	$150 \times 40 + 250 \times 16$ $= 10\ 000$	$10\ 000 = 10\ 000$

CHECKS!

Jeannine had 150 reserved seating tickets and 250 general admission tickets printed.

Check the answer against the given information.

Does the answer seem reasonable?

Guess and Check	1. Guess an answer that fits one of the facts. 2. Check the answer against the other facts. 3. If necessary, adjust your guess and check again.

Problems and Applications

1. Multiplying a number by 7 and adding 13 gives 55. What is the number?

2. Multiplying a number by 14 and subtracting 12 gives 114. What is the number?

3. What 3 consecutive numbers have a sum of 237?

4. What 4 consecutive even numbers have a sum of 196?

5. The square of the number of students in the band is close to 3000. About how many students are in the band?

6. The 7 Trudeaus went to the fair. Adult tickets cost $8. Children's tickets cost $5. The total cost was $47. How many adults were there?

7. In how many ways could 4 darts hit the board to give a total score of 19?

8. The perimeter of a rectangle is 60 m. The length is 4 m more than the width. What are the dimensions of the rectangle?

9. Karen wants to cut 56 m of television cable into 2 pieces, so that one is 6 m longer than the other. How long should she make each piece?

10. The cube of the number of people on the swim team is close to 4000. About how many are on the swim team?

11. Justine has some rare quarters and nickels. She has 8 more nickels than quarters. The face value of the coins is $2.50. How many are quarters?

12. The dimensions of a rectangular solid are whole numbers. The areas of the faces are 42 cm², 48 cm², and 56 cm². What are the dimensions of the solid?

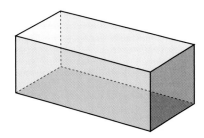

13. Piero works at the Snack Shack. He has been asked to make a mixture of 24 kg of cashews and peanuts that will cost $7.25/kg. Cashews cost $14/kg and peanuts cost $5/kg. Copy and complete the table to find how many kilograms of cashews and how many kilograms of peanuts should be mixed together so that the cost of the mixture is $7.25/kg.

GUESS				CHECK
Mass of Cashews (kg)	Mass of Peanuts (kg)	Total Cost of Mixture ($)	Cost per Kilogram ($)	Does cost equal $7.25/kg?

14. Canada's top honour is the Order of Canada. There are 3 categories—Companion, Officer, and Member. A total of up to 165 awards can be given in any year. If all the awards are given, the number of new Members is twice the number of new Officers. There are 35 more new Officers than new Companions. How many awards are made in each category?

15. Write a problem that can be solved using the guess and check strategy. Ask a classmate to solve the problem.

1.4 Exponents and Powers

Exponents are used as a short way to write repeated multiplication.

standard form ➝ $81 = \underbrace{3 \times 3 \times 3 \times 3}_{\text{repeated multiplication}} = 3^4$ ⬅ exponential form

$81 = 3^4$ exponent, base, power

Activity: Do an Experiment

When you repeatedly fold a piece of paper in half, the number of layers increases with the number of folds. Fold a standard piece of paper, and copy and complete the table.

Number of Folds	Number of Layers
1	$2 = 2$ or 2^1
2	$2 \times 2 = 4$ or 2^2
3	
4	
5	
6	

Inquire

1. If you were to fold the piece of paper the following numbers of times, how many layers would you have? Express each answer in exponential form.

a) 5   **b)** 7   **c)** 50

2. Explain how you found your answers to question 1.

3. If 10 layers of paper are about 1 mm thick, how thick is a piece of paper after 10 folds?

4. What is the maximum number of times you can fold a piece of paper?

$3 \times 3 = 3^2$ 3^2 is read as "three to the second" or more commonly "three squared" because it can be pictured as a square.

$2 \times 2 \times 2 = 2^3$ 2^3 is read as "two to the third" or "two cubed" because it can be pictured as a cube.

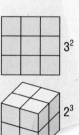
3^2
2^3

Exponents are also used with variables.
$3y^4$ means $3 \times y \times y \times y \times y$ xy^2 means $x \times y \times y$

A number that multiplies a variable is known as a **coefficient**. In $3y^4$, the coefficient is 3.

When an exponent is outside a pair of brackets, the exponent is applied to everything inside the brackets.

$(3y)^4$ means $(3y) \times (3y) \times (3y) \times (3y)$ $(xy)^2$ means $(xy) \times (xy)$
$= 3 \times 3 \times 3 \times 3 \times y \times y \times y \times y$ $= x \times x \times y \times y$
$= 81y^4$ $= x^2y^2$

Example 1

If $x = 2$ and $y = -3$, evaluate $5x^4 + 6xy$.

Solution

Substitute the values of x and y into the expression.

$$5x^4 + 6xy = 5(2)^4 + 6(2)(-3)$$
$$= 5(16) - 36$$
$$= 80 - 36$$
$$= 44$$

Practice

State the base and the exponent.

1. 5^3 **2.** 10^7 **3.** x^5 **4.** t^2

State the coefficient.

5. $2a$ **6.** $-7d^2$ **7.** $13x^5$ **8.** $-t^3$

Write in exponential form.

9. $4 \times 4 \times 4 \times 4 \times 4 \times 4$

10. $6 \times 6 \times 6 \times 6$

11. $m \times m \times m \times m \times m$

12. $r \times r \times r$

Write as a repeated multiplication.

13. 5^2 **14.** 1^6 **15.** 2^5 **16.** 10^4

17. 0^3 **18.** y^4 **19.** $5x^3$ **20.** $(2m)^3$

21. x^2y **22.** xy^3 **23.** $(xy)^3$ **24.** $(ab)^4$

Evaluate.

25. the third power of 2   **26.** 3 to the fourth

27. 5 cubed   **28.** 10 to the fifth

What power does each figure represent?

29. **30.** **31.** **32.**

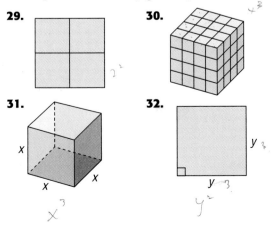

Write each number as a power of 10.

33. 100   **34.** 1000

35. 100 000   **36.** 1 000 000

37. 100 000 000   **38.** 10 000 000

Write in standard form.

39. 2^5 **40.** 5^3 **41.** 4^4 **42.** 7^3 **43.** 10^7

44. 3^6 **45.** 0.5^2 **46.** 1.1^3 **47.** 0.1^4

Write as a power of 2 or 3 and draw the square or cube represented by it.

48. 4   **49.** 27   **50.** 16

State which is smaller.

51. 5^3 or 3^5 **52.** 2^5 or 5^2

53. 4^2 or 2^4 **54.** 2^3 or 3^2

Evaluate.

55. $7^2 + 3^2$ **56.** $4^3 - 2^4$

57. 3×2^3 **58.** $4^4 \div 2^5$

59. 100×0.1^3 **60.** $0.8^2 \times 0.2^3$

61. 1000×0.2^4 **62.** 0.1×0.1^2

Evaluate.

63. $7^2 + 3^3$ **64.** $4^3 - 2^2$

65. $2^2 \times 2^3$ **66.** $4^2 \div 2^2$

67. Evaluate for $x = -4$.

a) x^3 **b)** $x^2 - 5$

c) $5x^2 - 7$ **d)** $(2x)^2$

68. Evaluate for $t = -3$ and $s = 2$.

a) $t^2 + s^2$ **b)** $(t + s)^3$ **c)** $t^3 - s^3$

d) $2t^2 - s^2$ **e)** $6s^3 - 2st$ **f)** $(3t)^2 - 4st$

CONTINUED

Problems and Applications

69. A scientist found that the number of bacteria in a culture doubled every hour. If there were 1000 bacteria at 08:00, how many were there at the following times?
a) 09:00   **b)** 11:00   **c)** 14:00

70. The ancestors of Ling Ling, the giant panda, included 2 parents and 4 grandparents. Her grandparents were 2 generations before her.
a) How many ancestors were in the seventh generation before Ling Ling? Express your answer in exponential form.
b) How many ancestors were in the tenth generation before Ling Ling? Express your answer in exponential form.

71. If a ball is thrown straight up at a speed of 30 m/s, its height in metres after t seconds is given by the formula $h = 30t - 5t^2$.
a) What is the height of the ball after 1 s? 3 s? 4 s?
b) After how many seconds will the ball hit the ground? State your assumptions.

72. a) Describe the pattern in this series.
$$1, 4, 27, 256, \ldots$$
b) Predict the fifth and tenth numbers in the series.

73. The product of the ages of a set of quadruplets is 16 times the sum of their ages. How old are they?

74. The product of the ages of a set of triplets is 12 times the sum of their ages. How old are they?

75. If $f(x) = 3x^2 + 1$
then $f(2) = 3(2)^2 + 1$
$= 3 \times 4 + 1$
$= 13$
Find the following.
a) $f(4)$ **b)** $f(10)$ **c)** $f(0)$

76. Decide whether each statement is always true, sometimes true, or never true for whole numbers greater than 1. Explain your reasoning.
a) Twice a number is smaller than the number squared.
b) The cube of a number is greater than the square of the number.
c) Powers with the same base but different exponents are equal.

77. A story says that the inventor of chess asked his ruler to give him 1 grain of wheat on the first square of the chessboard, 2 on the second, 4 on the third, 8 on the fourth, and so on for all 64 squares.

Suppose you could stack loonies on a chessboard in the same manner.
a) How many loonies would you stack on the fourth square? the fifth square? the sixth square? the seventh square?
b) About how high would the stack be on the sixty-fourth square? Compare your result with your classmates'.

CALCULATOR POWER

Many calculators have a $\boxed{Y^x}$ key to evaluate powers.
To evaluate 2^{12}
Press   2 $\boxed{Y^x}$ 12 $\boxed{=}$
Display   2   2   12 4096

Use a calculator to evaluate the following.
1. 2^6 **2.** 3^7 **3.** 4^8 **4.** 0.3^3

The Car of the Future

There are many examples of technology in modern cars. These range from simple devices, such as the levers and buttons that open the doors, to more complicated ones, like cellular telephones.

Activity ❶

List some examples of modern technology found in a new car. Think of the outside of the car as well as the inside.

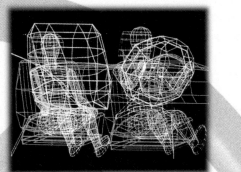

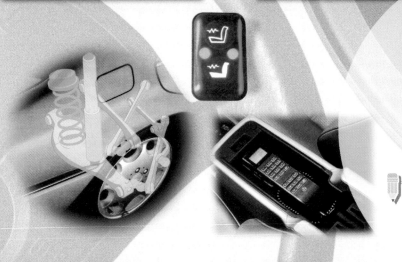

Activity ❷

Design a high technology car of the future and draw plans to show what it might look like. As you design the car, you will need to resolve such issues as the number of passengers it will carry, how the driver will steer it, the fuel the car will use, and so on.

Describe the uses of computers in your car of the future.

19

1.5 The Exponent Rules

The exponent rules are short cuts for multiplying and dividing powers with the *same base*.

Activity: Discover the Relationship

Copy and complete the table.

Exponential Form	Standard Form	Answer in Standard Form	Answer in Exponential Form
$2^3 \times 2^4$	8×16	128	2^7
$3^2 \times 3^2$			
$2^2 \times 2^3$			
$10^3 \times 10^3$			
$2^5 \div 2^2$			
$3^4 \div 3^2$			
$10^5 \div 10^3$			

Inquire

1. For the products, how are the exponents in the first column related to the exponents in the last column?

2. Write a rule for multiplying powers with the same base.

3. For the quotients, how are the exponents in the first column related to the exponents in the last column?

4. Write a rule for dividing powers with the same base.

Example 1	**Solution**	
Simplify $2^5 \times 2^3$.	**Method 1**	**Method 2**

Method 1
$$2^5 \times 2^3$$
$$= 2 \times 2 \times 2 \times 2 \times 2 \times 2 \times 2 \times 2$$
$$= 2^8$$

Method 2
To multiply powers with the same base, add the exponents.
$$x^m \times x^n = x^{m+n}$$
$$2^5 \times 2^3 = 2^{5+3}$$
$$= 2^8$$

Example 2

Solution

Simplify $y^7 \div y^2$.

Method 1
$$y^7 \div y^2$$
$$= \frac{y \times y \times y \times y \times y \times y \times y}{y \times y}$$
$$= y \times y \times y \times y \times y$$
$$= y^5$$

Method 2
To divide powers with the same base, subtract the exponents.
$$x^m \div x^n = x^{m-n}$$
$$y^7 \div y^2 = y^{7-2}$$
$$= y^5$$

Example 3

Simplify.
a) $(2^4)^3$ **b)** $(y^2)^4$

Solution

a) $(2^4)^3 = 2^4 \times 2^4 \times 2^4$
$\qquad = 2^{4+4+4}$
$\qquad = 2^{12}$

b) $(y^2)^4 = y^2 \times y^2 \times y^2 \times y^2$
$\qquad = y^{2+2+2+2}$
$\qquad = y^8$

To raise a power to a power, multiply the exponents.
$(x^m)^n = x^{m \times n}$

Practice

Simplify.

1. $5^3 \times 5^4$ **2.** $2^3 \times 2^7$ **3.** $7^5 \times 7^5$

4. $10^6 \times 10$ **5.** $4^2 \times 4^9$ **6.** 3×3^6

7. $y^2 \times y^4$ **8.** $x^3 \times x^6$ **9.** $a \times a^6$

Find the value of x.

10. $5^3 \times 5^x = 5^7$ **11.** $3^4 \times 3^x = 3^6$

12. $8^x \times 8^2 = 8^8$ **13.** $6^x \times 6^5 = 6^6$

14. $4^3 \times 4^x = 4^6$ **15.** $m^7 \times m^x = m^9$

16. $t^x \times t^3 = t^6$ **17.** $y^x \times y^4 = y^5$

Simplify.

18. $4^5 \div 4^3$ **19.** $3^7 \div 3^6$

20. $9^2 \div 9^2$ **21.** $10^6 \div 10^5$

22. $4^7 \div 4$ **23.** $5^8 \div 5^8$

24. $m^5 \div m^4$ **25.** $x^3 \div x$

Find the value of x.

26. $3^6 \div 3^x = 3^2$ **27.** $6^7 \div 6^x = 6^5$

28. $7^x \div 7^4 = 7^3$ **29.** $2^x \div 2^2 = 2^8$

30. $9^5 \div 9^x = 9^4$ **31.** $m^x \div m^2 = m^7$

32. $m^x \div m = m^3$ **33.** $y^6 \div y^x = y$

Simplify.

34. $(2^3)^4$ **35.** $(3^5)^2$ **36.** $(4^2)^7$

37. $(10^5)^3$ **38.** $(5^4)^4$ **39.** $(x^5)^4$

40. $(y^3)^3$ **41.** $(t^6)^7$ **42.** $(m^1)^5$

Find the value of x.

43. $(2^3)^x = 2^6$ **44.** $(3^x)^4 = 3^{12}$

45. $(5^x)^2 = 5^8$ **46.** $(7^5)^x = 7^{10}$

47. $(x^3)^x = x^9$ **48.** $(m^x)^5 = m^{15}$

49. $(t^4)^x = t^{20}$ **50.** $(z^x)^5 = z^5$

Problems and Applications

51. The approximate size of a quantity, expressed as a power of 10, is known as an **order of magnitude**. To the nearest orders of magnitude, the mass of the Earth is 10^{25} kg and the mass of the sun is 10^{30} kg. About how many times greater is the mass of the sun than the mass of the Earth?

52. On a test, a student wrote that $2^3 \times 3^2 = 6^5$.
a) What mistake did the student make?
b) What is the value of $2^3 \times 3^2$?

53. A student said that $6^3 \div 2^2 = 3^1$.
a) What mistake did the student make?
b) What is the value of $6^3 \div 2^2$?

54. Work with a partner. Use each of the digits from 1 to 6 only once. Write the largest and the smallest power possible.

NUMBER POWER

Here is one way to use the digits 1, 2, 3, 5, 7, and 9 to add to 648. Find 3 other ways.

$$\begin{array}{r} 251 \\ +397 \\ \hline 648 \end{array}$$

PROBLEM SOLVING

1.6 Make Assumptions

To solve some problems, you must make assumptions.

The Alaska Highway runs from Dawson Creek, B.C., to Fairbanks, Alaska. It is 2400 km long. The speed limit is 80 km/h. The De Marco family is leaving Dawson Creek at 09:00 on a Wednesday to drive to Fairbanks. They plan to stop for 10 h to eat and sleep on Wednesday night and on Thursday night. At what time on what day should they arrive in Fairbanks?

Understand the Problem

1. What information are you given?

2. What are you asked to find?

3. What assumptions should you make?

Think of a Plan

Assume that the De Marco family will drive at the speed limit. Calculate the time they will spend driving. Add 20 h to this time for eating and sleeping.

Carry Out the Plan

If the De Marco family drives at the 80 km/h speed limit, the time needed to drive 2400 km is found by dividing 2400 km by 80 km/h.

$$\frac{2400}{80} = 30$$

Thirty hours from 09:00 on Wednesday is 15:00 on Thursday. Add 20 h for eating and sleeping.

The De Marco family should arrive in Fairbanks at 11:00 on Friday.

Look Back

How could you use subtraction and multiplication to check your answer?

Make Assumptions	1. Decide what assumption(s) to make.
	2. Use your assumption(s) to solve the problem.
	3. Check that your answer is reasonable.

Problems and Applications

Solve the following problems and state each assumption that you make.

1. Frank earned $215.75 in the first month at his part-time job. How much can he expect to earn in a year?

2. The drama club sells oranges to raise money for charity. Last year, each member of the club sold 20 cases. How many cases can the 43 members of the club expect to sell this year?

3. Clara surveyed 40 students in the school. Ten of them said they would attend the dance. If the school has 800 students, how many can Clara expect to attend the dance?

4. The patrol boat travels at a speed of 15 km/h. How far can the boat travel in 5 h?

5. John trained for 5 weeks and reduced his time in the 100-m dash from 12.0 s to 11.5 s. He reasoned that with 20 more weeks of training he would be able to run 100 m in 9.5 s and break the world record. What assumption did he make? Is he necessarily correct? Explain.

6. Soo Lin surveyed 100 people who bought new bikes. Of those surveyed, 80 said the town needed new bike trails. There are 10 000 people in the town, so Soo Lin reported that 8000 people wanted new bike trails. What assumption did she make? Explain.

7. Six tents are placed 5.2 m apart in a straight line. What is the distance from the first tent to the last tent?

8. How many cuts must you make in a rope to make the following number of pieces?
a) 3   **b)** 4

9. How many seconds are there in February?

10. The distance from Eagle's Nest to Brewsterville is 425 km. The first part of the trip is 150 km of highway, where the speed limit is 100 km/h. The rest of the trip is along a country road, where the speed limit is 50 km/h.
a) How long will it take Paulina to drive from Eagle's Nest to Brewsterville?
b) If she leaves Eagle's Nest at 16:45, at what time will she arrive in Brewsterville?

11. Identify the next 3 terms in each of the following.
a) 200, 100, 50, 25, …
b) 14, 17, 21, 26, …
c) 3, 7, 15, 31, …

12. The world's longest sneezing fit lasted 977 days. In the first year of the fit, Donna Griffiths sneezed about a million times. How many seconds did she average between sneezes?

13. The price for a carton of juice doubles every 2 years for 50 years. What would a carton cost in 50 years? Find an alternative way of solving this problem using exponents.

14. Write a problem in which the solution requires at least one assumption. Have a classmate solve your problem and state the assumption(s).

LOGIC POWER

Move 3 sticks to form 4 squares of the same size.

1.7 Scientific Notation: Large Numbers

A leading Canadian astronomer, Dr. Helen Sawyer Hogg, studied huge balls of stars, known as globular clusters. The stars in these clusters are about 14 000 000 000 years old. The size of a number like 14 000 000 000 depends on the number of zeros. Writing another zero gives 140 000 000 000, which is ten times larger. Removing a zero from 14 000 000 000 gives 1 400 000 000, which is ten times smaller. To avoid mistakes when writing many zeros, we express large numbers in **scientific notation**.

Activity: Look for a Pattern

Copy and complete the table.

Standard Form	Product Form	Scientific Notation
410	4.1×100	4.1×10^2
4 100	$4.1 \times$ ▇	▇
41 000	$4.1 \times$ ▇	▇
410 000	$4.1 \times$ ▇	▇
4 100 000	$4.1 \times$ ▇	▇
41 000 000	$4.1 \times$ ▇	▇

Inquire

1. Use the completed table to write the rule for expressing numbers in scientific notation.

2. Why would you not write 2356 in scientific notation?

Example 1

Mercury is about 58 000 000 km from the sun. Write 58 000 000 in scientific notation.

Solution

In scientific notation, a number has the form $x \times 10^n$, where x is greater than or equal to 1 but less than 10, and 10^n is a power of 10.

The decimal point starts here.

58 000 000

Move the decimal point 7 places.

$= 5.8 \times 10\ 000\ 000$

$= 5.8 \times 10^7$

Notice that the number of places you moved the decimal point to the left is the exponent in the power of 10.

Example 2

Calculate $(4.5 \times 10^3) \times (8 \times 10^5)$. Write your answer in scientific notation.

Solution

$$(4.5 \times 10^3) \times (8 \times 10^5) = 4.5 \times 8 \times 10^3 \times 10^5$$
$$= 36 \times 10^{3+5}$$
$$= 36 \times 10^8$$
$$= 3.6 \times 10^9$$

Practice

1. Copy and complete the chart. The first line has been completed for you.

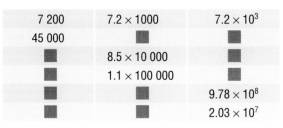

7 200	7.2×1000	7.2×10^3
45 000	■	■
■	$8.5 \times 10 000$	■
■	$1.1 \times 100 000$	■
■	■	9.78×10^8
■	■	2.03×10^7

State each value of n.

2. $6000 = 6 \times 10^n$

3. $7 100 000 = 7.1 \times 10^n$

4. $35 000 = 3.5 \times 10^n$

5. $54 000 000 = 5.4 \times 10^n$

6. $145 000 = 1.45 \times 10^n$

7. $460 000 000 = 4.6 \times 10^n$

Write the number that is 10 times as large as each of the following.

8. 77 000   **9.** 6700

10. 7.6×10^5 **11.** 9.8×10^7

Write the number that is one-tenth as large as each of the following.

12. 350   **13.** 2.3×10^5

14. 6.7×10^4 **15.** 1 300 000

Estimate, then calculate. Write each answer in scientific notation.

16. $(3.4 \times 10^5) \times (5 \times 10^4)$

17. $(4 \times 10^8) \times (1.2 \times 10^7)$

18. $(6.7 \times 10^3) \times (8.9 \times 10^{10})$

Round each number to the highest place value, then calculate using scientific notation.

19. $23 000 000 \times 341 000$

20. $870 600 000 \times 710 000$

21. $92 000 000 \div 56 000$

22. $83 000 000 000 \div 777 000 000$

Problems and Applications

23. Express each number in scientific notation.
a) Canada is the country with the longest coastline at about 91 000 km.
b) The distance across the universe has been estimated at
800 000 000 000 000 000 000 000 km.
c) Do you want to hunt for sunken treasure? The *HMS Edinburgh* went down with $95 000 000 in gold on board.

24. How far can you see? The Andromeda Constellation is the furthest object we can see with the unaided eye. It is about
22 000 000 000 000 000 km from Earth.
a) Express this distance in scientific notation.
b) Light travels in space at a speed of about 300 000 km/s. Calculate how many years light takes to reach Earth from the Andromeda Constellation.

25. Why is 56×10^6 not in scientific notation?

26. Work with a classmate.
a) Find the area of Canada in square metres.
b) Find the population of Canada.
c) Calculate how many square metres there are for each Canadian.

CALCULATOR POWER

1. Multiply $1 400 000 \times 3 000 000$ using your calculator. How does your calculator display the answer?

2. Scientific calculators display the answer as $\boxed{4.2 \qquad 12}$. What does it mean?

3. Many calculators have an $\boxed{EE}$ key. To input 2.3×10^7, press **2** $\boxed{\cdot}$ **3** $\boxed{EE}$ **7**. Use the $\boxed{EE}$ key to find
a) $(4.5 \times 10^4) \times (5.1 \times 10^7)$
b) $(7.8 \times 10^{11}) \times (6.7 \times 10^9)$

1.8 Working with Exponents

The leg span of the giant spider from South America is 25 cm. Like all spiders, it has 8 legs.

We can write the number 8 as the power 2^3. In this power, the exponent is 3 and the base is 2.

base $\rightarrow 2^3 \leftarrow$ exponent

power

The base of a power can also be a negative number. We can extend the exponent rules to simplify powers with integers as bases.

Activity: Look for a Pattern

Copy and complete the table.

Exponential Form	Result as a Repeated Multiplication	Result in Exponential Form	Result in Standard Form
$(-2)^2 \times (-2)^3$	$(-2) \times (-2) \times (-2) \times (-2) \times (-2)$	$(-2)^{2+3}$ or $(-2)^5$	-32
$(-2)^3 \times (-2)^4$			
$(+3)^2 \times (+3)^3$			
$(-2)^8 \div (-2)^3$			
$(-3)^4 \div (-3)^2$			
$(+5)^3 \div (+5)$			
$(-4)^3 \times (-4)^0$			
$(-3)^4 \div (-3)^0$			

Inquire

1. Write the exponent rule for multiplying powers with the same integral base.

2. Write the exponent rule for dividing powers with the same integral base.

3. Describe the difference between
a) $(1 + 3)^2$ and $1^2 + 3^2$?
b) $(1 - 3)^2$ and $1^2 - 3^2$?
c) $(-3)^2$ and -3^2?

Example 1

Simplify.
a) $(-0.25)^3 \times (-0.25)^5$
b) $(-y)^2 \times (-y)^3$

Solution

To multiply powers with the same base, add the exponents.
$x^m \times x^n = x^{m+n}$

a) $(-0.25)^3 \times (-0.25)^5$
     $= (-0.25)^{3+5}$
     $= (-0.25)^8$

b) $(-y)^2 \times (-y)^3$
     $= (-y)^{2+3}$
     $= (-y)^5$

Example 2

Simplify.

a) $(-6)^5 \div (-6)^2$

b) $\left(\frac{t}{2}\right)^3 \div \left(\frac{t}{2}\right)$

Solution

To divide powers with the same base, subtract the exponents.

$$x^m \div x^n = x^{m-n}$$

a) $(-6)^5 \div (-6)^2$

$= (-6)^{5-2}$

$= (-6)^3$

b) $\left(\frac{t}{2}\right)^3 \div \left(\frac{t}{2}\right)$

$= \left(\frac{t}{2}\right)^{3-1}$

$= \left(\frac{t}{2}\right)^2$

Example 3

Simplify.

a) $((-2)^2)^3$

b) $((-m)^4)^2$

Solution

a) $((-2)^2)^3$

$= (-2)^2 \times (-2)^2 \times (-2)^2$

$= (-2)^{2+2+2}$

$= (-2)^6$

b) $((-m)^4)^2$

$= (-m)^4 \times (-m)^4$

$= (-m)^{4+4}$

$= (-m)^8$

Example 3 suggests the following rule. To raise a power with an integral base to a power, multiply the exponents. $(x^m)^n = x^{m \times n}$

Example 4

Evaluate $(-5)^4(-5)^3$.

Solution

$(-5)^4(-5)^3 = (-5)^{4+3}$

$= (-5)^7$

$= -78\ 125$

$\boxed{\text{C}}\ 5\ \boxed{+/-}\ \boxed{\text{Y}^x}\ 7\ \boxed{=}\ \boxed{\quad -\ 78\ 125.}$

Example 5

Evaluate $\left(-\frac{1}{2}\right)^3 \times \left(-\frac{1}{3}\right)^2$.

Solution

Because the bases are not the same, evaluate each power before multiplying.

$$\left(-\frac{1}{2}\right)^3 \times \left(-\frac{1}{3}\right)^2$$

$= -\frac{1}{8} \times \frac{1}{9}$

$= -\frac{1}{72}$

$\boxed{\text{EST}}$

$\left(-\frac{1}{10}\right) \times \left(\frac{1}{10}\right)$

$= -\frac{1}{100}$

Example 6

Evaluate for $x = -2$ and $y = -1$.

a) $x^2 + y^3$

b) $\frac{x^3}{3} - \frac{y^2}{2}$

Solution

a) $x^2 + y^3$

$= (-2)^2 + (-1)^3$

$= 4 - 1$

$= 3$

b) $\frac{x^3}{3} - \frac{y^2}{2}$

$= \frac{(-2)^3}{3} - \frac{(-1)^2}{2}$

$= \frac{-8}{3} - \frac{1}{2}$

$= \frac{-16 - 3}{6}$

$= -\frac{19}{6}$

CONTINUED

Practice

State the base.

1. $\left(\frac{1}{2}\right)^6$ **2.** $(-5)^2$ **3.** -1^4 **4.** $(-9)^3$

State the exponent.

5. -2^5 **6.** 4^2 **7.** $(-4)^0$ **8.** -5

Write in exponential form.

9. $\left(\frac{1}{4}\right)\left(\frac{1}{4}\right)\left(\frac{1}{4}\right)$ **10.** $(-3)(-3)(-3)(-3)(-3)$

11. $p \times p \times p \times p \times p$ **12.** $(-n)(-n)(-n)(-n)$

13. $3 \times 3 \times 3 \times (-2) \times (-2) \times 3 \times (-2)$

Write as a repeated multiplication.

14. $(-2)^5$ **15.** -2^5 **16.** $\left(\frac{-1}{x}\right)^3$

Write in standard form.

17. 3^2 **18.** $(-3)^2$ **19.** $(-1)^4$

20. -1^5 **21.** $(-5)^3$ **22.** -5^3

23. $(-0.5)^3$ **24.** 1.1^4 **25.** $(-2.5)^2$

Simplify.

26. $5^3 \times 5^6$ **27.** $(-8)^2 \times (-8)^3$

28. $(-2)^3(-2)^4$ **29.** $\left(\frac{1}{2}\right)^3 \times \left(\frac{1}{2}\right)^4$

30. $(-2.1)^5(-2.1)^3$ **31.** $(-0.2)^3(-0.2)^2$

Simplify.

32. $5^4 \div 5^3$ **33.** $6^8 \div 6^2$ **34.** $\frac{(-0.4)^5}{(-0.4)^3}$ **35.** $\frac{(-9)^7}{(-9)^2}$

Simplify.

36. $(2^3)^2$ **37.** $((-3)^7)^4$

38. $\left(\left(-\frac{1}{5}\right)^2\right)^3$ **39.** $((-6)^5)^3$

40. $((-4)^6)^7$ **41.** $((-2.3)^3)^4$

Simplify.

42. $x^4 \times x^2$ **43.** $\left(\frac{1}{y}\right)^{12} \div \left(\frac{1}{y}\right)^5$

44. $z^8 \div z$ **45.** $(-m)^6(-m)^4$

46. $(s^2)^4$ **47.** $((-r)^3)^2$

Simplify, then calculate.

48. $(-5)^2 \times (-5)^3$ **49.** $6^2 \times 6^5$

50. $(-2)^3(-2)^5(-2)^2$ **51.** $(-1)^5(-1)^7$

52. $(-3.1)^5(-3.1)^3$ **53.** $(-3)^6 \div (-3)^4$

54. $(-10)^5 \div (-10)$ **55.** $(-4)^6 \div (-4)^5$

Calculate.

56. $2^8 \div 2^4$ **57.** $(-3)^7 \div (-3)$

58. $(-5)^2 \times (-5)^3$ **59.** $(3^2)^3$

60. $\frac{(-4)^3 \times (-4)^5}{(-4)^5}$ **61.** $\frac{4^9}{4^3 \times 4^2}$

62. $(-2)^3(-2)^5$ **63.** $(-3)^0(-3)^5$

64. $((-2)^3)^2$ **65.** $(6^2)^3 \div (6^2)^2$

Evaluate.

66. $(-8)^2$ **67.** $6(-4)^3$

68. $(-3)^2(6)^2$ **69.** $(-1)^5 + 3^3$

70. $4^5 - 3^5$ **71.** $(-2)^5 \times (-3)^4$

72. $9^2 \div (-2)^3$ **73.** $(-5)^2(-4)^4$

74. $(1.3)^2(-2)^4$ **75.** $(1.5)^2 \div (-5)^3$

76. Evaluate for $n = 3$.

a) $\frac{1}{5n^2}$ b) $-\frac{n^3}{6}$ c) $1 + 7n^5$ d) $n^3 - 6n$

77. Evaluate for $x = -2$ and $y = 3$.

a) x^3 b) $5y^4$ c) $\frac{x^2}{2} + \frac{y^2}{3}$

d) $\frac{x^3y^3}{3}$ e) $(x - y)^3$ f) $(y - x)^2$

g) $-\frac{x^2y^3}{8}$ h) $4x^3 - 5y$ i) $(3x^2)(-2y^2)$

Problems and Applications

78. Use the guess-and-check strategy to find the value of x.

a) $3^x = 81$ b) $(-2)^x = -512$

c) $x^5 = 1024$ d) $(-x)^3 = -1000$

e) $-5^x = -625$ f) $-x^2 = -1.69$

g) $(0.2)^x = 0.0016$ h) $x^3 = -0.216$

79. Find the value of x.

a) $x^2 \times x^3 = 32$ **b)** $x \times x^2 = 27$

c) $x^4 \div x^2 = 36$ **d)** $x^2 \div x = 64$

e) $(x^2)^2 = 81$ **f)** $(x^2)^3 = 64$

80. The formula for the volume, V, of a cube is

$$V = s^3$$

where s is the side length. Copy the chart and use the formula to complete it.

Side Length (cm)	Volume (cm³)
5	
7	
4.2	
	1000
	512

81. There are 10 bacteria in a culture at the beginning of an experiment. The number of bacteria doubles every 24 h. The table shows the number of bacteria present over the first few days.

Elapsed Time (days)	Number of Bacteria
1	10×2 $= 10 \times 2^1$ $= 20$
2	$10 \times 2 \times 2$ $= 10 \times 2^2$ $= 40$
3	$10 \times 2 \times 2 \times 2$ $= 10 \times 2^3$ $= 80$

a) Complete the table up to the end of day 8. How many bacteria are there after 8 days?

b) Use the pattern to calculate the number of bacteria after 2 weeks.

c) How many bacteria are there after 40 days?

82. If the base of a power is negative, and the exponent is even, is the standard form of the number positive or negative? Explain.

83. If the base of a power is negative, and the exponent is odd, is the standard form of the number positive or negative? Explain.

84. Any positive number has 2 square roots, but you can calculate only 1 side length if you are given the area of a square. Explain why.

85. a) Are the products $(-4)^3 \times (-4)^2$ and $(-4)^2 \times (-4)^3$ the same? Explain.

b) Are the quotients $(-4)^3 \div (-4)^2$ and $(-4)^2 \div (-4)^3$ the same? Explain.

c) Are the powers $((-4)^3)^2$ and $((-4)^2)^3$ the same? Explain.

86. A new student in your class does not know how to evaluate such powers as $(-2)^4$ and -2^4. Write an explanation and compare it with your classmates'.

PATTERN POWER

Many calculators have the bracket keys [(] and [)] to use with calculations involving the order of operations.

1. Estimate $(2.1 \times 3.2)^3$.

2. Calculate the expression in question 1 using this keying sequence:

[C] [(] 2.1 [×] 3.2 [)] [Yˣ] 3 [=]

3. Does your calculator give you the same answer if you omit the bracket keys in the keying sequence in question 2? Explain.

4. Why do some calculators give different answers for $(-2)^6$ and -2^6?

5. Estimate, then calculate.

a) $(4.2 \times 1.2)^3$

b) $(1.6 \times 1.3)^4$

c) $(2.5 \times 2.5)^3$

Patterns and Powers

What is the units digit of 2^{95}? To solve this problem, you might try using a calculator. What answer does your calculator give for 2^{95}? Another way to find the answer is to look for a pattern.

Activity ❶

To find the units digit of 2^{95}, complete the table and draw the graph.

$2^1 = 2$
$2^2 = 4$
$2^3 = \blacksquare$
$2^4 = \blacksquare$
$2^5 = \blacksquare$
$2^6 = \blacksquare$
$2^7 = \blacksquare$
$2^8 = \blacksquare$
$2^9 = \blacksquare$
$2^{10} = \blacksquare$
$2^{11} = \blacksquare$
$2^{12} = \blacksquare$

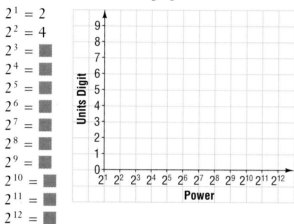

1. Describe the pattern in the units digits.

2. What is the units digit for the powers with exponents that are divisible by 4?

3. What is the units digit of
a) 2^{92}? **b)** 2^{93}? **c)** 2^{94}?

4. What is the units digit of 2^{95}?

Activity ❷

To find the units digit of 3^{100}, complete the table and draw the graph.

$3^1 = \blacksquare$
$3^2 = \blacksquare$
$3^3 = \blacksquare$
$3^4 = \blacksquare$
$3^5 = \blacksquare$
$3^6 = \blacksquare$
$3^7 = \blacksquare$
$3^8 = \blacksquare$
$3^9 = \blacksquare$

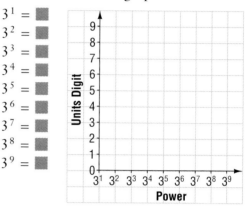

1. Describe the pattern in the units digits.

2. What is the units digit of 3^{100}?

Activity ❸

To find the units digit of 7^{111}, complete the table and draw the graph.

$7^1 = \blacksquare$
$7^2 = \blacksquare$
$7^3 = \blacksquare$
$7^4 = \blacksquare$
$7^5 = \blacksquare$
$7^6 = \blacksquare$
$7^7 = \blacksquare$
$7^8 = \blacksquare$
$7^9 = \blacksquare$

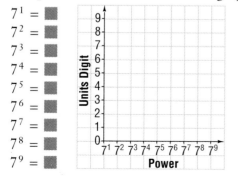

30

Activity ❹

1. Without drawing a graph, determine the units digit of 6^{80}.

2. What would the graph of the units digits versus the powers of 6 look like?

3. What other bases give similar graphs?

Activity ❺

1. Without drawing a graph, determine the units digit of

a) 4^{92} **b)** 4^{93}

2. What would the graph of the units digits versus the powers of 4 look like?

3. What other bases give similar graphs?

Activity ❻

1. How can you determine the last 2 digits of 6^{1000}?

2. Use your calculator to arrange 3^{666}, 4^{555}, 5^{444}, 6^{333} in increasing order.

Activity ❼

1. Write a problem using a power of 8.

2. Have a classmate solve your problem.

31

1.9 Powers of Monomials

There are 35 major pyramids in Egypt. The typical Egyptian pyramid has a square base. The area of the base is given by a power of a monomial, s^2, where s is the side length.

A **monomial** is a number or a variable, or the product of numbers and variables.

$$2 \qquad a \qquad -5b \qquad x^2 \qquad 15p^2q^3$$

Activity: Look for a Pattern

The following cubes have been built from interlocking cubes.

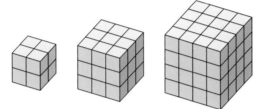

Inquire

1. Copy the table. Work with a partner to complete it. Consider each interlocking cube to have a side length of 1 unit.

Side Length of Large Cube	Total Number of Interlocking Cubes
2	
3	
4	
5	
10	
100	

2. To what exponent is the side length of each cube raised to express the volume?

3. What algebraic expression represents the volume of a cube with side length x?

4. What algebraic expression represents the volume of a cube with side length $2x$?

5. The volume of a cube with side length $2x$ can also be found by multiplying the lengths of the sides.
$2x \times 2x \times 2x = 8x^3$
How does the resulting expression compare with the expression you wrote in question 4?

6. Write a rule to find powers of a monomial.

The side lengths of a cube puzzle are represented by the monomial ab.

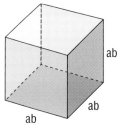

We can find the volume from the formula $V = s^3$, where s is the side length.

For the given cube, the volume is
$$V = (ab)^3$$
$$= (ab)(ab)(ab)$$
$$= (a \times a \times a)(b \times b \times b)$$
$$= a^3b^3$$

We obtain the same result by finding the third power of each factor in the monomial.
$$(ab)^3 = (a)^3(b)^3$$
$$= a^3b^3$$

In general,
$(xy)^m = x^my^m$

The power $\left(\dfrac{a}{b}\right)^3 = \dfrac{a \times a \times a}{b \times b \times b}$
$$= \dfrac{a^3}{b^3}$$

In general,
$\left(\dfrac{x}{y}\right)^m = \dfrac{x^m}{y^m}$

Example 1

Simplify.

a) $(x^3)^2$ **b)** $(y^3)^4$

Solution

a) $(x^3)^2 = x^{3 \times 2}$
$$= x^6$$

b) $(y^3)^4 = y^{3 \times 4}$
$$= y^{12}$$

Example 2

Simplify.

a) $(3x^4y^2)(-x^2y^3)^2$ **b)** $\left(\dfrac{2x^3}{3y^2}\right)^2$

Solution

a) $\quad (3x^4y^2)(-x^2y^3)^2$
$$= (3x^4y^2)(-1)^2(x^2)^2(y^3)^2$$
$$= (3x^4y^2)(1)(x^4)(y^6)$$
$$= (3 \times 1)(x^{4+4})(y^{2+6})$$
$$= 3x^8y^8$$

b) $\left(\dfrac{2x^3}{3y^2}\right)^2$
$$= \dfrac{(2x^3)^2}{(3y^2)^2}$$
$$= \dfrac{(2)^2(x^3)^2}{(3)^2(y^2)^2}$$
$$= \dfrac{4x^6}{9y^4}$$

CONTINUED ➤

Practice

Simplify.

1. $(x)^2$ **2.** $(a)^3$ **3.** $(p)^5$

4. $(n^2)^2$ **5.** $(-t^3)^2$ **6.** $(-y^2)^3$

Simplify.

7. $(x^2)^3$ **8.** $(y^3)^2$ **9.** $(m^2)^2$

10. $(n^3)^4$ **11.** $(x^3)^3$ **12.** $(y^2)^3$

13. $(z^4)^3$ **14.** $(m^4)^5$ **15.** $(p^{18})^2$

16. $(-s^{10})^2$ **17.** $(-x)^{31}$ **18.** $-(-b^0)^3$

Simplify.

19. $(xy)^2$ **20.** $(ab)^3$ **21.** $(-xy)^2$

22. $(mn)^4$ **23.** $(pq)^3$ **24.** $(-2xt)^2$

25. $(4xy)^2$ **26.** $(-2ax)^3$ **27.** $-(3rs)^3$

Simplify.

28. $(x^2y^2)^3$ **29.** $(x^2y^3)^2$ **30.** $(a^2b)^3$

31. $(ab^3)^2$ **32.** $(mn)^3$ **33.** $(-ab^2)^2$

34. $(-j^3k^4)^2$ **35.** $(x^2y)^2$ **36.** $-(s^3t^2)^0$

Simplify.

37. $(2x^2)^3$ **38.** $(3y^3)^2$ **39.** $(4x^4)^2$

40. $(5y^2)^2$ **41.** $(-m^2)^2$ **42.** $(-n^2)^3$

43. $(-2n^2)^3$ **44.** $(-3y^2)^2$ **45.** $(3pqr)^2$

46. $(-3yz)^3$ **47.** $(-4x^2y^3)^3$ **48.** $-(3xy^0)^2$

Simplify.

49. $\left(\dfrac{m}{2}\right)^4$ **50.** $\left(\dfrac{r}{t}\right)^8$ **51.** $\left(\dfrac{-d}{p}\right)^5$

52. $\left(\dfrac{2b}{5c}\right)^3$ **53.** $\left(\dfrac{-2x}{y^2}\right)^3$ **54.** $\left(\dfrac{3s^4}{2q^3}\right)^2$

Simplify.

55. $(2x^2y^3)^2(x^2y)$ **56.** $(-3xy)(-2xy)^2$

57. $(2xy^2)^3(3x^2y^2)$ **58.** $(10abc)^2(-2a^2bc)$

59. $(2a^4b^3)(-3ab)^3(10a^2b^2)$

Problems and Applications

60. Write and simplify an expression for the area of each square.

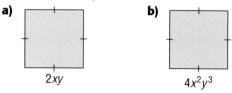

a) 2xy b) 4x²y³

61. Write and simplify an expression for the volume of each cube.

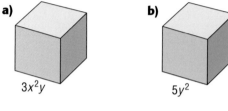

a) 3x²y b) 5y²

62. Find the volume of this cube if $a = 1$, $b = 2$, and $c = 3$.

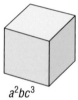

a²bc³

63. Does replacing the variables by their opposites, x by $-x$ and y by $-y$, result in the opposite of each monomial? Explain.

a) $(3x^2y^3)^2$ b) $(3x^2y^3)^3$

NUMBER POWER

Copy the diagram and place the numbers from 1 to 9 in the circles so that the consecutive sums of each side differ by 4.

1.10 Use a Flow Chart

A flow chart provides a way of describing or checking many processes. This flow chart shows how you might try to solve a problem.

When 15 is added to a number, and the result is squared, then multiplied by 3, the result is 243. What is the number?

Understand the Problem

1. What information are you given?

2. What are you asked to find?

3. Do you need an exact or approximate answer?

Think of a Plan

Construct a flow chart to show the operations on the original number.
Reverse the flow chart to work backward.

Carry Out the Plan

number → +15 → square → ×3 → 243

243 → ÷3 → square root → −15 → number

243 ÷ 3 = 81
The square roots of 81 are 9 and −9.
9 − 15 = −6   −9 − 15 = −24
The number is either −6 or −24.

Look Back

How can you use substitution to check your answer?

Use a Flow Chart
1. Use a flow chart to represent the problem.
2. Solve the problem.
3. Check that your answer is reasonable.

Problems and Applications

1. The cube of a number is divided by 20, then 36 is subtracted. The result is 14. What is the number?

2. Saskatchewan's population is about 1 000 000. This is about 6 000 000 less than Quebec's population, which is about 1.4 times smaller than Ontario's population. Find Ontario's population to the nearest million.

3. Troy has read 104 pages of a 496-page book. If he reads 32 pages a day, how many more days will he take to finish the book?

4. Draw a flow chart to represent each process. Compare your flow charts with a classmate's.
a) shopping for a new jacket
b) phoning a friend from your home
c) writing an essay

1.11 Zero and Negative Exponents

There are 8 A notes on a piano. They can be named as shown in the diagram.

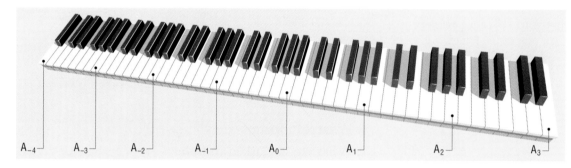

When tuning a piano, a tuner first adjusts the note A_0. This note, called "concert A," is the A above middle C. The formulas to determine the frequencies of the A notes are as follows. The units of frequency are hertz, symbol Hz.

$A_{-4} = 440 \times 2^{-4}$ $A_{-3} = 440 \times 2^{-3}$ $A_{-2} = 440 \times 2^{-2}$ $A_{-1} = 440 \times 2^{-1}$

$A_0 = 440 \times 2^0$ $A_1 = 440 \times 2^1$ $A_2 = 440 \times 2^2$ $A_3 = 440 \times 2^3$

Calculate the frequencies of notes A_1, A_2, and A_3.
To calculate the other frequencies, we need to know about zero and negative exponents.

Activity: Discover the Relationship

Copy and complete the table by doing each division twice. First expand and divide, and then use the exponent rule for division.

Division	Expand and Divide	Exponent Rule
$2^4 \div 2^4$	$\frac{2 \times 2 \times 2 \times 2}{2 \times 2 \times 2 \times 2} = ?$	$\frac{2^4}{2^4} = 2^{4-4} = 2^?$
$3^2 \div 3^2$		
$4^3 \div 4^3$		
$10^4 \div 10^4$		
$x^5 \div x^5$		

Inquire

1. How do the 2 answers in each row compare?

2. What is the value of 5^0? 7^0? y^0?

3. What is the value of any number raised to the exponent 0?

4. Calculate the frequency of A_0 on the piano.

Activity: Discover the Relationship

Copy and complete the table by doing each division twice. First expand and divide, and then use the exponent rule for division.

Division	Expand and Divide	Exponent Rule
$2^3 \div 2^5$	$\dfrac{2 \times 2 \times 2}{2 \times 2 \times 2 \times 2 \times 2} = \dfrac{1}{2^?}$	$\dfrac{2^3}{2^5} = 2^{3-5} = 2^?$
$3^2 \div 3^6$		
$5 \div 5^3$		
$10^4 \div 10^5$		
$x^5 \div x^9$		

Inquire

1. How do the 2 answers in each row compare?

2. State another way to write
a) 3^{-2} **b)** 4^{-3} **c)** 1^{-4}

3. Write a rule for writing a number with a negative exponent as a number with a positive exponent.

4. Evaluate.
a) 2^{-4} **b)** 5^{-2} **c)** 3^{-3} **d)** 4^{-2} **e)** 1^{-7}

5. Calculate the frequencies of the following notes on the piano.
a) A_{-4} **b)** A_{-3} **c)** A_{-2} **d)** A_{-1}

Example 1

Evaluate.
a) 4^0
b) $(-5)^0$
c) -2^0

Solution

$x^0 = 1$, where x can be any number except 0
a) $4^0 = 1$ **b)** $(-5)^0 = 1$ **c)** $-2^0 = -1$

Example 2

Evaluate.
a) 4^{-3}
b) $(-3)^{-3}$
c) $2^0 - 2^{-2}$

Solution

$x^{-m} = \dfrac{1}{x^m}$, where x can be any number except 0

a) $4^{-3} = \dfrac{1}{4^3}$
$= \dfrac{1}{64}$

b) $(-3)^{-3} = \dfrac{1}{(-3)^3}$
$= -\dfrac{1}{27}$

c) $2^0 - 2^{-2} = 1 - \dfrac{1}{2^2}$
$= 1 - \dfrac{1}{4}$
$= \dfrac{3}{4}$

CONTINUED

Example 3

Evaluate.

a) $3^{-3} \times 3^5 \times 3^{-4}$
b) $(-2)^{-5} \div (-2)^{-2}$
c) $(4^{-1})^2$
d) $\dfrac{1}{5^{-2}}$

Solution

a) $3^{-3} \times 3^5 \times 3^{-4}$
$= 3^{-3+5-4}$
$= 3^{-2}$
$= \dfrac{1}{3^2}$
$= \dfrac{1}{9}$

b) $(-2)^{-5} \div (-2)^{-2}$
$= (-2)^{-5-(-2)}$
$= (-2)^{-3}$
$= \dfrac{1}{(-2)^3}$
$= -\dfrac{1}{8}$

c) $(4^{-1})^2$
$= 4^{(-1)\times 2}$
$= 4^{-2}$
$= \dfrac{1}{4^2}$
$= \dfrac{1}{16}$

d) $\dfrac{1}{5^{-2}}$
$= \dfrac{1}{\dfrac{1}{5^2}}$
$= \dfrac{1}{\dfrac{1}{25}}$
$= 1 \times \dfrac{25}{1}$
$= 25$

Practice

1. Write each power with a positive exponent.

a) 9^{-8} **b)** 1^{-4} **c)** $(0.5)^{-6}$
d) $(-7)^{-6}$ **e)** $\dfrac{1}{5^{-4}}$ **f)** $\dfrac{1}{(-3)^{-5}}$

2. Write in exponential form.

a) $\dfrac{1}{8 \times 8}$ **b)** $\dfrac{1}{7 \times 7 \times 7}$ **c)** $\dfrac{1}{9 \times 9 \times 9 \times 9}$
d) $\dfrac{1}{4}$ **e)** $\dfrac{1}{27}$ **f)** $\dfrac{1}{64}$ **g)** $\dfrac{1}{243}$

Evaluate.

3. 5^0 **4.** 2^6 **5.** 3^{-1}
6. $(-10)^{-3}$ **7.** $(0.1)^{-3}$ **8.** $(-3)^{-6}$
9. $\dfrac{1}{3^{-1}}$ **10.** $\dfrac{1}{4^{-2}}$ **11.** $\dfrac{1}{(-3)^{-1}}$

Write each expression as a power.

12. $7^4 \times 7^5$ **13.** $9^6 \times 9^{-4}$
14. $8^{-3} \times 8^{-5}$ **15.** $6^7 \div 6^3$
16. $5^{-7} \div 5^{-2}$ **17.** $4^{-2} \div 4^6$
18. $(3^3)^4$ **19.** $(9^{-2})^4$
20. $(8^{-1})^{-5}$ **21.** $-(2^{-3})^{-2}$

Write each expression as a power.

22. $2^4 \times 2^{-3} \times 2^2$ **23.** $3^{-5} \times 3^{-3} \times 3^2$
24. $5^6 \times 5^{-9} \times 5$ **25.** $8^4 \times 8^{-5} \div 8^{-2}$
26. $(-2)^{-4} \times (-2)^{-3} \div (-2)^{-1}$
27. $(-3)^{-6} \div (-3)^{-2} \times (-3)^4$

Evaluate.

28. $3^2 \times 3^2$ **29.** $4^7 \div 4^5$
30. $5^2 \times 5^{-4}$ **31.** $6^{-2} \div 6^0$
32. $7^{-4} \div 7^{-5}$ **33.** $6^{-3} \div 6^{-3}$
34. $\dfrac{(6^0)^{-4}}{(10^2)^{-2}}$ **35.** $\dfrac{(7^{-3})^0}{(0.1^{-1})^{-2}}$

Evaluate.

36. $2^{-2} \times 2^{-2}$ **37.** $3^4 \div 3^5 \times 3$ **38.** $3^0 + 3^3$
39. $4^2 - 2^{-1}$ **40.** $5^3 + 3^2$
41. $2^{-2} + 5^0$ **42.** $2^3 \times 2^{-1} + 5$
43. $(6-3)^{-2}$ **44.** $(9^0 + 2^0)^{-1}$
45. $\dfrac{1}{2^{-2}} + \dfrac{1}{3^{-1}}$ **46.** $\dfrac{2^{-1}}{3^{-1}}$ **47.** $\dfrac{-3^{-2}}{4^{-1}}$

Evaluate.

48. $\left(\dfrac{1}{3}\right)^{-1}$ **49.** $\left(\dfrac{-1}{5}\right)^2$ **50.** $\left(\dfrac{-7}{8}\right)^0$
51. $\left(\dfrac{1}{10}\right)^{-2}$ **52.** $\left(\dfrac{-2}{3}\right)^{-3}$ **53.** $\left(\dfrac{-3}{4}\right)^{-2}$

Simplify.

54. $x^4 \times x^3$ **55.** $x^{-2} \times x^3$ **56.** $y^{-1} \times y^{-3}$
57. $t^8 \div t^4$ **58.** $m^6 \div m^{-2}$ **59.** $b^{-2} \div b^{-4}$
60. $(m^4)^2$ **61.** $(t^{-2})^4$
62. $(y^{-5})^{-2}$ **63.** $m^3 \times m^{-2} \times m^4$
64. $\dfrac{a^{-4} \times a^{-2}}{a^2}$ **65.** $\dfrac{t^4 \times t^3}{t^9}$
66. $y^{-3} \times y^7 \times y^{-5}$ **67.** $t^{-4} \div t^{-6} \times t^6$

Problems and Applications

68. a) Use your calculator to evaluate each power in this sequence.

$2^5 \qquad 2^4 \qquad 2^3 \qquad 2^2 \qquad 2^1 \qquad 2^0$

b) Describe the pattern.

69. a) Evaluate each power in this sequence with a calculator.

$2^3 \quad 2^2 \quad 2^1 \quad 2^0 \quad 2^{-1} \quad 2^{-2} \quad 2^{-3} \quad 2^{-4}$

b) Write each decimal answer as a fraction.

c) What is the exponential form for the next power in this sequence?

d) Without using a calculator, state the fraction that equals your answer to part c).

70. a) Use a calculator to evaluate each power in this sequence.

$3^3 \quad 3^2 \quad 3^1 \quad 3^0 \quad 3^{-1} \quad 3^{-2} \quad 3^{-3}$

b) Compare 3^3 and 3^{-3} written as a fraction. What do you notice?

c) What mathematical term describes your answer to part b)?

71. Evaluate. **a)** $\dfrac{6^3}{6^2} \times \dfrac{5^6 \times 5^{-2}}{(5^2)^2}$ **b)** $\dfrac{45 \times 4^{-2}}{(2^2)^2}$

72. Use the exponent laws to simplify these expressions. Leave your answers in the form $ax^b y^c$ where a, b, and c are integers.

a) $\dfrac{34x^{-3}y^4}{17x^3y^5}$ **b)** $\dfrac{39x^7y^6}{13x^{-4}y^8}$

73. Evaluate for $a = 2$ and $b = 3$.

a) a^3 **b)** b^4 **c)** a^0

d) a^{-3} **e)** b^{-2} **f)** a^{-4}

g) $(a \times b)^{-2}$ **h)** $(a - b)^{-1}$ **i)** $(b^2 - a^2)^{-2}$

74. Which is greater, 2^{-3} or 3^{-2}? Explain your reasoning. Compare your answer with your calculator answer.

75. Find the value of x.

a) $2^x = 8$ **b)** $3^x = 81$ **c)** $4^x = 1$

d) $3^x = \dfrac{1}{9}$ **e)** $5^x = \dfrac{1}{125}$ **f)** $x^3 = 27$

g) $x^{-2} = \dfrac{1}{4}$ **h)** $x^{-3} = \dfrac{1}{1000}$

76. Evaluate.

a) $\left(\dfrac{1}{2}\right)^0$ **b)** $\left(\dfrac{2}{3}\right)^{-3}$

c) $\left(\dfrac{1}{3}\right)^2 \left(\dfrac{-1}{2}\right)^{-3}$ **d)** $\left(\dfrac{4}{5}\right)^0 - \left(\dfrac{3}{4}\right)^2$

e) $\left(\dfrac{4}{5}\right)^6 \left(\dfrac{4}{5}\right)^{-8}$ **f)** $\left(\dfrac{5}{3}\right)^3 \div \left(\dfrac{5}{3}\right)^5$

77. The radioactivity of a sample of carbon-14 drops to $\dfrac{1}{2}$ or 2^{-1} of its original value in about 5700 years. After 11 400 years, the radioactivity is $\dfrac{1}{4}$ or 2^{-2} of its original value.

a) What fraction of the radioactivity remains after 28 500 years?

b) Write the fraction as a power with a negative exponent.

c) Write the fraction as a power with a positive exponent.

d) After how long is the radioactivity $\dfrac{1}{128}$ or 2^{-7} times its original value?

78. Is each statement always true, sometimes true, or never true? Explain.

a) The value of a power with a negative exponent is less than 0.

b) The value of a power with a fractional base is less than 1.

c) Two powers in which the exponents are both 0 have equal values.

79. On a test, 3 students evaluated $2^{-2} \times 2^0$ as follows.

$$\text{Terry} \quad 2^{-2} \times 2^0 = 4^{-2}$$
$$= \dfrac{1}{4^2} \text{ or } \dfrac{1}{16}$$
$$\text{Sean} \quad 2^{-2} \times 2^0 = 2^0 \text{ or } 1$$
$$\text{Michel} \quad 2^{-2} \times 2^0 = 4^0 \text{ or } 1$$

a) What errors did each student make? What did each do correctly?

b) What is the correct answer?

80. Describe how to evaluate such powers as $(-3)^{-2}$ and -3^{-2}. Use your calculator to justify your descriptions. Compare your descriptions with your classmates'.

The Binary Number System

The decimal system that we use has ten digits.

0, 1, 2, 3, 4, 5, 6, 7, 8, 9

The **binary system** consists of 2 digits, 0 and 1.

A computer stores information in a **bit**, which is a short form of "binary digit." The electrical current in a bit can be either off or on. Off is represented by 0 and on by 1. Bits are combined into groups of 8 called **bytes**.

Activity ❶ Binary Numbers

Copy and complete the table to write the first 16 decimal numbers in binary. The first 5 have been done for you.

Decimal Form	Binary Form
0	0
1	1
2	10
3	11
4	100

Activity ❷ Powers of Two

1. Copy the following table. To complete it, use your results from Activity 1 and look for a pattern.

Decimal Number	Power of 2	Binary Number
1	2^0	1
2	2^1	10
4	2^2	100
8		
16		
32		
64		
128		

2. How is the exponent in the power of 2 related to the number of zeros in the binary number?

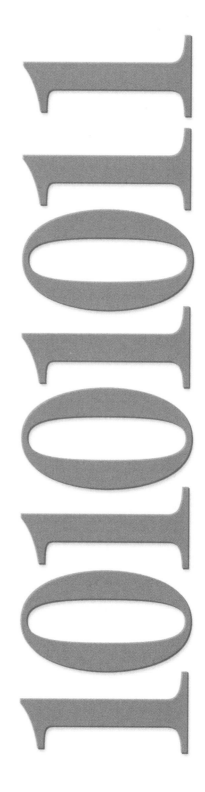

Activity ❸ Whole Numbers in Binary

You can use the results of Activity 2 to help you write whole numbers in binary form, because whole numbers can be written as sums of powers of 2. To write 43 as the sum of powers of 2, successively add the largest possible powers of 2.

$$43 = 32 + 11$$
$$= 32 + 8 + 3$$
$$= 32 + 8 + 2 + 1$$
$$= 2^5 + 2^3 + 2^1 + 2^0$$

In the binary system $2^5 + 2^3 + 2^1 + 2^0$
$$= 100000 + 1000 + 10 + 1$$
$$= 101011$$

Write each of these decimal numbers in binary form.

1. 20　　**2.** 37　　**3.** 56　　**4.** 78　　**5.** 147

Activity ❹ Binary Numbers to Whole Numbers

To write binary numbers as whole numbers, reverse the steps in Activity 3.

$$110110 = 100000 + 10000 + 100 + 10$$
$$= \quad 2^5 \quad + \quad 2^4 \quad + \quad 2^2 \quad + 2^1$$
$$= \quad 32 \quad + \quad 16 \quad + \quad 4 \quad + 2$$
$$= \quad 54$$

Write these binary numbers as whole numbers.

1. 10101　　　　**2.** 11001

3. 101010　　　　**4.** 110011

Activity ❺ Binary Codes

Some television stations scramble their signals so that viewers cannot use unauthorized satellite dishes. Authorized users receive a code to activate their descramblers. The code is a binary number.

If you had 1 bit to use, you could use one of 2 codes.　　　　0 or 1

If you had 2 bits, you could use one of 4 codes.
　　　　00　　01　　10　　11

1. How many different codes could you use if you had 3 bits? 4 bits? 5 bits?

2. Television stations have 2^{56} bits available to them. Approximately how many codes can they use? If you set about finding the code by trying 1 000 000 codes a day, about how many years would it take you to find the code if you succeeded on the last try?

1.12 Scientific Notation: Small Numbers

The wavelength is the distance from one peak of a wave to the next. The wavelength of red light is 0.000 07 cm. The wavelength of violet light is 0.000 04 cm. This is the range of wavelengths we can see. To work with these small numbers, we need to extend our knowledge of scientific notation.

Activity: Look for a Pattern

Copy and complete the table.

Inquire

1. Write a rule for writing numbers less than 1 in scientific notation.

2. Write in scientific notation the wavelength of
a) red light   **b)** violet light

3. Why would you not write 0.2347 in scientific notation?

Decimal Form	Product Form	Scientific Notation
0.52	$\frac{5.2}{10}$ or $5.2 \times \frac{1}{10^1}$	5.2×10^{-1}
0.052	$\frac{5.2}{?}$ or $5.2 \times \frac{1}{10^?}$	$5.2 \times 10^?$
0.0052	$\frac{5.2}{?}$ or $5.2 \times \frac{1}{10^?}$	$5.2 \times 10^?$
0.000 52	$\frac{5.2}{?}$ or $5.2 \times \frac{1}{10^?}$	$5.2 \times 10^?$

Example 1

Write in scientific notation.

a) 5100
b) 0.0051

Solution

Write the number in the form $x \times 10^n$, where x is greater than or equal to 1 but less than 10.

a) $5100 = 5.1 \times 1000$
$= 5.1 \times 10^3$

b) $0.0051 = 5.1 \times \frac{1}{1000}$
$= 5.1 \times \frac{1}{10^3}$
$= 5.1 \times 10^{-3}$

For 5100, the decimal point is moved 3 places to the left, and the exponent is 3. $5100 = 5.1 \times 10^3$

For 0.0051, the decimal point is moved 3 places to the right and the exponent is −3. $0.0051 = 5.1 \times 10^{-3}$

Example 2

Evaluate $(3.2 \times 10^{-2}) \times (5 \times 10^{-4})$.

Solution

$(3.2 \times 10^{-2}) \times (5 \times 10^{-4}) = 3.2 \times 5 \times 10^{-2} \times 10^{-4}$
$= 16 \times 10^{(-2)+(-4)}$
$= 16 \times 10^{-6}$
$= 1.6 \times 10^{-5}$

Practice

Write in scientific notation.

1. 4 500 000   **2.** 0.089

3. 0.2   **4.** 0.000 055

Write in scientific notation.

5. 45×10^7 **6.** 0.34×10^6

7. 33×10^{-8} **8.** 10^{-8}

9. 0.06×10^{-7} **10.** 100×10^{-14}

Write in decimal form.

11. 2.3×10^8 **12.** 4.7×10^{-6}

13. 7×10^{-9} **14.** 10^{-6}

Write the number that is 10 times as large as each of the following.

15. 2.3×10^6 **16.** 4.5×10^{-9}

17. 5×10^{-7} **18.** 10^{-11}

Write the number that is one-tenth as large as each of the following.

19. 7.8×10^9 **20.** 6.8×10^{-6}

21. 8×10^{-10} **22.** 10^{-7}

Estimate, then calculate. Write each answer in scientific notation.

23. $(2.5 \times 10^{-3}) \times (5 \times 10^{-4})$

24. $(8 \times 10^{-5}) \times (1.2 \times 10^{-1})$

25. $(3.2 \times 10^{-3}) \times (4.1 \times 10^{-2})$

26. $(5.2 \times 10^3) \div (2 \times 10^{-2})$

27. $(3.5 \times 10^{-4}) \div (7 \times 10^{-3})$

Problems and Applications

28. Order from highest to lowest.
a) 4.3×10^{-3}, 4.35×10^{-3}, 8.4×10^{-4}, 10^{-3}
b) 5.6×10^{-9}, 10^{-9}, $\frac{1}{10^8}$, 5.6×10^{-8}

c) $\frac{1}{1000}$, 2.1×10^{-3}, 10^{-2}, 2.12×10^{-3}

29. One water molecule has a mass of about 3×10^{-26} kg. Calculate the number of water molecules in Lake Superior, which holds about 1.2×10^{16} kg of water.

30. Energy is measured in joules, symbol J. If you tap your finger 10 times on your desk, you use about 1 J of energy. Express the following quantities of energy in scientific notation.
a) If you run for 1 h, you use about 2 000 000 J of energy.
b) When a cricket chirps, it uses about 0.0008 J of energy.
c) The food energy in a slice of apple pie is about 1 500 000 J.

31. Why is 0.23×10^{-9} not in scientific notation?

32. Is it possible to write the number 5 in scientific notation? Explain.

33. a) The waves that bombard us every day have wavelengths that range from 0.000 000 000 000 01 cm to 1 000 000 000 cm. Write these numbers in scientific notation.
b) Draw a number line showing the wavelengths in powers of 10.

$$\begin{array}{cccccccc} 10^{-3} & 10^{-2} & 10^{-1} & 1 & 10 & 10^2 & 10^3 \end{array}$$
Wavelength (cm)

Mark the range of wavelengths visible to humans.
c) Use your research skills to find out if there are creatures that can see outside the human range.

CALCULATOR POWER

1. On your calculator, multiply 0.000 000 4 × 0.000 055. How does your calculator display the answer?

2. Scientific calculators display
$$\boxed{2.2 \qquad -11}$$
. What does this answer mean?

3. Many calculators have an $\boxed{\text{EE}}$ key. To input 5.2×10^{-8}, press **5** $\boxed{\cdot}$ **2** $\boxed{\text{EE}}$ **8** $\boxed{+/-}$
Use the $\boxed{\text{EE}}$ key to evaluate the following. Describe your calculator key strokes in each case.
a) $(3.5 \times 10^{-4}) \times (4.8 \times 10^{-7})$
b) $(1.5 \times 10^{-8}) \div (5 \times 10^{-12})$
c) $\dfrac{(3.6 \times 10^6) \times (2.4 \times 10^{-8})}{2.7 \times 10^{-3}}$

Calculators and the Order of Operations

Activity ❶ Addition, Subtraction, Multiplication, and Division

1. a) Use your calculator to evaluate this expression.
$$3.2 \times 2.0 - 8.8 \div 2.2$$

b) In what order does your calculator perform operations when addition, subtraction, multiplication, and division are involved?

2. a) Is 7 the correct value for the following expression? Explain.
$$7 - 8 \times 0.5 - 0.5$$

b) If the correct value is not 7, what is it?

3. Use your calculator to evaluate each expression.

a) $\frac{7}{10} - 0.5 \times \frac{2}{5}$　　　　　　**b)** $\frac{9}{10} - 0.1 \div \frac{1}{10}$

c) $10 \div \frac{1}{2} \times 2.5$　　　　　　**d)** $10 + 10 \times 0.5 \div 0.5$

Activity ❷ Brackets and Exponents

1. a) Use your calculator to evaluate the expressions $-6.2 \div (0.5)^2 - 1.6$ and $-6.2 \div 0.5^2 - 1.6$.

b) Does the use of brackets, in this case, make any difference to the order in which your calculator evaluates the expressions? Explain.

2. a) Use your calculator to evaluate the expression $-3^2 \times (4 - 1)^3$.

b) In what order does your calculator perform operations for expressions that contain exponents and brackets?

3. What does the acronym BEDMAS mean?

4. a) Is 3.4 the correct value for the following expression? Explain.
$$8.8 \div 2.2 \times 3 + (6.1 - 1.1) \div 5$$

b) If the correct value is not 3.4, what is it?

5. Use your calculator to evaluate each expression.
a) $96 - 3(4.2 - 0.2)$
b) $(19.5 - 6.5)^2 - (8.4 - 4.4) - 7 \times 10$

6. Add brackets to make each statement true.
a) $\frac{2}{3} + 4 \times \frac{1}{2} + \frac{1}{4} \div 3 = \frac{5}{3}$　　　**b)** $0.5^2 - 0.1 \times 8 \div 2 = 0.6$
c) $-2 \times 18.5 - 6.3 \div 4 = -6.1$

7. Some calculators do not have square bracket keys. Use your knowledge of the order of operations to evaluate $-4[8 + 7(6 - 3)]$.

Activity ❸ Using the Memory Keys

Most calculators have one memory for storing and recalling data.

1. a) If your calculator does not have [M+] and [MRC] keys, what are the equivalent keys on your calculator?

b) Follow this keying sequence.
Press [C] 10 [M+] [C] [MRC] [=]

c) Describe the functions of the [M+] and [MRC] keys.

2. Do not clear the memory. Follow these keying sequences.

a) Press [C] 20 [+] [MRC] [=]

b) Press [C] 30 [−] [MRC] [=]

c) Press [C] 40 [×] [MRC] [=]

d) Press [C] 50 [÷] [MRC] [=]

3. a) Describe the use of the calculator's memory in question 2.

b) How did the calculator's memory save keystrokes?

4. a) Clear the memory by pressing [MRC] [MRC] when the display is zero. Then, follow this keying sequence.
Press [C] 35 [M+] 62 [+] 20 [+] [MRC] [=]

b) How was the calculator's memory used in this example?

Activity ❹ Using The Calculator Efficiently

1. a) Describe how you would use the [M+] and [MRC] keys to evaluate $(31.3 - 24.7) \times (15.7 + 4.6)$, without using bracket keys.

b) How many keystrokes did you use to calculate the answer in part a)?

2. Find and describe another keying sequence that uses less keystrokes.

3. Which keystroke method is more efficient? Explain.

4. a) Use your calculator to devise one way to calculate the answer to this expression to 4 decimal places, without using bracket keys. $\dfrac{31.5}{11.1 \times (24.5 - 6.8)}$

b) Record the type and number of keystrokes that you used to make the calculation.

5. a) Find another calculator method that uses less keystrokes to evaluate the expression in question 4.

b) Which of the two methods is more efficient? Explain.

6. a) Explore other calculator methods that can be used to make the calculation in question 4. Compare your answers with a classmate's.

b) Which method is the most efficient?

c) Which method do you prefer? Explain.

1.13 Rational Numbers and Formulas

Hailstones are balls of ice that grow as they are held up in the clouds by thunderstorm updrafts. While they are held up, supercooled water drops hit them and freeze, causing the hailstones to grow. Large hailstones can fall at speeds of up to 150 km/h and can have masses of up to 2 kg. Because of the damage that can occur during a hailstorm, weather forecasters try to warn people when hail is probable.

Activity: Use a Formula

Weather forecasters can use a formula to estimate the size of hailstones if the speed of the thunderstorm updraft is known. The formula is

$$d = 0.05s$$

where s is the speed of the updraft in kilometres per hour, and d is the diameter of a hailstone in centimetres.

Inquire

1. What is the predicted diameter of a hailstone when the updraft speed is 30 km/h? 80 km/h? 100 km/h?

2. The smallest hailstone possible is about 0.5 cm in diameter. What is the approximate updraft speed to produce this hailstone?

3. How might weather forecasters determine the speed of an updraft?

Example

Tidal waves are caused by underwater earthquakes or large storms at sea. Tidal waves can be very destructive if they crash into populated areas. The speed of a tidal wave in metres per second can be found using the formula

$$s = 3.1 \times \sqrt{d}$$

where d is the depth of the ocean in metres. To the nearest tenth of a metre per second, what is the speed of a tidal wave in 300 m of water? 50 m of water?

Solution

$s = 3.1 \times \sqrt{d}$

In 300 m of water
$s = 3.1 \times \sqrt{300}$
$\doteq 53.7$

In 50 m of water
$s = 3.1 \times \sqrt{50}$
$\doteq 21.9$

In 50 m of water, the speed is about 21.9 m/s.

© 3.1 × 300 √ ⊟ [53.693575]
In 300 m of water, the speed is about 53.7 m/s.

Problems and Applications

1. The stopping distance a car requires in good road conditions is given by the formula
$$d = 0.4s + 0.002s^2$$
where d represents the approximate stopping distance in metres and s represents the speed in kilometres per hour. Calculate the distance required to stop at the following speeds.
a) 50 km/h **b)** 80 km/h
c) 100 km/h **d)** 120 km/h

2. The drama club decided to raise money by performing in a drama marathon. Pledges averaged $5.50 per actor for every hour of acting. Write a formula to calculate the amount each member could earn for the club. Let h represent the number of hours each member performs and v represent the amount of money earned.

3. The Purple Cab Company needs a formula to program into its computers to calculate fares. The manager has decided that a minimum fare of $3.50 must be charged. There is also a charge of $0.70 per half kilometre.
a) Write the formula for the total fare.
b) Determine the cost of a 7.5 km ride.

4. A rental company charges for lawn ornament rentals according to the formula
$$C = 2.40n + 2.00$$
where n is the number of ornaments rented and C is the cost in dollars. Calculate the cost of renting 12 pink flamingos for a birthday party.

5. The face value, f dollars, of a collection of dimes and nickels is given by the equation
$$f = 0.1d + 0.05n$$
where d is the number of dimes and n is the number of nickels. What is the face value of 35 dimes and 48 nickels?

6. The following formula calculates the time, t seconds, it takes for an object to fall from a height, h metres.
$$t = \sqrt{h \div 4.9}$$
The High Level Bridge in Lethbridge, Alberta, is the highest railway bridge of its type in the world. It stands 96 m above the river valley below. How long does it take for an object to fall from the top of the High Level Bridge to the ground below it?

7. The period of revolution of a planet around the sun is the time it takes for the planet to complete one orbit of the sun. The period, P years, is given by Kepler's third law
$$P^2 = D^3$$
where D is the average distance of the planet from the sun in astronomical units (AU). One astronomical unit is the average distance of the Earth from the sun. Use the average distance from the sun to find the period of revolution for each of the following planets to the nearest tenth of a year.
a) Jupiter; 5.20 AU
b) Mercury; 0.387 AU
c) Uranus; 19.2 AU

8. Write a problem that requires a formula. Have a classmate solve your problem.

CALCULATOR POWER

Here is a way to write the digits from 1 to 9 in order, so that when + or − signs are included the answer is 100.
$$123 + 45 - 67 + 8 - 9 = 100$$
Find 4 other ways to do this.

1.14 Use a Data Bank

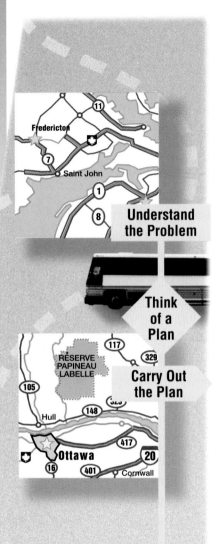

You must locate information to solve some problems. There are many sources of information, including computer files, libraries, newspapers, magazines, atlases, experts, and data banks.

A grade 9 history class is going from Saint John to Ottawa, then to Montreal, and back to Saint John. The students will spend 3 days in Ottawa and 2 days in Montreal. Their bus can average 70 km/h. The students plan to leave Saint John on a Monday morning. Draw up a schedule for the trip.

Understand the Problem

1. What information are you given?

2. What are you asked to find?

3. What information do you need to locate?

4. Do you need an exact or approximate answer?

Think of a Plan

You need the driving distances between the cities. You could use an atlas, almanac, or road map, or ask at a tourist information centre. To calculate the time required for each part of the trip, divide the distance by the average speed.

Carry Out the Plan

Use the Data Bank on pages 364 to 369 in this book. Use the chart of "Driving Distances Between Cities."

Saint John to Ottawa	1130 km
Ottawa to Montreal	190 km
Montreal to Saint John	940 km

Saint John to Ottawa takes $1130 \div 70 \doteq 16$ h. Allow 2 days.
Ottawa to Montreal takes $190 \div 70 \doteq 3$ h. Allow $\frac{1}{2}$ a day.

Montreal to Saint John takes $940 \div 70 \doteq 13$ h. Allow $1\frac{1}{2}$ days.

Schedule: Leave Saint John Monday morning. Arrive in Ottawa Tuesday evening. Spend Wednesday, Thursday, and Friday in Ottawa. Leave Saturday morning for Montreal. Arrive in Montreal at noon on Saturday. Spend the rest of Saturday and Sunday in Montreal. Leave Montreal for Saint John on Monday morning. Arrive in Saint John on Tuesday around noon.

Look Back

Does the schedule seem reasonable?

Use a Data Bank	
	1. Look up the information you need.
	2. Solve the problem.
	3. Check that the answer is reasonable.

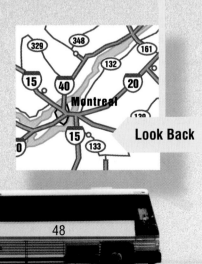

Problems and Applications

Use the Data Bank on pages 364 to 369 of this book to solve the problems.

1. a) What is the flying distance between Vancouver and Regina?
b) What is the driving distance between Vancouver and Regina?
c) How much longer is the driving distance than the flying distance?

2. The St. Joseph's High School Band is planning a tour. The band will leave from Halifax and stop in Saint John, Quebec City, Toronto, and Montreal, in that order. The band will play one concert at a high school in each city and will then return to Halifax. The band will travel on a bus that can average 80 km/h. The band will leave Halifax on a Monday morning. Draw up a schedule for the trip.

3. Sandra flew from Vancouver to Halifax to compete in a gymnastics competition. She left Vancouver at 11:00. The flight to Toronto took 4 h. She took 1 h and 15 min to change planes in Toronto. The flight to Halifax took 1 h and 30 min. What time was it in Halifax when she landed?

4. What is the wind chill temperature if the thermometer reading is $-23°C$ and the wind speed is 32 km/h?

5. If it is 09:00 on July 1 in Paris, France, what is the time and the date in Sydney, Australia?

6. Justine drove from Halifax to Vancouver. She drove on the Trans Canada Highway for the entire trip.
a) How far did she drive?
b) If she averaged 90 km/h, how many hours did she spend driving?
c) What major cities did she drive through?

7. The world's longest covered bridge is at Hartland, New Brunswick. The world's longest cantilevered bridge is the Pont de Quebec across the St. Lawrence River. How many times longer is the Pont de Quebec?

8. The population density of a country, city, or region is the average number of people living in each square kilometre of land. Use the area and the population of each Canadian province to work out the population density of each. Rank the population densities from highest to lowest.

9. a) You are the manager of a music group that wants to tour cities in Canada for two weeks to promote its new release. Make up a travel schedule for the group.
b) Compare your schedule with your classmates'. Decide the best features of each schedule.

NUMBER POWER

This puzzle appeared in the work of a Chinese mathematician, Sun Tzu, who lived in the 4th or 5th century A.D.

Pick a whole number less than 60 and greater than 5. Divide the whole number by 3. Call the remainder x. Divide the whole number by 4. Call the remainder y. Divide the whole number by 5. Call the remainder z.

Evaluate the expression
$$40 \times x + 45 \times y + 36 \times z$$
and divide the value by 60.
a) What do you notice about the remainder?
b) Compare your finding with your classmates'.

49

Radiocarbon Dating

One theory about how people first entered North and South America is that they crossed the Bering Strait over 40 000 years ago. One method that archaeologists use to establish such dates is called *radiocarbon dating*.

All living plants and animals contain the same amount of radioactive carbon–14, C–14, per kilogram of mass. When they die, the C–14 slowly changes to nitrogen–14, N–14, which is not radioactive. The level of radioactivity of the dead plant or animal slowly decreases with time. By measuring the level of radioactivity, archaeologists can find how much C–14 is left.

It takes about 5700 years for half the C–14 to change to N–14. Another way of saying this is that C–14 has a "half-life" of about 5700 years.

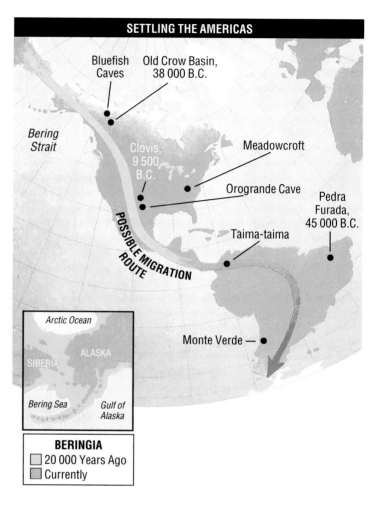

SETTLING THE AMERICAS

Activity ❶

Copy and complete the table. Graph the percent of C–14 remaining versus time after death.

Time After Death (Years)	Percent of C–14 Remaining
0	100
5700	50
11 400	25
17 100	
22 800	
28 500	
34 200	
39 900	

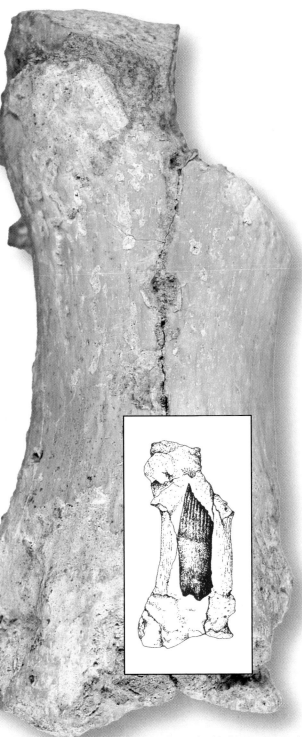

Spear point embedded in toe bone of a horse discovered in New Mexico.

Activity ❷

The map shows where archaeological digs have discovered evidence of human activity.

1. At the Bluefish Caves in the Yukon, Jacques Cinq-Mars of the Archaeological Survey of Canada found a caribou bone that was cut and shaped to form a tool. Six percent of the C–14 remained in the bone. How old is the bone? What was the date of the settlement at the Bluefish Caves?

2. At Monte Verde in southern Chile, dead plants from 15 species still used today for medicinal purposes were found under a peat bog. The plants came from the coast, 100 km away. The settlers probably trekked to the coast to get them. The plants had 20% of their C–14 remaining. How old are they?

3. At Taima-taima in Venezuela, the remains of a slain mastodon were found. The remains had 21% of their C–14 remaining. How old are the remains?

4. At Orogrande Cave in New Mexico, a horse's toe bone with a spear point in it had 5% of its C–14 remaining. How old is the bone?

5. In southwestern Pennsylvania, a mat woven from bark was found in a settlement that has been named Meadowcroft. The bark had 10% of its C–14 remaining. How old is the mat? What was the date of the settlement?

Review

Calculate.

1. 5^2

2. 7^2

3. 12^2

4. 31^2

5. $\sqrt{0.16}$

6. $\sqrt{81}$

7. $\sqrt{121}$

8. $\sqrt{400}$

9. $6\sqrt{36}$

10. $3^2 + 4^2 + 7^2$

11. $-8\sqrt{49}$

12. $\dfrac{6\sqrt{25} - 8}{2}$

Write both square roots of each number.

13. 25

14. 36

15. 64

16. 144

Estimate. Then, calculate to the nearest tenth.

17. $\sqrt{59}$

18. $\sqrt{372}$

19. $\sqrt{1273}$

20. $\sqrt{41\ 093}$

21. $\sqrt{4.93}$

22. $\sqrt{0.0187}$

Calculate to the nearest tenth.

23. $\sqrt{5} - \sqrt{7}$

24. $3\sqrt{17}$

25. $10\sqrt{7} - 6\sqrt{19}$

26. $(\sqrt{23})(\sqrt{8})$

27. $\sqrt{18} \div \sqrt{5}$

28. $\dfrac{\sqrt{30} - \sqrt{20}}{\sqrt{3}}$

Express in exponential form.

29. $2^3 \times 2^5$

30. $5^7 \div 5^3$

31. $(2^4)^2$

32. $7^8 \times 7^4$

33. $(3^3)^3$

34. $6^5 \div 6$

35. Evaluate for $c = 5, d = -6$.

a) $5c + 4d$

b) $3d + 4cd$

c) $c^2 + d^2$

Write in scientific notation.

36. 27 300 000

37. 0.000 000 019 3

Write in decimal notation.

38. 2.53×10^7

39. 9.71×10^{-4}

Calculate. Write your answer in scientific notation.

40. $(2.5 \times 10^3)(3.1 \times 10^5)$

41. $(6.2 \times 10^{-4})(3.7 \times 10^2)$

42. $(8.6 \times 10^{21}) \div (2.5 \times 10^7)$

Evaluate.

43. 3^5

44. 12^2

45. $(-5)^3$

46. $5(2)^5$

47. 6^0

48. $(-5)^0$

49. 2^{-1}

50. 3^{-2}

51. $\left(\dfrac{2}{3}\right)^3$

52. $\left(\dfrac{3}{5}\right)^{-2}$

53. $\dfrac{1}{3^{-2}}$

54. $\dfrac{5}{2^{-3}}$

Evaluate.

55. $3^{-1} - 3^0$

56. $2^{-3} + 2^{-2}$

Simplify.

57. $2^3 \times 2^{-5}$

58. $n^{-4} \div n^{-6}$

59. $((-3)^{-2})^4$

60. $((-x)^5)^{-1}$

61. $(-0.4)^{-5}(-0.4)^{-3}$

62. $4^2 \times 4^{-3} \times 4^{-1}$

Evaluate.

63. $5^3 \times 5^2 \times 5$

64. $2^0 \times 2^3$

65. $6^5 \div 6^3$

66. $(2^3)^4$

67. $2^{-3} \times 2^2$

68. $(4^2)^3 \div 4^4$

69. $(2^3)^{-2}$

70. $((-3)^2)^{-1}$

71. Evaluate for $x = 3$ and $y = -2$.

a) $x^2 y^2$

b) y^5

c) $-6xy$

d) $(x - y)^3$

e) $6x^3 - 5y$

f) $(-x)^2(-y)^2$

Calculate. Write your answer in decimal notation.

72. 4.716×100

73. 16.93×10^3

74. $0.63 \div 10$

75. $123.94 \div 10^3$

Simplify.

76. $(-2x^2y^3)^3$

77. $(-5x^2y^2)^2$

78. $(-2abc^4)^3$

Simplify.

79. $(2x^2yz^2)(x^2y^2z^2)^3$

80. $(3a^3b)^3(-a^3bx^4)$

Simplify.

81. $\left(\dfrac{f}{3}\right)^3$

82. $\left(\dfrac{-r}{q}\right)^7$

83. $\left(\dfrac{5m}{7n}\right)^2$

84. A box of mirror tiles contains 25 square tiles. Each tile covers 400 cm².
a) What are the dimensions of each tile?
b) What is the total area covered by the 25 tiles?
c) What length of edging is needed around the mirror?

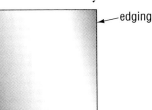

←—edging

85. Quebec City has a population of about 6.4×10^5 and an area of about 3.2×10^3 km².
a) How many square kilometres are there per person in Quebec City? Write your answer in scientific notation.
b) If each person's area was a square, what would its side be to the nearest metre?

86. a) Why is 0.45×10^7 not in scientific notation?
b) Write 0.45×10^7 in scientific notation.

87. The velocity of sound in air may be found from the formula
$$V = 20\sqrt{273 + T}$$
where V is the velocity in metres per second and T is the temperature in degrees Celsius. Calculate the velocity of sound in air when the temperature is
a) 18°C   **b)** 30°C

c) the temperature on Canada's coldest day ever

88. The formula that the Safety Taxi Co. uses to determine fares is
$$F = 2.50 + 0.125d$$
where F is the fare in dollars and d is the distance travelled in kilometres. Find the fare from Hyde Street to 34 Busy Road if the distance is 5.6 km.

Group Decision Making
Researching Earth Science Careers

To work effectively in groups.
a) Contribute ideas by speaking quietly.
b) Encourage others to participate, and listen to them carefully.
c) Respect the opinions of others.
d) Ask the teacher for help only when your whole group has the same difficulty.

1. Brainstorm as a class 6 earth science careers to investigate. They might include geographer, cartographer, geologist, paleontologist, and seismologist.

2. In home groups of 6, decide which career each person will research.

1 2 3 4 5 6	1 2 3 4 5 6

Home Groups

1 2 3 4 5 6	1 2 3 4 5 6

3. In your home group, decide what you want to know about each career. Make sure you include the ways in which math is used in each career.

4. Research your career individually.

5. Form an expert group with students who researched the same career as you. Combine your findings.

Expert Groups

6. In your expert group, prepare a report on the career. The report can take any form the group chooses.

7. In your expert group, evaluate the process and your presentation. What worked well and what would you do differently next time?

Chapter Check

Calculate.

1. $\sqrt{36}$ **2.** $5\sqrt{16}$ **3.** $-\sqrt{121}$

Estimate. Then, calculate to the nearest tenth.

4. $\sqrt{93}$ **5.** $(\sqrt{8})(\sqrt{39})$

Evaluate for $r = 4$ and $t = -5$.

6. $5r + 4t$ **7.** $3rt + t^2$

Evaluate for $x = 0.5$ and $y = 1.2$.

8. $3x + 5y$ **9.** $10xy - 2x$

Evaluate.

10. 4^2 **11.** 3^4 **12.** 5^3

Write the answer in exponential form.

13. $3^4 \times 3^5$ **14.** $2^7 \div 2^3$ **15.** $(5^2)^4$

Write in scientific notation.

16. 45 000 000   **17.** 213 000

Evaluate.

18. $(-3)^4$ **19.** $(-1)^{14}$

20. 6^0 **21.** 5^{-1}

22. $(3^{-2})^2$ **23.** $(-3)^{-2}$

24. -2^3 **25.** $(-0.7)^2$

26. $2^5 \div (-2)^3$ **27.** $5^{-2} \times 5^3 \times 5^{-2}$

28. $7^0 - 4^{-1}$ **29.** $(1 - 3)^4$

Write in scientific notation.

30. 0.0004

31. 0.000 000 000 002 31

Write in decimal form.

32. 4.6×10^{-3} **33.** 3.21×10^{-6}

Estimate, then calculate. Express your answer in scientific notation.

34. $(9.5 \times 10^{-2}) \times (5.1 \times 10^{-6})$

35. $(6.3 \times 10^{-4}) \div (1.9 \times 10^{-7})$

Simplify.

36. $(-3)^4 \div (-3)^5$

37. $s^2 \times s^{-5}$

38. $((2)^{-3})^{-1}$

39. $3^{-1} \div 3^{-2} \times 3^{-3}$

40. Evaluate for $m = -2$.
a) $3m^4$ **b)** $4m^3 + 5$

41. Forty percent of Canada's cropland is in Saskatchewan. The total area of cropland in Saskatchewan is about 134 000 km². What are the dimensions of a square that is big enough to hold all this land? Give your answer to the nearest kilometre.

Simplify.

42. $(-3x^4y^3)^3$ **43.** $(x^2y^4)(-3x^3y^2)^2$

Simplify.

44. $\left(\dfrac{g}{8}\right)^2$ **45.** $\left(\dfrac{-b}{d}\right)^9$ **46.** $\left(\dfrac{2y}{3k}\right)^4$

47. The cost of renting a car from a car rental agency is given by the formula
$$C = 50n + 0.25d$$
where C is the cost in dollars, n is the number of days the car is rented for, and d is the total distance driven in kilometres.
a) Calculate the cost of renting a car for 3 days and driving 350 km per day.
b) How much money do you have left for food and accommodations if you have $750 budgeted for the trip?

Using the Strategies

1. Copy the diagram. Place the digits from 1 to 5 in the squares so that the product is 3542.

2. What is the side of a cube that can be made with 294 cm² of cardboard? What assumptions have you made?

3. Jason chose a whole number less than 10. He multiplied the number by 6 and added 1. The result was a perfect square. What numbers could he have chosen?

4. Find 3 consecutive whole numbers whose sum is 144.

5. How many Friday the thirteenths will there be in the year you turn 21?

FRIDAY
13

6. Assume that the following pattern continues.

A, BBB, CCCCC, DDDDDDD, ...

a) How many letter Ms will there be?
b) How many letter Zs will there be?

7. In the figure, the side of each small square represents 1 cm.

Find the area of
a) the shaded region.
b) the unshaded region.

8. How many different combinations of coins have a value of $0.28? Copy and complete the table to find out.

	Coins			
Combinations	$0.25	$0.10	$0.05	$0.01
1	1	0	0	3
2	0	1	2	8
3				

9. The number 63 can be written as the sum of consecutive whole numbers as follows.

$$63 = 20 + 21 + 22$$

a) Find another way to write 63 as the sum of consecutive whole numbers.
b) Find 4 consecutive whole numbers that add to 138.

10. a) On a digital clock, how many times a day are the digits all the same?

b) Write another question about the numbers on a digital clock. Have a classmate solve your problem.

11. Draw a flow chart to represent each process. Compare your flow charts with a classmate's.
a) getting a driver's permit
b) writing a computer program

DATA BANK

Use the Data Bank on pages 364 to 369 to find the information you need.

1. If the Canadian province with the greatest area had the shape of a square, what would be the length of each side to the nearest kilometre?

2. Would you feel colder at a temperature of −7 °C with the wind at 32 km/h or at a temperature of −18 °C with the wind at 8 km/h? Explain.

CHAPTER 2

Patterns and Equations

Crime writers have used codes many times. "The Shadow" was a crime fighter in the 1930s. He was created by Walter B. Gibson. Here is a cipher used by "The Shadow."

A	B	C	D
E	F	G	H
I	J	K	L
M	N	O	P
Q	R	S	T
U	V	W	X
Y	Z		

Extra Symbols:

1   2   3   4

The extra symbols tell the decoder how far the letter symbols have been rotated to the right in the message in order to disguise them. The symbol means they have been rotated 90° to the right.

Decode this message.

Sir Arthur Conan Doyle used a code in the Sherlock Holmes story "The Adventure of the Dancing Men." Research how he used the code.

Activity ❶ Patterns in Tables

The patterns in the tables are found in the columns. Copy and complete the tables. Write the rules for completing each table.

1.

1	4	7	9	12	9		
3	3	4	5	4		7	9
4	7	11			16	20	
3	12	28					72

2.

1	4	6	9	11			
2	8	12			14		30
4	16	24			20		
7	28	42					

3.

1	4	6	9	3			
30	77	91				99	96
6	11	13			8		12
5	7	7	1	5	2	9	

4.

15	14	12			36	40	
3	2	3		3	4		
5	7	4	6	9		20	
2	5	1	2				

5.

3	5	6	4		7	5	
24	45	42		16	28	25	
35	59	55					
8	9	7	5	8			

6.

2	3	5	4			10	
6	9	15		18			
7	10	16		25			
13	19	31					

Activity ❷ Stamp Patterns

Two stamps can be attached to form two rectangular shapes.

1. In how many ways can 12 stamps be attached to form rectangular shapes? Sketch your solutions.

2. How many rectangular shapes can be made with 10 attached stamps?

3. How many rectangular shapes can be made with 24 attached stamps?

4. Without drawing the stamps, how can you determine how many rectangular shapes can be made with 100 attached stamps?

Activity ❸ Tile Patterns

A floor is being tiled using the following pattern. Each yellow tile is surrounded by white tiles.

1. How many tiles of each colour do you need to tile each of the following areas?
a) 3 tiles by 3 tiles   **b)** 5 tiles by 3 tiles
c) 5 tiles by 5 tiles   **d)** 7 tiles by 3 tiles
e) 7 tiles by 5 tiles   **f)** 7 tiles by 7 tiles

Activity ❹ Patterns in Drawings

Determine the pattern and then sketch the next figure in the sequence.

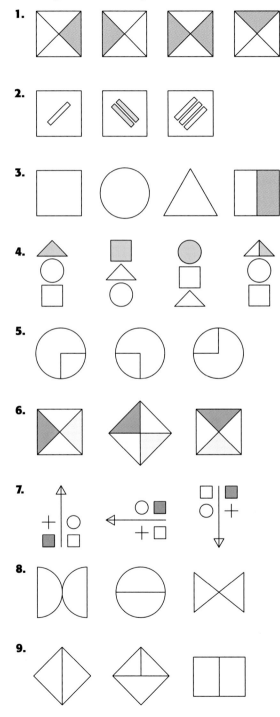

1.

2.

3.

4.

5.

6.

7.

8.

9.

Mental Math

Simplify.

1. $10 + 20 - 30$ **2.** $10 - 10 + 10$

3. $-10 + 2 + 2$ **4.** $15 - 5 - 4$

5. $-15 + 2 + 1$ **6.** $-10 - 10 - 10$

7. $-10 - 10 - 20$ **8.** $-15 + 5 - 15$

9. $-50 + 25 + 5$ **10.** $100 - 80 - 10$

Simplify.

11. $(2)^3$ **12.** $(-3)^2$ **13.** $(-1)^5$

14. $(-1)^8$ **15.** -5^2 **16.** -5^0

17. $(4)^2$ **18.** $(-2)^2$ **19.** -10^2

20. $(3)^3$ **21.** -1^3 **22.** -1^6

23. $(-8)^0$ **24.** $(-3)^3$ **25.** -3^2

Multiply.

26. $-2 \times (-3) \times 5$ **27.** $-2 \times (-2) \times (-5)$

28. $5 \times (-5) \times 2$ **29.** $5 \times 4 \times (-3)$

30. $-4 \times 3 \times 2$ **31.** $6 \times (-5) \times (-2)$

32. $10 \times 10 \times (-10)$ **33.** $-10 \times (-10) \times 2$

Divide.

34. $\dfrac{-18}{9}$ **35.** $\dfrac{21}{-7}$ **36.** $\dfrac{-42}{6}$

37. $\dfrac{-14}{-7}$ **38.** $\dfrac{-20}{-5}$ **39.** $\dfrac{-24}{-6}$

40. $\dfrac{21}{3}$ **41.** $\dfrac{-49}{7}$ **42.** $\dfrac{-54}{-6}$

43. $\dfrac{-33}{11}$ **44.** $\dfrac{44}{-4}$ **45.** $\dfrac{-50}{-5}$

Simplify. State each answer in exponential form.

46. 3×3^0 **47.** 2×2^2 **48.** $3^5 \times 3^{-2}$

49. $6^4 \times 6^{-2}$ **50.** $4^{-2} \times 4^3$ **51.** $5^{-3} \times 5^5$

52. $3^7 \div 3^5$ **53.** $4^{10} \div 4^8$ **54.** $2^8 \div 2^7$

55. $2 \div 2^{-2}$ **56.** $3 \div 3^{-1}$ **57.** $4 \div 4^{-1}$

58. $\dfrac{5^5}{5^3}$ **59.** $\dfrac{6^3}{6^2}$ **60.** $\dfrac{2}{2^{-2}}$

2.1 Look for a Pattern

Patterns are everywhere, and people often use them in their work. Scientists look for patterns in their research findings. Air traffic controllers use traffic patterns.

Using patterns to *predict results* is a very useful problem solving tool. Store managers and hotel managers use patterns to predict and plan for their busy times. Meteorologists use patterns to help predict the weather.

A group of towns has a phone network to call volunteer firefighters in the event of a forest fire. The fire chief phones 2 firefighters and gives them information about the fire. In the second round of calls, these 2 firefighters each phone 2 more. In the third round of calls, each person called in the second round phones 2 more people. How many firefighters are called in the ninth round of calls?

1. What information are you given?

Understand the Problem

2. What are you asked to find?

3. Do you need an exact or approximate answer?

Think of a Plan

Make a table. Write the numbers of people called in the first few rounds of calls and look for a pattern.

Round of Calls	1	2	3	4	5	6	7	8	9
Number of People Called	2 or 2^1	4 or 2^2	8 or 2^3	16 or 2^4					

Carry Out the Plan

The number of calls in a round equals 2 raised to an exponent that equals the round number.

From this pattern, we predict that 2^5 people are called in the fifth round, 2^6 people in the sixth round, and so on.

In the ninth round of calls, 2^9 or 512 people are called.

Does the answer seem reasonable?

Look Back

Can you think of another way to solve the problem?

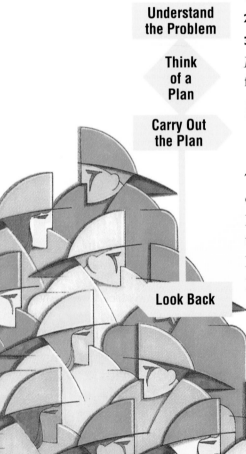

Look for a Pattern	1. Use the given information to find a pattern.
	2. Use the pattern to solve the problem.
	3. Check that the answer is reasonable.

Problems and Applications

In questions 1–5, determine the pattern in each set of numbers. Then, write the next 2 numbers.

1. 5, 8, 11, 14, ■ , ■

2. 14, 12, 10, 8, ■ , ■

3. 10, 12, 9, 11, 8, 10, 7, ■ , ■

4. 5, 10, 20, 40, ■ , ■

5. 256, 128, 64, 32, ■ , ■

6. If the pattern continues, how many toothpicks are needed for
a) the 5th diagram?
b) the 6th diagram?
c) the 50th diagram?

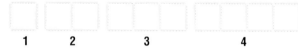

1   2   3   4

7. The numbers 1, 8, 27, and 64 are the first 4 cubes.
a) Find the sum of the first 2 cubes.
b) Find the sum of the first 3 cubes.
c) Find the sum of the first 4 cubes.
d) Describe the pattern in the sums.
e) Use the pattern to find the sum of the first 9 cubes.

8. Find the pattern and complete the chart.
$$1 \times 1 = \blacksquare$$
$$11 \times 11 = \blacksquare$$
$$111 \times 111 = \blacksquare$$
$$1111 \times 1111 = \blacksquare$$
$$11\ 111 \times 11\ 111 = \blacksquare$$
$$111\ 111 \times 111\ 111 = \blacksquare$$

9. A computer company donated money to a university scholarship fund for 10 years. In the first year, the company gave $1 000 000. Every year after that, it gave $100 000 more than in the previous year. How much did the university receive in the tenth year?

10. Six people entered a chess tournament. Each player played until losing a game. If there were no draws, how many games were played?

11. There are 10 rooms on each floor of a hotel. There are 9 floors. The rooms are numbered from 10 to 19 on the first floor, from 20 to 29 on the second floor, and so on. You have been hired to put new brass numbers on each room door. For example, you will put one brass "1" and one brass "0" on the door of the first room. To have enough brass numbers, how many will you need to buy for each digit from 0 to 9?

12. If you place a block on a table, 5 faces are showing. If you add another block as shown, 8 faces are showing. How many faces are showing when there are 21 blocks in a row?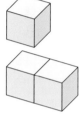

13. How many logs will be in a pile with 9 logs in the bottom row?

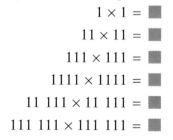

1   2   3   4

14. The staircase has 4 steps and is made up of 20 cubes. How many cubes are needed for a staircase with 12 steps?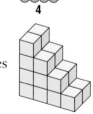

15. Eight people entered a tennis tournament. Each person played everyone else once. How many games were played?

16. A triangle has no diagonals. A quadrilateral has 2 diagonals. A pentagon has 5 diagonals. How many diagonals does a 12-sided figure have?

17. Write a problem you can solve by finding a pattern. Have a classmate solve your problem.

2.2 Evaluating Expressions

At the 1993 Juno Awards, the theme song from the movie *Beauty and the Beast* was voted best single of the year. It was sung by Quebec's Celine Dion and an American, Peabo Bryson.

Activity: Discover the Relationship

The prices of tickets for a recent Celine Dion concert are shown in the table. Copy and complete the table.

Number of Tickets Purchased	Main Floor	Balcony
1	$32.50	$28.50
2		
3		
4		
5		

Inquire

1. If n is the number of seats on the main floor, write an algebraic expression for the total cost of the main-floor tickets.

2. If m is the number of seats in the balcony, write an expression for the total cost of the balcony tickets.

3. Use the expressions from 1 and 2 to calculate the cost of tickets for everyone in your class to
a) sit on the main floor.
b) sit in the balcony.

A letter that represents one or more numbers is called a **variable**. Expressions such as $x + 2y + 10$, which include numbers and variables, are called **algebraic expressions**.

The expression $x + 2y + 10$ has 3 **terms**. The number 10 is called a **constant**. The letters x and y are variables. The **coefficient** of the variable x is 1. The coefficient of the variable y is 2.

Algebraic expressions can have many different values, depending on the value assigned to each variable. When we assign a specific value to a variable in an algebraic expression, the process is known as **substitution**.

Example 1

Evaluate for $x = 4$.
a) $2x + 1$
b) $-7x$
c) $x - 11.5$

Solution

a) $2x + 1 = 2(4) + 1$
$= 8 + 1$
$= 9$

b) $-7x = -7(4)$
$= -28$

c) $x - 11.5 = 4 - 11.5$
$= -7.5$

62

Example 2

Evaluate for $x = 3$, $y = -4$, and $z = 5$.

a) $5x + y - 2z$

b) $9x^{-2} - 5y^2 + 2z$

Solution

a) $5x + y - 2z = 5(3) + (-4) - 2(5)$
$$= 15 - 4 - 10$$
$$= 1$$

b) $9x^{-2} - 5y^2 + 2z = 9(3)^{-2} - 5(-4)^2 + 2(5)$
$$= 9 \times \frac{1}{9} - 5 \times 16 + 10$$
$$= 1 - 80 + 10$$
$$= -69$$

Practice

Name the variable in each expression.

1. $5a + 8$　　　**2.** $7c - 3$　　　**3.** $\frac{1}{4} + 3q$

4. $4b - 5$　　　**5.** $-k - 0.1$　　**6.** $6t^2 + 1$

Name each variable and constant.

7. $-2c + 10$　　　　　**8.** $a + 3b^2 - 6$

9. $x^3 - 11y^2 - 3$　　**10.** $xy + 4z^5 + 0.5$

State the number of terms and the coefficient of each variable in each expression.

11. $2a + 3b$　　　　　**12.** $7s + 9t - 5$

13. $1 - 5c + \frac{1}{4}d$　　**14.** $6jkl + 11mn$

15. Evaluate $5x$ for each value of x.

a) 2　　　**b)** −5　　　**c)** 0　　　**d)** −4

16. Evaluate $3y + 1$ for each value of y.

a) 0　　　**b)** 1　　　**c)** 5　　　**d)** −3

17. Evaluate $2z - 1$ for each value of z.

a) −1　　**b)** 2　　　**c)** −5　　　**d)** 10

18. Evaluate for $x = -2$.

a) $x + 3$　　　　　　**b)** $3x + 2$

c) $2x - 6$　　　　　　**d)** $8 - 2x$

19. Evaluate for $x = 2$, $y = 3$, and $z = -4$.

a) $x + y + z$　　　　**b)** xyz

c) $x + 2z$　　　　　　**d)** $xy - z$

20. Evaluate for $a = 1.5$, $b = 2.5$, and $c = 3.5$.

a) $a + b + c$　　　　　**b)** $ab - 0.75$

c) $5a - 3b$　　　　　　**d)** $1.2a + 3.2b$

e) $5.65 - ab$　　　　　**f)** $2.4b - a$

g) $ac - 2b$　　　　　　**h)** $ab - bc - ca$

Problems and Applications

21. a) In a basketball game, team A scored $7x + 46y + 15z$ points and team B scored $2x + 27y + 31z$ points. In these expressions, x is the value of a 3-point field goal, y is the value of a 2-point field goal, and z is the value of a 1-point free throw. Which team won?

b) At the end of the 1991–1992 season, the Chicago Bulls' Michael Jordan had the highest all-time scoring average in the NBA at 32.3 points per game. His total points were described by the expression $206x + 6881y + 4620z$. The variables have the same values as in part a). How many points had Michael Jordan scored?

22. An apple contains about 290 kJ of energy, a banana 360 kJ, and a grapefruit 210 kJ.

a) Write an expression for the energy in a mixture of apples, bananas, and grapefruit.

b) Calculate the energy in a fruit salad made from 2 apples, 3 bananas, and $1\frac{1}{2}$ grapefruit.

2.3 Like Terms

Activity: Use a Tangram

The tangram square is made up of 7 pieces. Copy the square into your notebook. Label the pieces with letters starting at A. Label pieces with equal areas with the same letter.

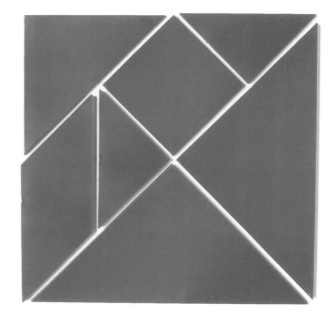

Inquire

1. How many different areas make the square?

2. Which areas are identical or *like*?

3. Which areas are not identical or *unlike*?

4. Write 2 different expressions that give the area of the tangram square.

5. Which of the 2 expressions in question 4 is simpler?

Like terms in algebra have the same variables raised to the same exponents. For example, the terms a, $3a$, and $7a$ are like terms. So are $2x^2$, $3x^2$, and $7x^2$.

Unlike terms in algebra have different variables, or the same variable but different exponents. For example, the terms $7b$, $3b^2$, $10q$, $5t$, $3x$, $4x^3$, and $17y$ are unlike terms.

Example 1

Simplify.
a) $x + 2x$ **b)** $3b - b$
c) $2y + y - 4$

Solution

Combine like terms.
a) $x + 2x = 3x$ **b)** $3b - b = 2b$
c) $2y + y - 4 = 3y - 4$

Example 2

Simplify.
a) $5x - 6y - 2x + 2y + 1$
b) $-11 + a - 2c + 16 + 3a - b - 5c$

Solution

a) $5x - 6y - 2x + 2y + 1$
$= 5x - 2x - 6y + 2y + 1$
$= 3x - 4y + 1$

b) $-11 + a - 2c + 16 + 3a - b - 5c$
$= a + 3a - b - 2c - 5c - 11 + 16$
$= 4a - b - 7c + 5$

Practice

Simplify.

1. $3x + 5x$ **2.** $11t - t$

3. $-10b + 3b$ **4.** $-12y - y$

5. $11m + 10m$ **6.** $15p - 9p$

Simplify.

7. $6r + 4r - r$ **8.** $2t + 3t - t$

9. $9p - p - 6p$ **10.** $11a - 10a - 5a$

11. $-5y - 2y + 9y$ **12.** $-8q - 9q + 10q$

Simplify.

13. $3t + 5 - 2t$ **14.** $2x - 5x - 7$

15. $2a - b + 3a$ **16.** $-4x + y - 6x$

17. $8y - 2z + 7y$ **18.** $-9p - 10q + 8p$

Simplify.

19. $5c + d - 2c - d$ **20.** $7p - q + p - 2q$

21. $3j + k - 5j - 2k$ **22.** $8a - 2b - 6a - 3b$

23. $-r + s + 2r - 2s$ **24.** $-5x + 5y + 5x - y$

Simplify.

25. $5x + 10 + 5y - 3x + 1$

26. $3a - 4b - 5 + a - b$

27. $-8 - 3z + 9x - 11 - 6z$

28. $8r - 11 - 18q + 5p + 7q$

29. $-4w + 7c - 8x - 9w - 3c$

30. $13j - 18d - 5d + 2j + 2c$

Simplify.

31. $-p + 5q - 8r - q + 3p + 9r + 1$

32. $-2z + 3y - 10x - 4y + 4z - 3x$

33. $5q - 9s - 8r + 8q - 7r + 13s$

34. $-10 - a + 6c - 11 - 9c + 8a - d$

Problems and Applications

35. Simplify, then evaluate.

a) $2a + 8a$, when $a = 2$

b) $7t - 3t$, when $t = 3$

c) $-6k - 8k$, when $k = -2$

d) $-6y - 9y - y$, when $y = -3$

e) $3 + 4x - 2x$, when $x = 5$

f) $-5p - 3p + 1 - 6$, when $p = -1$

36. Write an expression for each perimeter in 2 different ways.

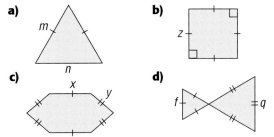

37. Write and simplify an expression for each perimeter.

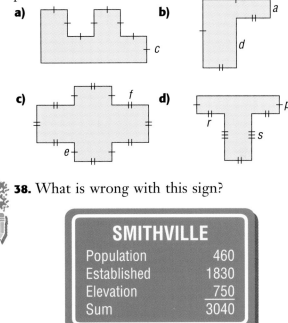

38. What is wrong with this sign?

SMITHVILLE	
Population	460
Established	1830
Elevation	750
Sum	3040

39. Work with a partner to calculate the perimeter of this figure. Describe the simplest method you can find.

Words to Symbols

Activity ❶

The longest parade in the world runs from March to July. The "floats" have masses between 500 000 t and 10 000 000 t. They are up to 10 000 years old. The parade consists of hundreds of icebergs that pass Newfoundland's east coast.

The part of an iceberg above the water is called the tip. The height, t, of the tip is $\frac{1}{7}$ of the total height of an iceberg. So, an expression for the total height of an iceberg is $7t$. Write an expression in terms of t for the height of the part of an iceberg that is under water.

Activity ❷

Match the words with the symbols.

1. a number increased by five $5x$
2. a number decreased by one $w + 3$
3. a number divided by nine $n - 1$
4. two less than a number $b + 5$
5. three more than a number $6 - t$
6. five times a number $m - 2$
7. six decreased by a number $2 + y$
8. two increased by a number $q \div 9$

If n represents a number, write an algebraic expression using numbers and symbols for each of the following statements.

9. three times a number
10. a number increased by one
11. a number decreased by five
12. the product of six and a number
13. a number divided by five
14. three more than twice a number
15. ten decreased by a number
16. seven divided by a number

In each case, let the number be x. Write an expression for each statement.

17. a number increased by four
18. seven times a number
19. a number multiplied by five
20. three divided by a number
21. seven more than a number
22. half of a number
23. a number diminished by eight
24. the product of a number and two

25. Write 3 new statements. Have a classmate write an expression for each.

Activity ❸
Copy and complete the tables.

1. The first number is 23 more than the second.

First Number	45	56		x		$3m$	$4t + 21$	
Second Number			18		y			$6r - 5$

2. Francine is 4 years younger than Terry.

Francine's Age		19		m		$4t$	
Terry's Age	16		x		$5y$		$3w + 8$

3. There are 6 times as many cars as motorcycles.

Number of Cars			72		y		
Number of Motorcycles	13			x		$m + 7$	$3t + 8$

Activity ❹
1. The length of a rectangle is 5 cm more than its width.
a) Which dimension is smaller?
b) Let the smaller dimension be x. Then, write the larger dimension in terms of x.
c) Draw and label a diagram of the rectangle.
d) Write an expression for the perimeter of the rectangle in terms of your variable.

2. The length of a rectangle is 4 m more than its width. Write an expression for its area.

3. The side length of a square is x metres. What is its perimeter?

4. a) Copy and complete the table for the dimensions of a rectangle. Its length is 3 m more than its width.

Width (m)	10	15	x	$10x$	$4x + 1$
Length (m)					

b) Write expressions for the perimeter and area of each rectangle. Compare your expressions with a classmate's.

5. Repeat question 4 for the following table. The length of the rectangle is now 7 m more than the width.

Width (m)	10		x		$3t$		$5z + 4$
Length (m)		24		y		$4n$	

2.4 Writing Equations

The Canadian Coast Guard patrols Canada's rivers and coastline. The Coast Guard is mainly involved in search-and-rescue operations.

Activity: Study the Information

A Coast Guard boat that travels at a speed of 15 km/h in still water was patrolling up a river with a current of 6 km/h. The boat's actual speed, s kilometres per hour relative to the river bank, was given by the equation $s = 15 - 6$.

When it patrolled down the river, the boat's actual speed, s kilometres per hour relative to the river bank, was given by the equation $s = 15 + 6$.

Inquire

1. Let the speed of the boat in still water be x kilometres per hour. Write an equation to find x if the boat patrols up a river where
a) the current is 6 km/h and the boat's actual speed is 11 km/h.
b) the current is 4 km/h and the boat's actual speed is 10 km/h.

2. Write an equation to find x if the boat patrols down a river where
a) the current is 5 km/h and the actual speed is 17 km/h.
b) the current is 7 km/h and the actual speed is 20 km/h.

Example 1

It costs 4 times as much to go to the movie theatre as it does to rent a movie. Together, both ways of seeing a movie cost $10. Write an equation to find each cost.

Solution

Let the smaller cost, a movie rental, be represented by x.
Then, the cost of going to a movie theatre is $4x$.
Together, both ways cost $10.
The total cost of both ways equals the sum of x and $4x$.

$$x + 4x = 10$$
$$5x = 10$$

Example 2

Lake Ontario is 77 km shorter than Lake Erie. The lengths of the 2 lakes total 699 km. Write an equation to find the length of Lake Ontario.

Solution

Let the length of Lake Ontario be represented by x.
Then, the length of Lake Erie is $x + 77$.
The sum of x and $x + 77$ is equal to 699.

$$x + (x + 77) = 699$$
$$2x + 77 = 699$$

Practice

Match each sentence with the correct equation.

1. Three times a number is equal to eighteen. $x - 4 = 10$

2. A number decreased by six is four. $3x = 18$

3. Kim's age in four years will be eighteen. $\frac{m}{4} = 18$

4. Shuji's age four years ago was ten. $y - 6 = 4$

5. A number divided by four is eighteen. $x + 4 = 18$

Write an equation for each sentence.

6. Four times a number is twenty.

7. A number divided by two equals five.

8. Six more than a number is fifteen.

9. A number increased by five is twelve.

10. A number decreased by six is ten.

11. Four less than a number is seven.

12. The square of a number is twenty-five.

13. Ten decreased by a number is two.

14. A number multiplied by three is nine.

15. A number divided by five is ten.

16. A number decreased by six is negative eight.

Problems and Applications

Write an equation for each statement in questions 17–22.

17. There are 16 more white keys than black keys on a full-sized piano keyboard. There are 88 keys on a piano.

18. Brad has $12 more than Pietro. Together they have $84.

19. Mike is seven years older than Carol. The sum of their ages is 29.

20. The area of the Pacific Ocean is twice the area of the Atlantic. The sum of their areas is 250 000 000 km².

21. The population of Japan is about 4.5 times the population of Canada. The sum of the populations is about 150 000 000.

22. Niagara Falls has 2 parts. The American Falls are 2 m higher than the Horseshoe Falls. Their average height is 58 m.

23. The perimeter of each rectangle is 36 cm. Write an equation to find the dimensions of each rectangle.

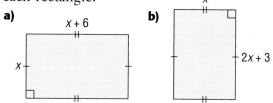

a) $x + 6$, x

b) x, $2x + 3$

24. It costs $30 to rent a VCR plus $15 a day. How much will it cost to rent a VCR for 2 days, 10 days, x days?

25. Compact discs cost $15 for the first one and $14 for each additional disc. Gina buys m compact discs and spends n dollars. Write an equation that shows the relationship between m and n. $n = 15 + 14(m-1) = 14m + 1$

WORD POWER

Lewis Carroll invented a word game called "doublets." The object is to go from one word to another by changing one letter at a time.

Change the word WARM to the word COLD by changing one letter at a time. You must form a real word each time you change a letter. The best solution has the fewest steps.

WARM
WARD
CARD
CORD
COLD

2.5 Solving Equations

Many horses take part in sports and shows in Canada. In the RCMP Musical Ride, 32 horses and their riders perform complex movements to music.

Activity: Solve the Problem

Suppose that you own a horse. The monthly cost to board your horse at a public stable is $100. You have $225 a month to spend, and you want to take riding lessons that cost $25 each. Use the equation $25n + 100 = 225$ to find the number of riding lessons you can take per month.

Inquire

1. How did you solve the equation $25n + 100 = 225$?

2. What is the value of x in each of the following equations?
   a) $x + 4 = 9$ b) $x - 7 = 11$ c) $3x = 27$ d) $4x + 11 = 31$

An **equation** is a statement that two expressions or numbers are equal.

This equation is true. $5 + 3 = 8$

This equation is false. $7 - 4 = 2$

This equation is neither true nor false. $x + 5 = 9$

The equation $x + 5 = 9$ is called an **open sentence**, because it is not possible to say whether it is true or false. It is true if x is replaced by 4. Other replacements make the statement false. A value of the variable that makes the statement true is called the **solution** or **root** of the equation. This value is said to *satisfy* the equation.

Example	**Solution**
Solve.	**a)** Simple equations like $x + 5 = 2$ can be solved mentally. This process
a) $x + 5 = 2$	is called **solving by inspection**. The solution is $x = -3$.
b) $7x + 13 = 55$	**b)** Use **systematic trial**. Substitute different values for the variable until you find the solution.

$$\text{Substitute 3 for } x. \quad 7x + 13 = 7(3) + 13$$
$$= 21 + 13$$
$$= 34 \quad \text{When } x = 3, 7x + 13 \text{ is less than 55.}$$

$$\text{Substitute 7 for } x. \quad 7x + 13 = 7(7) + 13$$
$$= 49 + 13$$
$$= 62 \quad \text{When } x = 7, 7x + 13 \text{ is greater than 55.}$$

$$\text{Substitute 6 for } x. \quad 7x + 13 = 7(6) + 13$$
$$= 42 + 13$$
$$= 55 \quad \text{The solution is } x = 6.$$

Practice

Solve by inspection.

1. $x + 3 = 7$ **2.** $x + 5 = 4$

3. $x + 5 = 5$ **4.** $x + 5 = 3$

5. $2 + m = 9$ **6.** $n + 1 = 6$

7. $p + 10 = 3$ **8.** $4 = 7 + s$

9. $y + 8 = 4$ **10.** $z + 8 = 12$

Solve by inspection.

11. $x - 5 = -7$ **12.** $x - 3 = 7$

13. $4 = -10 + y$ **14.** $y + 5 = -3$

15. $z - 1 = 6$ **16.** $t - 12 = 10$

17. $n + 5 = -2$ **18.** $4 - x = 0$

19. $m + 3 = 0$ **20.** $2 = x + 7$

Is the number in brackets the correct solution to the given equation?

21. $x + 7 = 10$ **(3)**   **22.** $x - 5 = 0$ **(-5)**

23. $3x = -18$ **(-6)**   **24.** $5x = 20$ **(-4)**

25. $\frac{x}{5} = \frac{4}{5}$ **(4)**   **26.** $\frac{2x}{7} = -\frac{6}{7}$ **(-3)**

27. $2x + 1 = 7$ **(-3)**   **28.** $10 = -2 + 3x$ **(4)**

Solve by systematic trial.

29. $6x + 17 = 65$ **30.** $73 - 7x = 45$

31. $14 + 9x = 86$ **32.** $35 = 83 - 8t$

33. $8k - 37 = 59$ **34.** $5b + 41 = 76$

35. $4 - 3s = -11$ **36.** $2m - 15 = -11$

37. $-15 = 7 - x$ **38.** $21 = 5b + 31$

Problems and Applications

Solve by inspection.

39. $x + 2.5 = 3.5$ **40.** $t - 4.3 = 1.7$

41. $6.6 - m = 2.6$ **42.** $2x = 4.8$

43. $0.5t = 16$ **44.** $7.1 + x = 10.2$

45. $5 = m - 3.7$ **46.** $12 = x + 4.6$

47. $9 - x = 8.2$ **48.** $1.2 + x = -5.3$

49. Solve the equation $9w = 36$ to find the width of the rectangle.

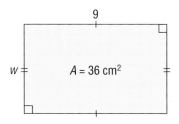

50. Point Pelee National Park has an area of 15 km², which is 7 km² less than the area of Prince Edward Island National Park. Solve the equation $x - 7 = 15$ to find the area of Prince Edward Island National Park.

51. London, Ontario, has thunderstorms on 36 days a year, the highest number in Canada. Prince Rupert, B.C., has the fewest days of thunderstorms. If you multiply the number for Prince Rupert by 10 and add 6, you get the number for London. Solve the equation $10d + 6 = 36$ to find the number of days of thunderstorms in Prince Rupert per year.

52. Use x, 2, and 6 to write equations with the following solutions. Check your answers by substitution.

a) 3   **b)** −4   **c)** 4

d) 8   **e)** 12   **f)** $\frac{1}{3}$

53. Find 2 solutions to each equation.

a) $x^2 = 16$ **b)** $t^2 - 6 = 19$

54. Write an equation that can be solved by inspection and in which the solution is $x = -4$. Have a classmate solve it.

55. Write an equation that can be solved by systematic trial and in which the solution is $x = 8$. Have a classmate solve it.

56. Write an equation that can be solved by systematic trial and in which the solution is $x = -15$. Have a classmate solve it.

Algebra Tiles

Each red tile represents +1.
Each white tile represents −1. **+1 −1**
Each long green tile represents +x or x. **x −x**
Each long white tile represents −x.
Each square green tile represents +x² or x². **x² −x²**
Each square white tile represents −x².

Activity ❶ Representing Variables with Tiles

1. Write the expression represented by each group of tiles and then evaluate each expression for $x = 2$ and $x = -3$.

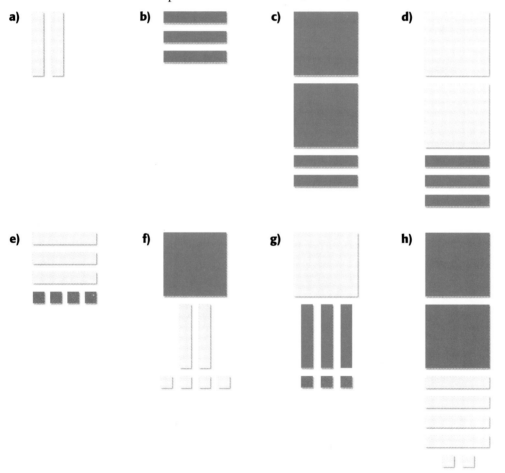

a)   b)   c)   d)

e)   f)   g)   h)

2. Use tiles to model the following expressions. Sketch your solutions.

a) $4x$ **b)** $2x^2$ **c)** $-4x$ **d)** $3x^2 - 2x$

e) $2x - x^2$ **f)** $-3x^2 + 4x + 3$ **g)** $-2x^2 - 2x - 1$ **h)** $3x^2 - 2x + 4$

Activity ❷ Representing Zero with Variables

Each pair represents zero.

1. Copy and complete the table. The first row has been done for you.

Tile Display	Simplified Form	Expression	Substituting $x = 3$ and $x = -2$
		$2x$	When $x = 3$, $2x = 6$ When $x = -2$, $2x = -4$

2. What is the smallest number of tiles you can add to each group to make zero? Explain.

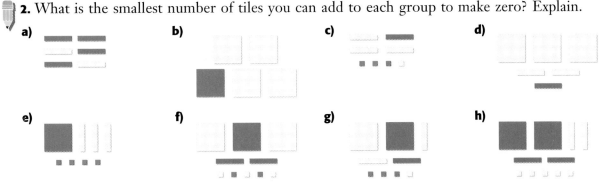

a)   **b)**   **c)**   **d)**

e)   **f)**   **g)**   **h)**

3. Represent each integer using exactly 10 tiles. Use only tiles that represent +1 and −1.

a) +8   **b)** −6   **c)** −4   **d)** −8   **e)** +2   **f)** −2

2.6 Using Addition to Solve Equations

One year, Canada won 2 gold medals at the Winter Olympics. This number was 4 less than the number of gold medals won by Canada at the Summer Olympics that same year.

If we let the number of gold medals Canada won at the Summer Olympics be x, we can represent the above information with the equation $x - 4 = 2$.

Activity: Use Algebra Tiles
Write the equation represented by the algebra tiles.

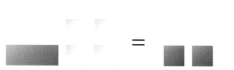

Inquire

1. How many red 1-tiles must be added to the left side so that only the value of the x-tile remains?

2. What must you do to the right side to keep the equation balanced?

3. What is the value of x?

4. How many gold medals did Canada win at the Summer Olympics?

5. Model the following equations using algebra tiles. Then, solve for x. Compare your answers with a classmate's.

a) $x - 2 = 5$ **b)** $x - 1 = 2$
c) $x - 4 = 2$ **d)** $x - 5 = -4$

6. Write a rule for solving equations by addition.

To solve an equation, isolate the variable on one side of the equation.

Example 1
Solve the equation $x - 2 = 6$.

Solution

Add 2 to both sides of the equation.

$$x - 2 = 6$$
$$x - 2 + 2 = 6 + 2$$
$$x = 8$$

The solution is $x = 8$.

$$\underline{x \quad -2} \quad = \quad \underline{6}$$

$$\underline{x \quad -2 + (+2)} \quad = \quad \underline{6 + (+2)}$$

$$\underline{x} \quad = \quad \underline{8}$$

74

Activity: Use Algebra Tiles

Write the equation represented by the algebra tiles in the box.

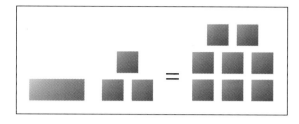

Inquire

1. How many white 1-tiles must be added to the left side so that only the value of the x-tile remains?

2. What must you do to the right side to keep the equation balanced?

3. What is the value of x?

4. Model the following equations using algebra tiles. Then, solve for x. Compare your answers with a classmate's.
a) $x + 1 = 5$ **b)** $x + 3 = 2$ **c)** $x + 4 = -2$ **d)** $x + 2 = -3$

Example 2

Solve and check $x + 7 = -2$.

Solution

To isolate the variable, add -7 to both sides of the equation.

$$x + 7 = -2$$
$$x + 7 + (-7) = -2 + (-7)$$
$$x = -9$$

Substitute $x = -9$ into the left side of the equation. The solution is correct if the value of the left side equals the value of the right side.

Check: **L.S.** $= x + 7$ **R.S.** $= -2$
$$= -9 + 7$$
$$= -2$$

The solution is $x = -9$.

CONTINUED ⟩

Practice

Write and solve the equations shown by the tiles.

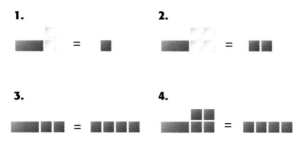

1.

2.

3.

4.

What number would you add to both sides to solve each equation?

5. $x - 3 = 11$ **6.** $x - 1 = 5$

7. $n - 7 = -8$ **8.** $-8 = -4 + m$

9. $3 = y - 10$ **10.** $z - 5 = -11$

11. $x + 6 = 13$ **12.** $8 = x + 1$

13. $y + 2 = -7$ **14.** $m + 5 = -5$

15. $x + 3 = 9$ **16.** $-10 = 7 + z$

Solve.

17. $m - 5 = -4$ **18.** $2 = -3 + n$

19. $p - 7 = -3$ **20.** $r + 7 = -9$

21. $-3 = s + 5$ **22.** $t - 8 = 10$

23. $2 + x = -4$ **24.** $7 = x - 5$

25. $x + 4 = -8$ **26.** $-11 = t - 1$

27. $13 = -2 + x$ **28.** $y - 5 = -8$

29. $12 + q = 10$ **30.** $d - 7 = -7$

Problems and Applications

Solve and check.

31. $x + 1.5 = 3.5$ **32.** $m - 3.2 = 4.8$

33. $4.6 = t - 1.4$ **34.** $5.7 = r + 3.6$

35. $4.3 + m = 1.3$ **36.** $y - 2.4 = -1.4$

37. $9 = 8.2 + x$ **38.** $3.7 + t = 6.4$

39. $-1.4 + q = 4.4$ **40.** $10.3 = x - 5.4$

41. $-8.8 = w - 1.1$ **42.** $x + 15.7 = -18.1$

In questions 43–45, find the equation that represents the problem and solve it.

43. Three more than a number, x, is eight. What is the number?
a) $x - 3 = 8$ b) $x + 8 = 3$
c) $x + 3 = 8$ d) $x - 8 = 3$

44. How many boxes are left to unload if there are 195 boxes in the shipment and 72 boxes have been unloaded?
a) $x + 72 = 195$ b) $x + 195 = 72$
c) $x - 72 = 195$ d) $x - 195 = 72$

45. In a triangle, the sum of the sides is 9.7 cm. The lengths of two of the sides are 3.2 cm and 4.5 cm. What is the length of the unknown side?
a) $x - 4.5 = 9.7 - 3.2$
b) $9.7 - x = 4.5 - 3.2$
c) $4.5 + x - 3.2 = 9.7$
d) $x + 3.2 + 4.5 = 9.7$

46. The number of moons around Uranus is 5 more than the number of rings. Uranus has 15 moons. Solve the equation $r + 5 = 15$ to find the number of rings around Uranus.

47. A nurse walks about 6.3 km a day, which is 0.8 km less than a letter carrier walks. Solve the equation $x - 0.8 = 6.3$ to find out how far a letter carrier walks in a day.

48. What is the result if you add 0 to both sides of an equation?

49. Find 2 solutions for each equation.
a) $x^2 - 1.8 = 7.2$ b) $82.2 = t^2 + 18.2$

50. Write 1 equation that can be solved by adding a positive number and 1 equation that can be solved by adding a negative number. Each equation should have $x = -3$ as its solution. Have a classmate solve your equations.

.7 Using Division and Multiplication to Solve Equations

In 1992, Canada won the Women's World Hockey Championships. In the semi-final game against Finland, Canada scored 6 goals, 3 times as many as Finland. If we let x be the number of goals Finland scored, we can represent the above information with the equation $3x = 6$.

Activity: Use Algebra Tiles
Write the equation represented by the algebra tiles.

Inquire

1. How many pairs of 1-tiles are shown?

2. How many x-tiles are shown?

3. How many 1-tiles does an x-tile represent?

4. Divide both sides of the equation $3x = 6$ by 3.
Compare your result with your answer to question 3.

5. How many goals did Finland score against Canada?

6. Represent the following equations using algebra tiles.
Then, solve for x.
a) $2x = 10$ **b)** $3x = -6$ **c)** $-2x = 4$ **d)** $-4x = -4$

7. Write a rule for solving equations by division.

Example 1
Solve the equation $2x = 6$.

Solution

Divide both sides of the equation by 2.
$$2x = 6$$
$$\frac{2x}{2} = \frac{6}{2}$$
$$x = 3$$
The solution is $x = 3$.

CONTINUED ▶

Activity ❷ Interpret the Diagram

The algebra tiles represent the equation $\frac{x}{2} = 1$.
What part of an x-tile is shown on the left side?

 $=$ ■

$$\frac{x}{2} = 1$$

Inquire

1. How many 1-tiles are shown on the right side?

2. How many 1-tiles does a whole x-tile represent?

3. Multiply both sides of the equation by 2.
What is the value of an x-tile? Compare this result
with your answer to question 2.

4. Write a rule for solving equations by multiplication.

Example 2	**Solution**

Solve the equation
$\frac{x}{2} = -5$.

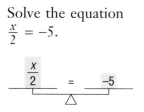

Multiply both sides of the equation by 2.

$$\frac{x}{2} = -5$$
$$2 \times \frac{x}{2} = 2 \times (-5)$$
$$x = -10$$

The solution is $x = -10$.

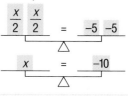

Example 3	**Solution**

Solve the equation
$\frac{12}{x} = -4$.

Multiply both sides of the equation by x.

$$x \times \frac{12}{x} = x \times (-4)$$
$$12 = -4x$$

Divide both sides of the equation by -4.

$$\frac{12}{-4} = \frac{-4x}{-4}$$
$$-3 = x$$

The solution is $x = -3$.

Example 4	**Solution**

Solve and check
$-2x = 18.4$.

Divide both sides of the equation by -2.

$$-2x = 18.4$$
$$\frac{-2x}{-2} = \frac{18.4}{-2}$$
$$x = -9.2$$

Check: **L.S.** $= -2x$ **R.S.** $= 18.4$
$$= -2(-9.2)$$
$$= 18.4$$

The solution is $x = -9.2$.

Practice

Write and solve the equation represented by the tiles.

1.

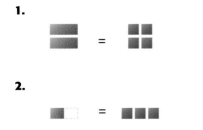

2.

By what number would you divide both sides to solve each equation?

3. $6x = 12$ **4.** $2x = -8$ **5.** $7z = -14$

6. $11r = 22$ **7.** $6n = -18$ **8.** $8y = 64$

By what number would you multiply both sides to solve each equation?

9. $\frac{x}{3} = 9$ **10.** $\frac{x}{2} = -4$ **11.** $\frac{y}{7} = 4$

12. $\frac{m}{5} = -6$ **13.** $\frac{t}{4} = -1$ **14.** $\frac{x}{6} = 0$

Solve.

15. $3x = 15$ **16.** $2y = -12$ **17.** $-8x = 16$

18. $-15 = 5p$ **19.** $-6t = -24$ **20.** $12 = 3s$

21. $2a = 24$ **22.** $-25 = 5j$ **23.** $-7x = -21$

Solve.

24. $\frac{x}{2} = 2$ **25.** $\frac{y}{2} = -4$ **26.** $\frac{x}{3} = 7$

27. $-4 = \frac{p}{3}$ **28.** $\frac{8}{m} = 4$ **29.** $-3 = \frac{6}{n}$

30. $\frac{10}{s} = 5$ **31.** $-2 = \frac{12}{t}$ **32.** $\frac{16}{u} = 4$

Solve and check.

33. $2x = 8.4$ **34.** $3m = -6.3$

35. $\frac{x}{5} = 2.4$ **36.** $\frac{3}{x} = -1.5$

37. $-4x = -2.8$ **38.** $1.6x = 4.8$

39. $4 = \frac{m}{1.5}$ **40.** $-8.4 = 0.2x$

Problems and Applications

In questions 41 and 42, find the equation that represents the problem and solve it.

41. Six dollars is to be divided equally among three people. How much money does each person receive?

a) $3x = 6$ **b)** $6x = 3$

c) $\frac{x}{3} = 6$ **d)** $\frac{x}{6} = 3$

42. One-third of the sum of the side lengths of an equilateral triangle is 4.2 cm. What is the sum?

a) $3x = 4.2$ **b)** $\frac{1}{3}x = 4.2$

c) $\frac{1}{3}x + 4.2 = 0$ **d)** $x = \frac{1}{3}(4.2)$

43. The average annual snowfall in Vancouver is about one-sixth of the average value for St. John's. Vancouver averages 60 cm of snow a year. Solve the equation $\frac{s}{6} = 60$ to find the average annual snowfall in St. John's.

44. The mass of a white-tailed deer is 1.4 times the mass of a cougar. White-tailed deer average 98 kg in mass. Solve the equation $1.4x = 98$ to find the mass of a cougar.

45. What is the result if you multiply both sides of an equation by 0?

46. Describe the solutions to these equations.

a) $3x = 0$ **b)** $0y = 2$

47. Find 2 solutions to each equation.

a) $2x^2 = 72$ **b)** $\frac{m^2}{4} = 1$

48. Write one equation that can be solved by division and one that can be solved by multiplication. Each equation should have $x = 7$ as its solution. Have a classmate solve your equations.

2.8 Use Logic

Problems that can be solved using logic do not require any special skills in mathematics. These problems sharpen your deductive thinking skills.

A cat, dog, monkey, and elephant are named Trixie, Wags, Snow, and Boots. Use the clues to name each animal.

- Trixie is a friend of the cat and the elephant.
- The dog and Boots enjoy popcorn.
- Snow and Boots play golf with the monkey.
- The elephant does not play outdoor sports.

Understand the Problem

1. What information are you given?
2. What are you asked to find?

Think of a Plan

Make a table and fill in the facts from the clues.

Carry Out the Plan

Trixie is a friend of the cat and the elephant. So, Trixie is not the cat or the elephant.

	C	D	M	E
Trixie	n			n
Wags				
Snow				
Boots				

The dog and Boots enjoy popcorn. So, the dog is not Boots.

	C	D	M	E
Trixie	n			n
Wags				
Snow				
Boots		n		

Snow and Boots play golf with the monkey. So, Snow and Boots are not the monkey.

	C	D	M	E
Trixie	n			n
Wags				
Snow			n	
Boots		n	n	

The elephant does not play outdoor sports. So, the elephant does not play golf and is not Snow or Boots. The table now shows that the Elephant must be Wags, and the cat must be Boots. We can now complete the table.

	C	D	M	E
Trixie	n			n
Wags				
Snow			n	n
Boots		n	n	n

	C	D	M	E
Trixie	n	n	y	n
Wags	n	n	n	y
Snow	n	y	n	n
Boots	y	n	n	n

Trixie is the monkey, Wags is the elephant, Snow is the dog, and Boots is the cat.

Look Back

Check that the answer agrees with the given facts.

Use Logic
1. Organize the information.
2. Draw conclusions from the information.
3. Check that your answer is reasonable.

Problems and Applications

1. Maria, Paula, and Shelly attend the same school. One is in grade 9, one is in grade 10, and one is in grade 11. Use the clues to find which grade each is in.

■ Maria and the grade 9 student eat lunch with Shelly.

■ Maria is not in grade 10.

2. Four students named Al, Bjorn, Carl, and Don each have a favourite sport. The sports are swimming, running, bowling, and golf. Use the clues to match each student with his sport.

■ The runner met Bjorn and the golfer for lunch.

■ Neither Bjorn's sport nor Carl's sport requires a ball.

■ Don is in the same math class as the golfer's sister.

3. Susan, Irina, Traci, and Debbie are a pilot, a dentist, a doctor, and a writer. Use the clues to match each person with her profession.

■ Debbie is a friend of the doctor.

■ Susan and the writer sail with Traci.

■ Neither Susan nor Irina has patients.

4. Four people are running a marathon. Manuel is 30 m behind Margaret. Coreen is 20 m behind Tom. Margaret is 75 m ahead of Coreen. How far ahead of Tom is Manuel?

5. Sonya had $1.19 in change. None of the coins was a dollar. Greg asked her for change for a dollar, but Sonya could not make change. What coins did she have?

6. The odometer on Anitha's car showed 25952 km. The number 25952 is called a **palindrome**. It reads the same forward and backward. Anitha drove for 2 h, and the odometer showed the next palindrome. How far did she drive in the 2 h?

7. A building has 5 doors. In how many ways can you enter the building by one door and leave by another?

8. A photographer wants to take a picture of the curling team. In how many ways can the 4 curlers be arranged side by side?

9. In a bacterial culture, the number of bacteria doubled every minute. At midnight, the glass jar was full and contained 1 000 000 bacteria. At what time was the jar half full?

10. Evans, Thompson, Smith, and DiMaggio are a teacher, plumber, artist, and banker. Use the clues to match each person with a profession.

■ Thompson met the artist when he hired her to paint a picture of his horse.

■ The plumber and DiMaggio are friends who have never had any business dealings.

■ Neither Evans nor the plumber has ever met Smith.

■ DiMaggio asked the banker for a loan.

11. Make your own logic puzzle like those in questions 2 and 3. First, set up a chart and mark the answers you want. Then, write the clues. Test your puzzle before asking a classmate to solve it.

Equations and Number Tiles

Prepare a set of 10 number tiles with the numbers from 0 to 9 written on them.

Activity ❶

1. Use each of the tiles only once to solve the equations. The x-value for each equation is shown in brackets. Three of the tiles have been placed for you.

$$x - \blacksquare = 2 \qquad (x = 5)$$

$$x - \blacksquare = \blacksquare - 3 \qquad (x = 5)$$

$$0 + x - \blacksquare = \blacksquare + 1 \qquad (x = 10)$$

$$x + \blacksquare - 8 = 9 + \blacksquare \qquad (x = 11)$$

Activity ❷

Use each of the tiles only once to solve the equations. The x-value for each equation is shown in brackets. Three of the tiles have been placed for you.

$$x + \blacksquare = 7 \qquad (x = 4)$$

$$x + \blacksquare = \blacksquare + 2 \qquad (x = 3)$$

$$\blacksquare + x + 6 = \blacksquare + 3 \qquad (x = 5)$$

$$x - 2 + \blacksquare = \blacksquare - 0 \qquad (x = 3)$$

82

Activity ❸

Use each of the tiles only once to solve the equations. The x-value for each equation is shown in brackets. Three of the tiles have been placed for you.

$$\blacksquare x = 8 \qquad\qquad (x = 2)$$

$$\blacksquare x + \blacksquare = 8 \qquad\qquad (x = 1)$$

$$\blacksquare + 2\,x = \blacksquare \qquad\qquad (x = 3)$$

$$0 + \blacksquare x = \blacksquare + 9 + 1 \qquad\qquad (x = 3)$$

Activity ❹

Use each of the tiles only once to solve the equations. The x-value for each equation is shown in brackets. Two of the tiles have been placed for you.

$$\frac{x}{\blacksquare} = 2 \qquad\qquad (x = 12)$$

$$\frac{x}{\blacksquare} + \blacksquare = 5 \qquad\qquad (x = 5)$$

$$\blacksquare + \frac{x}{2} = \blacksquare + 2 \qquad\qquad (x = 6)$$

$$\frac{x}{\blacksquare} + \blacksquare = 7 - \blacksquare \qquad\qquad (x = 18)$$

Activity ❺

Create a set of equations similar to those in Activities 1, 2, 3, and 4. Have a classmate solve your equations.

2.9 Work Backward

Working backward can be a very useful problem solving technique. To solve some crimes, a detective will start at the scene of the crime and retrace the criminal's steps, or work backward, until the crime is solved.

Understand the Problem

Think of a Plan

Carry Out the Plan

Look Back

The departure time for the Orient Express train from Calais to Paris is 21:20. Sam Orwell, a private detective, plans to board the train 35 min before departure. Orwell's hotel, the Rampant Lion, is a 25-min cab ride from the train station.

Before leaving the hotel, Orwell needs 30 min to eat dinner. After dinner, he needs 10 min to pack and 15 min to phone Interpol from his room. On the way to the train station, Orwell needs to stop for 15 min at the ambassador's residence to get a copy of a set of fingerprints. To reach the train on time, when should Orwell

a) leave his hotel for the train?   **b)** go to dinner?

1. What information are you given?

2. What are you asked to find?

3. Do you need an exact or approximate answer?

Start at the departure time of the train and work backward.

Train departure time	21:20
Time to arrive before departure	35 min
Orwell's arrival at the train	20:45
Time for cab ride and ambassador	25 + 15 = 40 min
When to leave hotel for the train	20:05
Time for dinner, packing, and phone call 30 + 10 + 15 = 55 min	
When to go to dinner	19:10

a) Orwell should leave the hotel at 20:05.
b) Orwell should go to dinner at 19:10.

Is the answer reasonable?
Can you think of another way to solve the problem?

Work Backward	1. Start with what you know.
	2. Work backward to get an answer.
	3. Check that the answer is reasonable.

Problems and Applications

1. Clara's plane leaves at 08:15. She has to be at the airport 40 min early. The cab ride to the airport is about 55 min. Clara wants to spend 30 min at her office on her way to the airport. When should she leave home?

2. Michiko went to the county fair. She spent half her money on rides. She spent half of what was left on food. Of the remainder, she spent half at the arcade. She had $6 left. How much money did she start with?

3. Sandra bought a gold chain for $150. The jeweller added one-half of his cost price to get the price of $150. What did the jeweller pay for the chain?

4. The exam starts at school at 09:00. You want to get there 15 min early. It takes 20 min to 30 min to get to school, depending on the buses. You plan to study for 1 h at home. It will take you 1 h to shower, dress, and eat breakfast. For what time should you set your alarm?

5. Jennifer wants a jacket that costs $230, including tax. She has saved $70. If she saves the rest in equal amounts over the next 4 months, how much will she save each month?

6. Ahmed's plane leaves at 12:30. Ahmed can drive 120 km to the airport at an average speed of 80 km/h. He needs to be at the airport 45 min before departure. When should he leave home?

7. Tanya saved for a band trip costing $725. She worked part-time at a convenience store and earned $7.50/h. Then, her aunt gave her $125 toward the trip. For how many hours did Tanya have to work to afford the trip?

8. Dino multiplied his age by 3. Then he subtracted 3, divided by 7, and added 12. The result was 18. How old was Dino?

9. The train left Sutton for Bent Creek. At Brownsville, 35 people got on and 27 got off. Next came Liberty, where 24 people got on and 11 got off. At Long Lake, 55 people got on and 42 people got off. At Bent Creek, 105 people got off and 10 got on. There were 203 people on the train when it left Bent Creek. How many people were on the train when it left Sutton?

10. Mike works for an art gallery. An art dealer offers him a painting for $72 000. The dealer says the painting has increased in value by one-half of the previous year's value in each of the past 2 years.
a) What was its value 2 years ago?
b) If the painting's value continues to increase at this rate, what will it be 3 years from now?

11. The Canadian population was about 27 300 000 in 1991. It had increased by about 3 000 000 since 1981. The 1981 figure was about 7 times the figure at Confederation in 1867. What was the Canadian population at Confederation to the nearest 100 000?

12. Write a problem that can be solved by working backward. Have a classmate solve your problem.

WORD POWER

In an anagram, the letters can be in any order except the right one. The word TEN has 5 anagrams.

NET   NTE   ETN   ENT   TNE

1. How many anagrams are there for
a) FOUR?   **b)** NINE?

2. Why are your answers different, even though FOUR and NINE both contain 4 letters?

Knowledge-Based and Expert Systems

Knowledge-based systems and **expert systems** are specialized types of computer software. Knowledge-based systems use facts and rules you might find in a manual or textbook. An example of a knowledge-based system is a chess-playing program. Expert systems provide you with the knowledge of human experts in a particular field. The programs are based on a combination of textbook knowledge and the decision-making processes supplied by experts. One example is the medical consultation system called CADUCEUS. This system is like many expert systems in that it is interactive. The user works with the system to solve a problem through a series of questions and answers, which eventually leads to a solution.

Activity ❶ Knowledge-Based Systems

1. Work with your classmates to list the knowledge-based systems that you know. You are probably familiar with more than you think.

2. Describe what each knowledge-based system is used for.

86

Activity ➋ Expert Systems

1. Describe what you would expect to find in an expert system called *Bird Species Identification*.

2. Use your research skills to find 5 areas in which expert systems have already been developed. Write a brief description of what each system does.

3. Predict 3 areas in which you think expert systems will be developed in the future. Describe how you think the systems will be used.

4. In what area would you like to see an expert system developed? What would you want the program to tell you?

5. There are many areas in which it is very difficult to create expert systems. A system that tells you how to predict the weather is one example. Why is an expert system difficult to create in this area? In what other areas do you think it would be difficult to have an expert system?

2.10 Solving Equations Using More Than One Step

A cow sleeps 7 h a day. This is 1 h less than twice the amount an elephant sleeps a day. If we let the hours that an elephant sleeps be x, we can represent this information with the equation $2x - 1 = 7$.

Activity: Use Algebra Tiles

Write the equation represented by the algebra tiles.

Inquire

1. How many red 1-tiles must be added to both sides so that only the value of the 2 x-tiles remains on the left?

2. How many red 1-tiles does an x-tile represent?

3. For how many hours does an elephant sleep each day?

4. Represent the following equations using algebra tiles. Solve the equations.

a) $3x + 2 = 8$ **b)** $4x - 1 = 11$ **c)** $2x + 3 = -9$ **d)** $5x - 1 = -11$

5. Write the steps for solving each equation in question 4.

6. The flow charts show the order of the steps to solve the equation $5x + 2 = 17$. First, isolate x on the left side.

Left Side START → $5x + 2$ → Add –2 → Divide by 5 → x → STOP

Then, apply the same steps to the right side.

Right Side START → 17 → Add –2 → Divide by 5 → 3 → STOP

Use flow charts to solve these equations.

a) $2x + 3 = 11$ **b)** $3x - 1 = 17$

Example 1

Solve the equation
$5x + 4 = -16$.

Solution

$$5x + 4 = -16$$

Add -4 to both sides: $\quad 5x + 4 + (-4) = -16 + (-4)$

$$5x = -20$$

Divide both sides by 5: $\quad \dfrac{5x}{5} = -\dfrac{20}{5}$

$$x = -4$$

The solution is $x = -4$.

Example 2

Solve and check
$7.2 = 3x - 4.2$.

Solution

$$7.2 = 3x - 4.2$$

Add 4.2 to both sides: $\quad 7.2 + 4.2 = 3x - 4.2 + 4.2$

$$11.4 = 3x$$

Divide both sides by 3: $\quad \dfrac{11.4}{3} = \dfrac{3x}{3}$

$$3.8 = x$$

Substitute $x = 3.8$.

Check: **L.S.** $= 7.2$ **R.S.** $= 3(3.8) - 4.2$

$$= 11.4 - 4.2$$
$$= 7.2$$

The solution is $x = 3.8$.

Example 3

Solve and check
$\dfrac{9x}{2} - 6 = 21$.

Solution

$$\dfrac{9x}{2} - 6 = 21$$

Add 6 to both sides: $\quad \dfrac{9x}{2} - 6 + 6 = 21 + 6$

$$\dfrac{9x}{2} = 27$$

Multiply both sides by 2: $\quad 2 \times \dfrac{9x}{2} = 2 \times 27$

$$9x = 54$$

Divide both sides by 9: $\quad \dfrac{9x}{9} = \dfrac{54}{9}$

$$x = 6$$

Substitute $x = 6$.

Check: **L.S.** $= \dfrac{9x}{2} - 6$ **R.S.** $= 21$

$$= \dfrac{9(6)}{2} - 6$$
$$= \dfrac{54}{2} - 6$$
$$= 27 - 6$$
$$= 21$$

The solution is $x = 6$.

CONTINUED ➤

Example 4

Solve the equation
$7x - 9x - 6 = 21 - 5$.

Solution

Simplify both sides of the equation.
Then, apply the rules for solving equations.

$$7x - 9x - 6 = 21 - 5$$
$$-2x - 6 = 16$$

Add 6 to both sides: $\quad -2x - 6 + 6 = 16 + 6$
$$-2x = 22$$

Divide both sides by -2: $\quad \dfrac{-2x}{-2} = \dfrac{22}{-2}$
$$x = -11$$

The solution is $x = -11$.

Example 5

Solve $3x - 2 = 5$.
Round your answer to the nearest tenth.

Solution

$$3x - 2 = 5$$

Add 2 to both sides: $\quad 3x - 2 + 2 = 5 + 2$
$$3x = 7$$

Divide both sides by 3: $\quad \dfrac{3x}{3} = \dfrac{7}{3}$
$$x \doteq 2.33$$

The solution is $x = 2.3$ to the nearest tenth.

Practice

Draw flow charts to show the solution steps for each equation.

1. $5x + 2 = 22$ **2.** $2x + 5 = 25$

Solve.

3. $3x = 11 + 1$ **4.** $2y - 5 = 9$

5. $5n + 2n = -14$ **6.** $3m + 7 = 19$

7. $4x + 2x = -18$ **8.** $4y - 9y = 35$

9. $5w + w = 7 + 23$ **10.** $6n + 3n = -18$

Solve.

11. $3y - 5y = 4$

12. $3t + 7t = -30$

13. $3x + 2x = -20$

14. $5 + 11 = 4y$

15. $15 = 2n + 3n$

16. $5 + n = -15$

17. $3 + m = -7$

18. $4 + x = 20$

Solve and check.

19. $\frac{x}{3} = 4 + 2$ **20.** $\frac{y}{2} = 6 - 3$

21. $\frac{n}{3} + 3 = 5$ **22.** $\frac{m}{5} - 5 = -9$

23. $4 + \frac{x}{3} = -7$ **24.** $\frac{y}{2} + 5 = 3$

25. $\frac{x}{4} - \frac{1}{4} = -\frac{3}{4}$ **26.** $\frac{y}{2} + \frac{1}{4} = \frac{3}{4}$

Solve and check.

27. $4x + 3x + 7 = 21$

28. $2y - 5y - 5 = 13$

29. $4t + 7t = 15 - 4$

30. $6s + 2s + s = 18$

31. $4t - 7t = 8 + 4$

32. $3y = 10 - 6 - 7$

33. $4 + 3t = -6 - 2$

34. $x + 2x = -15 - 6$

Solve and check.

35. $5n + 3n - 2n = 17 - 2 + 9$

36. $2m + 5m + m = -10 - 5 - 1$

37. $3x + 5x + 1 = 11 - 2$

38. $4 + 3t - 5t = 12$

39. $2s + 3s - 5 = 18 + 12$

40. $4y - 7 + 2y = -24 - 1$

Solve.

41. $2x + 1.4 = 7.8$ **42.** $5t - 2.1 = 8.9$

43. $1.4m - 3.6 = 3.4$ **44.** $9.2 = 1.5t + 1.7$

45. $6 - 1.2x = 8.4$ **46.** $9.3 + 2.5k = 1.3$

47. $2 - 1.8r = 11$ **48.** $4.2 + 0.5y = 8.1$

Solve. Round your answer to the nearest tenth.

49. $7x + 5 = -3$ **50.** $2.4n - 3.8 = 1.1$

51. $3 = 3y + 8$ **52.** $4 = -6z + 14$

Problems and Applications

53. The equation $(x + 12) + 3x + 8 = 40$ represents the perimeter of the triangle. Find the lengths of the sides.

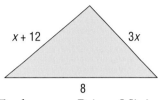

54. Pierre Trudeau was Prime Minister of Canada for 15 years. This was 3 years longer than twice the number of years that John Diefenbaker was Prime Minister. Solve the equation $2y + 3 = 15$ to find out how long John Diefenbaker was Prime Minister.

55. a) Solve the equation $2x + 5 = 11$, using the division rule first.
b) Is the result the same when you use the addition rule first?
c) Is one method better than the other? Explain.

56. Write an equation in which the solution requires at least 2 steps and is $x = -15$. Have a classmate solve your equation.

NUMBER POWER

Use each of the numbers from 1 to 9 only once to make each statement true.

$(\blacksquare - \blacksquare) \div \blacksquare = 1$

$\blacksquare + \blacksquare - \blacksquare = 1$

$\blacksquare - \blacksquare \times \blacksquare = 1$

2.11 Solving Equations with Variables on Both Sides

At the 1992 Summer Olympics, Canadians won medals in 19 events, including the demonstration sport of taekwondo. Marcia King won a silver medal for Canada in this event.

Canadians were more successful in rowing than in any other sport. If we let x be the number of rowing events in which Canadians won medals, we can write the equation $x + 9 = 19 - x$. This is an example of an equation with a variable on both sides.

Activity: Use Algebra Tiles
Write the equation represented by the algebra tiles.

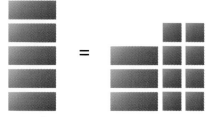

Inquire

1. Solve the equation for x. Describe your method.

2. Solve the equation $x + 7 = 2x + 3$ by isolating the variable on the right side of the equation.

3. Solve the equation $x + 7 = 2x + 3$ by isolating the variable on the left side of the equation.

4. Compare your results in questions 2 and 3.

5. Write the steps for solving equations with variables on both sides.

6. Solve the equation $x + 9 = 19 - x$ to find the number of rowing events in which Canadians won medals at the 1992 Summer Olympics.

Example	Solution
Solve the equation $5x - 8x = x + 8$.	Simplify before solving. $\quad\quad 5x - 8x = x + 8$
	$\quad\quad\quad\quad\quad\quad\quad\quad\quad\quad -3x = x + 8$
	Add $-x$ to both sides: $\quad -3x + (-x) = x + 8 + (-x)$
	$\quad\quad\quad\quad\quad\quad\quad\quad\quad\quad -4x = 8$
	Divide both sides by -4: $\quad\quad \dfrac{-4x}{-4} = \dfrac{8}{-4}$
	$\quad\quad\quad\quad\quad\quad\quad\quad\quad\quad x = -2$
	The solution is $x = -2$.

Practice

Write and solve the equations shown by the tiles.

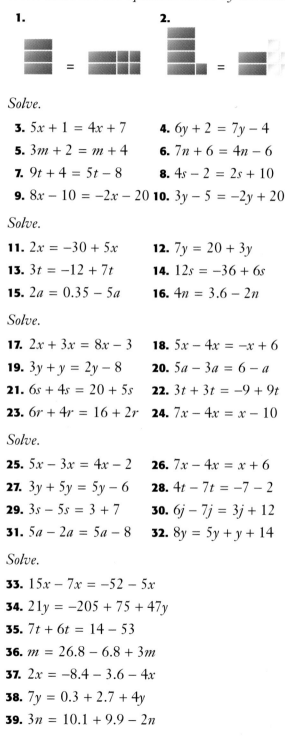

1.   2.

Solve.

3. $5x + 1 = 4x + 7$ **4.** $6y + 2 = 7y - 4$

5. $3m + 2 = m + 4$ **6.** $7n + 6 = 4n - 6$

7. $9t + 4 = 5t - 8$ **8.** $4s - 2 = 2s + 10$

9. $8x - 10 = -2x - 20$ **10.** $3y - 5 = -2y + 20$

Solve.

11. $2x = -30 + 5x$ **12.** $7y = 20 + 3y$

13. $3t = -12 + 7t$ **14.** $12s = -36 + 6s$

15. $2a = 0.35 - 5a$ **16.** $4n = 3.6 - 2n$

Solve.

17. $2x + 3x = 8x - 3$ **18.** $5x - 4x = -x + 6$

19. $3y + y = 2y - 8$ **20.** $5a - 3a = 6 - a$

21. $6s + 4s = 20 + 5s$ **22.** $3t + 3t = -9 + 9t$

23. $6r + 4r = 16 + 2r$ **24.** $7x - 4x = x - 10$

Solve.

25. $5x - 3x = 4x - 2$ **26.** $7x - 4x = x + 6$

27. $3y + 5y = 5y - 6$ **28.** $4t - 7t = -7 - 2$

29. $3s - 5s = 3 + 7$ **30.** $6j - 7j = 3j + 12$

31. $5a - 2a = 5a - 8$ **32.** $8y = 5y + y + 14$

Solve.

33. $15x - 7x = -52 - 5x$

34. $21y = -205 + 75 + 47y$

35. $7t + 6t = 14 - 53$

36. $m = 26.8 - 6.8 + 3m$

37. $2x = -8.4 - 3.6 - 4x$

38. $7y = 0.3 + 2.7 + 4y$

39. $3n = 10.1 + 9.9 - 2n$

Solve.

40. $2x + 10 = 9 + 11 - 3x$

41. $11s + 25 = 54 + 25 + 2s$

42. $65 + n = 85 - 16 + 3n$

Problems and Applications

43. Bill has x baseball cards. Abbas has $4x$ baseball cards. The number of cards Abbas has is equal to the number of cards Bill has plus 60. Solve the equation $x + 60 = 4x$ to find the number of cards Bill has.

44. Marlene scored y ringette goals. Lynn scored $3y$ goals. The number of goals that Marlene scored equals the number of goals Lynn scored minus 12. Solve the equation $y = 3y - 12$ to find the number of goals Marlene scored.

45. Solve for x. Assume the letters a, b, c, and y represent non-zero integers.
a) $x + a = b + c + y$ **b)** $a + (x - b) = c - y$
c) $ax + b = c - y$ **d)** $a(x - b) + y = c$
e) $b + y = cx - a$ **f)** $\frac{x}{a} + b - y = -c$

46. The average wind speed in Bonavista, Newfoundland, is twice the average wind speed in Whitehorse, Yukon Territory. The difference between the wind speeds is 14 km/h. Solve the equation $2x - 14 = x$ to find the average wind speed in Whitehorse.

47. The number of states in India is 1 more than 4 times the number of states in Australia. There are 19 more states in India than in Australia. Solve the equation $x + 19 = 4x + 1$ to find the number of states in Australia.

48. Write an equation with a variable on both sides and a solution of $x = -2$. Have a classmate solve your equation.

2.12 The Distributive Property

Activity: Use Algebra Tiles

An x-tile has an area of x square units.
A 1-tile has an area of 1 square unit.

How many units long are the sides of a 1-tile?
How many units long is each side of an x-tile?

Use x-tiles and 1-tiles to model these rectangles.

a)

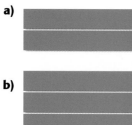

c)

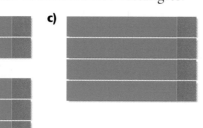

b)

Inquire

1. What is the area of each rectangle?

2. What are the length and width of each rectangle?

3. Describe a method for multiplying the length by the width to give the area of each rectangle.

To **expand** an expression means to remove the brackets and simplify. To do this, we use the **distributive property**.
$a(b + c) = ab + ac$

Example 1

Expand using the distributive property.
a) $3(x + 5)$
b) $-(2 - x)$

Solution

Multiply each term inside the brackets by the term outside the brackets.

a) $3(x + 5) = 3(x + 5)$
$\qquad = 3(x) + 3(5)$
$\qquad = 3x + 15$

b) $-(2 - x) = -1(2 - x)$
$\qquad = -1(2) - 1(-x)$
$\qquad = -2 + x$

Example 2

Expand.
a) $4(3x - 2y + 7)$
b) $-2(x + 3) - (x - 5)$

Solution

a) $4(3x - 2y + 7)$

$= 4(3x - 2y + 7)$
$= 12x - 8y + 28$

b) $-2(x + 3) - (x - 5)$

$= -2(x + 3) - 1(x - 5)$
$= -2x - 6 - x + 5$
$= -2x - x - 6 + 5$
$= -3x - 1$

Practice

Expand.

1. $5(x+1)$ **2.** $3(x-2)$ **3.** $4(x+2)$

4. $2(x-3)$ **5.** $7(x-1)$ **6.** $5(x+3)$

7. $2(x+6)$ **8.** $4(x-5)$ **9.** $7(x+3)$

10. $3(x-4)$ **11.** $10(x+2)$ **12.** $9(x-3)$

Expand.

13. $2(3x+2)$ **14.** $3(3x+1)$

15. $5(2x+1)$ **16.** $4(2x+3)$

17. $6(2x-1)$ **18.** $5(3x-2)$

19. $7(2x+1)$ **20.** $6(3x+2)$

Expand.

21. $-3(x+2)$ **22.** $-4(2x+1)$

23. $-2(5x-2)$ **24.** $-3(3x-2)$

25. $-5(2x-1)$ **26.** $-2(5x-3)$

27. $-4(x+5)$ **28.** $-(2x-1)$

Expand.

29. $-2(3x-2y)$ **30.** $-3(5x+3y)$

31. $-4(5x+2y)$ **32.** $-(2x+y)$

33. $-5(-x+y)$ **34.** $-7(x-3y)$

35. $-2(3x+7)$ **36.** $-4(2x-y)$

Expand.

37. $-4(2x+3y+z)$ **38.** $3(5x-2y+2)$

39. $6(-x+3y+4)$ **40.** $-(2x-3y+5)$

Expand and simplify.

41. $4(y-3)+2(y+4)$

42. $2(5x-1)-(3x+2)$

43. $4(x+7)-(3x+2)$

44. $3(2x-3)-3(2x-5)$

45. $3(2x-5)+3(2x+1)$

46. $4(-x+3)-2(3x+1)$

47. $-2(x-3y+2)-3(x-2y)$

Problems and Applications

Expand and simplify.

48. $3(x^2+4x-3)+2(x^2+5)$

49. $2(3x^2+7x-3)+4(x-3)$

50. $5(y^2+3y-4)+2(y^2-4y+1)$

51. $-(2x+3y-5)+5(2x-3y+6)$

52. $-(2x+3)+3(x-1)-4(x-2)$

53. $(2x+1)-4(2x-3)+2(3x-1)$

Expand and simplify.

54. $4(4x-3y+2)-(2x+5y-4)$

55. $-(3x-2y+7)+4(x+y-2)$

56. $2(x^2+y^2)-3x^2+4y^2+7$

57. $4(x^2+2x-3)-2(x^2+4y-1)$

58. $5(2y^2+3y-2)-2(y^2-4y+1)$

For each large rectangle, state
a) *the length and width.*
b) *the area in expanded form.*

59.   **60.**

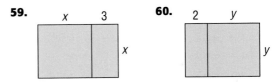

Write the area of the shaded rectangle in expanded form.

61.   **62.**

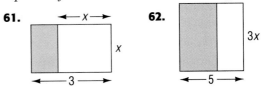

63. The money you deposit in a bank is called the principal, P. After your money earns interest, the new principal is given by the expression $P(1+rt)$, where r is the interest rate and t is the length of time your money was deposited.
a) Expand the expression $P(1+rt)$.
b) Evaluate the expression for $P = \$300$, $r = 0.05$, and $t = 2$ years.

2.13 Solving Equations with Brackets

Activity: Solve the Equation

Canada became a country in 1867. If we take the number of provinces in Canada at that time, add 1, and double the sum, the result is Canada's present number of provinces. Thus, we can find the number of provinces in 1867 by solving the equation $2(x + 1) = 10$.

Inquire

1. Expand to remove the brackets in the equation $2(x + 1) = 10$.

2. Solve for x to find the number of provinces in 1867.

3. Solve these equations.
a) $3(x - 1) = 12$
b) $-2(x + 1) = 6$
c) $2(x + 3) = -4$
d) $-(x + 1) = -7$

4. Write a rule for solving equations with brackets.

5. Research and list Canada's provinces in 1867.

Example 1

Solve the equation $2(x + 2) = -6$ and check.

Solution

Expand then solve.

$$2(x + 2) = -6$$
$$2x + 4 = -6$$

Add -4 to both sides:
$$2x + 4 + (-4) = -6 + (-4)$$
$$2x = -10$$

Divide both sides by 2:
$$\frac{2x}{2} = \frac{-10}{2}$$
$$x = -5$$

Substitute $x = -5$.

Check:

L.S.	$= 2(x + 2)$	**R.S.**	$= -6$
	$= 2(-5 + 2)$		
	$= 2(-3)$		
	$= -6$		

The solution is $x = -5$.

Example 2

Solve the equation $2(x - 3) - 5 = 13 - 4x$ and check.

Solution

To follow the order of operations, first expand to remove the brackets.

$$2(x - 3) - 5 = 13 - 4x$$
$$2x - 6 - 5 = 13 - 4x$$
$$2x - 11 = 13 - 4x$$
$$2x - 11 + 11 = 13 - 4x + 11$$
$$2x = 24 - 4x$$
$$2x + 4x = 24 - 4x + 4x$$
$$6x = 24$$
$$\frac{6x}{6} = \frac{24}{6}$$
$$x = 4$$

Substitute $x = 4$.

Check:

L.S. $= 2(x - 3) - 5$	**R.S.** $= 13 - 4x$
$= 2(4 - 3) - 5$	$= 13 - 4(4)$
$= 2(1) - 5$	$= 13 - 16$
$= 2 - 5$	$= -3$
$= -3$	

The solution is $x = 4$.

Example 3

Solve and check.
$$3(2x - 5) - (x + 3) = 2(x + 1) + 4$$

Solution

$$3(2x - 5) - (x + 3) = 2(x + 1) + 4$$
$$6x - 15 - x - 3 = 2x + 2 + 4$$
$$6x - x - 15 - 3 = 2x + 6$$
$$5x - 18 = 2x + 6$$
$$5x - 2x = 6 + 18$$
$$3x = 24$$
$$x = 8$$

Check:

L.S. $= 3(2x - 5) - (x + 3)$	**R.S.** $= 2(x + 1) + 4$
$= 3[2(8) - 5] - (8 + 3)$	$= 2(8 + 1) + 4$
$= 3(16 - 5) - (11)$	$= 2(9) + 4$
$= 3(11) - 11$	$= 18 + 4$
$= 33 - 11$	$= 22$
$= 22$	

The solution is $x = 8$.

CONTINUED ⟩

Practice

Solve.

1. $2(x + 1) = 4$ **2.** $2(x - 3) = 2$

3. $3(x + 1) = 6$ **4.** $2(x + 3) = -6$

5. $3(x + 2) = -9$ **6.** $2(x + 5) = -4$

Solve and check.

7. $2(3x + 4) = 14$ **8.** $14 = 2(3x - 2)$

9. $3(x + 5) = 18$ **10.** $3(2x + 3) = -3$

11. $-24 = 4(x + 3)$ **12.** $5(2x + 3) = -15$

Solve.

13. $2(x + 3) - 3 = 8 - 3x$

14. $3(x + 1) + 10 = 8 - 2x$

15. $8 - 3x = 4(x - 3) + 6$

16. $5(2x - 3) + 6 = -35 - 3x$

Solve.

17. $5(2x - 3) = 2(-3x - 2) + 5$

18. $2(5x - 6) = (3x - 2) + 4$

19. $3(5y + 4) = 5(2y - 3) + 22$

20. $2(8n + 7) = -50 + 2(-5n + 6)$

21. $5(2x - 3) = 2(3x + 7) + 11$

Solve and check.

22. $2(x - 3) + (x + 3) = 6x$

23. $5(x + 4) - (x + 2) = 8x + 2$

24. $4(m - 2) - (m + 3) = m - 1$

25. $4(n - 7) - 2(n + 3) = -15n$

26. $4(y + 2) - 5(y + 1) = y - 1$

Solve.

27. $3(2x + 1) - (x - 2) = 2(3x + 4)$

28. $12(2s - 1) - 4(-2s - 1) = 2(s + 11)$

29. $2(x - 8) - (x - 4) = 3(x + 5) + 3$

30. $7(2x - 1) - 2(5x - 6) = 2(4x - 5) + 7$

31. $3(4n - 1) = 4(-n + 9) - 7$

Problems and Applications

32. The equation $5(x + 1) = 20$ represents the area of the following rectangle.
a) Solve the equation.
b) Find the rectangle's width.

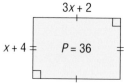

33. The equation $2(3x + 2) + 2(x + 4) = 36$ represents the perimeter of the rectangle shown below.

$3x + 2$

$x + 4$ $P = 36$

a) Solve the equation.
b) Calculate the rectangle's dimensions.

34. The Pacific Ocean accounts for 46% of the area of the water on the Earth's surface. If we take the percent that the Atlantic Ocean accounts for, subtract 1, and double the difference, the result is the percent that the Pacific Ocean accounts for. Solve the equation $2(x - 1) = 46$ to find the percent that the Atlantic Ocean accounts for.

35. Write an equation that has 1 bracketed expression on its left side and 1 bracketed expression plus a number on its right side. The equation should have a solution of $x = -2$. Have a classmate solve your equation.

WORD POWER

Change the word BARN to the word DOOR by changing one letter at a time. You must form a real word each time you change a letter. The best solution has the fewest steps.

Equivalent Forms of Algebraic Equations

An algebraic equation has an infinite number of equivalent forms. For example, dividing each term in the equation $4x + 2 = 6$ by 2 gives the equivalent form $2x + 1 = 3$. Because the forms are equivalent, the solution to both forms is the same, $x = 1$.

Activity ❶ Equivalent Whole-Number Forms

1. a) What whole numbers can be divided into each of the 3 terms of the equation $10x + 20 = 30$ to produce equivalent whole-number equations?

b) Write the equivalent whole-number equations you found by division.

c) Which equation from part b) is the least complex? Explain.

d) How could you write more whole-number equations equivalent to $10x + 20 = 30$?

2. a) Write three whole-number equations equivalent to $6x + 15 = 3$.

b) State the least complex whole-number equation that is equivalent to $6x + 15 = 3$.

c) Solve the equation you wrote in part b).

d) Without solving the equation $6x + 15 = 3$, state what the solution is. Check your answer by substitution.

3. Reduce each equation to its least complex equivalent whole-number form.

a) $8x - 4 = 12$

b) $100x + 300 = 1000$

c) $50x - 125 = 575$

d) $35x - 75 = 350$

BARN
BORN
BOON
BOOR
DOOR

Activity ❷ Equations with Decimal Coefficients

1. a) Multiply each of the three terms in the equation $1.5x + 0.7 = 3.7$ by 10.

b) What type of equation is the resulting equation?

c) What is its solution?

2. a) State the smallest whole number by which you can multiply each term in the equation $0.01p - 0.2 = 0.25$ to produce an equivalent whole-number equation.

b) What is the resulting equation?

c) What is its solution?

3. Can equivalent whole-number equations always be written for any equation written in decimal form? Explain.

CONTINUED

Activity ❸ Equations with Fractional Coefficients

1. What is the coefficient of the variable in each of these equations?

a) $\frac{1}{2}x + \frac{1}{5} = 5$ **b)** $\frac{3}{2}x + \frac{1}{3} = -4$

c) $\frac{x}{7} + 8 = -3$ **d)** $\frac{5x}{4} - 11 = 13$

2. a) What is the coefficient of x in the equation $\frac{2x}{5} + \frac{1}{5} = 1$?

b) Why can we write $\frac{2x}{5} + \frac{1}{5}$ in the equivalent form $\frac{2x + 1}{5}$?

c) The equation $2x + 1 = 5$ is the least complex whole-number form for the equation in part a). Explain how this equation was produced.

3. Write two other whole-number equations equivalent to the equation $2x + 1 = 5$.

4. Are these equations related? Explain.

$\frac{x}{3} + \frac{1}{2} = 1$ $2x + 3 = 6$ $34x + 51 = 102$

5. How are these equations related?

$\frac{x}{2} + \frac{3}{7} = 2$ $\frac{5x}{2} + \frac{15}{7} = 10$ $7x + 6 = 28$

Activity ❹ Alternate Equivalent Rational Forms

1. Is the expression $\frac{1}{3}(x + 1)$ an equivalent form of the expression $\frac{x + 1}{3}$? Explain.

2. Write the expression $\frac{x + 1}{3}$ as two separate expressions with a common denominator.

3. Which of the following expressions is equivalent to $\frac{3x - 4}{5}$?

a) $3x - 4 \div 5$ **b)** $\frac{3x}{5} - \frac{4}{5}$ **c)** $5(3x - 4)$

4. Explain how $\frac{x + 3}{2} = 5$, $\frac{3x + 9}{2} = 15$, and $2x + 6 = 20$ are related.

5. a) The equations $\frac{x}{2} + \frac{1}{5} = 5$, $\frac{3x}{2} + \frac{3}{5} = 15$, and $5x + 2 = 50$ are equivalent forms with the same solution. If you were asked to find the solution, which form would you solve? Explain.

b) Solve the equation.

6. Explain how $C = \pi d$ and $\pi = \frac{C}{d}$ are related.

7. If speed is distance divided by time, explain why time is distance divided by speed.

100

2.14 Solving Equations with Fractions and Decimals

In 1990, a survey of Canadian households found that the percent with camcorders was 2.1% less than one-half the percent with compact disc players. The percent of households with camcorders was 5.6%.

We can write the equation $0.5x - 2.1 = 5.6$, where x is the percent of households with compact disc players.

Activity: Solve the Equations

Solve these equations.

a) $1.2x - 0.4 = 2$ **b)** $0.25x - 5 = 2.75$
c) $3.14n + 2 = 12.99$ **d)** $2.3t - 1.47 = 6.85 + 0.7t$

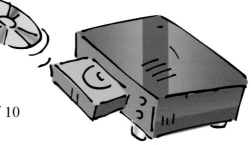

Inquire

1. Multiply the terms in the equations a) to d) by a power of 10 to produce an equation with whole-number coefficients.

2. Solve each equation you wrote in question 1.

3. Compare the 2 solution methods you used. Which method do you prefer? Explain.

4. Solve the equation $0.5x - 2.1 = 5.6$ to find the percent of Canadian households with compact disc players in 1990.

5. Research the percent of Canadian households with compact disc players today. Compare your findings with your answer to question 4.

Example 1

Solve the equation $5.84 - 2.2y = 18.6$.

Solution 1

The number 5.84 has the greatest number of decimal places. To obtain whole-number coefficients, multiply each term by 100.

$$5.84 - 2.2y = 18.6$$
$$100 \times (5.84 - 2.2y) = 100 \times 18.6$$
$$100 \times 5.84 - 100 \times 2.2y = 100 \times 18.6$$
$$584 - 220y = 1860$$
$$-220y = 1276$$
$$y = -5.8$$

EST $1000 \div (-200) = -5$

The solution is $y = -5.8$.

Solution 2

Keep the decimals and solve with a calculator.

$$5.84 - 2.2y = 18.6$$
$$-2.2y = 18.6 - 5.84$$
$$-2.2y = 12.76$$
$$y = -5.8$$

EST $10 \div (-2) = -5$

CONTINUED ▶

Example 2

Solve $\frac{x}{3} - \frac{3x}{2} = \frac{1}{6} - x$.

Solution

To eliminate the fractions, multiply each term in the equation by the lowest common denominator, 6.

$$\frac{x}{3} - \frac{3x}{2} = \frac{1}{6} - x$$

$$6 \times \left(\frac{x}{3}\right) - 6 \times \left(\frac{3x}{2}\right) = 6 \times \left(\frac{1}{6}\right) - 6 \times x$$

$$2x - 9x = 1 - 6x$$

$$-7x = 1 - 6x$$

$$-7x + 6x = 1$$

$$-x = 1$$

$$x = -1$$

The solution is $x = -1$.

Example 3

Solve and check
$\frac{x-2}{3} + \frac{x+1}{2} = 4$.

Solution

Multiply all terms by the lowest common denominator, 6.

$$\frac{x-2}{3} + \frac{x+1}{2} = 4$$

$$6 \times \frac{(x-2)}{3} + 6 \times \frac{(x+1)}{2} = 6 \times 4$$

$$2(x-2) + 3(x+1) = 24$$

$$2x - 4 + 3x + 3 = 24$$

$$5x - 1 = 24$$

$$5x = 25$$

$$x = 5$$

> The division bar is a grouping symbol. It acts like a bracket.

Check: L.S. $= \frac{x-2}{3} + \frac{x+1}{2}$ R.S. $= 4$

$$= \frac{5-2}{3} + \frac{5+1}{2}$$

$$= \frac{3}{3} + \frac{6}{2}$$

$$= 1 + 3$$

$$= 4$$

The solution is $x = 5$.

Practice

Solve.

1. $x + 0.2 = 0.8$

3. $s + 1.2 = 1.5$

5. $m + 5.2 = 2.2$

2. $y - 0.5 = 1.2$

4. $t + 4.5 = -3.0$

6. $-2.3 = 4.6 + n$

Solve.

7. $0.3x = 0.3$

9. $1.2m = -3.6$

11. $4.8 = 2.0n$

8. $-5 = 0.5y$

10. $0.3n = 1.2$

12. $1.1s = -4.4$

Solve and check.

13. $3x - 0.4 = 0.8$ **14.** $3.64 = 2m + 4.7$

15. $4y + 0.88 = 5.24$ **16.** $2.5 = 3.7 + 0.2x$

17. $0.3r + 0.54 = -3$ **18.** $1.2s + 3.6 = 4.8$

Solve.

19. $\frac{x}{4} = \frac{1}{2}$ **20.** $\frac{y}{12} = \frac{1}{3}$ **21.** $\frac{8}{10} = \frac{n}{5}$

22. $\frac{m}{6} = -\frac{1}{3}$ **23.** $-\frac{1}{9} = \frac{y}{27}$ **24.** $\frac{x}{8} = -\frac{1}{4}$

Solve and check.

25. $\frac{y}{2} = \frac{y}{3} - 1$ **26.** $\frac{y}{4} = \frac{y}{5} + 1$

27. $\frac{5n}{2} = \frac{4n}{3} - \frac{7}{6}$ **28.** $\frac{p}{2} - \frac{3p}{4} = \frac{3}{4} - p$

29. $\frac{n}{3} + 2 = \frac{n}{5} + 4$ **30.** $\frac{(x+1)}{3} = \frac{(x-1)}{5}$

31. $\frac{(3-y)}{5} = \frac{(-2-3y)}{4}$ **32.** $\frac{(2x-3)}{2} = \frac{(-x-1)}{4}$

Solve and check.

33. $\frac{1-x}{4} - \frac{x}{2} = 7$

34. $\frac{x-1}{3} + \frac{x+2}{6} = 7$

35. $\frac{x+1}{2} - \frac{x-7}{6} = 3$

36. $\frac{2n+10}{4} - \frac{n}{3} = 1$

37. $\frac{4x+5}{3} - \frac{3x}{2} = -x$

38. $4 = \frac{x+1}{3} + \frac{x+5}{5}$

39. $\frac{x+1}{3} + \frac{2-3x}{2} = -1$

40. $\frac{x+1}{3} + \frac{x-2}{7} = 1$

Problems and Applications

41. On the average, the mass of a raccoon is 1 kg more than $\frac{1}{4}$ of the mass of a coyote. The mass of a raccoon is 9.5 kg. To find the mass of a coyote, solve the equation $\frac{m}{4} + 1 = 9.5$.

42. On the average, a Canadian adult spends 35% or 0.35 of the time sleeping. Solve the equation $9t - 0.01 = 0.35$ to find the fraction of the time spent shopping.

PATTERN POWER

1. Take a 20 cm by 20 cm square piece of paper and cut out a 1-by-1 square from each corner. Fold up the sides to make a box. Calculate the volume of the box.

2. Cut out a 2-by-2 square from each corner and calculate the volume of the new box.

3. Repeat the procedure for a 3-by-3 square, a 4-by-4 square, and so on. Copy and complete the table.

Dimensions of Corners (cm)	Volume of Box (cm³)
1 × 1	
2 × 2	
3 × 3	
...	

4. What are the dimensions of the box with the greatest volume?

5. What was the size of the square you removed from each corner to give the box with the greatest volume?

6. To get the box with the greatest volume, what size of square must you remove from each corner of each of the following squares?
a) 14 cm by 14 cm
b) 25 cm by 25 cm

Rolling Balls and Inductive Reasoning

Inductive reasoning is the process of drawing conclusions from a number of specific cases. In the following activities, you will consider a number of cases in which a ball rebounds from the sides of a table.

When a ball moves on a flat table with raised sides, the angle at which the ball strikes a side equals the angle at which the ball rebounds.

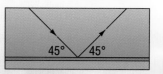

In the following activities, assume that:
a) The corners of the table are named top right (TR), top left (TL), lower right (LR), and lower left (LL).
b) The ball always starts from the lower left (LL) corner at an angle of 45° to the sides.
c) The ball keeps rolling until it hits a corner. Then, the ball stops.
d) The table dimensions are stated as height first and then width. A 3-by-2 table is shown here.

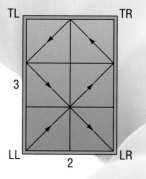

Activity ❶

The diagram shows the path of a ball on a 3-by-2 table. The ball stops at the lower right (LR) corner.

1. Draw tables with the following dimensions on grid paper. For each grid, draw the path of a ball that starts at the LL corner.

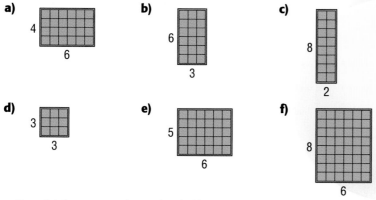

2. In which corner does the ball stop on each table?

3. What are the dimensions of the table that gives
a) the most complicated path?   **b)** the simplest path?

4. On which table does the ball cross every square?

5. Will a ball ever stop at the LL corner? Explain.

Activity ❷

1. Draw tables with the following dimensions and draw the path of the ball.

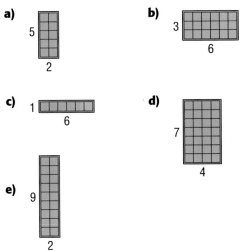

2. What kind of number is the height of each table?

3. What kind of number is the width of each table?

4. Where does the ball always stop?

Activity ❸

1. Draw each table and the path of the ball.

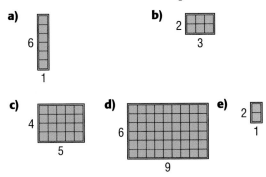

2. What kind of number is the height of each table?

3. What kind of number is the width of each table?

4. Where does the ball always stop?

Activity ❹

1. Draw tables with the following dimensions and draw the path of the ball.

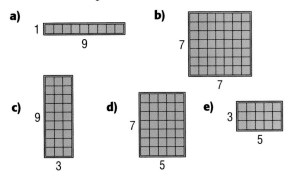

2. What kind of number is the height of each table?

3. What kind of number is the width of each table?

4. Where does the ball always stop?

Activity ❺

1. Use inductive reasoning to write a rule that states where the ball stops if the dimensions are
a) odd-by-even   **b)** even-by-odd
c) odd-by-odd

2. State where the ball stops on tables with the following dimensions.
a) 32-by-13   **b)** 37-by-37
c) 29-by-28   **d)** 101-by-101
e) 244-by-133   **f)** 79-by-88

Review

Evaluate $3x + 2y$ for the following values of the variables.

1. $x = 1, y = 3$ **2.** $x = 4, y = 2$

3. $x = 7, y = 1$ **4.** $x = 3, y = 3$

5. $x = -4, y = 0$ **6.** $x = -2, y = -1$

7. $x = 3, y = -5$ **8.** $x = -1, y = -3$

Evaluate each expression for $a = 2.5$, $b = -3.5$, and $c = 5.5$.

9. $a + 2b - 3c$ **10.** $2a - b + 4c$

Simplify.

11. $7x + 10 + 7y - 4x + 1$

12. $2a - 3b - 5 + a - b$

13. $-q + 4q - 9r - a + 2r + 1$

In questions 14–18, write an equation for each statement.

14. Eight more than a number is twenty.

15. A number multiplied by six is seventy-two.

16. Hadib is eight years older than Cam. The sum of their ages is twenty-four.

17. Sonya has ten dollars less than Paula. Together they have ninety dollars.

18. Carl has three times as many stamps as Tim. Together they have 2400 stamps.

19. The perimeter of each figure is 64 m. Write an equation to find the dimensions of each figure.

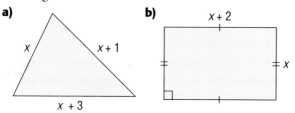

Solve.

20. $3x = 12$ **21.** $y + 7 = 12$

22. $2 = -4 + s$ **23.** $3 + z = 7$

24. $x + 1 = -2$ **25.** $5m = 40$

26. $3n = -21$ **27.** $-24 = 12x$

28. $5p = 3.0$ **29.** $7z = -2.8$

Solve.

30. $\frac{x}{2} = 5$ **31.** $\frac{y}{2} = -5$

32. $\frac{b}{3} = -3$ **33.** $\frac{z}{4} = 6$

Solve.

34. $\frac{x}{3} + 2 = 4$ **35.** $\frac{y}{2} - 3 = 2$

36. $4 + \frac{b}{3} = -1$ **37.** $2 - \frac{z}{4} = -1$

Solve and check.

38. $2x - 3 = 9$ **39.** $3y - 2 = 13$

40. $5y - 7 = 3$ **41.** $-22 = 7y - 8$

42. $3x + 2x = -25$ **43.** $4x + 5x = -81$

44. $3 + 2q = 21$ **45.** $2.9 + 6x = 1.1$

Solve.

46. $3x - 17 = 13$ **47.** $56 = 5y + 11$

48. $2x + 3.1 = 1.1$ **49.** $5m + 25 = -65$

50. $3y + 10 = 82$ **51.** $0.3x + 2.6 = 4.4$

52. $-39 = 25 + 4a$ **53.** $-54 = 6z - 18$

54. $-33 + 7t = -61$ **55.** $8q - 42 = -26$

Solve.

56. $6a - 3a + 2a = 10 - 2 + 7$

57. $2p + 3p - p = 9 - 15 - 6$

58. $10j - 5j - 8j = -6 + 15 + 12$

59. $12k - 8k - 6k = -18 + 20 - 6$

Solve and check.

60. $3x - 4 = 8 - x$ **61.** $6x - 6 = 4x - 10$

62. $7 - x = -7 + 6x$ **63.** $4 + x = 36 - 7x$

64. $2 + 3j = 5j - 24$ **65.** $-3 + 2r = -30 - 7r$

Solve.

66. $2x + 15 = -12 - 13 - 3x$

67. $b - 17 = 15 + 3b + 18$

68. $21 + 4q = q + 13 + 17$

Solve and check.

69. $4(y - 4) + 3(y + 7) = -30$

70. $-38 = 5(2y - 1) + y$

71. $6(3x - 4) - (1 - 3x) = -67$

Solve.

72. $5y + 0.4 - 3y = -6$

73. $1.6m - 2.4 + 0.1m = 0.1m + 0.8$

74. $8.4x - 0.8 = 4.4x - 4$

75. $12.2x + 0.3 = 20.7 + 5.4x$

Solve.

76. $\dfrac{y}{2} + \dfrac{y}{3} = \dfrac{5}{6}$ **77.** $\dfrac{5y}{4} - \dfrac{y}{2} = \dfrac{-3}{4}$

78. $\dfrac{2y + 1}{3} = -5$ **79.** $\dfrac{x - 2}{6} = \dfrac{x + 2}{2}$

80. $\dfrac{x + 2}{4} = \dfrac{2x - 5}{2}$ **81.** $\dfrac{x - 2}{2} - \dfrac{x}{6} = -2$

Solve and check.

82. $\dfrac{2x - 1}{3} - \dfrac{x + 2}{4} = -5$

83. $\dfrac{3y + 5}{3} - \dfrac{y - 3}{6} = -2$

84. $\dfrac{2y + 1}{3} - \dfrac{y + 4}{5} = 7$

85. The number of Members of Parliament (MPs) elected from Ontario is 99. This number is 5 less than 4 times the number elected from Alberta. Solve the equation $4n - 5 = 99$ to find the number of MPs elected from Alberta.

Group Decision Making
Designing a Rube Goldberg Invention

The cartoonist Rube Goldberg is famous for his impractical inventions, which are shown as one-scene cartoons. This cartoon is like a Rube Goldberg cartoon. It shows a different way of pouring water into a sink.

Sources of power for Goldberg inventions might include:
• the sun melting a block of ice that releases a rope that was frozen into it
• the rays of the sun being focused through a magnifying glass
• a cat chasing a dog

1. Work in home groups. Decide on a Rube Goldberg invention designed to do something in an original way. Some tasks might include sharpening a pencil, travelling to school, or cleaning the chalkboard.

2. As a group, design a flow chart to show the sequence of events in your invention before you start to draw the cartoon.

3. In your group, draw and discuss rough sketches of the cartoon. Draw the final version and present it to the class.

4. As a class, evaluate the cartoons for originality and humour.

Chapter Check

1. Evaluate $ab + bc - ca$ for $a = 2$, $b = 3$, and $c = 4$.

Collect like terms and simplify.

2. $3x - 2y - 3x + 3y + 2$

3. $-15 + 2a - 3c + 10 + 4a - b - 7c$

4. Burt is four years older than Anna and the sum of their ages is 36. Write the equation to find their ages.

Solve and check.

5. $x - 12 = -4$ **6.** $x + 15 = 12$

7. $x + 2 = 8$ **8.** $x - 10 = -19$

9. $5 = x - 3$ **10.** $15 - x = -5$

Solve.

11. $6x = -54$ **12.** $4x = 44$

13. $\frac{x}{5} = 7$ **14.** $\frac{x}{3} = 4$

Solve.

15. $5x + 8 = 3x + 2$

16. $5x + 12 = 7x + 16$

17. $6z + 8 = 9z - 7$

18. $2y - 6 = 10 + 11y + 2$

Solve.

19. $3(2x - 4) = 9x + 3$

20. $5(2x - 1) + 9 = 2(x - 2)$

Solve.

21. $10x - 0.4 = 2x - 3.6$

22. $7.6x - 0.7 = 5.6x - 6.5$

Solve.

23. $\frac{2x}{3} = -6$ **24.** $\frac{y}{3} + \frac{1}{3} = -\frac{2}{3}$

25. $\frac{y}{3} - \frac{5y}{6} = -\frac{1}{2}$

Solve.

26. $\frac{3y + 1}{2} = 5$ **27.** $\frac{x + 2}{2} = \frac{x - 1}{5}$

28. $\frac{x + 2}{2} + \frac{x - 2}{5} = 2$

29. The average Canadian spends 23% or 0.23 of the time on leisure activities. This fraction is 0.01 less than 4 times the fraction of the time spent eating. Solve the equation $4t - 0.01 = 0.23$ to find the fraction of the time spent eating.

Using the Strategies

1. Determine the pattern and write the next 3 rows.

1	1	1						
1	2	3	2	1				
1	3	6	7	6	3	1		
1	4	10	16	19	16	10	4	1

2. The perimeter of an isosceles triangle is 8 cm. The length of each side is a whole number. How long is the shortest side?

3. The number 72 can be factored as follows.

$$72 = 36 \times 2$$
$$= 18 \times 2 \times 2$$
$$= 9 \times 2 \times 2 \times 2$$
$$= 3 \times 3 \times 2 \times 2 \times 2$$

Use this technique to find the age of each person in a group of teenagers if the product of their ages is 661 500.

4. The first 4 triangular numbers are shown.

1   **3**   **6**   **10**

What are the next 3 triangular numbers?

5. There are 20 students in the gym. The teacher wants them in 3 groups, with an even number of students in each group. In how many ways can the teacher put them into groups?

6. Your train leaves at 08:15. The bus trip to the train station takes 25 min. The bus stop is a 5-min walk from your place. You should get to the train station to buy your ticket 15 min before the train leaves. It will take you 55 min to get dressed, eat breakfast, and pack. For what time should you set your alarm clock?

7. Determine the pattern and predict the next 2 lines.

$$101 \times 101 = \blacksquare$$
$$202 \times 202 = \blacksquare$$
$$303 \times 303 = \blacksquare$$

8. The number 8 is a perfect cube.
$$2^3 = 2 \times 2 \times 2 = 8 \text{ or } 2^3 = 8$$
The number 27 is also a perfect cube.
$$3^3 = 3 \times 3 \times 3 = 27 \text{ or } 3^3 = 27$$

We can write 8 as the sum of 2 consecutive odd numbers.
$$3 + 5 = 8$$
We can write 27 as the sum of 3 consecutive odd numbers.
$$7 + 9 + 11 = 27$$

a) The next perfect cube is 64 because $4^3 = 64$. Write 64 as the sum of 4 consecutive odd numbers.

b) The next perfect cube is 125. Write 125 as the sum of 5 consecutive odd numbers.

c) The next perfect cube is 216. Write 216 as the sum of 6 consecutive odd numbers.

d) How does the square of the number that is cubed fit into the sum of the consecutive odd numbers?

e) Use this pattern to write 7^3 as the sum of 7 consecutive odd numbers.

9. Sketch a graph to show the length of time you spend watching TV versus the day of the week.

DATA BANK

1. How much higher above sea level is Mexico City than Calgary?

2. Express Venezuela's annual gold production as a percent of Canada's annual gold production.

Using Equations to Solve Problems

The following are the times for a typical space shuttle launch.

At $t - 3.8$ s, the shuttle's 3 main engines are ignited.

At $t + 2.88$ s, the twin boosters are ignited, and the hold-down bolts are released.

At $t + 2$ min 12 s, the boosters burn out and are jettisoned.

At $t + 8$ min 32 s, just before the shuttle reaches orbital velocity, the engines are shut down.

The huge external tank is jettisoned at $t + 8$ min 50 s.

The shuttle's own orbit-adjust engines put the shuttle into orbit.

If t is 08:00, at what time does each of the above events take place? For how long is the shuttle bolted to the lift-off platform while the engines are on? Why?

Activity ❶ A Scavenger Hunt

When you solve problems in mathematics, you often replace words with symbols.

1. The following are some symbols that have been used to replace words. State what each symbol means and, if possible, give an example of where you have seen it.

2. Design an international symbol of your own. Ask your classmates to tell you what they think it means.

Activity ❷ Equations

Solve.

1. $x - 4 = -6$

2. $y - 5 = -8$

3. $8 = m + 3$

4. $n + 5 = 8$

5. $s - 7 = 7$

6. $t + 7 = 7$

7. $x + 5 = 11$

8. $-9 = -3 + y$

9. $q + 9 = -1$

Solve.

10. $3y = 12$

11. $5x = -20$

12. $-m = 6$

13. $-n = -3$

14. $18 = 6s$

15. $-45 = 9t$

16. $\frac{x}{3} = 5$

17. $\frac{y}{4} = 1$

18. $\frac{y}{2} = -3$

Solve and check.

19. $2x + 7 = -13$

20. $1 = -5 + 3y$

21. $m + 6 = 4m + 18$

22. $4n - 5 = 2n + 1$

23. $6 = 2(x - 1)$

24. $3(y + 2) + 1 = y + 9$

25. $2(m + 3) + 4 = 3(m - 7) + 19$

Activity ❸ Perimeter and Area

Calculate each perimeter.

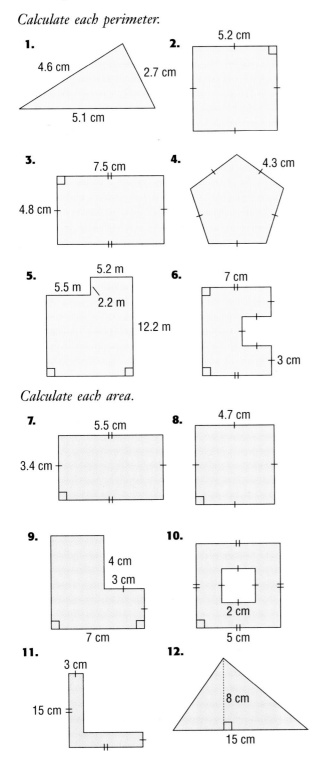

1.

4.6 cm

2.7 cm

5.1 cm

2.

5.2 cm

3.

7.5 cm

4.8 cm

4.

4.3 cm

5.

5.2 m

5.5 m

2.2 m

12.2 m

6.

7 cm

3 cm

Calculate each area.

7.

5.5 cm

3.4 cm

8.

4.7 cm

9.

4 cm

3 cm

7 cm

10.

2 cm

5 cm

11.

3 cm

15 cm

12.

8 cm

15 cm

Mental Math

Add.

1. $18 + 2$ **2.** $18 + 12$ **3.** $25 + 5$

4. $25 + 25$ **5.** $46 + 5$ **6.** $46 + 15$

7. $54 + 6$ **8.** $54 + 16$ **9.** $54 + 26$

Subtract.

10. $36 - 6$ **11.** $36 - 16$ **12.** $54 - 4$

13. $54 - 24$ **14.** $65 - 6$ **15.** $65 - 16$

16. $71 - 2$ **17.** $71 - 12$ **18.** $71 - 22$

Multiply.

19. $(25)(4)$ **20.** $(25)(40)$ **21.** $(4)(5)$

22. $(400)(5)$ **23.** $(5)(8)$ **24.** $(5)(800)$

25. $(4)(9)$ **26.** $(40)(9)$ **27.** $(400)(9)$

Divide.

28. $28 \div 4$ **29.** $280 \div 4$ **30.** $35 \div 7$

31. $3500 \div 7$ **32.** $2000 \div 5$ **33.** $2000 \div 50$

Simplify.

34. $(3)(2) + 5$ **35.** $4 + (2)(5)$

36. $5(2 + 6)$ **37.** $(8 - 3) \times 4$

38. $5 + 9 - 2$ **39.** $24 - (8 - 2)$

40. $27 - 9 - 3$ **41.** $30 - (10 + 5)$

Simplify.

42. $4 + 6 + 5 + 7$ **43.** $7 - 3 + 4 - 5$

44. $(2)(6) - 3 + 4$ **45.** $12 - 3 + 6 - 5$

46. $24 - (4)(2)(1)$ **47.** $20 - 5 - (4)(3)$

48. $(6 + 4)(3 - 1)$ **49.** $5 + 7 - (7 - 4)$

Simplify.

50. $\frac{4}{8} + \frac{1}{8}$ **51.** $\frac{3}{9} + \frac{1}{9}$ **52.** $\frac{5}{10} + \frac{2}{10}$

53. $\frac{5}{10} - \frac{1}{5}$ **54.** $\frac{5}{6} - \frac{1}{6}$ **55.** $\frac{3}{10} - \frac{1}{5}$

3.1 Solving Problems Using Equations

The ground speed of a jet depends on its air speed and the speed of the headwind or tailwind.

Activity: Study the Information

The equation for the ground speed of a jet, y, flying at 450 km/h with a headwind, x, is:

$$y = 450 - x$$

If there is a tailwind, the equation is:

$$y = 450 + x$$

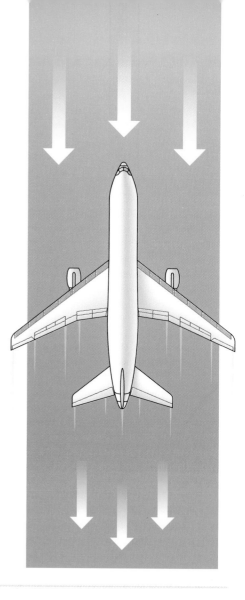

Inquire

1. What is the ground speed when there is
a) a headwind of 80 km/h?
b) a tailwind of 120 km/h?

2. What is the headwind if the ground speed is 390 km/h?

3. What is the tailwind if the ground speed is 515 km/h?

4. Write the equation to find the ground speed when the headwind is 60 km/h. Solve the equation.

5. Write the equation to find the ground speed when the tailwind is 100 km/h. Solve the equation.

6. Write the equation to find the headwind when the ground speed is 400 km/h. Solve the equation.

7. Write the equation to find the tailwind when the ground speed is 475 km/h. Solve the equation.

Example 1

A compact disc player costs $75 more than a tape deck. Together, they cost $725. How much does each cost?

Solution

Let the cost of the tape deck be x dollars.
Then, the cost of the compact disc player is $(x + 75)$ dollars.
The sum of the costs is $725.

$$
\begin{aligned}
x + (x + 75) &= 725 \\
2x + 75 &= 725 \\
2x &= 725 - 75 \\
2x &= 650 \\
x &= 325
\end{aligned}
$$

The cost of the tape deck is $325.
The cost of the compact disc player is $325 + $75 or $400.
Check: $325 + $400 = $725

Example 2

The sides of a triangle are 3 consecutive whole numbers of centimetres. The perimeter of the triangle is 48 cm. How long is each side?

Solution

Let x represent the length of the shortest side in centimetres. Then, the lengths of the other 2 sides are $x + 1$ and $x + 2$. The sum of the 3 sides is 48 cm.

$$x + (x + 1) + (x + 2) = 48$$
$$x + x + x + 1 + 2 = 48$$
$$3x + 3 = 48$$
$$3x = 45$$
$$x = 15$$

If $x = 15$, $x + 1 = 16$, and $x + 2 = 17$.
The lengths of the sides are 15 cm, 16 cm, and 17 cm.
Check: The numbers 15, 16, and 17 are consecutive whole numbers, and $P = 15 + 16 + 17$ or 48 cm.

Example 3

A parking meter contains $27.05 in quarters and dimes. There are 146 coins. How many quarters are there?

Solution

Let x represent the number of quarters.
Then, $(146 - x)$ is the number of dimes.
If there are x quarters, then the value of the quarters is $25x$ cents.
If there are $(146 - x)$ dimes, the value of the dimes is $10(146 - x)$ cents.
The total value of the coins is $27.05 or 2705 cents.

$$10(146 - x) + 25x = 2705$$
$$1460 - 10x + 25x = 2705$$
$$1460 + 15x = 2705$$
$$15x = 1245$$
$$x = 83$$

The number of quarters is 83.
The number of dimes is $146 - 83$ or 63.
Check: The value of the coins in dollars is $(0.25)(83) + (0.10)(63)$ or $27.05.

CONTINUED ➤

Example 4

One number is 2 times another number. If you subtract 10 from each number, the sum is 40. What are the numbers?

Solution

Let the smaller number be x. Then, the larger number is $2x$. Subtract 10 from each number to give $x - 10$ and $2x - 10$. The sum equals 40.

$$(x - 10) + (2x - 10) = 40$$
$$x + 2x - 10 - 10 = 40$$
$$3x - 20 = 40$$
$$3x = 60$$
$$x = 20$$

If $x = 20$, $2x = 40$. The numbers are 20 and 40.

Check: $20 - 10 = 10$ $40 - 10 = 30$ $10 + 30 = 40$

Practice

Each statement has two unknowns. Represent both in terms of x.

1. The sum of two numbers is 35.

2. There are 50 nickels and dimes.

3. There are 125 quarters and dimes.

4. The length and width of a rectangle total 36 cm.

5. There is a total of 32 males and females in the class.

6. The cafeteria sold 758 hamburgers and hot dogs.

7. Jim and Janice sold 468 kg of cheese.

8. The parking meter had 246 coins in quarters and dimes.

Find the length of each side.

9.

10.

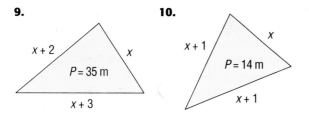

11.

12.

13.

14.

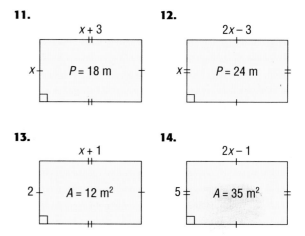

Problems and Applications

15. The sum of 2 numbers is 46. One number is 12 more than the other. What are the numbers?

16. The Mackenzie river is 1183 km longer than the St. Lawrence. The sum of their lengths is 7299 km. How long is each river?

17. The length of a rectangle is 5 m more than its width. Its perimeter is 90 m. What are its dimensions?

116

18. The sum of 3 consecutive numbers is 105. Find the numbers.

19. The number of frost-free days per year in Quebec City is 18 less than the number in Halifax. The total number in both cities is 292. How many frost-free days are there per year in Halifax?

20. The maximum life span of a brown bear is 10 times the maximum life span of a mouse. The sum of their maximum life spans is 33 years. What is the maximum life span of a mouse?

21. When Canada won the Women's World Hockey Championships, the Canadian team scored 35 more goals than were scored against it. The total number of goals scored in the games that Canada played was 41.
a) How many goals were scored against Canada?
b) How many goals did Canada score?

22. There are 2.25 times as many days of fog per year in Vancouver as in Winnipeg. The total number of days of fog in both cities is 65. How many days of fog does Winnipeg have per year?

23. One of the equal sides of an isosceles triangle is 3 m less than twice its base. The perimeter is 44 m. Find the lengths of the sides.

24. The cost of a pen is 3 times the cost of a pencil. The cost of 4 pencils and 3 pens is $9.75. What is the cost of a pencil?

25. Sally has twice as many dimes as nickels. The total value is $3.50. How many nickels does she have?

26. Aretha has $0.85 in nickels and dimes. She has 2 more nickels than dimes. How many nickels and dimes does she have?

27. A box contains 140 dimes and nickels. The total value is $11.15. How many dimes and how many nickels are there?

28. A picture is 5 cm longer than it is wide. The perimeter of the picture is 90 cm.
a) What is the width of the picture?
b) The picture is surrounded by a border, which is 6 cm wide. What are the outside dimensions of the border?

29. The sum of 2 numbers is 39. Twice the first number plus 3 times the second number is 101. Find the numbers.

30. One number is 5 more than another number. Three times the first plus twice the second is 30. Find the numbers.

31. A jar contains $18.50 in dimes and quarters. There are 110 coins in the jar. How many quarters are in the jar?

32. Pietra sells tickets at the theatre. At the end of the evening, she had $524.00 in $2.00 and $5.00 bills. The total number of bills was 145. How many of each kind of bill were there in total?

33. Large pizzas cost $12.50 and small pizzas cost $9.00. The pizza parlor sold 38 pizzas with a total value of $415.50. How many of each type of pizza did the parlor sell?

34. Tickets to the concert cost $9.00 for adults and $6.50 for students. A total of 950 people paid $7675.00 to attend. How many students attended the concert?

35. A garden is 20 m by 25 m. It is surrounded by a walk-way. The outside perimeter of the walk-way is 114 m. What is the width of the walk-way?

36. A picture measures 40 cm by 30 cm. The outside perimeter of the frame around the picture is 156 cm.
a) What is the width of the frame?
b) What is the area of the frame?

37. Write a problem that can be solved using an equation. Have a classmate solve your problem.

3.2 Use a Formula

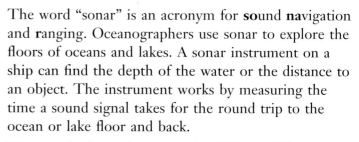

The word "sonar" is an acronym for **so**und **na**vigation and **r**anging. Oceanographers use sonar to explore the floors of oceans and lakes. A sonar instrument on a ship can find the depth of the water or the distance to an object. The instrument works by measuring the time a sound signal takes for the round trip to the ocean or lake floor and back.

The speed of sound in water is 1500 m/s. The formula for the distance to an object is

$$d = \frac{1500 \times t}{2}$$

where d is the distance in metres, and t is the time in seconds for a sonar signal to reach the object and bounce back.

It takes 0.35 s for sound to reach a wreck and bounce back. How deep is the water above the wreck?

Understand the Problem

1. What information are you given?

2. What are you asked to find?

3. What formula should you use?

Think of a Plan

Substitute for t in the formula.

$$d = \frac{1500 \times t}{2}$$

Carry Out the Plan

$$= \frac{1500 \times 0.35}{2}$$

> **EST** $1500 \times 0.4 = 600$
> $600 \div 2 = 300$

$$= \frac{525}{2}$$

$$= 262.5$$

The water is 262.5 m deep.

Look Back

To check your answer, how could you use the depth to calculate the time?

Use a Formula	
	1. Write the formula.
	2. Replace variables with known values.
	3. Calculate the remaining variable.
	4. Check that your answer is reasonable.

Problems and Applications

1. The following formula gives the ideal amount of sleep needed each night by people 19 years old or younger.

$$s = \frac{35 - n}{2}$$

The amount of sleep is s hours, and n is the age in years.

a) How much sleep does a 14-year-old need? *10.5*
b) Jason is 10. He gets 9 h of sleep each *12.5* night. Is this enough?

2. You are a sonar operator searching for a wreck that is known to be in 900 m to 1000 m of water. Your sonar has generated the table below, which includes time measurements at 16 locations, A_1, A_2, and so on. Use the formula $d = \frac{1500 \times t}{2}$ to decide where the wreck might be.

	Sonar Measurements (s)			
	1	**2**	**3**	**4**
A	0.9	0.8	1.1	1.0
B	1.0	1.4	1.2	0.7
C	0.6	1.3	1.5	1.6
D	1.1	1.2	0.5	2.1

3. To find the distance to an object in space, a radio telescope bounces radio signals off the object and measures the time it takes for the signals to make a round trip. Radio signals travel at 298 000 km/s in space. The formula for the distance to an object is

$$d = \frac{298\ 000 \times t}{2}$$

where d is the distance in kilometres, and t is the time for the round trip in seconds.

a) When the moon is closest to the Earth, the round-trip time is 2.45 s. How far is the moon from the Earth?
b) When the moon is furthest from the Earth, the round-trip time is 2.71 s. How far is the moon from the Earth?

4. In the following formula, T is the air temperature in degrees Celsius at an altitude of h metres, and t is the ground temperature in degrees Celsius.

$$T = t - \frac{h}{150}$$

If the ground temperature is 25°C, what is the temperature outside an aircraft at the following altitudes?

a) 8000 m   **b)** 4500 m

5. The formula relates the time, t seconds, an object takes to fall to the Earth from a height of h metres.

$$h = 4.9t^2$$

The table gives the time it takes an object to fall to the ground from the top of several structures. Calculate the height of each.

Structure	Time (s)		
Eiffel Tower	8.08	*320m*	*1050'*
CN Tower	10.63	*534m*	*1752'*
Washington Monument	5.88	*169m*	*554'*

6. If you stand on the Earth and jump up at a speed of 5 m/s, your approximate height, h metres, above the ground after t seconds is given by this formula.

$$h = 5t - 5t^2$$

If you stand on the moon and jump up at the same speed, the corresponding formula is

$$h = 5t - 0.8t^2$$

a) How far would you be from the Earth after 0.5 s? 1 s?
b) How far would you be from the moon after 0.5 s? 1 s? 3 s? 6 s?
c) About how much longer would you stay off the ground on the moon than on the Earth? Explain.

7. Write a problem that can be solved with one of the formulas on this page. Have a classmate solve your problem.

3.3 Working with Formulas

A squid has 8 arms and 2 tentacles. The arms and the ends of the tentacles are covered with tooth-rimmed suction pods. The squid uses its tentacles to pull prey into its arms. Giant squids prey on sharks and, in turn, are preyed upon by sperm whales.

Activity: Use the Formula

Scientists can determine the length of a giant squid by measuring the diameter of the suction-pod scars left on its prey. The formula $l = 180d$ gives the length of a squid in centimetres from the diameter of its suction pods in centimetres.

Inquire

1. How long is a squid whose suction pods have a diameter of 0.5 cm?

2. Squids found off the coast of Newfoundland have suction pods with diameters of 5 cm. How long are these squids in metres?

3. The longest squid, to date, was found in New Zealand. The suction pods were 5.4 cm in diameter. How long was this squid in metres?

4. A sperm whale was found with suction-pod scars that measured 35 cm in diameter. How many metres long was the squid that made these scars?

Example

a) Given $P = 2(l + w)$, solve for w.

b) Evaluate w for $P = 350$ cm and $l = 120$ cm.

Solution

a) Since we want the value of w, isolate this variable.

$$P = 2(l + w)$$
$$P = 2l + 2w$$

Subtract $2l$ from both sides: $P - 2l = 2l + 2w - 2l$
$$P - 2l = 2w$$

Divide both sides by 2: $\dfrac{P - 2l}{2} = \dfrac{2w}{2}$

$$\frac{P - 2l}{2} = w$$

b) Substitute $P = 350$ and $l = 120$ into the formula.

$$w = \frac{P - 2l}{2}$$
$$= \frac{350 - 2(120)}{2}$$
$$= \frac{350 - 240}{2}$$
$$= \frac{110}{2}$$
$$= 55$$

So, $w = 55$ cm.

Check: Substitute into $P = 2(l + w)$.

$350 = 2(120 + 55)$
$350 = 2(175)$
$350 = 350$

Practice

1. For the formula $A = lw$,
a) find A if $l = 8$ cm and $w = 5$ cm.
b) find w if $A = 40$ m^2 and $l = 10$ m.
c) find l if $A = 238$ m^2 and $w = 14$ m.

2. Assume $\pi = 3.14$. For the formula $C = 2\pi r$,
a) find C if $r = 10$ cm.
b) find r if $C = 628$ cm.

3. For the formula $A = \frac{1}{2}bh$,
a) find A if $b = 6$ cm and $h = 8$ cm.
b) find h if $A = 40$ cm^2 and $b = 4$ cm.
c) find b if $A = 60$ m^2 and $h = 20$ m.

4. For the formula $P = 2(l + w)$,
a) find P if $l = 9$ m and $w = 6$ m.
b) find w if $P = 60$ m and $l = 16$ m.
c) find l if $P = 84$ m and $w = 5$ m.

Solve each formula for the indicated variable.

5. $A = lw$ for w **6.** $A = \frac{1}{2}bh$ for b

7. $I = Prt$ for P **8.** $C = 2\pi r$ for r

9. $E = mc^2$ for m **10.** $A = \frac{1}{2}h(a + b)$ for b

Problems and Applications

11. The maximum desirable pulse rate for a person exercising can be found using the formula
$$m = 220 - a$$
where m is the pulse rate in beats per minute and a is the person's age in years.
a) Copy and complete the table.

Age (years)	Maximum Desirable Pulse Rate (beats/min)
20	
27	
39	
44	
61	

b) To what ages do these maximum desirable pulse rates correspond?
198   171   183

12. The distance travelled by a spaceship is given by the formula
$$d = 40\ 000t$$
where d is the distance in kilometres and t is the time in hours.
a) How far does a spaceship travel in 12 h? in 17.5 h?
b) How long does it take a spaceship to travel 130 000 km?

13. The amount of food energy required per day by military personnel on active duty is given by the formula
$$E = -125T + 15\ 250$$
where E is the amount of food energy in kilojoules (kJ) and T is the outside temperature in degrees Celsius. Copy and complete the table.

Temperature (°C)	Energy (kJ)
40	
23	
0	
−10	
−45	

14. Shawna is at an outdoor concert in Vancouver. She is sitting 100 m from the band. The formula that gives the length of time for the band's sound to reach her is
$$t = \frac{d}{330}$$
where t is the time in seconds and d is Shawna's distance from the band in metres. Paul is listening to the same concert on a radio in Halifax. The formula that gives the length of time for the band's sound to reach him is
$$t = \frac{d}{300\ 000}$$
where t is the time in seconds and d is the distance from Halifax to Vancouver in kilometres. Who hears each sound first, Shawna or Paul?

Developing Pick's Formula for Area

Activity ❶ No Points in the Interior

Each polygon has been constructed so that there are no points in its interior.

1. Construct the polygons on grid paper or on a geoboard.

2. Copy and complete this table. The first line has been completed for you.

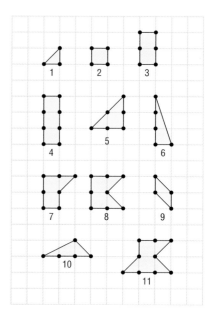

Polygon	Points on the Perimeter (P)	Area (square units)
1	3	$\frac{1}{2}$
2	4	1
3	6	2
4	8	3
5	6	2
6	5	$1\frac{1}{2}$
7	7	$2\frac{1}{2}$
8	8	3
9	4	1
10	5	$1\frac{1}{2}$
11	9	$3\frac{1}{2}$

3. If 2 figures have the same number of points on the perimeter, what can you say about their areas?

4. List the areas from smallest to largest. Do not repeat areas. The first two are:

3 points, 0.5 square units

4 points, 1 square unit

$A = \frac{1}{2}n - 1$

5. Predict the area of a figure with 10 points on the perimeter and no points in its interior. Check your prediction by making 2 such shapes and finding their areas.

6. Use the pattern in the table to write a formula for the area of a polygon with no points in the interior if you know the number of perimeter points.

7. Draw 3 different figures with no interior points. Verify your formula.

8. Use your formula to determine the area of a figure with 99 points on the perimeter and no interior points.

122

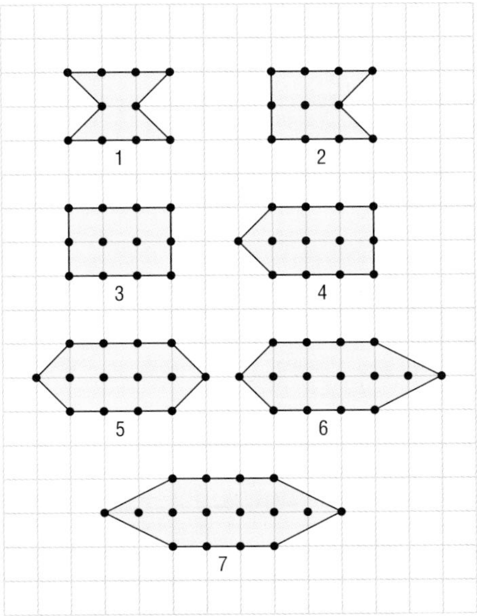

Activity ❷ Points in the Interior

Each polygon has 10 points on the perimeter. The number of points in the interior, *I*, increases from 0 to 6.

1. Calculate the area of each polygon.

2. Copy and complete the table, calculating each area in square units.

Polygon	Points on the Perimeter (*P*)	Interior Points (*I*)	Area (square units)
1	10	0	4
2		1	5
3		2	6
4		3	7
5		4	8
6		5	9
7		6	10

3. What happens to the area of the polygon as the number of interior points increases by 1?

4. Predict the area of figures with 10 points on the perimeter and 7 and 8 points in the interior. Check your prediction by making 2 such shapes and finding their areas.

5. Use the pattern in the table and the formula for area you found in Activity 1. Write a formula for the area of a polygon if you know the number of perimeter points and interior points. This formula is called **Pick's formula** after the mathematician who discovered it.

6. Draw 3 different figures with points in the interior. Verify your formula.

7. Use your formula to determine the areas of the following figures.

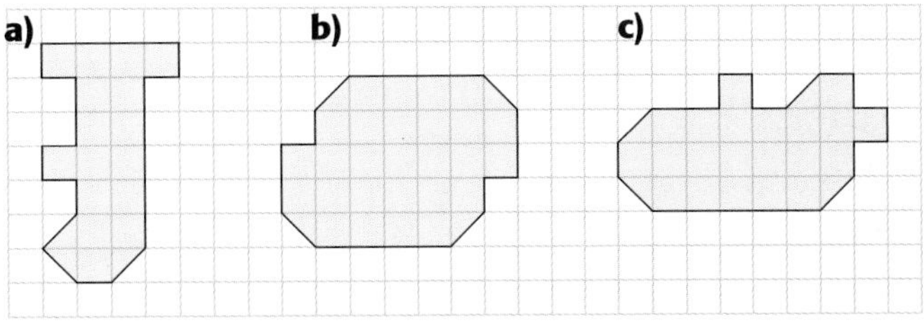

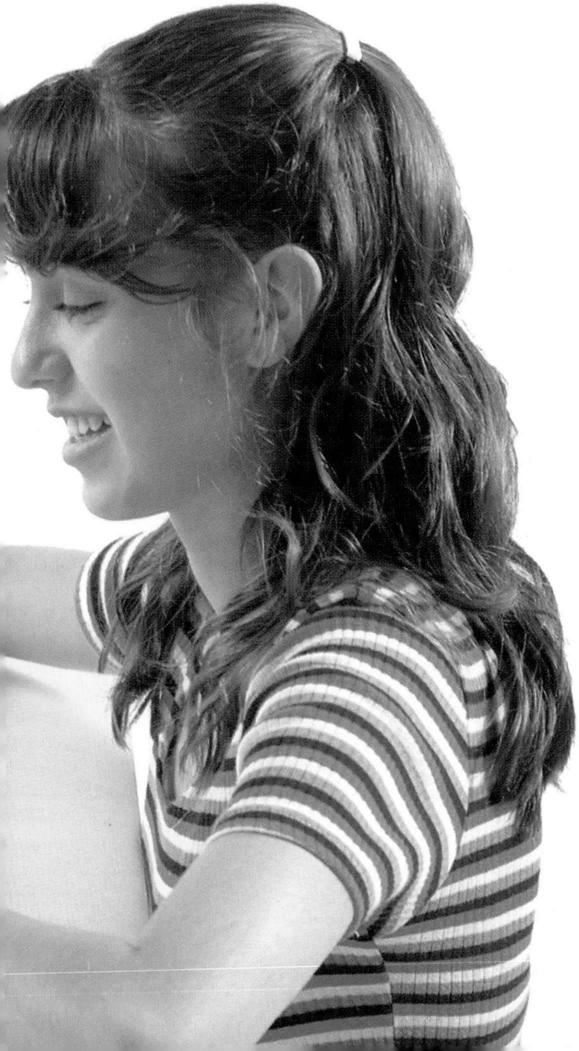

3.4 Developing Formulas

The *Bluenose* was Canada's most famous sailing ship. It was launched in Lunenburg, Nova Scotia, in 1921. It was the fastest racing schooner of its time, winning many championships until its last race in 1938.

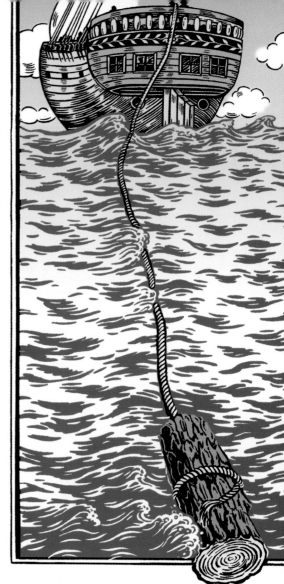

Activity: Study the Information

In the early days of sailing ships, navigators estimated the speed of their ship by tying a rope to a log and tossing the log into the water behind the ship. After 30 s, the length of the rope was measured, showing how far the ship had travelled in this amount of time.

Inquire

1. If the length of the rope after 30 s was 90 m, what was the speed of the ship in metres per second?

2. Let the length of the rope after 30 s be *l*. Write a formula for the speed of the ship in metres per second.

3. If the length of the rope after 30 s was 240 m, what was the speed of the ship in metres per second?

4. Use the formula to calculate the speed of the ship if the length of the rope after 30 s is 210 m.

5. Rewrite the formula to calculate the speed of the ship in kilometres per hour.

Example

Many early navigators also estimated the speed of a ship by measuring the number of seconds it took a piece of wood to float from one end of the ship to the other.

a) Write a formula to estimate the speed of a galleon in metres per second.

b) Use the formula to find the speed of a 40 m long galleon if $t = 8$ s.

Solution

a) Let the time in seconds be t. Let the speed in metres per second be s.
The distance travelled in metres is the length of the galleon, l.

$$\text{Speed} = \frac{\text{Distance}}{\text{Time}}$$

$$s = \frac{l}{t}$$

b) $s = \dfrac{40}{8}$

$= 5$

The speed of the galleon was 5 m/s.

Practice

Complete the table and state a rule for each pattern.

1.

a	1	2	3	4	5	6	7
b	3	6	9	12			

2.

m	2	4	6	8			
n	5	7	9	11	13	15	17

3.

t	25	24	23	22			
a	100	96	92	88	84	80	76

Complete the table. Then, use the variables to write a formula for each pattern.

4.

Number of Books (*n*)	1	2	3	4
Cost (*c*)		4	8	12

5.

Hours (*h*)		5	10	15	20
Wages (*w*)		37.50	75.00	112.50	

6.

Selling Price (*s*)		300	400	500	600
Profit (*p*)		60	80	100	

Problems and Applications

7. The cost to rent a bus is $100 plus a certain amount per kilometre. The table gives the cost of 3 bus trips. Write a formula to calculate the cost of a bus trip in terms of distance.

Trip	Distance, *d* (km)	Cost, *C* ($)
1	50	250
2	100	400
3	150	550

8. This table shows the cost of a taxi ride. Write a formula that relates kilometres driven, *d*, to the cost of the ride, *C*.

d (km)	0	5	10	15	20
C ($)	3.00	10.50	18.00	25.50	33.00

9. The map shows an area where there are 6 towns, 9 roads, and 4 regions.

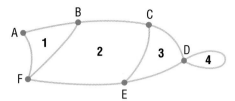

Roads start and end at a town. If roads cross, there is a town where they cross. A road can connect a town to itself. Regions are completely surrounded by roads. Each town is connected to at least 1 other town.
In such maps, there is a relationship between the numbers of towns, regions, and roads.
a) Make at least 5 maps, each with 4 regions. Complete a table like the one shown.

Map	Regions	Towns	Roads
1	4		
2	4		
3	4		
4	4		
5	4		

Look for a pattern in the Towns and Roads columns.
Write a formula that lets you determine the number of regions if you know the numbers of towns and roads.
Regions = ▨
Test your formula on another map.
b) Make at least 5 maps, each with 6 towns. Complete a table like the one in part a).
Write a formula that lets you determine the number of towns if you know the numbers of roads and regions. Test your formula on another map.
c) Make at least 5 maps, each with 6 roads. Complete a table like the one in part a).
Write a formula that lets you determine the number of roads if you know the numbers of towns and regions. Test your formula on another map.

3.5 Uniform Motion Problems

Problems involving **uniform motion** are those in which the speeds of the objects do not change. The formula $D = r \times t$ is used to solve these problems, where D is the distance, r is the rate of speed, and t is the time.

Activity: Study the Information

Frank left the ranch for town on horseback. He rode at 15 km/h. One hour later, his brother Jesse left the ranch and tried to catch up with Frank. Jesse rode at 20 km/h. How long did it take Jesse to catch up with Frank?

Inquire

1. Let x be the time in hours that Frank rode before Jesse caught up with him. Write an expression for how far Frank rode in x hours.

2. If x is the time Frank rode, write an expression in terms of x for the time Jesse rode.

3. Use your expression from question 2 to write an expression for the distance Jesse rode.

4. When Jesse caught up with Frank, the distances they had ridden were the same. Write an equation stating the 2 distances were equal.

5. Solve the equation for x.

6. a) How long had Frank been riding when Jesse caught up with him?
b) How long had Jesse been riding?

Example

A plane left Montreal for Calgary, a distance of 3000 km, travelling at 550 km/h. At the same time, a plane left Calgary for Montreal travelling at 450 km/h. How long after take-off did the planes pass each other?

Solution

Set up a table and let x be the time from take-off until the planes passed. Write expressions for D using r and t.

	t (h)	r (km/h)	D (km)
Montreal to Calgary	x	550	$550x$
Calgary to Montreal	x	450	$450x$

The sum of the distances is 3000 km.

$$550x + 450x = 3000$$
$$1000x = 3000$$
$$x = 3$$

The planes passed each other 3 h after take-off.

Check:
In 3 h, the plane from Montreal flew 3×550 or 1650 km.
In 3 h, the plane from Calgary flew 3×450 or 1350 km.
1650 km + 1350 km = 3000 km

Practice

Calculate the distance travelled.

1. 3 h at 60 km/h   **2.** 2 h at 85 km/h

3. $\frac{1}{2}$ h at 90 km/h   **4.** $\frac{3}{4}$ h at 60 km/h

How long does each trip take?

5. 40 km at 80 km/h

6. 400 km at 50 km/h

7. 20 km at 100 km/h

8. 360 km at 80 km/h

Calculate each speed.

9. 300 km in 3 h   **10.** 400 km in 5 h

11. 360 km in 4 h   **12.** 40 km in $\frac{1}{2}$ h

Complete the table.

	Distance (km)	Rate (km/h)	Time (h)
13.	450	100	
14.		65	3
15.	600		8
16.		80	x
17.		90	$x + 1$
18.		85	$x - 1$
19.	200	x	
20.	400		x
21.		r	t
22.	D	r	
23.	D		t

Problems and Applications

24. A cruise ship left Halifax for Bermuda at 20 km/h. A private boat left for Bermuda 1 h later and travelled at 25 km/h. After how long did the private boat overtake the cruise ship?

25. Two cars left a service centre at 16:30. One car travelled in one direction at 75 km/h. The other car travelled in the opposite direction at 85 km/h.
a) After how long were they 600 km apart?
b) At what time were they 600 km apart?

26. Two friends, one living in Winnipeg and one living in Edmonton, decided to meet on the TransCanada Highway. The distance from Edmonton to Winnipeg is about 1360 km. They both left home at 08:00 Winnipeg time. The friend from Winnipeg drove at 80 km/h, and the friend from Edmonton drove at 90 km/h.
a) After how long did they meet?
b) What was the time in Winnipeg when they met?
c) What assumptions have you made?

27. A plane left Vancouver for Los Angeles at 08:30 and flew at 600 km/h. Fifteen minutes later, another plane left Vancouver for Los Angeles and flew at 700 km/h.
a) How long did it take the second plane to overtake the first one?
b) At what time did it happen?

28. A car left a garage on the highway at 100 km/h. Fifteen minutes later, a police cruiser left the same garage at 120 km/h in pursuit of the car. How long did it take the cruiser to catch up with the car?

29. Write a problem involving uniform motion and ask a classmate to solve it.

NUMBER POWER

Place the digits from 1 to 9 in the boxes to make the statements true. Use the order of operations.

$$\blacksquare + \blacksquare - \blacksquare = 10$$
$$\blacksquare \div \blacksquare + \blacksquare = 10$$
$$\blacksquare - \blacksquare + \blacksquare = 10$$

3.6 Rate of Work Problems

Activity: Study the Process

Tania and Justine own a cruise boat that takes people out to the Atlantic Ocean to show them how lobsters are caught. At the end of the day, Tania and Justine take turns cleaning the boat for the next day's cruise. Tania is older and cleans the boat in 2 h. It takes Justine 3 h. We want to know how long it would take them to clean the boat together. Problems of this type are known as **rate of work problems**.

Inquire

1. What fraction of the boat does Tania clean in 1 h?

2. What fraction of the boat does Justine clean in 1 h?

3. What is the sum of these fractions?

4. If they clean $\frac{5}{6}$ of the boat in 1 h, how long will it take to clean the last $\frac{1}{6}$?

5. What is the total time to clean the boat?

Example	Solution

Example

After the restaurant closes, Roberto takes 2 h to clean it. Bill is new to the job and takes 4 h. How long would it take them if they worked together?

Solution

One way to solve this type of problem is to use an equation. Let x hours represent the time the job takes if they work together. Then, $\frac{x}{2}$ represents the part cleaned by Roberto and $\frac{x}{4}$ the part cleaned by Bill. Together, the 2 parts must add to the whole job.

$$\frac{x}{2} + \frac{x}{4} = 1$$

Multiply by 4: $\quad 4 \times \frac{x}{2} + 4 \times \frac{x}{4} = 4 \times 1$

$$2x + x = 4$$
$$3x = 4$$
$$x = \frac{4}{3} \text{ or } 1\frac{1}{3}$$

Roberto and Bill can clean the restaurant in $1\frac{1}{3}$ h by working together.

Check:

In $\frac{4}{3}$ h, the fraction of the restaurant cleaned by Roberto is $\dfrac{\frac{4}{3}}{2}$ or $\frac{4}{3} \times \frac{1}{2} = \frac{2}{3}$.

In $\frac{4}{3}$ h, the fraction of the restaurant cleaned by Bill is $\dfrac{\frac{4}{3}}{4}$ or $\frac{4}{3} \times \frac{1}{4} = \frac{1}{3}$.

$\frac{2}{3} + \frac{1}{3} = 1$ or the entire restaurant

Practice

Write 2 fractions for each question.

1. Ahmed takes 2 h to mow his lawn. His brother, Sami, takes 4 h. What fraction of the lawn does each mow in 1 h?

2. Athena takes 6 h to paint an apartment. Helena takes 8 h to do the same job. What fraction of the apartment do they each paint in 1 h?

Problems and Applications

Solve. Round answers to the nearest tenth, where necessary.

3. Julio can fill a water tank in 4 min using a large hose. He takes 6 min using a smaller hose. How long will he take if he uses both hoses?

4. Andrea can deliver 500 handbills in 2 h. Althea can deliver the same number in 3 h. How long will they take to deliver 500 handbills if they work together?

5. Murray can tile a floor in one hour. His partner can do the same job in half the time. How long will it take them to tile the floor if they work together?

6. Mario can take inventory at the store in 30 min. His partner, Carmen, can take inventory in 20 min. If they work together, how long will the inventory take?

7. Ken and Milan are office cleaners. Ken earns $10/h and takes 8 h to clean an office. Milan earns $8/h and takes 10 h to clean it.
a) How long will it take Ken and Milan to clean the office together?
b) What is the cost of cleaning the office using only Ken? only Milan? Ken and Milan together?

8. Uri, Max, and Boris work for a company that installs carpet tiles in offices. Uri can install 2000 tiles in 10 h. It takes Max 12 h to do the same job. Boris installs 2000 tiles in 15 h. How long would it take them to install 2000 tiles if they work together?

9. Mary takes 3 h to complete a task. Mary and Jim together take 2 h to complete the same task. How long will it take Jim to complete the task working alone?

10. Dan and Brad are brothers who attend the same school. Brad can walk to school in 15 min. Dan takes 20 min.
a) How long will it take them to walk to school together?
b) What makes this problem different from the others in this section?

11. Write a rate of work problem. Have a classmate solve your problem.

LOGIC POWER

Draw the grid and place 3 pennies, a nickel, and a dime on it as shown. By sliding one coin at a time into a neighbouring empty square, make the nickel and the dime change places. You can move horizontally or diagonally. Make the switch in as few moves as possible.

129

3.7 Interpret Graphs

Much of the information you receive from newspapers and magazines is displayed on graphs. Therefore, the ability to interpret graphs correctly is an important life skill. The graph shows the distance from Port Colborne to Brampton and the time taken for a car to travel this distance. What is happening between P and Q; Q and R; R and S; S and T?

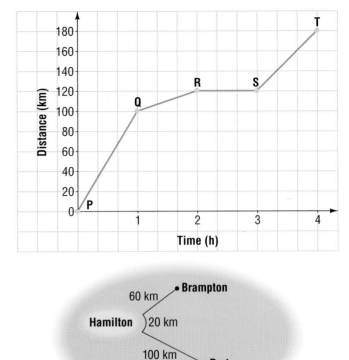

1. What information are you given?

2. What are you asked to find?

3. Do you need an exact or approximate answer?

Read the information from the graph. Use it to solve the problem.

From P to Q The car covered 100 km in 1 h, so it travelled at 100 km/h from Port Colborne to Hamilton.

From Q to R The car took 1 h to drive 20 km around Hamilton. It averaged 20 km/h.

From R to S The car stopped for 1 h on the outskirts of Hamilton on the Brampton side.

From S to T The car travelled the 60 km from Hamilton to Brampton in 1 h. The car travelled at 60 km/h.

Does the answer seem reasonable?

Understand the Problem

Think of a Plan

Carry Out the Plan

Look Back

Interpret Graphs	1. Interpret the graph.
	2. Use the information to solve the problem.
	3. Check that the answer is reasonable.

Problems and Applications

1. The graph shows the amount of gasoline in the tank of a salesperson's car at different times of a work day. Describe how the salesperson might have spent the day.

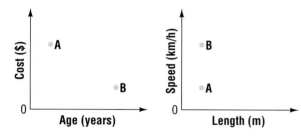

2. The 2 graphs describe 2 pleasure boats. Compare the boats by age, cost, speed, and length.

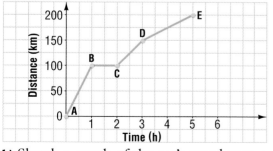

3. a) The graph shows the distance versus time for a car travelling from Fredericton to Moncton. Describe what is happening between A and B; B and C; C and D; D and E.

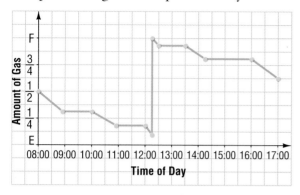

b) Sketch a graph of the car's speed versus time.

4. You are the first person to get on and off a Ferris wheel with 8 cars. Once the cars are loaded, the Ferris wheel makes 3 revolutions before letting people off. Sketch a graph of your height versus time.

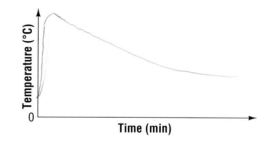

5. Suppose someone turned on the hot-water tap on a kitchen sink and left it running. Sketch a graph of the water temperature versus time as the tap is running.

6. Sketch a graph of the number of minutes of daylight versus the month of the year.

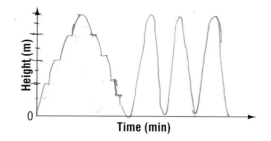

7. Write a graph-sketching problem that involves each of the following. Have a classmate solve each problem.
a) the temperature of water in a kettle versus time
b) the depth of water in a bathtub versus time

131

3.8 Solving Inequalities

Dr. Roberta Bondar was the second Canadian in space. She wore a space suit that protected her against pressure and temperature changes. The mass of a space suit is 23 kg. The combined mass of an astronaut plus space suit must be less than 110 kg.

Activity: Complete the Table

Copy and complete the table.

Astronaut's Mass (kg)	Mass of Astronaut Plus Space Suit (kg)	Astronaut's Mass (kg)	Mass of Astronaut Plus Space Suit (kg)
71		91	
76		96	
81		101	
86		106	

Inquire

1. From the table, what is the maximum mass that an astronaut can have without exceeding the mass restriction?

2. Let the mass of an astronaut be x. Write an equation to show that the mass of an astronaut plus space suit can equal 110 kg.

3. What is the difference between the equation you wrote in question 2 and the statement about combined mass given in the introduction?

4. Which symbol, greater than, ">," or less than, "<," should you use to replace the "=" sign in the equation you wrote in question 2?

5. Rewrite your equation using the symbol you chose in question 4.

An **inequality** is a mathematical sentence that contains one of these symbols: >, <, ≥, or ≤. The following table shows each symbol and its meaning.

Symbol	Meaning
<	is less than
>	is greater than
≤	is less than or equal to
≥	is greater than or equal to

Activity: Discover the Relationships

Copy the table. Complete it by writing the correct inequality after each operation.

Inequality	Operation on Both Sides	New Inequality	Inequality	Operation on Both Sides	New Inequality
6 > –4	Add 2		6 > –4	Add (–2)	
6 > –4	Subtract 2		6 > –4	Subtract (–2)	
6 > –4	Multiply by 2		6 > –4	Multiply by (–2)	
6 > –4	Divide by 2		6 > –4	Divide by (–2)	

Inquire

1. Repeat the table for the inequality $-8 < -2$.

2. Does the direction of the inequality sign stay the same when you do each of the following?
a) add the same positive or negative number to both sides
b) subtract the same positive or negative number from both sides
c) multiply both sides by the same positive number
d) divide both sides by the same positive number
e) multiply both sides by the same negative number
f) divide both sides by the same negative number

Example 1

Solve the inequality $5x - 2 \geq 2x + 4$ and graph the solution.

Solution

Add 2 to both sides:

$$5x - 2 \;{+2} \geq 2x + 4 \;{+2}$$
$$5x \geq 2x + 6$$

Subtract $2x$ from both sides:

$$5x \;{-2x} \geq 2x + 6 \;{-2x}$$
$$3x \geq 6$$

Divide both sides by 3:

$$\frac{3x}{3} \geq \frac{6}{3}$$
$$x \geq 2$$

The solution is $x \geq 2$.

The closed dot at $x = 2$ means that 2 is included in the solution.

Example 2

a) Solve the inequality $2(x - 3) > 4x + 2$ and graph the solution.
b) Check the solution.

Solution

a)

$$2(x - 3) > 4x + 2$$
$$2x - 6 > 4x + 2$$
$$2x - 4x > 2 + 6$$
$$-2x > 8$$

Divide both sides by –2:

$$\frac{-2x}{-2} < \frac{8}{-2}$$
$$x < -4$$

Remember to reverse the symbol when multiplying or dividing by a negative number.

The open dot at $x = -4$ means that –4 is not included in the solution. CONTINUED

b) Substitute -4 for x in the original inequality, $2(x-3) > 4x + 2$.

L.S. $\quad 2(-4-3) = 2(-7)$ $\qquad$ **R.S.** $\quad 4(-4)+2 = -16+2$

$\qquad\qquad\qquad\qquad = -14$ $\qquad\qquad\qquad\qquad\qquad = -14$

$\not{>}$ means "is not greater than" As $-14 \not{>} -14$, -4 is not a solution.

To check solutions less than -4, substitute -5 for x in $2(x-3) > 4x + 2$.

L.S $\quad 2(-5-3) = 2(-8)$ $\qquad$ **R.S.** $\quad 4(-5)+2 = -20+2$

$\qquad\qquad\qquad\qquad = -16$ $\qquad\qquad\qquad\qquad\qquad = -18$

As $-16 > -18$, -5 is a solution.

Practice

1. Which inequalities are true?

a) $5 > 4$ $\qquad$ **b)** $10 > 6$ $\qquad$ **c)** $15 \geq 17$

d) $6 < 8$ $\qquad$ **e)** $7 \leq -7$ $\qquad$ **f)** $11 < 13$

g) $-3 > -2$ $\qquad$ **h)** $-1 > -5$ $\qquad$ **i)** $-1 \geq -2$

j) $-4 \leq -4$ $\qquad$ **k)** $-5 < -8$ $\qquad$ **l)** $-6 < -5$

2. Which of the x values shown make each inequality true?

a) $x + 2 < 8$ $\qquad$ **(3, 6)** $\quad$ **b)** $-5 > x - 2$ $\quad$ **(−5, 0)**

c) $x + 5 < 7$ $\qquad$ **(4, 1)** $\quad$ **d)** $x - 3 > 3$ $\qquad$ **(0, 8)**

e) $x + 3 \leq 8$ $\qquad$ **(7, −1)** $\quad$ **f)** $x - 5 \geq -9$ $\quad$ **(−5, 1)**

g) $6 \leq -1 + x$ $\quad$ **(−4, 7)** $\quad$ **h)** $x + 2 \leq -2$ $\quad$ **(−2, −4)**

Solve each inequality and graph its solution.

3. $x - 2 > 0$ $\qquad\qquad$ **4.** $10 > x + 5$

5. $x - 3 < 1$ $\qquad\qquad$ **6.** $x - 5 > 2$

7. $y - 4 > -3$ $\qquad\qquad$ **8.** $y + 3 < 4$

9. $1 < -2 + z$ $\qquad\qquad$ **10.** $z - 5 < -2$

Solve, then check your solution.

11. $4x < 8$ $\qquad$ **12.** $2y > -8$ $\qquad$ **13.** $4m < 20$

14. $5n < -20$ $\qquad$ **15.** $3s > 0$ $\qquad$ **16.** $21 \geq 7y$

17. $6p \leq -12$ $\qquad$ **18.** $-15 \geq 5t$ $\qquad$ **19.** $8b \leq 24$

Solve.

20. $-3m < 9$ $\qquad\qquad$ **21.** $-4n > 12$

22. $-15 > -5x$ $\qquad\qquad$ **23.** $-6 > -2y$

24. $-3t \geq -18$ $\qquad\qquad$ **25.** $-10y \leq -50$

26. $21 \geq -7x$ $\qquad\qquad$ **27.** $4x \geq -12$

Solve. Graph the solution.

28. $2x < 10$ $\qquad$ **29.** $2y > -8$ $\qquad$ **30.** $-8 > 4m$

31. $2n > 6$ $\qquad$ **32.** $5t \leq -15$ $\qquad$ **33.** $4 \leq 4s$

34. $3y \leq -6$ $\qquad$ **35.** $8x \leq 40$ $\qquad$ **36.** $2x \geq -2$

Solve and check.

37. $4x + 2 < 3x + 5$ $\qquad$ **38.** $2x - 4 > x + 2$

39. $7y - 4 \geq 6y + 3$ $\qquad$ **40.** $5y + 7 \leq 4y - 2$

41. $2t + 7 < t - 1$ $\qquad$ **42.** $10a + 4 > 9a + 2$

43. $3n + 4 < 2n + 2$ $\qquad$ **44.** $5n + 2 > 4n - 1$

Solve.

45. $4(x-3) > 3x + 1$

46. $3y + 9 < 2y + 12$

47. $4(2m-1) \geq 7m - 3$

48. $3x - 10 > 2x - 9$

49. $3y + 2 \leq 2y + 1$

50. $3m + 14 < 2(m+6)$

51. $17 - 6x > 12 - 7x$

52. $20m - 7 < 19m - 2$

53. $2(5 - 3b) \geq -7b + 2$

54. $5w - 7 \leq 4w - 3$

55. $7p + 11 \geq 6p + 17$

56. $10x + 10 \leq 9x + 15$

57. $19 - 13x \geq -14x + 16$

Solve. Graph the solution.

58. $7x + 4 < 5x + 8$ **59.** $5y - 2 \leq 2y + 7$

60. $2m - 3 < 9 - 2m$ **61.** $3x + 10 < -2 - 3x$

62. $4y + 5 \geq 6y - 1$ **63.** $6t - 5 \leq 8t + 3$

64. $7 + y < 4y + 13$ **65.** $6x - 13 \geq 8x - 15$

Solve.

66. $6(y - 2) + 7 > 8y - 25$

67. $4(t - 1) < 8t + 20$

68. $8(x - 2) > 8 - 4x$

69. $24x + 18 > 12 + 7(3x - 3)$

70. $3(5 - 5x) + 3 \geq 34 - 7x$

71. $2(7x - 11) \leq 9x - 32$

72. $15 + 4x \geq 5(2x - 1) - 10$

73. $2(8x - 13) + 4 < 18x + 26$

74. $3t + 45 \geq 6(t - 4)$

75. $6(m - 4) - 2(m + 2) < 7(m - 4) - 6$

76. $5(y + 1) - 2(y + 3) \leq 5(y - 1)$

77. $3(2x - 5) \geq 2(1 + 2x) + 5$

Problems and Applications

78. In her last math test, Giselle got 10 marks more than on any other test this year. Her mark was less than 100. Solve the inequality $x + 10 < 100$ to find her highest possible mark on any other test.

79. On Saturdays, Campus Clothes sells at least 25 more jackets than on any other day of the week. The store has never sold more than 84 jackets in one day. Solve the inequality $84 \geq n + 25$ to find the number of jackets that could have been sold on any other day of the week.

80. Matt wants to keep his annual travel expenses under $4680. Solve the inequality $52x < 4680$ to find how much Matt can spend each week.

81. Bianca must keep her phone bill below $55/month. The basic charge is $15, and it costs her $2/min to phone her friend in Taiwan. Solve the inequality $2t + 15 < 55$ to determine how long Bianca can spend talking to her friend each month.

82. A peregrine falcon can dive at up to 350 km/h. This speed is 50 km/h faster than 3 times the top speed of the fastest land animal, the cheetah.

a) Solve the inequality $350 \geq 3s + 50$ to determine the speed of a cheetah.

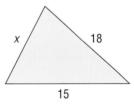 **b)** Does a cheetah have a minimum speed? Explain.

83. a) Solve the inequality $x + 15 + 18 \leq 50$ to find the values of x that give this triangle a perimeter of no more than 50.

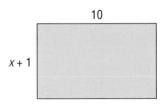

b) Does x have a minimum value? Explain.

84. a) Solve the inequality $10(x + 1) < 50$ to find values of x that give this rectangle an area of less than 50.

10

$x + 1$

b) Does x have a minimum value? Explain.

85. Write an inequality that has variables and numbers on both sides and has a solution of $x \leq -1$. Have a classmate solve your inequality.

135

Solving Problems Using Spreadsheets

A spreadsheet consists of rows and columns. It allows you to quickly analyze and change data. A spreadsheet can be an important problem solving tool.

The following problem solving activities show both the power and simplicity of a spreadsheet.

Activity ❶

A collection of 48 coins has a total value of $7.32. The collection consists of pennies, nickels, dimes, quarters, and half dollars. How many coins of each type are there?

1. Set up the following spreadsheet. Each formula in Column C is typed into that particular cell as indicated.

	A	B	C
1	Coin	Number	Value
2	Penny		0.01*B2
3	Nickel		0.05*B3
4	Dime		0.1*B4
5	Quarter		0.25*B5
6	Half Dollar		0.5*B6
7	Totals	@SUM(B2. .B6)	@SUM(C2. .C6)

2. Enter the number of each type of coin into Column B of the spreadsheet until the total number of coins is 48, and the total value of all the coins is $7.32.

3. What strategy did you use to solve the problem?

4. Is there more than one solution?

Activity ❷

You can use a spreadsheet to help select a store for shopping.

1. Obtain advertising flyers from several stores.

2. Find several items that are common to all stores.

3. Set up a spreadsheet similar to the one shown to determine which store gives you the best value for your money.

	A	B	C	D
		STORE 1	**STORE 2**	**STORE 3**
1	**ITEM**			
2		Cost	Cost	Cost
3	Toothpaste			
4	Shampoo			
.				
.				
	Totals			

Activity ❸

1. Make up a problem of your own that can be solved using a spreadsheet.

2. Give your problem to a classmate to solve.

137

Fingerprints

Because your fingerprints never change and are different from everyone else's, they can be used to identify you. There are 3 different patterns of fingerprints, known as arches, whorls, and loops.

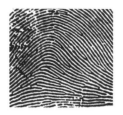

Plain Arch
The ridge lines enter on one side and curve up and exit on the other side.

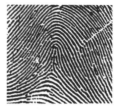

Tented Arch
The ridge lines are the same as a plain arch, except that they make a sharp point or tent in the middle.

Whorls
The ridge lines are circles or ovals.

Loops
The ridge lines enter on one side of the print, curve, and exit on the same side. An **ulnar loop** slants toward the ulna bone in the wrist. A **radial loop** slants toward the radius bone in the wrist.

Right-hand ulnar loop or left-hand radial loop.

Right-hand radial loop or left-hand ulnar loop.

The RCMP receives many sets of prints with requests to identify the people they belong to. It is impossible to check the prints against all the prints on file. The RCMP first classifies the prints.

Activity ❶

1. Identify each of your fingerprints as an arch, a loop, or a whorl.

2. According to fingerprint experts, there are 5% arches, 65% loops, and 30% whorls on fingerprints. Are these percents true for your class?

Activity ❷

The primary fingerprint classification is based on the number of whorls. Prints are assigned the following values.

Whorl = 1   Arch = 0   Loop = 0

These values are substituted into the following formulas.

(Rt Index) × 16 + (Rt Ring) × 8 + (Lt Thumb) × 4 + (Lt Middle) × 2 + (Lt Little) × 1 + 1

(Rt Thumb) × 16 + (Rt Middle) × 8 + (Rt Little) × 4 + (Lt Index) × 2 + (Lt Ring) × 1 + 1

For example, Yoshiko has whorls on her left thumb, left little finger, and right thumb. All her other prints are arches and loops. Her primary classification is as follows.

(0) × 16 + (0) × 8 + (1) × 4 + (0) × 2 + (1) × 1 + 1

(1) × 16 + (0) × 8 + (0) × 4 + (0) × 2 + (0) × 1 + 1

0 + 0 + 4 + 0 + 1 + 1 = 6

16 + 0 + 0 + 0 + 0 + 1 = 17   Her primary classification is $\frac{6}{17}$

1. What is your primary classification?

2. How many different primary classifications are there in your class?

3. How many different primary classifications are possible?

Activity ❸

The secondary classification is a fraction made up of letters based on the prints on the index fingers. The fraction is

$$\frac{\textit{right index finger}}{\textit{left index finger}}.$$

The letters are A for plain arch, T for tented arch, W for whorl, U for ulnar loop, and R for radial loop. If the right index finger is a whorl and the left index finger is a radial loop, the secondary classification is $\frac{W}{R}$.

1. What is your secondary classification?

2. How many different secondary classifications are there in your class?

3. How many different secondary classifications are possible?

Activity ❹

The combined classification of a set of prints is written in the form $\frac{6\ W}{17\ R}$.

1. What is your combined classification?

2. How many different combined classifications are there in your class?

3. How many different combined classifications are possible?

Review

Solve.

1. One number is five times another and their sum is 36. What are the numbers?

2. The length of a rectangle is 3 m greater than the width. The perimeter is 26 m. What are the dimensions of the rectangle?

3. The sum of three consecutive numbers is 183. Find the numbers.

4. The length of a rectangular field is three times the width. The perimeter is 1688 m. What are the dimensions of the field?

5. The lengths of the sides of a triangle are 3 consecutive numbers. The perimeter of the triangle is 126 m. How long is each side?

6. One number is 4 times another. If you subtract 5 from each number, the sum is 50. What are the numbers?

7. The mass of synthetic material in a hockey puck is 9 times the mass of natural rubber. A regulation hockey puck has a mass of 170 g. What mass of natural rubber is there in a hockey puck?

8. Find the length of each side.

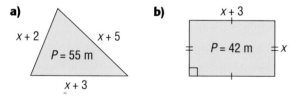

a) $x + 2$, $x + 5$, $x + 3$, $P = 55$ m

b) $x + 3$, x, $P = 42$ m

9. The sum of two numbers is 51. Twice the first plus 4 times the second is 128. What are the numbers?

10. One number is 5 more than another number. Four times the larger number plus 3 times the smaller is 97. Find the numbers.

11. A jar contains $36.25 in dimes and quarters. There are 250 coins in the jar. How many quarters are in the jar?

12. In a pile of coins, there are 15 more quarters than loonies. The total value of the coins is $21.25. How many quarters are there?

Solve. Graph each solution.

13. $2x < 10$ **14.** $3y > -15$ **15.** $4 + x > 8$

16. $8 > 4x$ **17.** $3x \geq 12$ **18.** $-3 \leq 3x$

19. $-2x < 6$ **20.** $-5x > -5$ **21.** $-8x \leq 16$

Solve and check.

22. $3(x - 2) \leq 3$ **23.** $18 \geq 10 + 4x$

24. $4t - 3 \geq -15$ **25.** $4 - 2x \geq 8$

26. $7x - 8 < 4x + 1$ **27.** $7t + 7 \leq 10t - 14$

28. $6t - 5 > 2t - 1$ **29.** $3(s + 6) \leq -9$

Solve.

30. $4y - 2 \leq 2y + 8$

31. $5(x + 6) - 2(x - 1) > 2$

32. $2(x + 4) \leq 5 - 11$

33. $4(x - 5) - (x + 1) < 3$

34. $7 - 3(2x - 5) - x > 1$

35. The world's largest rodent is the capybara of South America. The mass of a capybara can be up to 113 kg. This mass is 8 kg more than 5 times the greatest known mass of a domestic cat. Solve the inequality $5m + 8 \leq 113$ to find the masses of domestic cats.

36. The formula $Q = 12t + 35$ gives the amount of water in a tank after t minutes. The tank originally contained 35 L of water, and water runs into it at a rate of 12 L/min.
a) How much water will be in the tank after 5 min? 8 min?
b) How long will it take to fill the tank if it holds 203 L?

37. A hot water tank holds 200 L of water. When the tap is opened, the water drains at a rate of 15 L/min. The amount of water left in the tank after t minutes is given by $A = 200 - 15t$.
a) How much water will be in the tank after 5 min? 10 min?
b) How long, to the nearest minute, will it take to drain the tank?

38. Marie started jogging at 08:30 at 9 km/h. Heather started jogging 15 min later in the same direction. Heather jogged at 12 km/h.
a) How long did it take Heather to catch up to Marie?
b) At what time did she catch up to her?

39. Two cars left the same highway restaurant at the same time but in opposite directions. One travelled at 65 km/h, the other at 55 km/h. After how long were they 600 km apart?

40. Heidi and Kelly drove in an antique car rally. Kelly left a checkpoint at 09:00 travelling at 45 km/h. One hour later, Heidi left the same checkpoint travelling at 50 km/h.
a) After how long did Heidi overtake Kelly?
b) At what time did Heidi overtake Kelly?

41. A plane left Darwin for Beijing, a distance of 6000 km, travelling at 450 km/h. At the same time, a plane left Beijing for Darwin travelling at 550 km/h. How long after take-off did the planes pass each other?

42. It takes Renate 3 h to cut the lawn. It takes her older sister Adrianna 2 h to cut the same lawn. How long will it take them to cut the lawn if they cut it together?

43. A small gas barbecue will cook for 4 h on a tank of propane. A larger barbecue will only cook for 3 h on a tank of propane. For how long can you cook if both barbecues are attached to the same tank?

Group Decision Making
Researching Medical Careers

1. Brainstorm as a class possible careers to investigate. They could include careers like dentist, doctor (general practitioner), doctor (specialist), nurse, X-ray technician, psychologist, dietition, dental hygienist, or physiotherapist. Decide as a class on 6 careers.

2. Go to home groups. Decide as a group what career each member will research.

| 1 2 3 4 5 6 | 1 2 3 4 5 6 |

Home Groups

| 1 2 3 4 5 6 | 1 2 3 4 5 6 |

3. Form an expert group with students who have the same career as you to research. Decide on the questions you want answered, including how math is used in the career. Research the career in your expert group.

| 1 1 1 1 | 2 2 2 2 | 3 3 3 3 |

Expert Groups

| 4 4 4 4 | 5 5 5 5 | 6 6 6 6 |

4. Return to your home group and tell the others what you found out in your expert group. Ask for questions and comments from your home group.

5. Return to your expert group and report what you have learned from your home group. In your expert group, prepare a report on the career. The form of the report is to be decided by the group.

6. In your expert group, evaluate the process and your report.

Chapter Check

1. When 47 is subtracted from a certain number, the result is 34. Find the number.

2. The length of a rectangle is 15 m longer than the width. The perimeter of the rectangle is 74 m. Find the length and width.

3. The lengths of the sides of a triangle are 3 consecutive whole numbers. The perimeter of the triangle is 102 m. Find the lengths.

Solve and graph.

4. $-3x > 21$ **5.** $-2x + 5 < 9$

6. $4r + 4 > r + 1$

Solve.

7. $2(3x + 1) - 2(x - 1) \geq -16$

8. $4(x - 1) - 6(x + 1) < 10$

9. A Boeing 747 is about 60 m long. This length is about 4 m longer than 8 times the length of the longest known earthworm. Solve the inequality $8x + 4 \leq 60$ to find the lengths of earthworms.

10. The formula for the perimeter of a rectangle is $P = 2(l + w)$. Find w if $P = 200$ m and $l = 56$ m.

11. The formula for the area of a triangle is $A = \frac{1}{2}bh$. Solve for h.

12. A cargo ship left Montreal for Halifax at 15 km/h. One hour later, a patrol boat left Montreal at 20 km/h, trying to overtake the cargo ship. After how long did the patrol boat overtake the cargo ship?

13. Mark lived 350 km from his agent. Mark had to sign a contract his agent had. Mark and his agent left their apartments at the same time in their cars and drove along the same road toward each other. Mark drove at 65 km/h and his agent drove at 75 km/h. After how long did they meet?

14. You see lightning flash before you hear thunder because light travels much faster than sound. The light reaches you almost instantaneously. The sound travels at a speed of 330 m/s. Write a formula to find your distance, *d* metres, from a thunderstorm in terms of the number of seconds between the lightning flash and when you hear the thunder.

15. Sunil and Kim both do volunteer work at Ronald McDonald House. It takes Sunil 6 h to cut the lawns and trim the hedges, and it takes Kim 4 h to do the same. How long would it take them to cut the lawns and trim the hedges if they worked together?

THE FAR SIDE   By GARY LARSON

"Yes, yes, I know that, Sidney ... everybody knows that! ... But look: Four wrongs squared, minus two wrongs to the fourth power, divided by this formula, do make a right."

Using the Strategies

1. If the pattern continues, find the following product.

$$\left(1 - \tfrac{1}{2}\right)\left(1 - \tfrac{1}{3}\right)\left(1 - \tfrac{1}{4}\right)\cdots\left(1 - \tfrac{1}{24}\right)$$

2. The figure is made up of 11 identical squares. The area of the figure is 539 cm^2.

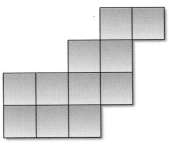

What is the perimeter of the figure?

3. Your plane is scheduled to leave for Casablanca at 18:15. You must arrive at the airport 25 min before the flight to pick up your tickets. It takes a taxi 30 min to drive to the airport from your hotel. Before you leave for the airport, the naval attaché is delivering some documents to you in the lobby of your hotel. It will take the attaché 10 min to explain the documents to you. Before meeting the attaché, you need 1 h 15 min to shower, pack, change clothes, and eat. It is now noon. You want to spend some time sightseeing. What is the latest time you can return to the hotel?

4. A train travelling at 90 km/h passed a car sitting at a railway crossing. It took 45 s for the train to pass. How long was the train in metres?

5. An engine plant built 485 automobile engines. There were 2 models of engines, 4-cylinder and 6-cylinder. The total number of cylinders in the engines was 2224. How many of each model of engine did the plant build?

6. A 2-digit number is changed by decreasing the tens digit by 1 and increasing the units digit by 1. When the new number is added to the original number, the result is 59. What was the original number?

7. If you disregard the year on a calendar, only a limited number of calendars is necessary. For example, you need only one calendar for any year in which January 1 is on a Monday, providing the year is not a leap year.

a) How many different calendars are necessary?

b) Start with the year 2001 and determine how many years must pass before each of the calendars you found in part a) is used at least once.

8. The graphs show the motion of Xenia's car. The vertical axis shows the distance from her house and the horizontal axis shows time. Write a story to explain each graph.

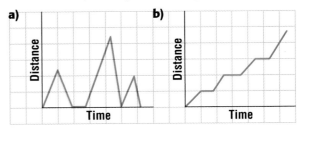

DATA BANK

1. Before he left to sail down the Nile River, Livingstone, who was in Cairo, called his friend Stanley, who was in Edmonton. Livingstone called at 10:00 Cairo time. What time was it in Edmonton?

2. Use the Data Bank on pages 364 to 369 to write a uniform motion problem. Have a classmate solve it.

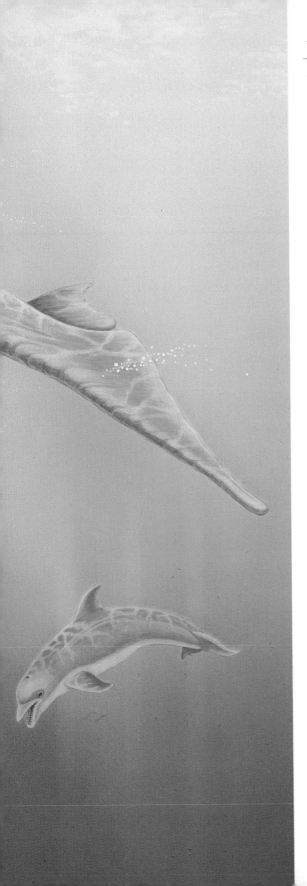

CHAPTER 4

Polynomials

Whales, sharks, and dolphins have shapes that minimize water resistance. The ideal shape for minimum water resistance is a torpedo shape, with a width that is one-quarter the length.

The equations below show how the widths of a blue whale, a shark, and a dolphin are related to their lengths.

Blue Whale	$w = 0.21l$
Shark	$w = 0.26l$
Dolphin	$w = 0.25l$

About how wide is a shark that is 18 m long?

The blue whale is the world's largest mammal. Is a 30-m long blue whale wider than your classroom?

What objects made by humans have torpedo shapes? Explain why they are made in this shape.

Activity ❶ Like Tiles I

1. a) What is the name of each type of algebra tile shown?

b) How many are there of each type?

2. a) Group the same types of tiles together.
b) Write the simplified algebraic expression represented by your group of tiles.
c) Evaluate the expression for $x = -3$.

Activity ❷ Like Tiles II

1. In each set, group the same types of tiles together.

a)

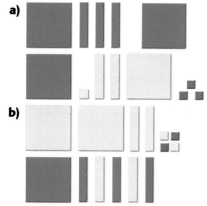

b)

2. Simplify each set of tiles and explain your reasoning.

3. a) Write an algebraic expression represented by each simplified set of tiles.
b) Evaluate each expression for $x = 2$.

Mental Math

Calculate.

1. $101 - 765$	**2.** $432 + 333$
3. $723 + 145$	**4.** $-824 + 134$
5. $666 + 121$	**6.** $545 + 232$
7. $-616 + 303$	**8.** $876 + 123$

Calculate.

9. $555 - 121$	**10.** $-656 - 234$
11. $875 - 662$	**12.** $285 - 164$
13. $-742 - 141$	**14.** $637 - 237$
15. $567 - 456$	**16.** $973 - 663$

Calculate.

17. $7 + 8 - 3$	**18.** $11 - 6 + 7$
19. $13 + 2 - 9$	**20.** $17 + 8 - 20$
21. $21 - 6 + 8$	**22.** $55 - 15 + 11$
23. $44 - 22 - 11$	**24.** $21 + 21 - 20$

Calculate.

25. 102×3	**26.** 111×7
27. $2002 \times (-4)$	**28.** -1010×6
29. -3434×2	**30.** 1212×4
31. $3003 \times (-3)$	**32.** 44×4

Calculate.

33. $5555 \div 5$	**34.** $606 \div 3$
35. $-8080 \div 4$	**36.** $963 \div (-3)$
37. $8642 \div 2$	**38.** $147 \div 7$
39. $-515 \div 5$	**40.** $246 \div (-6)$

Calculate.

41. $5 \times 6 \div 2$	**42.** $3 \times 4 \times 5$
43. $-3 \div 3 \times 4$	**44.** $8 \div (-2) \times (-2)$
45. $6 \times 0 \div 2$	**46.** $6 \times 5 \div 2$
47. $14 \div 4 \times (-2)$	**48.** $8 \times (-1) \times 9$

4.1 Polynomials

The Olympic biathlon consists of 2 events. The events are cross-country skiing and shooting. At one winter Olympics, Canada's Miriam Bedard won two gold medals in the biathlon.

Just like combination Olympic events, algebraic expressions have special names. A monomial is a number or variable or the product of numbers and variables. A **polynomial** is a monomial or the sum of monomials. A polynomial with 2 terms is called a **binomial**. A polynomial with 3 terms is called a **trinomial**.

Activity: Use the Diagrams
Copy the diagrams into your notebook.

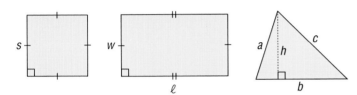

Inquire

1. Write the formulas for the perimeter and area of each figure. Combine like terms where possible.

2. Which expressions are monomials?

3. Which expression is a binomial?

4. Which expression is a trinomial?

5. Explain why it is appropriate to call expressions with 1, 2, and 3 terms monomials, binomials, and trinomials.

Example 1
Classify each of the following as a monomial, binomial, or trinomial.

a) $a - 2b$ **b)** $x^2 + y^2 + z^2$ **c)** 10

Solution

a) The expression $a - 2b$ is a binomial because it contains 2 terms.

b) The expression $x^2 + y^2 + z^2$ is a trinomial because it contains 3 terms.

c) The number 10 is a monomial because it contains 1 term.

CONTINUED ▶

The **degree of a monomial** is the sum of the exponents of its variables.

Monomial	Degree
$4x^3$	3
$5a^2b^3c$	$2 + 3 + 1 = 6$

The **degree of a polynomial in one variable** is the highest power of the variable in any one term.

Polynomials	Degree
$6x^2 + 3x$	2
$x^5 + 7x^2 - 3$	5

The **degree of a polynomial in two variables or more** is the largest sum of the exponents in any one term.

Polynomials	Degree
$x^2y^3 + xy^4 + xy^5$	6
$3x^3y^4 + 7xy^3 - 2xy$	7

$$3 + 2 + 4 = 9$$

$$2x^3y^2z^4$$

Example 2

Classify each polynomial and state its degree.

a) $3abc$ **b)** $2x^2 + x$ **c)** $3xy + 5x^2y^2 - 3$

Solution

a) $3abc$ is a monomial. The sum of the exponents is $1 + 1 + 1 = 3$. It is a third-degree polynomial.

b) $2x^2 + x$ is a binomial. The highest power, 2, is contained in the term $2x^2$. It is a second-degree polynomial.

c) $3xy + 5x^2y^2 - 3$ is a trinomial. The largest exponent sum is contained in the term $5x^2y^2$. It is a fourth-degree polynomial.

The terms of a polynomial are usually arranged so that the powers of one variable are in either ascending order or descending order.

Descending Order	Ascending Order
$x^3 + 2x^2 - 5x + 7$	$7 - 5x + 2x^2 + x^3$
(in x) $5x^2 + 7xy + 3y^2$	(in x) $3y^2 + 7xy + 5x^2$

Practice

Identify as a monomial, binomial, or trinomial.

1. $5xyz$ **2.** $x + 2y$ **3.** $a - 2b + 3c$

4. $x^2 + y^2$ **5.** 23 **6.** $x - y + 2$

State the degree of each monomial.

7. $25x$ **8.** $25x^2y^2$ **9.** 17

10. $2x^2y^3$ **11.** $-5x^3y^4$ **12.** $-6xy^4z$

State the degree of each polynomial.

13. $5x^2y^2 + 3xy^3$

14. $3x + 2y - 5z$

15. $x^4 + 2x^3 + 3x^2 + 4$

16. $4x^4y^2 + 2x^3y^5 - 23$

17. $3x - 2y + z^2$

18. $25m^3n + 36m^3n^3$

19. $-5x^4y^2z + 2x^2y^2z^2$

Arrange the terms in each polynomial in descending powers of x.

20. $1 + x^3 + x^2 + x^5$

21. $5 - 3x^3 + 2x$

22. $5y^2 + 2xy - x^2$

23. $25xy^2 - 5x^2y + 3x^3y^3 - 4x^4$

24. $5ax + 7b^2x^4 - 3x^3 + 4abx^2$

Arrange the terms in each polynomial in ascending powers of x.

25. $3x^2 - 2x^3 + 5x^5 + x - 2$

26. $4x^4 + x^2 - 3x^3 + 5 - x$

27. $4xy^2 - 2x^2y^2 - 3x^4 + 2x^3y$

28. $5x^2yz^2 + 2xy^4z + 3x^3y^4z^2 - 3$

29. $z - xy + x^2$

30. $x^2 - 2xy - 3x^3 + 16$

31. $2x^3y + 3xy - x^5$

32. $3x^3y^2 + x^4y + xy - 1$

Problems and Applications

33. Identify each type of polynomial.

a) $\dfrac{4\pi r^3}{3}$ **b)** $\pi r^2 + 2\pi rh$ **c)** $4\pi r$

34. What type of polynomial is represented by the perimeter of each of these figures?

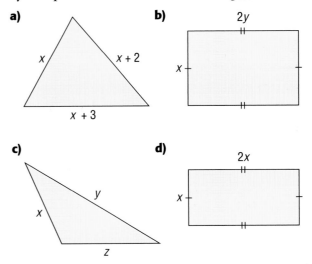

35. a) Calculate the area of each face of this box.

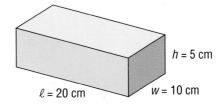

b) What is the total area of the box?
c) Write a polynomial that can be used to calculate the answer you gave in part b).

36. The formula for the volume of a rectangular jewellery box is lwh. Its dimensions are 25 cm × 18 cm × 17 cm. It has 2 cm thick walls. What is the volume of the box's interior to the nearest cubic centimetre?

37. Write a problem that can be solved with a polynomial. Have a classmate solve your problem.

149

4.2 Adding Polynomials

A sports car has 4 wheels, 2 seats, and 1 engine.
To build 2 sports cars, we need

4 + 4 or 8 wheels,
2 + 2 or 4 seats,
and 1 + 1 or 2 engines.

We have added the like parts of the 2 cars.
Algebra tiles model the addition of like parts
of 2 polynomials.

To model polynomials, we can use x^2-tiles,
x-tiles, and 1-tiles. When the x^2 or x-tile is
green side up, it means x^2 or x. When the
x^2 or x-tile is white side up, it means $-x^2$ or
$-x$. When the 1-tile is red side up, it means $+1$.
When the 1-tile is white side up it means -1.

Activity: Use Algebra Tiles

Use x^2-tiles, x-tiles, and 1-tiles to duplicate
the algebraic expressions in Set A and Set B.

Set A

Set B

Inquire

1. How many x^2-tiles, x-tiles, and 1-tiles are in Set A? in Set B?

2. Write an algebraic expression to represent
a) Set A   **b)** Set B

3. Combine the tiles in Set A and Set B into 1 set, so that like
tiles are placed together.

4. Write the algebraic expression that represents the combined
set in 3.

5. Use tiles to represent the following pairs of expressions.

a) $x^2 + 2x + 3$ **b)** $x^2 - 2x + 6$ **c)** $3x^2 + 4x - 2$
  $2x^2 + 3x + 2$ $3x^2 + 5x - 2$ $5x^2 - 2x + 3$

6. Combine each pair in 5 and write its algebraic sum.

7. Write a rule for adding polynomials.

Example 1

Add $(x^2 + 4x + 3) + (2x^2 + 5x + 1)$.

Solution

Remove the brackets, collect like terms, and add.

$$(x^2 + 4x + 3) + (2x^2 + 5x + 1) = x^2 + 4x + 3 + 2x^2 + 5x + 1$$
$$= x^2 + 2x^2 + 4x + 5x + 3 + 1$$
$$= 3x^2 + 9x + 4$$

Note that the answer to Example 1, $3x^2 + 9x + 4$, is in **simplest form**. A polynomial is in simplest form when it contains no like terms.

Example 2

Use column form to add these polynomials.
a) $(5x^2 - 3x + 5) + (2x^2 - 7x - 10)$
b) $(3y^3 - 3y + 2y^2 + 8) + (-5 - 6y^2 + 2y)$

Solution

a) Write the like terms of the polynomials in columns, then add.

$$\begin{array}{r} 5x^2 - 3x + 5 \\ +2x^2 - 7x - 10 \\ \hline 7x^2 - 10x - 5 \end{array}$$

b) Rewrite the terms in descending powers of y before arranging them in columns and adding.

$$3y^3 - 3y + 2y^2 + 8 \longrightarrow 3y^3 + 2y^2 - 3y + 8$$
$$-5 - 6y^2 + 2y \longrightarrow \underline{\qquad - 6y^2 + 2y - 5}$$
$$3y^3 - 4y^2 - y + 3$$

Practice

Find the sums of the expressions, A and B, represented by the algebra tiles.

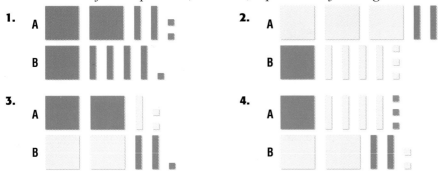

1. A   B

2. A   B

3. A   B

4. A   B

CONTINUED

Identify the like terms in each expression.

5. $2x + 3y - 4xy + 5x - 2y + 6xy$

6. $2a + 5a - 6b + 8b - 2c + 3c$

7. $3s^2 + 5s - 2 + 7s^2 + s - 3$

Add.

8. $(3x + 1) + (4x - 2)$

9. $(3x^2 + 5x - 4) + (x^2 - 7x + 2)$

10. $(-y^2 + 7y - 5) + (2y^2 + 7y - 4)$

11. $(2y^3 - 3y^2 - 1) + (-5y^2 - 4y^3 + 3)$

Add.

12. $\quad x + 7$
$\quad +5x + 2$

13. $\quad 3y^2 + 2y + \ 8$
$\quad +4y^2 + 7y + 11$

14. $\quad 5x - 2y + 6$
$\quad +3x - 6y + 9$

15. $\quad 5x^2 - 3x + \ 7$
$\quad +2x^2 - 5x - 12$

16. $\quad 5x^2 + 7x - \ 9$
$\quad +4x^2 - 8x + 11$

17. $\quad 3y^2 - 8y + 3$
$\quad +2y^2 + 8y - 9$

Simplify.

18. $(5z + 6 - 3z^2) + (4 - 7z + 2z^2)$

19. $(3x^2 + 2y^2 - 5) + (4x^2 + 3y^2 - 11)$

20. $(2x^4 + 7x - 5x^2 + 3) + (2x^3 - 7)$

Add.

21. $(5x^2 + 7x - 7) + (4x^2 - 8x + 12)$

22. $(3y^2 - 8y + 3) + (2y^2 + 8y - 9)$

23. $(m^3 + 5m^2 + 3) + (4m^2 + 7)$

24. $(x^2 + x + 3) + (x^2 - 6) + (x^2 - 2x - 3)$

Simplify.

25. $(4x^2 + 3xy - 2y^2) + (-x^2 - 5xy + 7y^2)$

26. $(5y^2 + 3y - 7) + (-2y^2 - 5y + 8)$

27. $(3x^2y - 2xy + 4y^2) + (x^2y + y^2)$

Problems and Applications

28. Explain how these algebra tiles can be used to model a solution to $(2x^2 - 3x + 4) + (2x - 3)$.

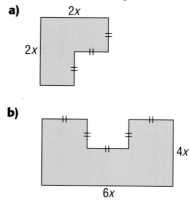

29. a) Write an expression in simplest form for the perimeter of the figure.

$4x + 7$ $\quad$ $5x + 3$ $\quad$ $3x + 2$

b) If $x = 4$ cm, what is the perimeter?

30. a) Write an expression in simplest form for the perimeter of the figure.

$2x - 3$ $\quad$ $3x + 5$

b) If $x = 7$ cm, what is the perimeter?

31. a) The perimeter of historic Fort York is expressed by the following polynomial.

$$x + (x + 171) + (x + 156)$$

What geometric shape is the perimeter of Fort York?

b) If $x = 153$ m, what is the perimeter?

32. Add $(3x^2 + x - 1) + (x^2 - 3x - 2)$. How can you use $x = 1$ to check your solution?

33. Work with a partner to write a monomial that describes the perimeter of each figure.

a) $2x$ $\quad$ $2x$

b) $4x$ $\quad$ $6x$

Budgets from a Spreadsheet

A spreadsheet is a useful tool for keeping track of expenses and the amount of money that remains in a budget.

Activity ❶

1. Work with a partner. Use magazines, catalogues, and newspapers to choose 5 prizes of different values. They will be 1st, 2nd, 3rd, 4th, and 5th prizes for the students who raise the most in a fund-raising project. Keep the total cost below $500.00.

2. Copy the following spreadsheet into your notebook. Calculate and record the entries.

You will need to enter the rate of provincial tax for your province. You may need to correct the rate of the GST.

		B	C	D	E	F
1		Prize	Price	Provincial Tax	GST	Item Cost
2	1st			+C2*▪	+C2*.07	+C2+D2+E2
3	2nd					
4	3rd					
5	4th					
6	5th					
7					Total Cost	@SUM(F2..F6)

3. Is the calculation method shown in the spreadsheet correct for all provinces? Explain.

Activity ❷

1. Set up the spreadsheet from Activity 1 on a computer and have the computer calculate the total cost.

2. Adjust your prizes until you have spent no more than $350.00 and no less than $300.00.

3. Challenge another group of students to come closer to $350.00 than your total cost does.

Activity ❸

1. Redo the spreadsheet to allow for 8 prizes, but leave the total cost at no more than $350.00.

2. Challenge another group of students to come closer to $350.00 than your total cost does.

4.3 Subtracting Polynomials

Activity: Use Algebra Tiles

Use tiles to duplicate Set A and Set B.

Inquire

1. Write the algebraic expression represented by each group of tiles.

2. How many x^2-tiles, x-tiles, and 1-tiles are there in each set?

3. If the x^2-tiles, x-tiles, and 1-tiles in Set B are subtracted from those in Set A, how many of each type of tile are left?

4. Turn Set B over to make its opposite or **additive inverse**. Write the sum of Set A and the opposite of Set B. Compare with your answer in 3.

5. Use algebra tiles to represent each pair of expressions.

a) $x^2 + 5x - 7$
$ - 2x + 3$

b) $3x^2 - 4x + 3$
$x^2 + 3x - 5$

c) $-2x^2 + 4x - 5$
$-x^2 + x - 3$

6. In each pair, add the opposite or additive inverse of the second polynomial to the first polynomial.

7. Write a rule for subtracting polynomials.

Example 1

Use column form to subtract $2x^2 + 2x + 5$ from $5x^2 - 7x + 4$.

Solution

When we subtract 1 polynomial from another, we add the opposite of the polynomial that is being subtracted.

The opposite of $2x^2 + 2x + 5$ is $-2x^2 - 2x - 5$.

$$\begin{array}{r} 5x^2 - 7x + 4 \\ -2x^2 - 2x - 5 \\ \hline 3x^2 - 9x - 1 \end{array}$$

How can you check your answer by addition?

Example 2

Simplify
$(4x^2 - 5x + 7) - (3x^2 + 2x - 5)$.

Solution

Write the opposite of $3x^2 + 2x - 5$ and add.

$$\begin{aligned} &(4x^2 - 5x + 7) - (3x^2 + 2x - 5) \\ &= (4x^2 - 5x + 7) + (-3x^2 - 2x + 5) \\ &= 4x^2 - 5x + 7 - 3x^2 - 2x + 5 \\ &= 4x^2 - 3x^2 - 5x - 2x + 7 + 5 \\ &= x^2 - 7x + 12 \end{aligned}$$

154

Practice

Write the additive inverse.

1. $x^2 + 4x + 1$ **2.** $x^2 - 2x - 3$

3. $2x^2 + x - 5$ **4.** $-3x^2 - 7x + 2$

Subtract.

5. $(3x - 5) - (x + 2)$ **6.** $(x + 5) - (3x - 1)$

7. $(x + 4) - (-x - 3)$ **8.** $(3x - 5) - (x + 4)$

Subtract.

9. $5x^2 + 3x - 5$ **10.** $-3x^2 + 5x - 7$
$2x^2 - 5x - 4$ $2x^2 + 3x - 3$

11. $-4x^2 - 4x + 3$ **12.** $x^2 - 5x + 1$
$-3x^2 + 4x - 8$ $x^2 - 5x + 6$

13. $x^2 + 7x - 1$ **14.** $12x^3 + 3x^2 - 5x$
$x^2 + 4x + 1$ $9x^3 + 4x^2 - 4x$

Subtract.

15. $(2y^2 + 3y - 5) - (-2y^2 + 4y + 6)$

16. $(4s^2 + s - 2) - (-3s^2 + s - 5)$

17. $(y^2 - 5y + 3) - (-2y^2 + 7y + 5)$

Subtract.

18. $3x^2 + 7x - 3$ from $2x^2 - 2x + 3$

19. $5y^2 + 7y - 5$ from $-2y^2 + 3y - 2$

20. $-t^2 + 5t - 1$ from $2t^2 + 3t + 6$

Simplify.

21. $(-5n^2 - n - 8) - (-2n^2 + 7n - 3)$

22. $(4 + 2x - x^2) - (3 - 7x^2 + 5x)$

23. $(-t^2 + 4t - 7) - (3t^2 + 4t - 2)$

24. $(x^2 + 5x + 3) - (-x^2 - 7x + 11)$

25. $(3m^2 + 7m - 8) - (-m^2 + m - 1)$

26. $(-5y^2 + 7y - 12) - (-3y^2 + 4y - 2)$

Problems and Applications

27. Explain how these algebra tiles can be used to model a solution to
$(2x^2 - 2x + 1) - (2 + x - 2x^2)$.

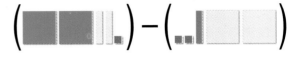

28. Find the length of *PQ*.

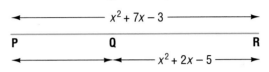

29. Given the perimeter, *P*, of a figure and 2 or 3 sides, find the missing length.

a)   **b)**

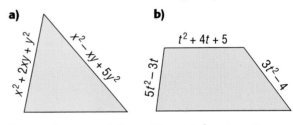

$P = 5x^2 + xy + 5y^2$ $P = 11t^2 + 6t + 9$

30. The area of the large rectangle is $3x^2 + 2x + 1$. What is the area of the shaded region?

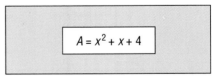

$A = x^2 + x + 4$

31. What is the result of adding a polynomial and its additive inverse? Explain why.

32. a) If you add 2 polynomials, A and B, does it matter if you add A + B or B + A? Explain and give an example.
b) If you subtract 2 polynomials, A and B, does it matter if you subtract A − B or B − A? Explain and give an example.

155

4.4 Use a Diagram

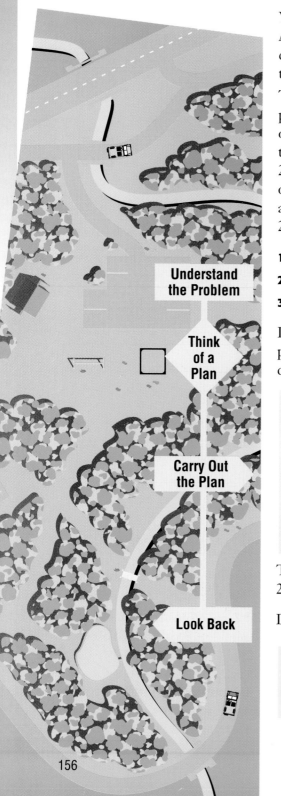

You can simplify many problems by drawing a diagram. Architects and interior designers use diagrams to solve design problems. The director of a play uses a diagram to block out where the actors should be.

Tom and Margarita are park rangers. They patrol the park by driving around the outside in jeeps. They start on opposite sides and drive at different speeds. Margarita takes 15 min to drive halfway around the park. Tom takes 20 min. They start their patrols at 20:00 and travel in opposite directions. If they stay on schedule, what are the approximate times at which they pass each other between 20:00 and 22:00?

Understand the Problem

1. What information are you given?

2. What are you asked to find?

3. Do you need an exact or approximate answer?

Think of a Plan

Draw a diagram to show the time taken to drive around the park. Show Tom in red. Show Margarita in blue. Use the diagram to find when they pass each other.

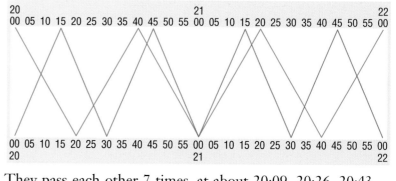

Carry Out the Plan

They pass each other 7 times, at about 20:09, 20:26, 20:43, 21:00, 21:17, 21:34, and 21:51.

Look Back

Does the answer seem reasonable?

Use a Diagram	**1.** Draw a diagram to represent the situation.
	2. Use the diagram to solve the problem.
	3. Check that the answer is reasonable.

Problems and Applications

1. How many different-sized rectangles have a perimeter of 16 m and side lengths that are whole numbers?

2. In a scalene triangle, no 2 sides are equal. How many scalene triangles have a perimeter of 12 cm or less, if the side lengths are whole numbers?

3. Roberto bought 4 stamps attached as shown.

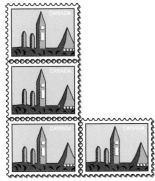

In how many different ways can 4 stamps be attached to each other?

4. Lenore wants to fence a rectangular yard that measures 15 m by 9 m. She wants posts at the corners and every 3 m. How many posts does she need?

5. Yoshiko and Carla are water polo players. Part of their training program is to swim widths of the pool. Carla swims a width in 15 s. Yoshiko swims a width in 12 s. They start swimming widths at the same time from opposite sides of the pool. How many times do they pass each other in 2 min? What assumptions have you made?

6. Terry, Rocky, Indu, and Lennox went out for dinner. They sat at a square table. They decided to use a math problem to see who would leave the tip. The problem was: "In how many different ways can 4 people sit at a square table if there must be 1 person on each side?"

7. Ships at sea use flags to send signals. Different orders of the same flags mean different messages. How many different messages could you send by using 3 flags?

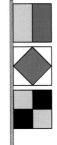

8. You can cut a round pie into 4 pieces with 2 straight cuts.
If you do not care about the sizes of the pieces, you can cut a round pie into 7 pieces using 3 straight cuts.
What is the greatest number of pieces you can get using 5 straight cuts?

9. A farmer must get a wolf, a goat, and some cabbages across a river. The boat will hold the farmer and one of the wolf, the goat, or the cabbages. Only the farmer can row the boat. The farmer cannot leave the goat alone with the cabbages, because the goat will eat them. The farmer cannot leave the wolf alone with the goat, because the wolf will chase the goat away. How does the farmer get the goat, wolf, and cabbages safely across the river?

10. A photography expedition planned an 8-day crossing of a desert. Each person could carry, at most, a 5-day supply of water. What is the smallest number of people needed to start the trip so that one person can cross the desert and the others can return to the starting point?

11. Write a problem that can be solved with a diagram. Have a classmate solve your problem.

Multiplication with Algebra Tiles

Activity ❶ Multiplication with 1-tiles

1. a) Draw a frame with a square corner.
b) Place three 1-tiles along the horizontal frame line and two 1-tiles along the vertical frame line, as shown.

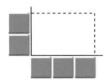

2. a) Fill the outlined rectangular space with 1-tiles.
b) Count the number of 1-tiles to find the product.
c) What two numbers are multiplied together to give this product?

3. Draw a frame. Then, use 1-tiles to model these products.

a) 6×2 **b)** 4×3 **c)** 5×2

4. What type and number of tiles should be used to fill each rectangular space? Explain.

a)   **b)**

Activity ❷ Multiplication with x-tiles and 1-tiles

1. Draw a frame and use algebra tiles to model the situation shown.

2. a) Can 1-tiles be used to exactly fill the rectangular space? Explain.
b) Can x-tiles be used to exactly fill it? Explain.

3. a) Count the number of tiles that exactly fill the space to find the product.
b) What number and variable are multiplied together to give this product?

4. Use algebra tiles to model and find these products.

a) $x \times 3$ **b)** $x \times 1$ **c)** $2x \times 2$

Activity ❸ Multiplication with *x*-tiles

1. Use algebra tiles to model the situation shown.

2. a) State the length and the width of the shape.
b) What is the geometric name for this shape?

3. a) Can the space be exactly filled with *x*-tiles? Explain.
b) Can the space be exactly filled with x^2-tiles?

4. a) What is the product?
b) What two algebraic expressions are multiplied together to give this product?

5. What type and number of tile represent each product?

a)   **b)**

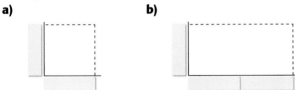

Activity ❹ Multiplication with *x*²-tiles

1. Count x^2-tiles to find the product.

2. Write the two algebraic expressions, each including *x*, that have been multiplied together to create this product.

3. Use algebra tiles to model and find these products.
a) $x \times 2x$ **b)** $2x \times 2x$ **c)** $2x \times 3x$

Activity ❺ Multiplication with *x*-tiles and *y*-tiles

1. Compare a green *x*-tile and an orange *y*-tile.
a) Do an *x*-tile and a *y*-tile have the same width?
b) Which of the 2 tiles is longer?

2. a) Use algebra tiles to model this product.

b) Can the space be exactly filled with *x*-tiles or *y*-tiles? Explain.
c) Can the space be exactly filled with grey *xy*-tiles?
d) What is the product?

3. Use algebra tiles to model and find these products.
a) $x \times 2y$ **b)** $2x \times y$ **c)** $2x \times 2y$

4.5 Multiplying Monomials by Monomials

The first male killer whale born in captivity in North America was born at Marineland in Niagara Falls. The volume of the tank in which *Splash* lives can be expressed as the product of 3 monomials, $l \times w \times h$, where l is the length, w is the width, and h is the height of the tank.

Activity: Use Algebra Tiles

Arrange six xy-tiles to form a rectangle as shown.

Inquire

1. What is the area of the rectangle?

2. What is the length of the rectangle?

3. What is the width of the rectangle?

4. Write the area of the rectangle as a product of its dimensions.

5. Use xy-tiles to model these products. State the product in each case.

a) $2x \times 3y$ **b)** $x \times 3y$ **c)** $3x \times y$

6. Write a rule for multiplying a monomial by a monomial.

Example

Find the product.

a) $(30x)(4y)$ **b)** $-5x^2(-3yz)$

Solution

a)
$$(30x)(4y)$$
$$= 30 \times x \times 4 \times y$$
$$= 30 \times 4 \times x \times y$$
$$= 120xy$$

b)
$$-5x^2(-3yz)$$
$$= -5 \times x^2 \times (-3) \times y \times z$$
$$= -5 \times (-3) \times x^2 \times y \times z$$
$$= 15x^2yz$$

Practice

Multiply.

1. $5x \times 3y$ **2.** $2m \times 3n$ **3.** $5s \times 7t$

4. $4a \times 6b$ **5.** $3x^2 \times 2y$ **6.** $4a \times 5b^2$

7. $4b \times 3c$ **8.** $3a \times 2b^2$ **9.** $6s \times 3t$

Multiply.

10. $(3x)(2y)$ **11.** $(3a)(4b)$ **12.** $(5x^2)(2y^2)$

13. $(5ab)(3c)$ **14.** $(4x)(3y)$ **15.** $(6xy)(5z)$

16. $(2a^2)(3b^2)$ **17.** $(3a)(3b)$ **18.** $(7a)(5b)$

Multiply.

19. $(3x^2)(-5y^2)$ **20.** $-2t^3(-4a)$

21. $(6ab)(-2c^2)$ **22.** $-8a^2(3y^2)$

23. $(5x)(5yz)$ **24.** $-12x^2(4y^2)$

Multiply.

25. $(-2xy)(-7xy)$ **26.** $-5m^2(-2mn)$

27. $4s^2t^3(-3st)$ **28.** $-3abx(-2a^2b^4y)$

29. $-2s^2t^3(-5s^4t^2)$ **30.** $-5x^2y^2(4c^2x^3y^8)$

Multiply.

31. $-3x^2yz(5yz)$ **32.** $-2x^2(-3cy^2z^3)$

33. $-2x^2(-2y^2)(z)$ **34.** $-5x^2(-7y)(-2z)$

35. $-5x(-7y)(-2z)$ **36.** $-6xy(-5z^2)(3t^2)$

Multiply.

37. $(4a^2x^3z)(-2x^3y^2z^2)$

38. $(2b^2xy^4z^2)(-3xyz)$

39. $-5a^2b^3(-2a^2b^2)$

Multiply.

40. $(3abc)(-4abc)(2abc)$

41. $(-x^2yz)(2xy^2z)(-2xyz^2)$

42. $(-2jkl)(-3jkl)(-4jkl)$

Problems and Applications

43. Find the area of each figure.

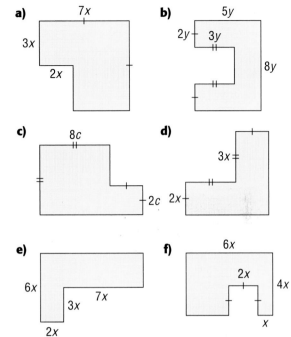

44. a) If x is the time needed in minutes to make a hat, and y is the cost of production in dollars per minute, what does the expression $24xy$ mean?

b) Use $x = 3$ and $y = 0.5$ to evaluate your expression in part a).

45. Write an expression for the volume of each prism.

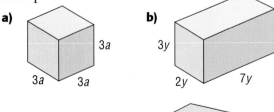

46. What is the length of the side of a cube that has the same volume as this rectangular solid?

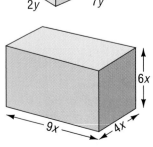

4.6 Solve a Simpler Problem

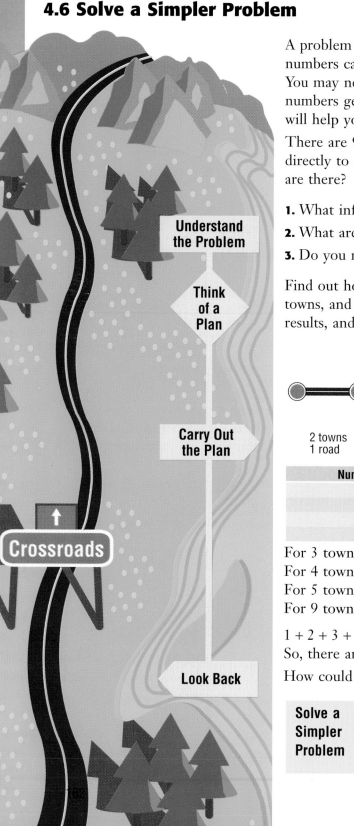

Crossroads

Understand the Problem

Think of a Plan

Carry Out the Plan

Look Back

A problem that appears to be difficult because of large numbers can often be simplified if you use smaller numbers. You may need to solve a series of simpler problems, with the numbers getting larger, until you see a pattern. This pattern will help you solve the original problem.

There are 9 towns in the county. Each town is connected directly to each of the others by a road. How many roads are there?

1. What information are you given?

2. What are you asked to find?

3. Do you need an exact or approximate answer?

Find out how many roads connect 2 towns, 3 towns, 4 towns, and so on. Draw diagrams, make a table of the results, and look for a pattern.

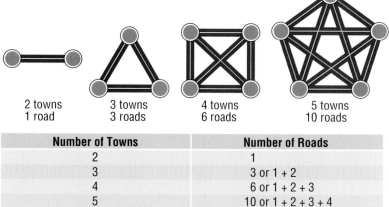

2 towns 1 road	3 towns 3 roads
4 towns 6 roads	5 towns 10 roads

Number of Towns	Number of Roads
2	1
3	3 or 1 + 2
4	6 or 1 + 2 + 3
5	10 or 1 + 2 + 3 + 4

For 3 towns, add the first 2 non-zero whole numbers.
For 4 towns, add the first 3 non-zero whole numbers.
For 5 towns, add the first 4 non-zero whole numbers.
For 9 towns, add the first 8 non-zero whole numbers.

$1 + 2 + 3 + 4 + 5 + 6 + 7 + 8 = 36$
So, there are 36 roads.

How could you check the answer?

Solve a Simpler Problem	1. Break the problem into smaller problems.
	2. Solve the problem.
	3. Check that your answer is reasonable.

Problems and Applications

1. How would you estimate the number of listings in the white pages of a telephone book?

2. How would you estimate the thickness of 1 page of this textbook?

3. How would you estimate how long it would take you to read a 250-page novel?

4. Caroline owns a rectangular field of length 60 m and width 40 m. She

40 m

60 m

wants to put a fence around the field. The fence posts are to be 2 m apart and there must be a post in each corner. How many posts will she need?

5. Find the sum of the first 100 odd numbers.
$1 + 3 + 5 + 7 + 9 + \cdots$

6. Find the sum of the first 100 even numbers.
$2 + 4 + 6 + 8 + 10 + \cdots$

7. Calculate the following.
$80 - 79 + 78 - 77 \cdots + 2 - 1$

8. Sixteen teams play in a basketball tournament. Each team plays until it loses 1 game. There are no ties. How many games are played?

9. For the final game of an international hockey tournament, each team had 18 players. Before the game, each player shook hands with every player on the opposing team. How many handshakes were exchanged?

10. Each of the 10 provinces sent 1 student to Ottawa for the opening of Parliament. Each student gave each of the other students a provincial pin. How many pins were exchanged?

11. About how many breaths do you take in 1 year?

12. If 1 bacterium divides into 2 bacteria in 1 min, how many bacteria come from 1 bacterium in 12 min? What assumptions have you made?

13. Write a problem that can be solved by means of a simpler problem. Have a classmate solve your problem.

LOGIC POWER

The Riddler has invited you to a party at his apartment. The elevator buttons are shown below. They are lettered from A to I, but the letters are hidden. You must press the buttons in order from A to I to get to the party. Use the clues to find the button letters.

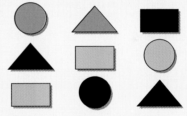

1. The D button is green.

2. The G button is red.

3. The F button is directly below a triangle.

4. The I button is in the left column.

5. The B button is not round.

6. The E button is in the middle row.

7. The H button is in the top row.

8. The F button is lower than the C button.

9. The C button is directly to the left of a round button.

4.7 Dividing Monomials by Monomials

When Patricia Hy became Canadian Women's Tennis Champion, she played on a regulation court. If we know the area of the court and its length or width, we can calculate the other dimension. Dividing the area, A, by the length, l, or width, w, involves the division of a monomial by a monomial.

Recall that for the multiplication statement $3 \times 2 = 6$, there are 2 division statements.

$$6 \div 2 = 3 \qquad 6 \div 3 = 2$$

Activity: Discover the Relationship

Copy and complete.

a) $2a \times 3b$ **b)** $3x \times 5x$ **c)** $4x^2 \times 2x$

Inquire

1. Write 2 division statements for each multiplication statement above.

2. Write 2 division statements for each of the following.

a) $3g \times 4h = 12gh$ **b)** $5y \times 2y^2 = 10y^3$
c) $2x \times 3y = 6xy$ **d)** $x^2 \times 2y^3 = 2x^2y^3$

3. Write a rule for dividing monomials by monomials.

Example

Divide. Express each answer with positive exponents.

a) $10x^3y^4 \div 2y^3$ **b)** $\dfrac{-8x^6y^7}{4x^5y^5}$ **c)** $\dfrac{60a^2b^2c^2}{30a^4b^3c^2}$

Solution

a) $10x^3y^4 \div 2y^3$
$= \dfrac{10x^3y^4}{2y^3}$
$= (102)\left(\dfrac{x^3}{1}\right)\left(\dfrac{y^4}{y^3}\right)$
$= 5x^3y$

b) $\dfrac{-8x^6y^7}{4x^5y^5}$
$= \left(\dfrac{-8}{4}\right)\left(\dfrac{x^6}{x^5}\right)\left(\dfrac{y^7}{y^5}\right)$
$= -2xy^2$

c) $\dfrac{60a^2b^2c^2}{30a^4b^3c^2}$
$= \left(\dfrac{60}{30}\right)\left(\dfrac{a^2}{a^4}\right)\left(\dfrac{b^2}{b^3}\right)\left(\dfrac{c^2}{c^2}\right)$
$= 2a^{-2}b^{-1}$
$= \dfrac{2}{a^2b}$

Practice

Divide.

1. $\frac{6x}{3}$ **2.** $\frac{-15a}{5}$ **3.** $\frac{24y}{8}$

4. $\frac{36m}{9}$ **5.** $\frac{-30x}{6}$ **6.** $\frac{-25y}{5}$

7. $\frac{12x}{4x}$ **8.** $\frac{-18y}{3y}$ **9.** $\frac{24a}{a}$

10. $\frac{-32b}{-b}$ **11.** $\frac{-40x}{40}$ **12.** $\frac{-32m}{-8}$

Divide.

13. $\frac{15xyz}{5xy}$ **14.** $\frac{-18ab}{6a}$ **15.** $\frac{12pqr}{4pqr}$

16. $\frac{36abc}{-4a}$ **17.** $\frac{28xy}{7y}$ **18.** $\frac{-15rst}{3rt}$

Divide.

19. $25xy \div 5xy$ **20.** $22ab \div 11ab$

21. $21xyz \div 3xyz$ **22.** $9amn \div amn$

23. $36rst \div 3rs$ **24.** $39jkl \div 13kl$

25. $52pqrs \div 13ps$ **26.** $51defg \div 3eg$

Simplify.

27. $5x^4y^2 \div x^3y$ **28.** $-3a^3b^4 \div ab$

29. $18j^7k^7 \div (-9j^4)$ **30.** $-20x^5y^{15} \div 4x^2y$

31. $7a^3b^2c \div (-7ab)$ **32.** $-8x^2y^9 \div (-2xy^8)$

Simplify.

33. $\frac{10a^6b^3}{5a^4b^2}$ **34.** $\frac{-15x^6y^8}{-5x^5y^7}$ **35.** $\frac{-12m^6n^2}{4m^3n^2}$

36. $\frac{22x^2y^4z^3}{11xy^3z}$ **37.** $\frac{20a^4b^6c}{15a^4b^6c}$ **38.** $\frac{-18x^5y^8}{12x^3y^6}$

Simplify. Express each answer with positive exponents.

39. $\frac{10x^3y}{5x^5y^3}$ **40.** $\frac{-12a^4b^{-3}}{3a^2b^{-5}}$ **41.** $\frac{-16m^7n^3}{4m^8n^6}$

42. $\frac{-9x^4y^3}{-3x^5y^2}$ **43.** $\frac{-24x^{-6}y^{-3}}{18x^{-7}y}$ **44.** $\frac{9p^5q^{15}}{p^2q^3r^2}$

Problems and Applications

45. Find the missing dimension in each rectangle.

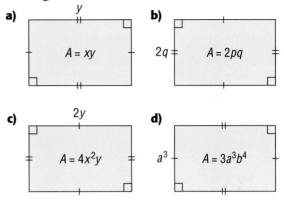

a) $A = xy$, y

b) $2q$, $A = 2pq$

c) $2y$, $A = 4x^2y$

d) a^3, $A = 3a^3b^4$

46. What are the dimensions of each rectangle if each area is 160 cm²?

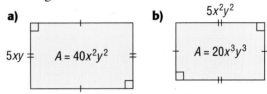

a) $5xy$, $A = 40x^2y^2$

b) $5x^2y^2$, $A = 20x^3y^3$

47. Find the quotient of the volume of this box divided by its area.

x, x, x

48. A and B represent monomials. When you multiply A × B, the result is A. When you divide A ÷ B, the result is A. What is the monomial B?

49. Write a problem similar to problem 46. Have a classmate solve your problem.

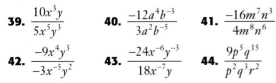

PATTERN POWER

There are x cars in a bumper-to-bumper lineup. The cars' bumpers are touching. How many bumpers are touching?

4.8 Sequence the Operations

The solutions to some problems have several steps, which must be performed in the proper sequence.

Bob Robertson is a gold miner in the Klondike. He has 400 claims and pays the Canadian government $10 per year to operate each one. Bob employs 14 people during the "season," which runs from April to freeze-up in October. Each employee works 12 h a day for $19.75/h. One year, 9 people worked 143 days, and the other 5 worked 131 days. If gold was worth $15 000/kg, how many kilograms of gold did Bob's claims have to produce to cover the salaries and government costs? Write your answer to the nearest kilogram.

Understand the Problem

1. What information are you given?

2. What are you asked to find?

3. What is the proper sequence of steps?

Think of a Plan

Calculate the wages of the 14 employees. Add the amount paid to the government. Divide the total expenses by $15 000 to find out how many kilograms were needed. Use a calculator to find the exact answer.

Carry Out the Plan

Wages of 9 employees
$= 9 \times 143 \times 12 \times \$19.75$
$= \$305\ 019$

EST $10 \times 140 \times 10 \times 20$
$= 280\ 000$

Wages of 5 employees
$= 5 \times 131 \times 12 \times \$19.75$
$= \$155\ 235$

EST $5 \times 100 \times 10 \times 20$
$= 100\ 000$

Payment to government
$= 400 \times \$10$
$= \$4000$

Total expenses
$= \$305\ 019 + \$155\ 235 + \$4000$
$= \$464\ 254$

EST $300\ 000 + 160\ 000 + 4000$
$= 464\ 000$

Kilograms of gold needed
$= \dfrac{\$464\ 254}{\$15\ 000}$
$= 30.950\ 266\ 67$

EST $450\ 000 \div 15\ 000$
$= 30$

Bob's claims had to produce 31 kg of gold to cover salaries and government costs.

Look Back

How can you work backward to check your answer?

Sequence the Operations	1. List the given facts.
	2. Decide on the proper solution sequence.
	3. Complete the calculation.
	4. Check that your answer is reasonable.

Problems and Applications

1. At ages 3, 4, and 5, a child learns about 3 new words each day. About how many words does a child learn in these 3 years?

2. The average person normally speaks about 125 words/min. How many words can the average person speak in 2.5 h?

3. The sports arena has 17 624 seats. Tickets for the track meet cost $22.50 each. If 1057 tickets remain unsold, what is the value of the tickets sold?

4. Tamar and Ken left the highway service centre at the same time and travelled in the same direction. Tamar drove at 90 km/h, and Ken drove at 70 km/h.
a) How far did Tamar drive in 3.5 h?
b) How far did Ken drive in 4 h?
c) How far apart were they after 4.5 h?

5. The parking garage charges $5.50 for the first hour or part of an hour. The charge is $2.00 for each additional half hour or part of a half hour. Eileen arrived at 08:17 and left at 11:45. How much was she charged?

6. Mohammed works on a highway survey crew during the summer. He earns $11.70/h for up to 35 h/week. He earns time-and-a-half for hours over 35 h/week. If he works 41 h in one week, how much does he earn?

7. Light travels through space at a speed of 298 000 km/s. A **light year** is the distance light travels through space in one year. How far is a light year?

8. What time will it be 213 000 h from now?

9. Twenty-four students are planning a trip to a theatre festival. The total cost is $10 466. The school will pay $1100 towards the total cost. The students will equally share the rest of the cost. Each student will pay in 5 equal monthly instalments. How much is each instalment?

10. The passenger pigeon was a North American migratory bird. At one time, there were huge numbers of these pigeons, but they became extinct in 1914. A flock of passenger pigeons was once described as follows.

"The column was 500 m wide and flew overhead at 500 m/min. It took three hours to fly by. Each square metre was occupied by ten pigeons."

How many pigeons were in the flock?

LOGIC POWER

Examine the map. Use your knowledge of geography to decide which province this area is in. Then find this area on a complete map.

167

The Solar System

The table shows the diameters of the star and planets in the solar system relative to the Earth's diameter.

Planet or Star	Diameter (Earth = 1)
Sun	109
Mercury	0.38
Venus	0.95
Earth	1.00
Mars	0.53
Jupiter	11.2
Saturn	9.4
Uranus	4.0
Neptune	3.8
Pluto	0.2

Activity ❶ Diameters in the Solar System

1. Work with a partner to explain what is meant by the heading "Earth = 1" in the diameter column of the table.

2. How were the diameters of the other planets calculated? Compare your answer to a classmate's.

3. a) Estimate how many times the smallest planet could fit across the diameter of the sun.
b) Use your calculator to check your estimate. How close was your estimate?

4. Prepare some arguments that would support the statement, "Some planets are approximately the same size."

5. If the diameter of the Earth is approximately 12 756 km, what are the diameters of the other planets?

6. Use circles, or parts of circles, to make a scale drawing that shows how the sizes of the planets and the sun compare.

7. Write three English words that are derived from *sol*, the Latin word for sun.

Activity ❷ Distances in the Solar System

This table shows how far from the sun each planet is relative to the Earth.

Planet	Average Distance from Sun (Earth = 1)
Mercury	0.39
Venus	0.72
Earth	1.00
Mars	1.52
Jupiter	5.2
Saturn	9.5
Uranus	19.2
Neptune	30.1
Pluto	39.6

1. Work with a partner to explain why the numbers are increasing from the beginning to the end of this table.

2. Compare the meaning of the heading "Earth = 1" in this table to its meaning in the previous table.

3. If the average distance of the Earth from the sun is 149.6 million kilometres, calculate the average distance from the sun for the rest of the planets.

4. What sort of orbit does Pluto make as it revolves around the sun?

5. Make a scale drawing to show how the distances of the planets from the sun compare.

Activity ❸ Researching a Space Probe

1. Research the latest space probe. Then, write a press release to describe what was supposed to happen.

2. List 3 points supporting the view that the money spent on all the space probes to date is well worth it.

3. List 3 points supporting the view that the money spent on all the space probes to date is not worth it.

4. a) Work with a classmate to compare the lists that each of you prepared in questions 2 and 3 of this activity.
b) On the basis of your lists, discuss whether space probes should continue.

5. Divide the class into small groups to prepare a debate on this topic.

6. Choose a side, elect a speaker for each side of the argument, and hold the debate.

Review

Identify each polynomial type and state its degree.

1. xyz **2.** $3x^2y^3$

3. $5xy^2 - 5xy$ **4.** $x^2 + y$

5. $ab^3 + b^2 + 1$ **6.** $3m^2n^3 + 5mn$

7. $x^2 + 2x^4 + 5x^2$ **8.** $3x^3 - 5x + 3$

9. $x^2yz + 2yz$ **10.** $b^2x^3 - 2x^3 - 4xy^2$

Arrange each polynomial with its powers in descending order.

11. $x^2 + 3x - 5x^3$

12. $5 + 2y^2 - 3y + y^4$

13. $2m + 6 - 3m^2 - m^4 + 6m^3$

14. $3 + x + x^2 + x^3 + x^4$

15. $y^5 - 2y^7 + 3y - 4y^2 + 5y^6$

16. What type of polynomial is represented by the perimeter of each figure?

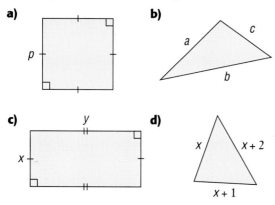

a)   b)

c)   d)

17. a) Calculate the area of each face of this box.

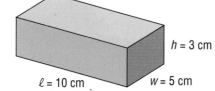

$h = 3$ cm
$\ell = 10$ cm $w = 5$ cm

b) What is the total area of the box?
c) Write a polynomial that can be used to calculate the answer you gave in part b).

Add.

18. $(m^2 + 3m - 5) + (2m^2 - 5m + 7)$

19. $(5a + 3a^2 - 2) + (a^2 + 3a + 4)$

20. $(b + 5 - 2b^2) + (1 - 2b + b^2)$

Add.

21. $\begin{array}{r} 2x^3 - 3x^2 + 5x \\ - \ x^2 + 3x \\ \hline \end{array}$ **22.** $\begin{array}{r} 3x^2 - 7x + 5 \\ -x^2 - \ x - 3 \\ \hline \end{array}$

23. $\begin{array}{r} -5a^2 - 2a - 7 \\ 6a^2 + 4a + 3 \\ \hline \end{array}$ **24.** $\begin{array}{r} 7t^2 + \ 8t - 9 \\ 2t^2 - 10t - 5 \\ \hline \end{array}$

Subtract.

25. $(5a^2 - 3a + 6) - (2a^2 + 3a + 7)$

26. $(3m^2 + 5m + 1) - (5m^2 + 2m - 1)$

27. $(3x^2 + 2x - 5) - (x^2 + x + 1)$

Subtract.

28. $\begin{array}{r} 5x^2 - 3x + 2 \\ -x^2 - 2x + 4 \\ \hline \end{array}$ **29.** $\begin{array}{r} 4x^2 - 7x + 5 \\ 7x^2 - 9x + 3 \\ \hline \end{array}$

30. $\begin{array}{r} 2x^2 + \ 8x - \ 4 \\ -3x^2 + 13x - 11 \\ \hline \end{array}$ **31.** $\begin{array}{r} 8x^2 - 2x - 1 \\ 3x^2 + \ x + 7 \\ \hline \end{array}$

Simplify.

32. $(-3n^2 - n - 7) - (-2n^2 + 8n - 4)$

33. $(5 + 3x - 2x^2) - (4 - 8x^2 + 6x)$

34. $(-p^2 + 5p - 8) - (2p^2 + 3p - 1)$

35. $(4x^2 + 6x + 4) - (-x^2 - 8x + 12)$

36. $(2m^2 + 8m - 9) - (-m^2 + 2m - 3)$

37. $(-4y^2 + 5y - 14) - (-5y^2 + 3y - 1)$

38. Given the perimeter, P, of a figure and 2 or 3 sides, find the missing length.

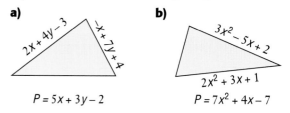

a) $2x + 4y - 3$ $-x + 7y + 4$

$P = 5x + 3y - 2$

b) $3x^2 - 5x + 2$

$2x^2 + 3x + 1$

$P = 7x^2 + 4x - 7$

Multiply.

39. $(10x)(4y)$

40. $(-30y)(5xy)$

41. $(3ax)(4bx)$

42. $(-2ap)(-5ab)$

43. $(3xy)(-5xy)$

44. $-4a^2(-ab)$

45. $4x^2(-2xy^2z)$

46. $-s^2t^2(3s^3t^3)$

47. Find the area of each figure.

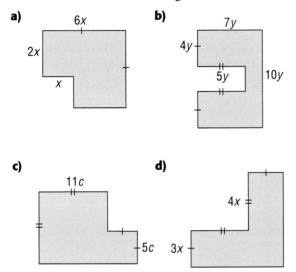

a) 6x, 2x, x

b) 7y, 4y, 5y, 10y

c) 11c, 5c

d) 4x, 3x

Divide. Express each answer with positive exponents.

48. $\dfrac{20x^5y^3}{5x^4y^6}$

49. $\dfrac{36x^2y^4}{4x^5y^8}$

50. $\dfrac{45a^3b^3}{9ab^4}$

51. $\dfrac{-20a^4b^{-5}}{10a^3b^{-3}c^2}$

52. Find the missing dimension in each rectangle.

a)

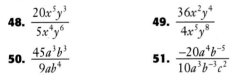

$7x^3y^3$

$A = 28x^5y^5$

b)

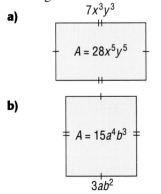

$A = 15a^4b^3$

$3ab^2$

Group Decision Making
Researching Computer Careers

1. Brainstorm the computer careers that you would like to investigate. They could include careers such as programming, systems design, sales, marketing, and hardware technician. As a class, select six careers to research. Number the careers from 1 to 6.

2. Go to home groups. As a group, decide which career each group member will research.

Home Groups

3. Form an expert group with students who have the same career to research. In your expert group, decide what questions you want to answer about the career. Then, research the answers.

Expert Groups

4. Return to your home group and tell the others in the group what you learned in your expert group.

5. In your home group, prepare a report on the 6 careers. As a group, decide what form the report will take. It could be written, acted out, presented as a video, displayed on a poster, or presented in any other appropriate form.

6. In your home group, evaluate the process and your presentation.

Chapter Check

Classify each polynomial and state its degree.

1. $x^2 + 3x + 7$ **2.** $3x^3 + x^2$

3. $3x^2y$ **4.** 200

Arrange each of the following in descending powers of x.

5. $1 + x^3 + x^5 + x^4$

6. $5x^3 + 2xy - yx^4$

7. $x^3y - 3x^4 - 2x^2y + 10xy^2$

8. $3ax - 5b^2x^3 - 1 + 5abx^2$

Simplify.

9. $(5a^2 - x + 9) + (a^2 + x - 13)$

10. $(b^3 + b^2 - 2y + 7) + (3y - 8 - 2b^2)$

Simplify.

11. $(6y^2 - 6x + 3) - (y^2 + 6x - 3)$

12. $(-8t^2 + 4t - 1) - (4 - 7t^2 + 5t)$

Simplify.

13. $(10x^2 - 3x + 8) + (-11x^2 - 4x - 2)$

14. $(8y^2 + 6y - 1) - (3y^2 - 8y - 2)$

Add.

15. $\begin{array}{r} 3x^2 + 2x - 7 \\ +5x^2 - 11x - 5 \end{array}$

16. $\begin{array}{r} 10x^2 + 4x - 5 \\ -12x^2 + 6x + 6 \end{array}$

Subtract.

17. $\begin{array}{r} 7x^2 - 5x + 4 \\ -3x^2 - 3x + 8 \end{array}$

18. $\begin{array}{r} 5x^2 - 8x + 6 \\ 9x^2 - 11x + 5 \end{array}$

19. $\begin{array}{r} x^2 + 7x - 5 \\ -2x^2 + 15x - 13 \end{array}$

20. $\begin{array}{r} 10x^2 - 3x - 2 \\ 2x^2 - x + 9 \end{array}$

Multiply.

21. $-10x(5y)$ **22.** $(15x^2y)(-3xy^2)$

23. $-2x^5(3b^2yz)$ **24.** $3x^3yz(-5xyz^2)$

25. Find the area of each figure.

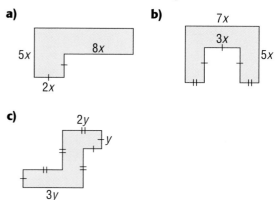

a)

b)

c)

Divide. Express each answer with positive exponents.

26. $\dfrac{-6a^5b^3}{3a^8b^5}$ **27.** $\dfrac{-39j^5k^4l^5}{-13j^7k^5l^3}$

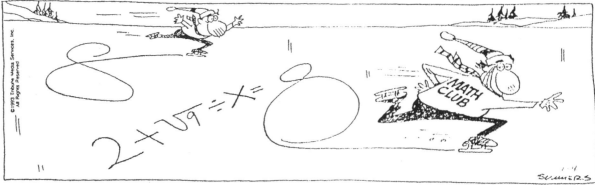

Using the Strategies

1. How many hours are in 1000 s?

2. a) What is the largest 2-digit number that is a perfect square?

b) What is the largest 3-digit number that is a perfect square?

3. Find 3 consecutive numbers that have a sum of 111.

4. There are 4 boys, Barry, Bob, Hans, and Joe and 5 girls, Marie, Sue, Paola, Natasha, and Oba, who wish to enter a badminton mixed doubles tournament. How many different 2 player teams can these nine players make?

5. A picture 20 cm by 20 cm is to be bordered by 1-cm squares. How many squares are needed for the border?

6. The sides of a triangular field are 40 m, 44 m, and 52 m. A fence is to be built around the field with a post in each corner and the posts 4 m apart. How many fence posts are needed?

7. Sue is 4 years older than Alex. In four years, the sum of their ages will be 36. How old are they today?

8. A restaurant offers a choice of how to pay for a class lunch.

Plan A: $8 per person
Plan B: $20 service charge plus
             $7 per person

a) For what number of students is Plan A better?

b) For what number of students is Plan B better?

c) For what number of students are the 2 plans the same?

9. In a bean toss game, each person throws 2 bags.

Scoring A and B gives 18 points.
Scoring A and C gives 15 points.
Scoring B and C gives 13 points.

What will you score if you toss both bags in B?

10. Two grade 6 students and two grade 9 students want to cross a river in a canoe. The canoe is big enough to hold the two grade 6 students or one grade 6 student and one grade 9 student. How many times must the canoe cross the river to get all the students to the other side?

11. Find the 4-digit perfect square that is a pair of 2-digit perfect squares written side by side.

12. Chicken pieces come in boxes of 6, 9, and 20. You can buy 21 pieces by buying 2 boxes of 6 pieces and 1 box of 9 pieces.

$$6 + 6 + 9 = 21$$

a) How can you buy 44 pieces?

b) How can you buy 41 pieces?

c) How can you buy 42 pieces?

d) Can you buy 43 pieces?

DATA BANK

1. You leave Halifax at 09:00 on a Friday and drive to Vancouver. You average 80 km/h and drive for 9 h/day, starting at 09:00. On what day and at about what time will you arrive in Vancouver?

2. The Canadian city with the greatest elevation is 561 m higher than Saskatoon. What is the elevation of Saskatoon?

Chapter 1

Estimate the square root.

1. 80　　　　　　　　　**2.** 291

Calculate.

3. $\sqrt{81}$

4. $3\sqrt{9} - \sqrt{4}$

5. $\sqrt{3^2 + 4^2 + 12^2}$

6. $\dfrac{5\sqrt{16} - 8}{3}$

Evaluate.

7. 3^3　　**8.** 2^4　　**9.** 5^2　　**10.** 10^4

Calculate.

11. $3^4 + 3^0$　　　　　**12.** 2^{-1}

13. $3^{-1} - 3^{-2}$　　　　**14.** $(2^3)^2$

15. $(-1)^{12}$　　　　　**16.** $(-1)^{21}$

17. -5^3　　　　　　**18.** $(3 - 2)^{-1}$

Write in scientific notation.

19. 37 300 000

20. 0.000 000 000 015 4

Write in standard form.

21. 3.4×10^8　　　　**22.** 4.0×10^5

23. 8.88×10^3　　　**24.** 3.01×10^{10}

Simplify.

25. $\left(\dfrac{6}{7}\right)^2$　　**26.** $\left(\dfrac{-s}{t}\right)^5$　　**27.** $\left(\dfrac{3p}{4q}\right)^3$

28. The approximate diameter of a circle can be found using the formula

$$d = \sqrt{\dfrac{4A}{3.14}}$$

where A is the area. Determine the diameter of circles with the following areas. Round each answer to the nearest tenth of a unit.

a) 78 cm^2　　　　　**b)** 1000 m^2

Chapter 2

1. Evaluate for $x = -2$ and $y = -3$.

a) $4x - 3y$　　　　　**b)** $5x + 2y$

c) $x - y$　　　　　　**d)** $y - x$

Write an equation for each statement.

2. Three times a number is fifteen.

3. Five more than a number is six.

4. Two times a number is equal to the number increased by 10.

5. A number increased by 2 and then multiplied by 5 is 20.

Solve.

6. $x - 2 = 10$　　　　**7.** $y - 9 = 3$

8. $y + 3 = 4$　　　　　**9.** $x + 4 = 8$

Solve.

10. $7y = 21$　　　　　**11.** $3x = 12$

12. $\dfrac{x}{2} = 8$　　　　　**13.** $\dfrac{y}{3} = 5$

Solve.

14. $2x = 10 + 2$　　　**15.** $5x = 15 - 10$

16. $\dfrac{x}{2} - 3 = 5 + 2$　　**17.** $\dfrac{x}{5} - 1 = 4 + 6$

Solve.

18. $6x + 12 = 3x$　　　**19.** $4x + 3x = 5x + 2$

20. $\dfrac{4x}{3} - 3 = \dfrac{x}{3} + 2$　　**21.** $\dfrac{x}{6} - 2 = -\dfrac{x}{6} + 1$

Solve.

22. $2(x - 1) - 2 = 11 - 3x$

23. $2(x + 3) - (2x - 5) = 2(x + 1) + 1$

Solve.

24. $\dfrac{x - 1}{2} = \dfrac{x + 3}{3}$　　**25.** $\dfrac{3n + 1}{2} - \dfrac{n}{3} = 4$

Chapter 3

Solve.

1. The sides of a triangle are 3 consecutive numbers. Its perimeter is 54 cm. How long is each side?

2. a) Copy and complete the table for the areas of 4 triangles, each with a fixed height of 10 cm.

Base (cm)	4	6	8	10
Area (cm)^2				

b) Write a formula for the areas of the triangles with a fixed height of 10 cm.
c) Use the formula to find the area of a triangle with a height of 10 cm and a base of 15 cm.

3. One painter paints a room in 1 h. A second paints it in 2 h. How long will they take to paint a room together?

4. An aircraft flew at 400 km/h to its destination and returned at 500 km/h. If the total trip took 9 h, how far did the aircraft fly?

5. The sum of 2 numbers is 26. Four times the first number plus twice the second is 70. What are the numbers?

Solve each inequality and graph the solution on a number line.

6. $7x - 3 \geq 5x - 1$ **7.** $3x - 2 < 2x - 4$

8. $3x - 1 > 5x - 3$ **9.** $6x - 4 \leq 9x + 5$

10. A swinging pendulum is often used to keep time. The period of a pendulum is defined as the time it takes for a complete swing to and fro. At sea level on the surface of the Earth, the period, T seconds, is given by the formula

$$T = 2.01\sqrt{l}$$

where l is the length of the pendulum in metres. What is the period of a pendulum of length 1 m? 2 m? 3 m? Write each answer to the nearest hundredth of a second.

Chapter 4

Simplify.

1. $(3x^2 + 2x - 3) + (x^2 + x + 1)$
2. $(2y^2 - 3y + 1) + (3y^2 - y - 1)$
3. $(x^2 + x - 7) - (2x^2 + 3x + 2)$
4. $(2x^2 - x - 1) - (3x^2 - x + 2)$

Simplify.

5. $(3x)(5y)$ **6.** $(-6s)(2t)$

Add.

7. $3x^2 - 5x + 2$
$\underline{+\ x^2 + 2x + 1}$

8. $4x^2 + x - 2$
$\underline{+3x^2 - 4x + 4}$

9. $-6x^2 + 7x + 5$
$\underline{2x^2 - 5x - 14}$

10. $-2x^2 + 3x - 4$
$\underline{-\ x^2 - 8x - 5}$

Subtract.

11. $10x^2 - 5x + 1$
$\underline{-\ 2x^2 - 3x + 6}$

12. $6x^2 - 4x + 9$
$\underline{7x^2 - 10x + 3}$

13. $-7x^2 + 11x - 3$
$\underline{2x^2 + 13x - 7}$

14. $-3x^2 - 5x - 2$
$\underline{-2x^2 + x + 15}$

Multiply.

15. $(4ax)(5bx)$ **16.** $(-2pw)(-6pb)$
17. $(5xy)(-7xy)$ **18.** $-5b^2(-5ab)$
19. $3x^2(-4x^2yz^2)$ **20.** $-p^2q^3(2p^4q)$

Divide. Express each answer with positive exponents.

21. $\dfrac{15x^4y}{5x^7y^2}$ **22.** $\dfrac{-21a^5b^{-4}}{3a^3b^{-4}}$ **23.** $\dfrac{-16p^3q^5}{8p^4q^9}$

24. $\dfrac{-18x^5y^5}{-3x^{-6}y^{-2}}$ **25.** $\dfrac{-48x^{-8}y^{-6}}{-32x^{-7}y^{-1}}$ **26.** $\dfrac{15s^2t^7}{-21rs^5t^2}$

Find the area of each figure.

27. **28.**

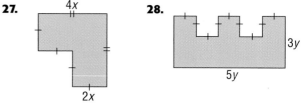

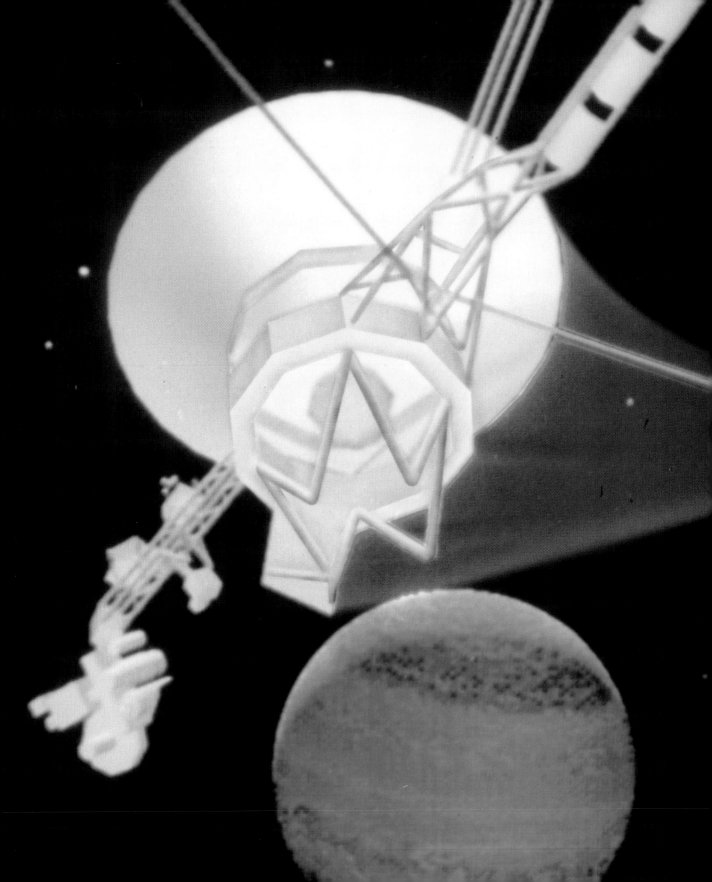

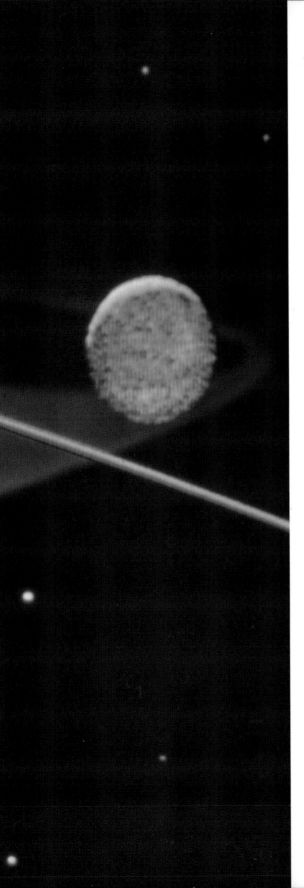

CHAPTER 5

Special Products and Factoring

The formula $v = 1.15 \times 10^{-5} \times \sqrt{\dfrac{m}{r}}$ gives the minimum velocity that space probes, such as *Voyager 1* and *Voyager 2*, must have to escape the Earth's gravitational pull. In this formula, v is the minimum velocity in metres per second, m is the mass of the Earth in kilograms, and r is the radius of the Earth in metres.

The mass of the Earth is 5.98×10^{24} kg, and the radius of the Earth is 6.38×10^{6} m.

Use these data to calculate the escape velocity in metres per second. What is the escape velocity in kilometres per hour?

Activity ❶ Factors

List the whole-number factors for these numbers.

1. 12   **2.** 15   **3.** 21

4. 8   **5.** 45   **6.** 36

7. 52   **8.** 17   **9.** 100

10. 24   **11.** 80   **12.** 39

Write each number as a product of prime factors.
For example, $12 = 2 \times 2 \times 3$.

13. 8   **14.** 15   **15.** 24

16. 20   **17.** 36   **18.** 42

19. 28   **20.** 19   **21.** 26

22. Copy and complete this table.

First Number	Second Number	Sum	Product
3	4	7	12
-2	-3		
7	-5		
-9	2		
-5		-9	
	-6		-18
	10		-10
-3		1	
		9	20
		-7	12
		12	20
		-11	30

Determine the missing factor in each of the following expressions.

23. $6a = (3a)(\blacksquare)$ **24.** $-7ab = (-7a)(\blacksquare)$

25. $4x = (\blacksquare)(2x)$ **26.** $4x^2 = (-2x)(\blacksquare)$

27. $15a^2 = (5a)(\blacksquare)$ **28.** $-18xy = (9y)(\blacksquare)$

29. $12xy = (3x)(\blacksquare)$ **30.** $-4x^2 = (x)(\blacksquare)$

31. $12xy = (\blacksquare)(6xy)$ **32.** $36xy^3 = (\blacksquare)(-6y)$

33. $7x^2 = (\blacksquare)(7x^2)$ **34.** $20abc = (\blacksquare)(-5bc)$

Activity ❷ Division by Monomials

Divide.

1. $x^5 \div x^2$ **2.** $p^3 \div p^2$

3. $a^7 \div a$ **4.** $x^5 \div x$

5. $\dfrac{-5t^5}{t^2}$ **6.** $\dfrac{a^4 b^2}{a^2 b^2}$

7. $\dfrac{-12x^4}{4x}$ **8.** $\dfrac{8a^4}{-2a}$

9. $\dfrac{-30x^3 y^2}{-6xy^2}$ **10.** $\dfrac{72m^2 n^2}{12mn}$

11. The area of a rectangle is $45a^2 b^2$ and its length is $9ab$. Find an expression for its width.

Use this example to simplify each expression.

$$\frac{4a^2 b - 6ab^2}{2ab} = \frac{4a^2 b}{2ab} - \frac{6ab^2}{2ab}$$
$$= 2a - 3b$$

12. $\dfrac{6a + 12}{6}$ **13.** $\dfrac{9x - 6y}{3}$

14. $\dfrac{6t - 18}{6}$ **15.** $\dfrac{33xy - 22y}{11y}$

16. $\dfrac{27m - 18n + 9}{9}$ **17.** $\dfrac{4x^3 - 10x^2 + 6x}{2x}$

18. $\dfrac{6a^2 b + 4ab^2}{2ab}$ **19.** $\dfrac{12xy^4 - 9x^3 y}{3xy}$

Activity ❸ Square Roots and Squares

State each square root. Assume that variables are positive.

1. $\sqrt{25}$ **2.** $\sqrt{121}$

3. $\sqrt{36}$ **4.** $\sqrt{x^2}$

5. $\sqrt{4a^2}$ **6.** $\sqrt{49x^2}$

Square.

7. 2^2 **8.** $(-5)^2$

9. 9^2 **10.** $(2x)^2$

11. $(-3a)^2$ **12.** $(5x^3)^2$

Activity ❹ Area

Write an expression for each area.

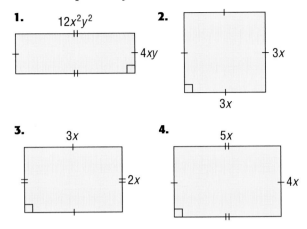

1. $12x^2y^2$ ... $4xy$

2. $3x$ ... $3x$

3. $3x$ ... $2x$

4. $5x$ ... $4x$

Add the areas of the smaller rectangles to write an expression for the area of each complete figure.

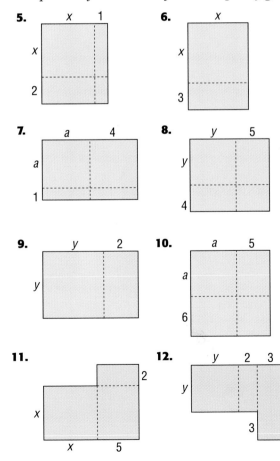

5. x ... 1 ... x ... 2

6. x ... x ... 3

7. a ... 4 ... a ... 1

8. y ... 5 ... y ... 4

9. y ... 2 ... y

10. a ... 5 ... a ... 6

11. 2 ... x ... x ... 5

12. y ... 2 ... 3 ... y ... 3

Mental Math

Calculate.

1. $12 + 6 - 3$ **2.** $20 - 12 + 6$

3. $24 \div 6 \times 4$ **4.** $18 \times 2 \div 4$

5. $12 \times 3 - 4 \div 2$ **6.** $24 - 18 \div 3 \times 4$

7. $3 + 8 \times 3 \div 4$ **8.** $(10)(3^2)$

9. $(2 + 3)^2$ **10.** $(4)(5^2)$

11. $3^2 + 4^2$ **12.** $2^3 + (4 + 1)^2$

Calculate.

13. $(8 + 4) \div 2$

14. $(20 - 8) \div 4$

15. $6 \times (5 + 4)$

16. $3 \times 4 + 6 \times 4$

17. $8 \times (12 - 9) + 2$

18. $15 \times (10 - 8) + 1$

19. $(20 + 10) \div 2 - 3 + 1$

20. $40 + 24 \div 8 - 3 + 1$

21. $(40 + 24) \div 8 - 3 + 1$

Simplify.

22. $\frac{1}{2} \times \frac{1}{3}$ **23.** $\frac{1}{4} \times \frac{1}{5}$ **24.** $\frac{3}{4} \times 4$

25. $\frac{2}{3} \times 3$ **26.** $\frac{1}{3} + \frac{1}{3}$ **27.** $\frac{5}{8} + \frac{1}{8}$

28. $\frac{1}{2} \div \frac{1}{2}$ **29.** $\frac{1}{2} \div \frac{1}{4}$ **30.** $\frac{2}{3} - \frac{1}{3}$

31. $\frac{5}{8} - \frac{1}{8}$ **32.** $\frac{3}{4} + \frac{3}{4}$ **33.** $\frac{3}{5} + \frac{4}{5}$

34. $\frac{1}{4} \times \frac{1}{3}$ **35.** $\frac{1}{2} \div 2$ **36.** $4 \div \frac{1}{2}$

37. $\frac{1}{4} + \frac{1}{2}$ **38.** $\frac{1}{2} - \frac{1}{4}$ **39.** $\frac{7}{8} - \frac{3}{4}$

40. $\frac{1}{3} - \frac{1}{5}$ **41.** $\frac{1}{4} - \frac{1}{8}$ **42.** $\frac{2}{5} - \frac{1}{10}$

43. $3 \div \frac{1}{3}$ **44.** $\frac{1}{2} \times \frac{2}{3}$ **45.** $\frac{1}{3} + \frac{1}{6}$

Activity ❶ Patterns on a Calendar

Examine the following monthly calendar.
What month might it be?

S	M	T	W	T	F	S
		1	2	3	4	5
6	7	8	9	10	11	12
13	14	15	16	17	18	19
20	21	22	23	24	25	26
27	28	29	30	31		

1. Copy any 3-by-3 block, such as the one shaded in the table.

2. Choose 3 numbers by circling only 1 number from each column and each row of the block.

3. Record the sum of the 3 numbers.

4. Choose 3 other numbers in the same block. Again, choose only 1 number from each column and each row. Record the sum of the 3 numbers.

5. Compare your results from steps 3 and 4.

6. Describe how you can use 1 number in the block to find the sum of the 3 numbers you chose.

7. Compare your findings with your classmates'.

8. How many 3-by-3 blocks can you make from the above calendar month?

9. How many 3-by-3 blocks could you make if the first of the month was a Sunday?

10. Complete these 3-by-3 calendar blocks to show the patterns.

a)

x	x + 1	x + 2
x + 7		

b)

x		

c)

	x	

11. Investigate the historical development of the calendar.

Activity ❷ Patterns in Tables

1. Copy and complete the table.

Addition				
+	3	5	7	9
2				
4				
6				
8				

2. Choose 4 sums by circling only 1 sum in each row and each column of the table.

3. Add the 4 numbers you circled.

4. Compare the sum of your 4 numbers with that of a classmate. Is the result always the same?

5. Copy and complete the following table. Then carry out steps 2 and 3 above. Explain why the sum is always the same.

+	b	d	f	h
a				
c				
e				
g				

6. Work with a partner to rewrite steps 1, 2, 3, and 4 to deal with multiplication, instead of addition.

7. Copy and complete the table.

Multiplication				
×	1	2	3	4
1				
2				
3				
4				

8. Use your instructions to investigate the products in the table. Compare your results with your classmates'.

181

5.1 Common Factors and the GCF

On the average, Yellowknife has blowing snow on 10 days of the year, and Halifax has blowing snow on 14 days of the year.

The number 10 has 4 factors: 1, 2, 5, and 10. The number 14 also has 4 factors: 1, 2, 7, and 14.

The **greatest common factor** (GCF) of the numbers 10 and 14 is 2.

Activity: Discover the Relationship

Write all the factors of each number.

a) 6 **b)** 12 **c)** 18

Inquire

1. Which prime factors are common to all 3 numbers?

2. What is the GCF of the 3 numbers?

3. Write a rule for finding the GCF of a set of numbers from their prime factors.

4. Write 3 different numbers that have a GCF of

a) 3 **b)** 8 **c)** 10

5. Write 4 different numbers that have a GCF of

a) 4 **b)** 5 **c)** 12

Example 1

Find the common factors of 15 and 18.

Solution

Write each number as a product of its prime factors.

$15 = 3 \times 5$
$18 = 2 \times 3 \times 3$

The numbers 15 and 18 have only 1 common factor, 3.

Note that the factor 1 is common to all numbers. Therefore, we do not include it as a common factor.

Example 2

Determine the GCF of each pair of numbers.

a) 24 and 48   **b)** 36 and 42

Solution

a) Write each number as a product of its prime factors.

$24 = 2 \times 2 \times 2 \times 3$
$48 = 2 \times 2 \times 2 \times 2 \times 3$

Multiply the common factors to calculate the GCF.
The GCF of 24 and 48 is $2 \times 2 \times 2 \times 3$ or 24.

b) $36 = 2 \times 2 \times 3 \times 3$
$\quad\;\; 42 = 2 \times 3 \times 7$
The GCF of 36 and 42 is 2×3 or 6.

Example 3

a) Determine the common factors of the monomials $2x^2$ and $4x$.
b) Write their GCF.

Solution

For algebraic expressions, the variable must also be factored. Write each expression as a product. Write the factors common to both.

a) $2x^2 = 2 \times x \times x$
$\quad\;\; 4x = 2 \times 2 \times x$
The common factors of $2x^2$ and $4x$ are 2 and x.
b) The GCF of $2x^2$ and $4x$ is $2x$.

Example 4

Find the GCF of $2x^3y$, $4x^2y^2$, and $2x^2y$.

Solution

$2x^3y = 2 \times x \times x \times x \times y$
$4x^2y^2 = 2 \times 2 \times x \times x \times y \times y$
$2x^2y = 2 \times x \times x \times y$

The GCF of $2x^3y$, $4x^2y^2$, and $2x^2y$ is $2 \times x \times x \times y$ or $2x^2y$.

(CONTINUED)

Practice

Write the prime factors of each number.

1. 12   **2.** 16   **3.** 28

4. 63   **5.** 144   **6.** 225

Factor fully.

7. $4xy^2$ **8.** $18a^2b^3$ **9.** $36x^2yz^2$

10. $10x^2y$ **11.** $54x^5$ **12.** $125a^4b^2$

Determine the GCF of each pair.

13. 15, 20   **14.** 16, 24   **15.** 27, 36

16. 28, 42   **17.** 48, 72   **18.** 64, 96

Determine the GCF of each pair.

19. $4a$, $6a$ **20.** $2x^2$, $3x$

21. $12m^3$, $10m^2$ **22.** $12abc$, $3abc$

23. $2x$, $4y$ **24.** $14a$, $7b$

25. $5x^2$, $10x$ **26.** $4xy$, $5xy$

27. $9mn^2$, $8mn$ **28.** $2a^3$, $8a^2$

29. $15bc$, $25b^2c$ **30.** $6x^2y^2$, $9xy$

Determine the GCF of each set.

31. $5xyz$, $10abc$, $25pqr$

32. $20x$, $10x^3$, $8x^2$

33. $12abc$, $18ab$, $6ac$

34. $10x^2y$, $15xy^2$, $25xyz$

35. $21a^2b$, $35a^2b^2c$, $49ab^2c$

36. $12xy$, $16x^2y$, $20xyz$

37. $56abc$, $64a^2b$, $36ab^2c$

Find the GCF.

38. x^2y^2, x^2y^3, x^3y^4

39. $2x^3y$, $4x^2y^4$, $2x^2y^4$

40. $3x^2y^3$, $3x^3y^2$, $6xy^2$

41. $4a^3b^3$, $8a^2b^3$, $16ab^3$

42. $10s^4t^5$, $5s^5t^4$, $15s^3t^4$

Problems and Applications

43. Montreal has 162 wet days a year, whereas Beijing has 66. What is the GCF of these numbers?

44. Two rectangles are attached as shown.

$A = xy$	$A = 2xy$

What is the length of the common side? Explain.

45. Suppose students can get to school by walking at 5 km/h, riding a bike at 10 km/h, or being driven in a car at 30 km/h. Bob rides a bike, as does Karin. Bob lives the same distance from the school as Collette, who walks. Gustav and Shirley come by car. Karin and Gustav live the same distance from school. The graph gives the times the five students take to get to school one day.

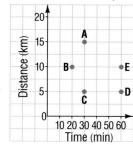

a) Which person does each point represent? Give reasons for your answers.

b) Draw a map of the area, showing where each student could live. Compare your map with a classmate's.

LOGIC POWER

If the outside of the large cube is painted red, how many of the smaller cubes have the following numbers of red faces?

a) 3   **b)** 2

c) 1   **d)** 0

5.2 Factoring Expressions with Common Factors

The world's narrowest commercial building is in Vancouver, British Columbia. The Sam Kee building is 30 m long by 1.8 m wide. In how many ways can you determine the perimeter?

Activity: Discover the Relationship

Examine the diagram of an x-tile.

Inquire

1. What is the sum of the length and width of the x-tile?

2. Write an expression for twice the sum of the length and width. Do not expand.

3. Add the sides of the x-tile to find the perimeter. Collect like terms.

4. How do the quantities represented in questions 2 and 3 compare?

5. Write a rule for removing a common factor from the terms in a polynomial.

6. Use your rule to remove a common factor from each of the following.

a) $3x + 6$ **b)** $4x + 4$ **c)** $2x - 8$

Example

a) Factor the expression $6x^2 - 14x$.
b) Check your answer by expanding.

Solution

a) Determine the GCF of both terms. Then, divide both terms by the GCF.

$6x^2 = \boxed{2} \times 3 \times x \times x$
$14x = \boxed{2} \times 7 \times x$

The GCF is $2x$.

The second factor is $\dfrac{6x^2}{2x} - \dfrac{14x}{2x}$ or $3x - 7$.

The factors of $6x^2 - 14x$ are $2x$ and $3x - 7$.

Therefore, $6x^2 - 14x = 2x(3x - 7)$.

b) $2x(3x - 7) = 2x(3x - 7)$
$\qquad\qquad\quad = 6x^2 - 14x$ Checks!

CONTINUED

Practice

State the missing factor.

1. $12x + 18y = (\ \blacksquare\ )(2x + 3y)$

2. $3x^2 - 5x = (\ \blacksquare\ )(3x - 5)$

3. $4ab + 3ac = (\ \blacksquare\ )(4b + 3c)$

4. $5x^2 + 10x = (\ \blacksquare\ )(x + 2)$

5. $8abc - 12ab = (\ \blacksquare\ )(2c - 3)$

Copy and complete.

6. $3y^2 + 18y = 3y(y + \blacksquare)$

7. $14a - 12b = 2(\blacksquare - 6b)$

8. $4a^3 - 8a^2 = 4a^2(\blacksquare - 2)$

9. $10x^3 - 5x^2 + 15x = 5x(2x^2 - \blacksquare + \blacksquare)$

Copy and complete.

10. $33ab - 22b = 11b(\blacksquare - \blacksquare)$

11. $4a^3 - 10a^2 + 6a = 2a(\blacksquare - \blacksquare + \blacksquare)$

12. $27a^2b^2 - 18ab + 9b = 9b(\blacksquare - \blacksquare + \blacksquare)$

13. $6x^2y - 4xy^2 = 2xy(\blacksquare - \blacksquare)$

14. $9a^3b - 12ab^4 = 3ab(\blacksquare - \blacksquare)$

Factor each binomial.

15. $10x + 15$ **16.** $28y - 14$

17. $2mn - n$ **18.** $5x^2 + 10x$

19. $8x^2 + 4x^3$ **20.** $9a^3b^2 - 6a^2b$

21. $4x^2y^2 - 6xy^2z^2$ **22.** $14a^2b^4 - 21b^2c^2$

23. $6x^2y^3z + 12xy^2z$ **24.** $15a^2b^5 - 9b^4c^5$

Problems and Applications

Factor each trinomial.

25. $9a - 6b + 3$

26. $4a - 8b + 16$

27. $12x^3 - 6x^2 + 24x$

28. $10x^3 - 5x^2 + 15x$

29. $24x^4y - 18x^3y + 12x^2y^2$

30. $8a^2b + 16ab - 24a$

31. $25m^3n - 15m^2n^2 + 5mn^3$

32. a) Write the rectangle's perimeter as the sum of 2 different products and as the product of a number and a sum.

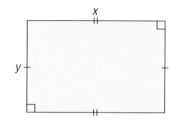

b) Which of the 2 forms in part a) is the factored form?

33. The perimeter of a rectangle is 46 cm. The length is 1 cm longer than the width. What are the rectangle's dimensions?

34. Find the GCF of each expression and factor fully.

a) $(a + b)x + (a + b)y$

b) $x(x - 2) + 3(x - 2)$

c) $x(2x - 3) - 5(2x - 3)$

d) $2a(a - b) + b(a - b)$

35. If you stand on the Earth and jump up at 5 m/s, your approximate height in metres above the ground after t seconds is given by the expression $5t - 5t^2$.
a) Factor the binomial.
b) Evaluate for $t = 0.4$ s.

PATTERN POWER

Find the missing number.

4	7	8	5
3		3	4
2	5	7	3
2	3	5	2

Fitness Centres

Activity ❶

Many Canadians are members of local fitness centres. There are many examples of modern technology in fitness centres. Describe some examples of how technology is used. Consider the office, weight rooms, pool area, aerobics room, and so on.

Activity ❷

Design a fitness centre that has all of the technology that you would like to have available. Create your own machines and explain what physical activities they would measure or involve. Describe how the machines would make use of mathematics.

187

5.3 Multiplying a Polynomial by a Monomial

Northern Dancer was one of the fastest thoroughbred horses that ever raced. He was born, raised, and trained at Winfields Farm in Oshawa. The 500 ha of Winfields Farm contains many different sizes and shapes of rectangular fields attached to each other, like the rectangles shown below.

Activity: Explore the Pattern

Copy or trace this diagram onto a blank sheet of paper.

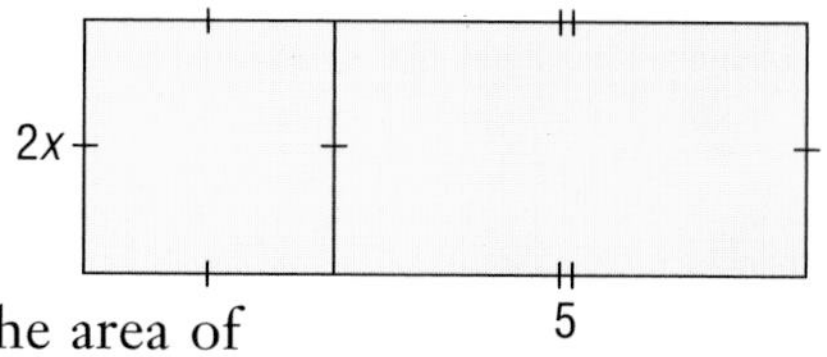

Inquire

1. In simplest form, what is the area of
a) the square?   **b)** the rectangle attached to the square?

2. Write the sum of the areas for the square and the rectangle.

3. Consider the larger rectangle that includes the square.
a) What is the length of the larger rectangle?
b) What is the width of the larger rectangle?
c) Use your answers to parts a) and b) to write an expression for the area.
d) How can you multiply the monomial in your expression by the binomial in your expression to arrive at the answer you gave in question 2?

4. Write a rule for multiplying a polynomial by a monomial.

Example 1

Expand and simplify.
a) $2x(x^2 - 2x + 5)$
b) $4x(x - 3) - 2(x + 3)$

Solution

Use the distributive property to expand each expression. Then, collect like terms and simplify.

a) $2x(x^2 - 2x + 5)$

$= 2x(x^2 - 2x + 5)$
$= 2x^3 - 4x^2 + 10x$

b) $4x(x - 3) - 2(x + 3)$

$= 4x(x - 3) - 2(x + 3)$
$= 4x^2 - 12x - 2x - 6$
$= 4x^2 - 14x - 6$

Example 2

Expand and simplify
$2(3x^2 - 4x + 5) - 2x(x - 3)$.

Solution

$2(3x^2 - 4x + 5) - 2x(x - 3)$

$= 2(3x^2 - 4x + 5) - 2x(x - 3)$
$= 6x^2 - 8x + 10 - 2x^2 + 6x$
$= 4x^2 - 2x + 10$

188

Practice

Expand.

1. $x(x + 2)$ **2.** $x(x - 3)$ **3.** $a(a + 1)$

4. $t(t - 1)$ **5.** $y(y + 4)$ **6.** $m(m + 5)$

7. $x(x - 5)$ **8.** $y(y - 7)$ **9.** $a(a - 10)$

Expand.

10. $3x(x + 2)$ **11.** $4b(b - 11)$

12. $5t(t + 3)$ **13.** $2x(3 + x)$

14. $7y(y - 5)$ **15.** $-2x(x + 4)$

16. $-x(x + 2)$ **17.** $-y(y - 3)$

Expand and simplify.

18. $x(x + 3) - x(x - 2)$

19. $y(2 + y) + y(y - 1)$

20. $m(m - 1) + m(m - 1)$

21. $x(x + 2) - (2x - 2)$

22. $y(y - 4) - y(3 - 2y)$

23. $a(2a - 1) + a(a + 1)$

24. $x(x - 2) - x(x + 1)$

Expand and simplify.

25. $3x(x + 2) + 2x(x + 5)$

26. $2x(x - 3) - x(x - 5)$

27. $3x(2x + 1) + x(3x + 2)$

28. $-2y(y - 3) - y(y + 1)$

29. $2a(a + 3) + 3a(a - 2)$

30. $-x(3x - 4) - 2x(1 - x)$

31. $4x(x + 2) + 2x(7 - 2x)$

Expand.

32. $x(x^2 + 2x + 3)$ **33.** $3(x^2 + 2x - 5)$

34. $5x(x^2 + 2x - 7)$ **35.** $-(x^2 - 3x - 1)$

36. $4m(m^2 - 5m + 6)$ **37.** $3y(2y^2 - 4y + 3)$

38. $-3b(3b^2 - 5b + 1)$ **39.** $-5z(z^2 - 2z - 5)$

Problems and Applications

Expand and simplify.

40. $3(x^2 + 2x - 5) - x(x + 1)$

41. $5(x^2 + 2x - 7) + 3x(x + 1)$

42. $-(x^2 - 3x - 1) + x(3x + 2)$

43. $4(2x + 3) + 3x(x^2 - x + 3)$

44. $3m(m - 2) + 4(m^2 - 5m + 6)$

45. $5y(1 - y) + 3(2y^2 - 4y + 3)$

46. $-3x(x + 2) + 2x(2x - 1)$

47. Write, expand, and simplify an expression for the area of each figure.

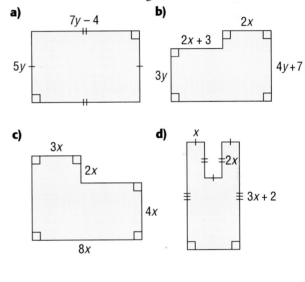

a)
b)
c)
d)

48. Explain why the area of the algebra tiles models the product $2x(x + 3)$.

49. Use algebra tiles to model each of the following products. Expand each expression to check that the model is correct.
a) $4x(x + 1)$ **b)** $x(3x + 2)$ **c)** $2x(2x + 1)$

50. Write a problem similar to those in question 47. Have a classmate solve your problem.

189

5.4 Dividing Polynomials by Monomials

An x^2-tile has an area of x^2 square units.
An x-tile has an area of x square units.

Activity: Use Algebra Tiles

Use an x^2-tile and an x-tile to model this rectangle.

Inquire

1. What is the area of the rectangle?

2. What is the length of the rectangle?

3. What is the width of the rectangle?

4. Describe how you can divide the area by the width to give the length.

5. Write a rule for dividing a polynomial by a monomial.

The distributive property applies to division as well as to multiplication.
$$\frac{a + b}{c} = \frac{1}{c}(a + b) = \frac{a}{c} + \frac{b}{c}$$

Example 1

Simplify.

a) $\dfrac{5xyz + 10xy}{5xy}$

b) $\dfrac{8x^5 + 12x^3 - 4x^2}{4x}$

Solution

Divide each term of the polynomial by the monomial.

a) $\dfrac{5xyz + 10xy}{5xy} = \dfrac{5xyz}{5xy} + \dfrac{10xy}{5xy}$
$$= z + 2$$

b) $\dfrac{8x^5 + 12x^3 - 4x^2}{4x} = \dfrac{8x^5}{4x} + \dfrac{12x^3}{4x} - \dfrac{4x^2}{4x}$
$$= 2x^4 + 3x^2 - x$$

Example 2

Simplify.

a) $\dfrac{15y^4 - 12y^5 + 9y^3}{-3y^2}$

b) $\dfrac{16a^5b^3 - 20a^4b^4 + 24a^5b^3}{4a^3b^3}$

c) $\dfrac{9a^4b^7z^5 - 15ab^3z^2}{-3ab^3z}$

Solution

a) $\dfrac{15y^4 - 12y^5 + 9y^3}{-3y^2}$

$= \left(\dfrac{15y^4}{-3y^2}\right) - \left(\dfrac{12y^5}{-3y^2}\right) + \left(\dfrac{9y^3}{-3y^2}\right)$

$= -5y^2 + 4y^3 - 3y$

$= 4y^3 - 5y^2 - 3y$

b) $\dfrac{16a^5b^3 - 20a^4b^4 + 24a^5b^3}{4a^3b^3}$

$= \dfrac{16a^5b^3}{4a^3b^3} - \dfrac{20a^4b^4}{4a^3b^3} + \dfrac{24a^5b^3}{4a^3b^3}$

$= 4a^2 - 5ab + 6a^2$

c) $\dfrac{9a^4b^7z^5 - 15ab^3z^2}{-3ab^3z}$

$= \dfrac{9a^4b^7z^5}{-3ab^3z} - \left(\dfrac{15ab^3z^2}{-3ab^3z}\right)$

$= -3a^3b^4z^4 - (-5z)$

$= -3a^3b^4z^4 + 5z$

Practice

Divide.

1. $\dfrac{12xy}{4xy}$ 2. $\dfrac{24ab}{-4ab}$ 3. $\dfrac{-12mn}{3m}$

4. $\dfrac{-30xy}{-5xy}$ 5. $\dfrac{11ab}{ab}$ 6. $\dfrac{5xy}{5x}$

7. $\dfrac{24x^2y}{6xy}$ 8. $\dfrac{15ab^3}{-5ab}$ 9. $\dfrac{36x^3y^2}{-6x^2y^2}$

Divide.

10. $\dfrac{12xy - 15y^2 + 24y}{3y}$ 11. $\dfrac{5x^3 + 10x^2 - 15x}{5x}$

12. $\dfrac{7y^4 + 7y^3 - 21y}{-7y}$ 13. $\dfrac{4m^3 + 8m^2 - 12m}{4m}$

14. $\dfrac{9x^3 - 24x^2 - 15x}{-3x}$ 15. $\dfrac{6j^5 + 12j^4 + 18j^3}{-6j}$

Divide.

16. $\dfrac{10x^4 + 5x^3 - 15x^2}{-5x^2}$

17. $\dfrac{-21m^2 + 14m^3 - 21m^4}{-7m^2}$

18. $\dfrac{10p^2q^2 - 15pq^3 + 25p^3q^4}{-5pq^2}$

19. $\dfrac{-12a^3b^2 + 9a^2b^3 + 24a^4b^4}{3a^2b^2}$

Divide.

20. $\dfrac{-20x^3yz + 30x^2y^2z - 40xy^3z}{-10xyz}$

21. $\dfrac{8a^3b^2c^3 - 12a^2b^2c^2 + 16a^2b^3c}{4a^2b^2}$

22. $\dfrac{-12x^4y^6 - 16x^5y^5 - 24x^6y^4}{-4x^4y^4}$

23. $\dfrac{30m^3n^5 - 36m^4n^4 - 30m^5n^3}{6m^3n^3}$

24. $\dfrac{25a^3b^3c^5 - 40a^4b^3c^4 + 35a^6b^4c^3}{-5a^2b^2c^2}$

Problems and Applications

25. Determine the length, *l*, of the unknown side, given the area and the length of one side.

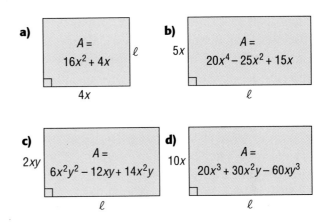

26. Write a problem similar to those in question 25. Have a classmate solve your problem.

LOGIC POWER

Four students entered a problem solving contest. Each student represented a different zone of the town. Use the clues to determine which zone each student represented and in which order the students finished.

1. David came second, just behind the student from the west zone.

2. Petra represented neither the east nor the west zones.

3. The student from the north zone finished second last, just ahead of Frank.

4. David and Jarvi represented opposite zones in the town.

191

The Möbius Strip

Activity ❶ Making a Möbius Strip

1. Take a strip of paper about 30 cm long and 5 cm wide and tape it together to make a ring. You could paint this ring with 2 colours, red on the inside and blue on the outside, because the ring has 2 sides. To get from one side to the other, you have to cross an edge.

2. Take another strip of paper about 30 cm long and 5 cm wide. Turn 1 end of the paper to make a half twist. Then, tape the 2 ends together. The result is called a Möbius strip after the German mathematician, Augustus Möbius, who discovered it.

3. Use a coloured pencil and start "painting" the strip. You will notice you can "paint" the whole strip with just one colour. You never have to cross an edge. The strip has only one side.

Activity ❷ Cutting a Möbius Strip in Half

If you cut a paper ring around the middle, you get 2 paper rings, each one-half the width of the original.

1. Predict what you will get when you cut a Möbius strip around the middle.

2. Cut the Möbius strip around the middle and describe the results. How many sides does the resulting figure have? Is it a Möbius strip? Explain.

Activity ❸ Cutting a Möbius Strip into Thirds

If you cut a paper ring into thirds, you get 3 paper rings, each one-third the width of the original.

1. Predict what you will get if you cut a Möbius strip into thirds.

2. Cut a Möbius strip starting one-third the way in from its edge. The scissors will make 2 trips around the strip. Describe the result. How many sides does each of the resulting figures have? Are they both Möbius strips? Explain.

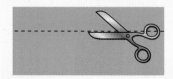

5.5 Binomial Products

Activity: Use Algebra Tiles

Use algebra tiles to model this rectangle.

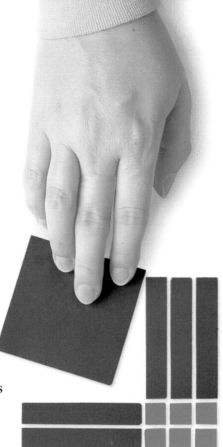

Inquire

1. Write an expression for the area of the rectangle by counting the numbers of x^2-tiles, x-tiles, and 1-tiles. Collect like terms and write the expression in descending powers of x.

2. Write an expression for the length of the rectangle.

3. Write an expression for the width of the rectangle.

4. Use the expressions for the length and width to write an expression for the area of the rectangle. Do not expand.

5. How do the quantities you represented in questions 1 and 4 compare?

6. Write a rule for multiplying 2 binomials.

7. Use your rule to multiply the following. Check your results by modelling with algebra tiles.

a) $(x + 1)(x + 3)$ **b)** $(x + 2)(x + 4)$

8. Check your results in question 7 by substituting 1 for x.

Example

Find the product of these binomials.

a) $(x + 1)(x + 2)$ **b)** $(3x - 4)(5x + 1)$

Solution

To expand a binomial, use the distributive property.

a)
$$(x + 1)(x + 2) = x(x + 2) + 1(x + 2)$$
$$= x^2 + 2x + x + 2$$
$$= x^2 + 3x + 2$$

b)
$$(3x - 4)(5x + 1) = 3x(5x + 1) - 4(5x + 1)$$
$$= 15x^2 + 3x - 20x - 4$$
$$= 15x^2 - 17x - 4$$

The same result can be obtained by multiplying each term in the first binomial by each term in the second binomial.

You can remember this method with the acronym FOIL, which stands for First terms, Outside terms, Inside terms, and Last terms.

$$(x + 1)(x + 2) = (x + 1)(x + 2)$$

$$= \overset{F}{x^2} + \overset{O}{2x} + \overset{I}{x} + \overset{L}{2}$$
$$= x^2 + 3x + 2$$

	x	$+$	2
x	x^2		$2x$
$+$			
1	x		2

CONTINUED ▶

Practice

Express each area as a product and in expanded form.

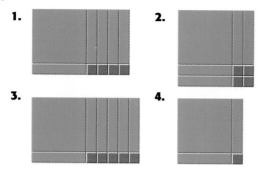

1. **2.**

3. **4.**

Expand.

5. $3(x-5)$ **6.** $x(2x+3)$

7. $-7(2x-6)$ **8.** $4x(3x-1)$

9. $5a^2(3a-4b)$ **10.** $-2x(3x+5y)$

Find the product.

11. $(x+1)(x+2)$ **12.** $(x+4)(x+3)$

13. $(a+4)(a+4)$ **14.** $(y+5)(y+6)$

15. $(x-4)(x-3)$ **16.** $(a-4)(a-2)$

17. $(b-1)(b-5)$ **18.** $(y-9)(y-9)$

19. $(x-6)(x+3)$ **20.** $(c+2)(c-8)$

21. $(t+10)(t-10)$ **22.** $(q-2)(q+5)$

Expand.

23. $(c+3)(c-4)$ **24.** $(x+2)(x-5)$

25. $(y+6)(y-2)$ **26.** $(a+9)(a-5)$

27. $(x-3)(x+3)$ **28.** $(b-7)(b+10)$

29. $(y-12)(y+3)$ **30.** $(x-7)(x+1)$

Multiply.

31. $(x+5)(2x+1)$ **32.** $(3y+1)(y+2)$

33. $(x-1)(2x-1)$ **34.** $(a-3)(-2a-5)$

35. $(5y-7)(y+3)$ **36.** $(x-5)(4x+3)$

37. $(-2x+3)(2x+1)$ **38.** $(5y-2)(3y-4)$

39. $(4x+1)(3x-5)$ **40.** $(2y-9)(5y+2)$

41. $(7y-3)(2y-7)$ **42.** $(-3x-2)(8x+5)$

Problems and Applications

Multiply.

43. $(x+0.5)(x+2)$ **44.** $(x-1.2)(x+3)$

45. $(x-2.5)(x-10)$ **46.** $(x-3)(x+2.1)$

Expand the following.

47. $2(x+3)(x+5)$ **48.** $4(x-9)(x+5)$

49. $-1(a+3)(a-2)$ **50.** $10(x+7)(x-5)$

51. $3(2x-1)(3x-2)$ **52.** $2x(x+7)(x-10)$

53. $0.5(x-1)(x+3)$ **54.** $1.8(x+1)(x+1)$

55. Evaluate each area in 2 different ways for $x = 3$ cm.

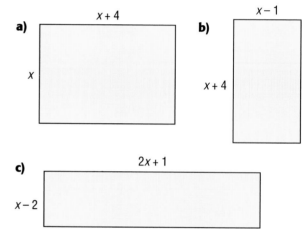

a)

$x+4$

x

b)

$x-1$

$x+4$

c)

$2x+1$

$x-2$

56. a) Verify that $(x+6)(x+2) \neq x^2 + 12$ by substituting 1 for x.

b) Expand $(x+6)(x+2)$ correctly.

57. A square building of side x metres is extended by 10 m on one side and 5 m on the other side to form a rectangle.

a) Express the new area as the product of 2 binomials.

b) Evaluate the new area for $x = 20$.

58. After 2 years, an investment of $1000 compounded annually at an interest rate r grows to the amount $1000(1+r)^2$ in dollars.

a) Expand the expression.

b) Evaluate for $r = 0.08$.

6.6 Factoring Trinomials: $x^2 + bx + c$

Many trinomials can be written as a product of 2 binomials.

Activity: Use Algebra Tiles

Use algebra tiles to model this rectangle.

Inquire

1. Write an expression for the area of the rectangle by counting tiles. Collect like terms and write the expression in descending powers of x.

2. Use expressions for the length and width to write an expression for the area of the rectangle. Do not expand.

3. How are the quantities represented by your 2 expressions related?

4. How is the numerical term in the expression from question 1 related to the numerical terms in the expression from question 2?

5. How is the coefficient of the x-term in the expression from question 1 related to the numerical terms in the expression from question 2?

6. How is the x^2-term in the expression from question 1 related to the x-terms in the expression from question 2?

7. Use your findings to factor each of the following.

a) $x^2 + 5x + 6$ **b)** $x^2 - 3x + 2$ **c)** $x^2 - x - 2$

Expanding 2 general binomials gives the following results.

$$(x + m)(x + n) = x^2 + nx + mx + mn$$
$$= x^2 + mx + nx + mn$$
$$= x^2 + (m + n)x + mn$$

Compare the above result to the general trinomial $x^2 + bx + c$.

$$x^2 + \quad bx \quad + c$$
$$\uparrow \qquad \uparrow \qquad \uparrow$$
$$x^2 + (m + n)x + mn$$

When we make this comparison, we see that $b = m + n$ and $c = mn$.

Therefore, the general trinomial $x^2 + bx + c = x^2 + (m + n)x + mn$
$$= (x + m)(x + n)$$

CONTINUED ▶

Example 1

Factor $x^2 - 10x + 16$.

Solution

To factor $x^2 - 10x + 16$, find m and n so that $m + n = -10$ and $mn = 16$.

This means that both factors are negative. List pairs of factors of 16 and choose the correct pair.

Therefore, $m = -2$ and $n = -8$.

$$x^2 - 10x + 16 = x^2 + (-2 - 8)x + (-2)(-8)$$
$$= (x - 2)(x - 8)$$

Pairs of Factors of 16	Sum of Pairs of Factors
1, 16	17
−1, −16	−17
2, 8	10
−2, −8	−10
4, 4	8
−4, −4	−8

Example 2

Factor $x^2 + 4x - 21$.

Solution

Find m and n so that $m + n = 4$ and $mn = -21$.

This means that one factor is positive and one factor is negative.

Therefore, $m = -3$ and $n = 7$.

$$x^2 + 4x - 21 = (x - 3)(x + 7)$$

Pairs of Factors of −21	Sum of Pairs of Factors
1, −21	−20
−1, 21	20
3, −7	−4
−3, 7	4

Example 3

Factor $2x^2 - 4x - 70$.

Solution

Factor the trinomial first to remove the GCF, which is 2.

$$2x^2 - 4x - 70 = 2(x^2 - 2x - 35)$$

Find m and n so that $m + n = -2$ and $mn = -35$.

One value is positive and one value is negative.

Therefore, $m = 5$ and $n = -7$.

$$2x^2 - 4x - 70 = 2(x + 5)(x - 7)$$

Pairs of Factors of −35	Sum of Pairs of Factors
1, −35	−34
−1, 35	34
5, −7	−2
−5, 7	2

Practice

Natasha modelled the process of factoring $x^2 + 2x + 1$ and $x^2 + 4x + 3$ as shown.

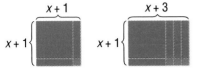

Use algebra tiles and her method to factor these expressions.

1. $x^2 + 5x + 4$ **2.** $x^2 + 6x + 9$

State the values of m and n that satisfy the given conditions.

3.

	Sum $m + n$	Product mn
a)	7	12
b)	8	15
c)	13	12
d)	18	77
e)	−8	15
f)	−10	25
g)	−7	12

4.

	Sum $m + n$	Product mn
a)	−1	−12
b)	1	−12
c)	−3	−40
d)	25	150
e)	4	−5
f)	−1	−42
g)	−7	−60

Factor.

5. $x^2 + 7x + 10$ **6.** $y^2 - 8y + 15$

7. $w^2 - w - 56$ **8.** $z^2 + 3z - 40$

9. $x^2 - x - 30$ **10.** $a^2 - 17a + 16$

11. $x^2 - 9x - 10$ **12.** $x^2 + 12x + 20$

13. $x^2 + 10x + 25$ **14.** $m^2 - 9m + 18$

15. $a^2 - 6a + 9$ **16.** $y^2 + 11y + 30$

17. $x^2 + 10x + 9$ **18.** $x^2 - 15x - 16$

19. $a^2 + 6a - 16$ **20.** $x^2 + 9x + 20$

21. $a^2 - 25a + 24$ **22.** $y^2 - 9y + 14$

23. $y^2 - 7y - 18$ **24.** $x^2 - x - 72$

25. $s^2 - 2s - 80$ **26.** $a^2 - 18a + 81$

Simplify by combining like terms, if possible. Then, remove the GCF and factor fully.

27. $2x^2 - 21x + 36 + x^2$ **28.** $5x^2 - 2x - 10 - 3x$

29. $7x^2 + 35x + 42$ **30.** $b^2 + 3b + 4 + b^2 + 5b$

31. $bx^2 - 28bx + 75b$ **32.** $x^2 - 3x + 8 - 9x + x^2$

33. $5jx^2 - 40jx + 75j$ **34.** $3tx^2 + 12tx + 12t$

35. $t^3 + t^2 - 12t$ **36.** $3k^3 + 15k^2 - 18k$

Problems and Applications

Factor, if possible.

37. $x^2 + x + 1$ **38.** $a^2 - 7a - 8$

39. $b^2 + 14b + 48$ **40.** $y^2 + 7y - 12$

41. $z^2 - 20z + 100$ **42.** $m^2 - 2m + 5$

43. $x^2 - 4x - 4$ **44.** $y^2 + 8y - 20$

45. The area of a rectangle is represented by the expression $x^2 + 9x + 20$.
a) Factor the expression.
b) A smaller rectangle is 1 unit shorter on each side than the first rectangle. Write a factored expression for the area of the smaller rectangle.
c) Expand the expression for the area of the smaller rectangle.

46. Write 4 trinomials in the form $x^2 + 12x + \blacksquare$ that can be factored.

47. a) Use algebra tiles to factor $x^2 - 2x - 3$. Explain your method.
b) Use your method to factor $x^2 - 3x - 4$ using algebra tiles.

48. a) Complete the factoring by supplying the missing terms.

$x^2 + 6x + \blacksquare = (x + \blacksquare)(x + \blacksquare)$

$x^2 - 5x + \blacksquare = (x - \blacksquare)(x - \blacksquare)$

$x^2 + \blacksquare x + 12 = (x + \blacksquare)(x + \blacksquare)$

$x^2 - \blacksquare x + 5 = (x - \blacksquare)(x - \blacksquare)$

$x^2 - \blacksquare x - 12 = (x - \blacksquare)(x + \blacksquare)$

b) Compare your answers with a classmate's. Which cases have more than one solution? Explain.

49. Make up 5 trinomials in the form $x^2 + bx + c$. Make 3 factorable and 2 impossible to factor. Exchange trinomials with a classmate. Try to factor each other's trinomials.

197

5.7 Special Product: $(a - b)(a + b)$

How are the binomials $x + 4$ and $x - 4$ the same and how are they different?

Activity: Look for a Pattern

Copy and complete this table.

Binomials	Product	Simplified Product
$(x + 4)(x - 4)$	$x^2 + 4x - 4x + 16$	
$(a - 7)(a + 7)$		
$(k + 5)(k - 5)$		
$(x - y)(x + y)$		
$(2a - 1)(2a + 1)$		

Inquire

1. a) What do you notice about the 2 middle terms in each product?

b) What is the algebraic sum of the middle terms in each product?

2. How many terms are there in each simplified product?

3. Write a rule for expanding 2 binomials that are identical except for the signs in the middle.

Example

Expand.

a) $(x + 3)(x - 3)$ **b)** $(7x - 1)(7x + 1)$

Solution

a) $(x + 3)(x - 3) = (x + 3)(x - 3)$
$$= x^2 - 3x + 3x - 9$$
$$= x^2 - 9$$

b) $(7x - 1)(7x + 1) = (7x - 1)(7x + 1)$
$$= 49x^2 + 7x - 7x - 1$$
$$= 49x^2 - 1$$

These expanded forms represent a special case of the product of 2 binomials, called the **difference of squares**.

$$(a + b)(a - b) = a^2 - b^2$$

Practice

Write the missing factor.

1. $(a - 7)(\blacksquare) = a^2 - 49$

2. $(x + 2)(\blacksquare) = x^2 - 4$

3. $(\blacksquare)(3m - 7) = 9m^2 - 49$

4. $(9x + 8)(\blacksquare) = 81x^2 - 64$

5. $(x - y)(\blacksquare) = x^2 - y^2$

6. $(\blacksquare)(2a + 3b) = 4a^2 - 9b^2$

Expand.

7. $(x + 1)(x - 1)$ **8.** $(a + 5)(a - 5)$

9. $(p + 6)(p - 6)$ **10.** $(x - 9)(x + 9)$

11. $(y - 8)(y + 8)$ **12.** $(t - 10)(t + 10)$

Multiply.

13. $(2x - 1)(2x + 1)$ **14.** $(3y + 1)(3y - 1)$

15. $(4a + 3)(4a - 3)$ **16.** $(6t - 5)(6t + 5)$

17. $(x - y)(x + y)$ **18.** $(10t - 3)(10t + 3)$

19. $(p + q)(p - q)$ **20.** $(3a - b)(3a + b)$

21. $(x - 6y)(x + 6y)$ **22.** $(j - 10r)(j + 10r)$

23. $(x^2 + 3)(x^2 - 3)$ **24.** $(k^2 + 9)(k^2 - 9)$

Problems and Applications

25. Factor each of the numbers as shown and complete the table.

Numbers	$(a + b)(a - b)$	Product
33×27	$(30 + 3)(30 - 3)$	891
24×16		
47×53		
62×58		

Multiply each of the following, using the method in question 25.

26. $(10 + 2)(10 - 2)$ **27.** $(15 + 3)(15 - 3)$

28. $(20 - 2)(20 + 2)$ **29.** 14×6

30. 17×23 **31.** 32×28

Expand.

32. $(x - 1)(x + 1)(x^2 + 1)$

33. $(a + 2)(a - 2)(a^2 + 4)$

34. $(x - 9)(x + 9)(x^2 + 81)$

35. $(3x - 2)(3x + 2)(9x^2 + 4)$

36. $(x - 1)(x + 1)(x^2 + 1)(x^4 + 1)$

37. If a square field is made into a rectangle by shortening 2 opposite sides by 50 m each and lengthening the other 2 sides by 50 m each, how do the areas of the original field and the new field compare? Explain.

38. Which of the following numbers of terms are not possible as the product of 2 binomials?

     1 term

     2 terms

     3 terms

     4 terms

     5 terms

Give reasons for your answers.

LOGIC POWER

Use your knowledge of geography to find out what province this area is in. Then find the area on a complete map.

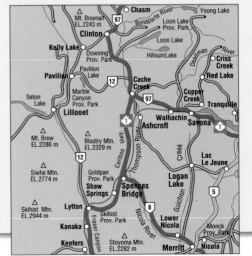

5.8 Factoring the Difference of Squares

Activity: Complete the Table

Copy and complete the table.

Factored Form	Product
$(x-5)(x+5)$	$x^2 - 25$
$(b+8)(b-8)$	
$(z+9)(z-9)$	
	$a^2 - 36$
	$y^2 - 100$
	$r^2 - 81$

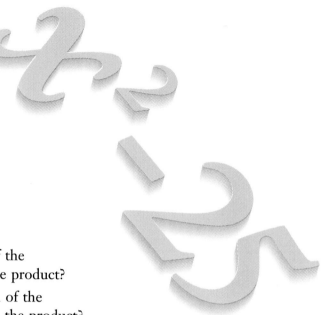

Inquire

1. How is the first term in each binomial of the factored form related to the first term in the product?

2. How is the second term in each binomial of the factored form related to the second term in the product?

3. Write a rule for working backward from the product to the factored form.

4. Use your rule to factor each of the following.

a) $x^2 - 4$ **b)** $y^2 - 49$ **c)** $4z^2 - 25$

Example

Factor.

a) $x^2 - 49$ **b)** $25a^2 - 81b^2$ **c)** $9y^2 - 81$ **d)** $12b^2 - 27c^2$

Solution

Remove any common factors.
Take the square root of each term in the difference of squares.
Write 2 binomial factors that are identical except for the signs in the middle.

a) $x^2 - 49$
   $= (x+7)(x-7)$

b) $25a^2 - 81b^2$
   $= (5a - 9b)(5a + 9b)$

c) $9y^2 - 81z^2$
   $= 9(y^2 - 9z^2)$
   $= 9(y + 3z)(y - 3z)$

d) $12b^2 - 27c^2$
   $= 3(4b^2 - 9c^2)$
   $= 3(2b - 3c)(2b + 3c)$

Practice

Determine the missing factor.

1. $x^2 - 25 = (x - 5)(\ \blacksquare\ )$
2. $w^2 - 100 = (w + 10)(\ \blacksquare\ )$
3. $k^2 - 81 = (k - 9)(\ \blacksquare\ )$
4. $4a^2 - 121 = (2a - 11)(\ \blacksquare\ )$
5. $9 - 16x^2 = (3 + 4x)(\ \blacksquare\ )$
6. $x^4 - 36 = (x^2 + 6)(\ \blacksquare\ )$

Factor, if possible, using a difference of squares.

7. $t^2 - 4$
8. $x^2 - 16$
9. $b^2 - 9$
10. $m^2 - 49$
11. $p^2 - 25$
12. $w^2 - 36$
13. $a^2 - 81$
14. $q^2 - 100$
15. $y^2 + 144$
16. $1 - c^2$
17. $64 - x^2$
18. $121 + w^2$
19. $s^2 - t^2$
20. $z^2 - x^2$
21. $b^2 - g^2$
22. $p^2 - q^2$

Factor.

23. $4a^2 - 9b^2$
24. $16p^2 - 81$
25. $25a^2 - 49$
26. $9b^2 - 25$
27. $16 - x^2$
28. $25 - 36b^2$
29. $16 - 49x^2$
30. $81 - 4a^2$
31. $16x^2 - 1$
32. $144 - 121x^2$
33. $169 - 100t^2$
34. $225 - 49w^2$

Factor, if possible.

35. $6x^2 - 25$
36. $16y^2 - 49$
37. $9 - 4z^2$
38. $25a^2 - 36$
39. $x^2y^2 - 4$
40. $m^2 + 64$
41. $(a + b)^2 - (a - b)^2$
42. $25 - 81p^2q^2$

Remove the common factor, then factor using a difference of squares.

43. $2m^2 - 50$
44. $9x^2 - 36$

45. $20r^2 - 45$
46. $8a^2 - 50$
47. $10y^2 - 1000$
48. $x^3 - x$
49. $50y^2 - 72$
50. $x^3 - 9x$
51. $8y^2 - 8$
52. $4p^2 - 16$
53. $27k^2 - 12$
54. $16t^2 - 16$
55. $64 - x^2$
56. $50 - 18x^2$
57. $12x^2 - 75y^2$
58. $50x^2 - 98y^2$

Problems and Applications

59. Cut a 10-by-10 square out of grid paper. Remove a 3-by-3 square from one corner.

$100 - 9 = 91$

a) The area of the new figure is $10^2 - 3^2$. What is the area?

$13 \cdot 7 = 91$

b) Cut off one of the 7-by-3 rectangles and add it to the larger rectangle to make one rectangle. What are the dimensions of this rectangle?

c) How do the dimensions of the rectangle compare with the result of factoring $10^2 - 3^2$?

d) Repeat parts a) to c) for a square that is 6-by-6, with a 2-by-2 square removed. The area of the resulting figure is $6^2 - 2^2$.

e) Repeat parts a) to c) for a starting square of side length x, with a square of side length y removed.

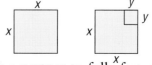

60. Work with a partner to fully factor the following expressions.

a) $x^4 - 1$ **b)** $x^8 - 1$ **c)** $x^4 - 625$

5.9 Special Products: Perfect Squares

An Austrian monk, Gregor Mendel (1822–1884), began the modern study of genetics. He found that the seeds from some tall pea plants produced dwarf plants, as well as tall ones.

We can represent Mendel's findings with a diagram called a Punnett square. Each parent plant, represented outside the square, has a dominant gene (T) for tallness and a recessive gene (t) for dwarfism. Because the tallness gene is dominant, each parent is tall.

The genes inherited by the offspring appear inside the square. Offspring with the combinations TT, Tt, and tT are tall plants. Offspring with 2 recessive genes (tt) are dwarf plants. If both tall parents have a recessive gene for dwarfism, what fraction of their offspring are dwarf plants?

	T	t
T	TT	Tt
t	tT	tt

A Punnett square is an example of a perfect square. Many algebraic expressions are also perfect squares.

Activity: Use Algebra Tiles

Use algebra tiles to model these squares.

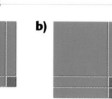
a) b) c)

Inquire

1. Count tiles to write a polynomial that represents the area of each square. Collect like terms and write each polynomial in descending powers of x.

2. Record an expression for the side length of each square.

3. Use your expression for the side length to write an expression for the area of each square. Do not expand.

4. How are the quantities represented by your expressions from questions 1 and 3 related?

5. Write a rule for finding the square of a binomial.

6. Use your rule to expand each of the following.

a) $(x + 4)^2$ b) $(x - 1)^2$ c) $(x - 2)^2$

Example

Expand the following binomials.

a) $(x + 6)^2$ b) $(x - 5)^2$ c) $(2x - 7)^2$

202

Solution

A **perfect square** consists of 2 identical binomial factors.
Expand, collect like terms, and simplify.

a) $(x + 6)^2$

$= (x + 6)(x + 6)$
$= x^2 + 6x + 6x + 36$
$= x^2 + 12x + 36$

b) $(x - 5)^2$

$= (x - 5)(x - 5)$
$= x^2 - 5x - 5x + 25$
$= x^2 - 10x + 25$

c) $(2x - 7)^2$

$= (2x - 7)(2x - 7)$
$= 4x^2 - 14x - 14x + 49$
$= 4x^2 - 28x + 49$

In general, the following are true for the product of 2 identical binomials.

$(a + b)^2 = (a + b)(a + b)$
$\qquad = a^2 + ab + ab + b^2$
$\qquad = a^2 + 2ab + b^2$

$(a - b)^2 = (a - b)(a - b)$
$\qquad = a^2 - ab - ab + b^2$
$\qquad = a^2 - 2ab + b^2$

Practice

Square.

1. $(-7)^2$ **2.** $(-9)^2$ **3.** $(-6)^2$

4. $(-12)^2$ **5.** $(2x)^2$ **6.** $(-3a)^2$

7. $(11y)^2$ **8.** $(-x)^2$ **9.** $(-4y)^2$

What is the first term in each product?

10. $(x + 7)^2$ **11.** $(a - 9)^2$ **12.** $(2x - 1)^2$

13. $(9t + 5)^2$ **14.** $(10b - 3)^2$ **15.** $(3y + 6)^2$

16. $(7p - 2)^2$ **17.** $(4j + 1)^2$ **18.** $(6q - 8)^2$

What is the middle term, including its sign, in each product?

19. $(x - 3)^2$ **20.** $(y + 8)^2$

21. $(x + y)^2$ **22.** $(a - b)^2$

23. $(2x + 3)^2$ **24.** $(4a - 5)^2$

25. $(3x + 2y)^2$ **26.** $(6p - 7)^2$

Square.

27. $(y - 10)^2$ **28.** $(3a - 1)^2$

29. $(5x + 2)^2$ **30.** $(3 - x)^2$

31. $(5 - y)^2$ **32.** $(5a + b)^2$

33. $(3x + y)^2$ **34.** $(4x - 3y)^2$

35. $(7a - 2b)^2$ **36.** $(4m + 5n)^2$

Problems and Applications

Rewrite in the form $(a + b)^2$ or $(a - b)^2$.

37. $x^2 + 14x + 49$ **38.** $x^2 - 16x + 64$

39. $4a^2 + 12a + 9$ **40.** $9b^2 - 24b + 16$

41. $64m^2 - 32m + 4$ **42.** $81n^2 + 90n + 25$

None of the following trinomials is a perfect square. Change 1 term to make the trinomial a perfect square.

43. $x^2 + 12x + 18$ **44.** $a^2 + 7a + 16$

45. $y^2 - 9y + 9$ **46.** $m^2 - 4m + 16$

47. $4x^2 - 4x + 2$ **48.** $9y^2 + 10y + 4$

49. Verify that $(x + 3)^2 \neq x^2 + 9$ by substituting 1 for x.

50. Use the diagram to expand $(a + b + c)^2$. Collect like terms.

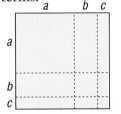

51. Explain how you can recognize a perfect square trinomial. You might use a sketch. Discuss terms and coefficients.

203

5.10 Products of Polynomials

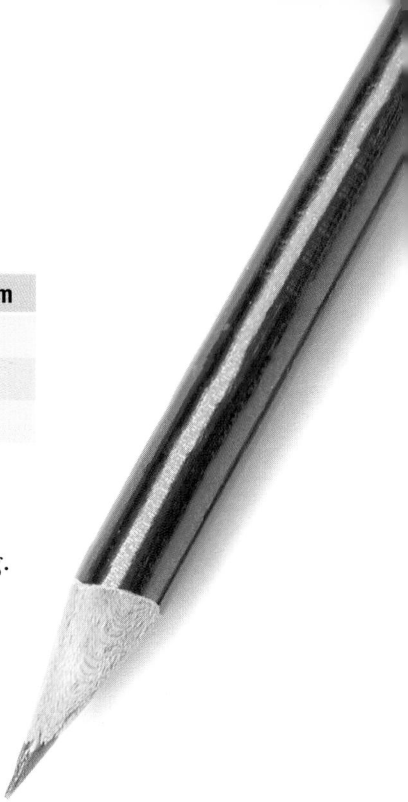

Activity: Complete the Table

Copy and complete this table.

Product Form	Expanded Using the Distributive Property	Simplified Form
$(x+2)(x+3)$	$(x+2)x+(x+2)3$	
$(x+3)(x^2+x+2)$	$(x+3)x^2+(x+3)x+(x+3)2$	
$(x-1)(x^2-2x+4)$	$(x-1)x^2+(x-1)(-2x)+(x-1)4$	

Inquire

1. Find the products in the first column by multiplying each term of the first factor by each term of the second factor and simplifying.

2. How do the answers you found in 1 compare with the answers in the simplified form in the table?

3. Write a rule for multiplying polynomials.

Example

Expand.

a) $(x+1)(x^2+2x+1)$ **b)** $(x-2)(x^2-3x-5)$ **c)** $(x-5)(2x^2-x+2)$

Solution

Multiply each term in the first expression by each term in the second expression and simplify.

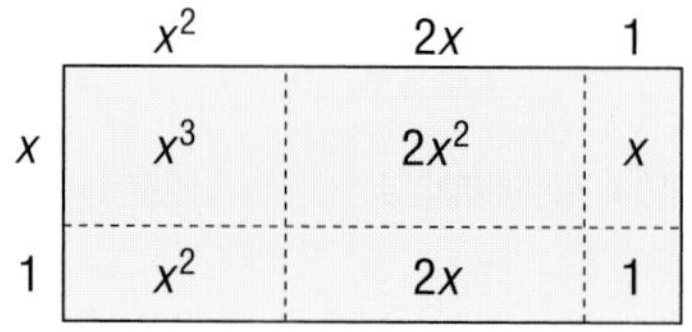

a) $(x+1)(x^2+2x+1) = (x+1)(x^2+2x+1)$

$$= x^3+2x^2+x+x^2+2x+1$$
$$= x^3+2x^2+x^2+x+2x+1$$
$$= x^3+3x^2+3x+1$$

	x^2	$2x$	1
x	x^3	$2x^2$	x
1	x^2	$2x$	1

b) $(x-2)(x^2-3x-5) = (x-2)(x^2-3x-5)$

$$= x^3-3x^2-5x-2x^2+6x+10$$
$$= x^3-3x^2-2x^2-5x+6x+10$$
$$= x^3-5x^2+x+10$$

c) $(x-5)(2x^2-x+2) = (x-5)(2x^2-x+2)$

$$= 2x^3-x^2+2x-10x^2+5x-10$$
$$= 2x^3-x^2-10x^2+2x+5x-10$$
$$= 2x^3-11x^2+7x-10$$

204

Practice

Expand.

1. $3(x^2 + 3x - 5)$ **2.** $2(3a^2 - 5a + 7)$

3. $2(x^2 + 7x + 12)$ **4.** $3(a^2 + 7a + 10)$

5. $5(y^2 + 4y + 10)$ **6.** $x(x^2 - 10x + 25)$

7. $x(x^2 + 11x + 28)$ **8.** $a(2a^2 + 8a + 15)$

9. $x(4x^2 - 3x - 4)$ **10.** $x(6x^2 - 23x + 20)$

Expand and simplify.

11. $(x + 1)(x^2 + 2x + 3)$

12. $(x + 2)(x^2 - 3x + 1)$

13. $(x + 3)(x^2 + 2x - 3)$

14. $(x - 3)(x^2 + 6x + 5)$

15. $(x - 4)(x^2 - 8x - 7)$

16. $(x - 2)(x^2 - 5x + 6)$

17. $(x - 5)(x^2 + 10x - 11)$

Expand and simplify.

18. $(a - 1)(3a^2 + a + 5)$

19. $(b - 7)(5b^2 - b - 2)$

20. $(x - 8)(2x^2 - 3x + 3)$

21. $(x - 5)(4x^2 - 3x - 7)$

22. $(x - 2)(3x^2 - 5x - 4)$

23. $(a - 1)(7a^2 - a + 1)$

24. $(y - 5)(2y^2 + 5y + 2)$

Expand and simplify.

25. $(2x^2 + 3x - 2)(x + 5)$

26. $(3a^2 - 5a - 6)(a + 3)$

27. $(5b^2 - 7b + 10)(b + 1)$

28. $(7w^2 - w - 1)(w - 1)$

29. $(2y^2 + 3y + 2)(y - 2)$

30. $(4t^2 - 2t - 1)(t - 5)$

31. $(x^2 + 2xy + y^2)(x + 1)$

32. $(x^2 - 3xy + y^2)(x - 2)$

33. $(b^2 - 3by - y^2)(x + 3)$

Problems and Applications

Expand and simplify.

34. $(3x + 2)(5x^2 - 2xy + y^2)$

35. $(2y - 5)(2y^3 - 3y^2 + 7)$

36. $(4x + 9)(7x^2 + x - 3)$

37. $(3a - 7)(2a^2 - 3a + 5)$

38. $(2y + 1)(3y^2 + 4y + 2)$

39. $(3a^2 - 6a - 7)(3a - 5)$

40. Determine the area of each figure.

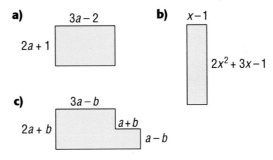

41. Determine the volume of each box.

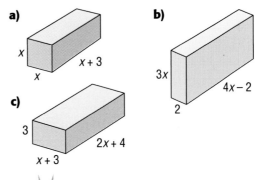

WORD POWER

Change the word NAIL to the word FILE by changing one letter at a time. You must form a real word each time you change a letter. The best solution has the fewest steps.

5.11 Rational Expressions

Duane Ward had the lowest earned run average of all the Blue Jays' pitchers the first year they won the World Series. His ERA was 1.95, meaning that, on average, about 2 runs were scored against him for every 9 innings he pitched. The ERA is a fraction, calculated by dividing 9 times the number of runs, r, by the number of innings pitched, i. The expression $\frac{9r}{i}$ is an example of a rational expression.

Activity: Discover the Relationship

Copy and complete the table.

Fraction	$\frac{2}{5} + \frac{1}{5}$	$\frac{2}{5} - \frac{1}{5}$	$\frac{2}{5} \times \frac{1}{5}$	$\frac{2}{5} \div \frac{1}{5}$
Simplified Fraction				

Inquire

1. Substitute x for the 2 in each expression and perform the operations.

2. Substitute x for 2 and y for 1 in each expression and perform the operations.

3. Substitute x for 5 in each expression and perform the operations.

4. Substitute x for 5 and y for 2 in each expression and perform the operations.

5. Use your findings to simplify the following.

a) $\frac{3}{x} + \frac{2}{x}$ **b)** $\frac{3}{x} - \frac{2}{x}$ **c)** $\frac{3}{x} \times \frac{2}{x}$ **d)** $\frac{3}{x} \div \frac{2}{x}$

Recall that rational numbers are numbers that can be written as the quotient of two integers, $\frac{a}{b}$, where a is any integer, and b can be any integer except zero.

A **rational expression** is an expression that can be written as the quotient of two polynomials. Some examples of rational expressions are shown.

$$\frac{a}{2} \qquad \frac{4}{y} \qquad \frac{x}{x-2}$$

Since division by zero is not defined, restrictions must sometimes be placed on the variables.

For the expression, $\frac{4}{y}$, y cannot be zero. We write $\frac{4}{y}$, $y \neq 0$.

For the expression, $\frac{x}{x-2}$, x cannot be 2. We write $\frac{x}{x-2}$, $x \neq 2$.

Example 1

Simplify. State the restrictions on the variables.

a) $\frac{3x^2y}{4x} \times \frac{2xy^3}{5y}$

b) $\frac{-8x^5y^8}{4x^3y^5}$

c) $\frac{3x^2y}{4} \div \frac{2x}{5}$

Solution

a) $\frac{3x^2y}{4x} \times \frac{2xy^3}{5y}$

$= \frac{6x^3y^4}{20xy}$

$= \left(\frac{6}{20}\right)\left(\frac{x^3}{x}\right)\left(\frac{y^4}{y}\right)$

$= \frac{3}{10}x^2y^3$

$= \frac{3x^2y^3}{10}$, $x \neq 0$, $y \neq 0$

b) $\frac{-8x^5y^8}{4x^3y^5}$

$= \left(\frac{-8}{4}\right)\left(\frac{x^5}{x^3}\right)\left(\frac{y^8}{y^5}\right)$

$= -2x^2y^3$, $x \neq 0$, $y \neq 0$

c) $\frac{3x^2y}{4} \div \frac{2x}{5}$

$= \frac{3x^2y}{4} \times \frac{5}{2x}$

$= \frac{15x^2y}{8x}$

$= \left(\frac{15}{8}\right)\left(\frac{x^2}{x}\right)\left(\frac{y}{1}\right)$

$= \frac{15xy}{8}$, $x \neq 0$

Example 2

Simplify.

a) $\frac{x-1}{2} + \frac{x-2}{3}$

b) $\frac{(x+1)}{2} - \frac{2(x-1)}{5}$

Solution

To add or subtract rational expressions with different denominators, find equivalent fractions with a common denominator.

a) $\frac{x-1}{2} + \frac{x-2}{3}$

$= \frac{3(x-1)}{3 \times 2} + \frac{2(x-2)}{2 \times 3}$

$= \frac{3x-3+2x-4}{6}$

$= \frac{3x+2x-3-4}{6}$

$= \frac{5x-7}{6}$

b) $\frac{(x+1)}{2} - \frac{2(x-1)}{5}$

$= \frac{5(x+1)}{5 \times 2} - \frac{2[2(x-1)]}{2 \times 5}$

$= \frac{5(x+1) - 2(2x-2)}{10}$

$= \frac{5x+5-4x+4}{10}$

$= \frac{5x-4x+5+4}{10}$

$= \frac{x+9}{10}$

CONTINUED ▶

Practice

For each pair of fractions, write the lowest common denominator.

1. $\dfrac{1}{4}, \dfrac{3}{8}$ **2.** $\dfrac{5}{12}, \dfrac{7}{24}$ **3.** $\dfrac{1}{3}, \dfrac{1}{6}$

4. $\dfrac{5}{3x}, \dfrac{1}{7x}$ **5.** $\dfrac{6}{5a}, \dfrac{2}{3a}$ **6.** $\dfrac{7}{8x}, \dfrac{5}{6x}$

Simplify. State the restrictions on the variables.

7. $\dfrac{12x}{4xy}$ **8.** $\dfrac{20}{10y}$ **9.** $\dfrac{9x^2}{3x}$

10. $\dfrac{6abc}{3ab}$ **11.** $\dfrac{-10x^3y^4}{5x^2y^2}$ **12.** $\dfrac{20a^2b^2}{-5ab}$

Simplify.

13. $\dfrac{x}{2} \times \dfrac{3}{x}$ **14.** $\dfrac{2}{m} \times \dfrac{m}{4}$ **15.** $\dfrac{x}{y} \times \dfrac{y}{x}$

16. $\dfrac{m}{3} \div \dfrac{m}{4}$ **17.** $\dfrac{2}{y} \div \dfrac{4}{y}$ **18.** $\dfrac{x}{y} \div \dfrac{x}{y}$

Multiply.

19. $\dfrac{x^2y}{x} \times \dfrac{xy}{y}$ **20.** $\dfrac{2xy^2}{2x} \times \dfrac{5x^2y}{3x}$

21. $\dfrac{3p^2q^2}{2p^2} \times \dfrac{4pq}{3qr}$ **22.** $\dfrac{7a^2b}{2a} \times \dfrac{2ab}{2}$

Divide these monomials.

23. $\dfrac{x^2y^3}{3} \div \dfrac{xy}{3}$ **24.** $\dfrac{2x^2y}{5} \div \dfrac{2xy}{5}$

25. $\dfrac{xy^2}{10} \div \dfrac{2xy^5}{5x^3y^3}$ **26.** $\dfrac{3x^3y^2}{2x^2y^2} \div \dfrac{3}{xy}$

Simplify these fractions.

27. $\dfrac{7}{y} + \dfrac{12}{y}$ **28.** $\dfrac{x}{a} - \dfrac{11}{a}$

29. $\dfrac{7}{12x} - \dfrac{4}{12x}$ **30.** $\dfrac{45xy}{4z} - \dfrac{9xy}{4z}$

Simplify.

31. $\dfrac{2}{x} + \dfrac{3-x}{x}$ **32.** $\dfrac{x+3}{3x^2} + \dfrac{4-x}{3x^2}$

33. $\dfrac{3}{x^2} - \dfrac{(7-x)}{x^2}$ **34.** $\dfrac{2-x}{5x^2} - \dfrac{1}{5x^2}$

Simplify.

35. $\dfrac{x-2}{2} + \dfrac{x+5}{4}$ **36.** $\dfrac{x-2}{3} - \dfrac{x-6}{4}$

37. $\dfrac{x+2}{2} - \dfrac{4-x}{3}$ **38.** $\dfrac{2-x}{5} - \dfrac{3-x}{3}$

39. $\dfrac{x-1}{4} - \dfrac{2(x-3)}{6}$ **40.** $\dfrac{2(x-2)}{5} + \dfrac{x+1}{2}$

Problems and Applications

41.

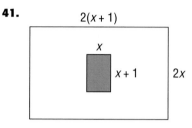

a) What is the total area of the figure? Leave your answer in factored form.
b) What is the area of the red rectangle in factored form?
c) What is the quotient of the area of the red rectangle divided by the total area of the figure? Write your answer in simplest form.
d) Check your answer by substituting 1 for x.

42.

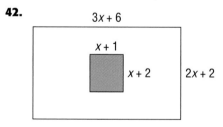

a) What is the total area of the figure in factored form?
b) What is the area of the green rectangle in factored form?
c) What is the quotient of the area of the green rectangle divided by the total area of the figure? Write your answer in simplest form.
d) Verify your answer by substituting 2 for x.

Computers and Connectivity

Connectivity means connecting a computer by telephone lines or other methods to other computers or other sources of information. The connected system can be as simple as the computer at your desk and a regular telephone. A simple system for a car is a laptop computer and a cellular telephone. Both systems allow you to send and receive information. They give you access to many resources.

Activity ❶ Electronic Bulletin Boards

Like the public bulletin boards you sometimes see in grocery stores, electronic bulletin boards are usually open to everyone. There are bulletin boards for almost every subject.

1. How would sports cards collectors use an electronic bulletin board?

2. How would mystery novelists use one?

3. What kind of service could a newspaper provide on an electronic bulletin board?

4. One of the biggest electronic bulletin boards is called CompuServe. What kind of service does it supply? How much does it cost to use the service?

Activity ❷ Commercial Services

Some businesses offer services for computer users. One type of service is travel reservations. You can get information on airline schedules and fares, then order your tickets and charge the cost to a credit card.

1. Describe how home banking would work on a computer.

2. Describe how teleshopping would work.

3. What other commercial services do you think would be useful?

Activity ❸ Electronic Mail

Electronic mail is also called E-mail. It is used within companies, so that employees can send messages to each other. To send a message, you type it into your computer and send the message to the receiver's electronic mailbox. You can also put the message in several mailboxes at once, or broadcast it to everyone on the E-mail system. To open your own mailbox, you type your password into your computer and "open" your mail.

1. What advantages does E-mail have over a telephone?

2. Why do E-mail users have passwords?

3. Would E-mail be useful in homes?

209

Activity ❶ Designing a Theatre

You have been asked to submit a design for the seating in a theatre that will be located in an old movie house. The floor slopes to the stage and orchestra pit, so all you need to do is to place the seats and the aisles. The stage and orchestra pit are centred and measure 30 m across.

Each seat measures 50 cm by 50 cm, including arm rests. There is to be a 50-cm space in front of each seat for leg room and access. The seating area measures 40 m wide by 50 m deep. Aisles must be at least 2 m wide.

There must be an aisle across the front and the back of the seating area, plus aisles to get customers to their seats. Aisles may be curved or straight.

There should be no more than 20 seats in a row. There are 2 doors evenly spaced at the back of the theatre and a door in the middle of each side. There is no balcony.

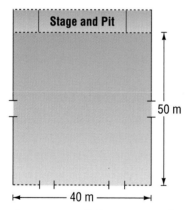

Design the placement of the seats and aisles so that people have easy access to their seats. The owners of the theatre want you to decide how many seats to put in. The owners want a pleasant, comfortable arrangement, but keep in mind that they are in the business of selling tickets. If you include too few seats, your design may not be accepted. You must label each aisle and each seat for the purpose of ticket sales.

Activity ❷ Designing a Circular Track

Suppose there is to be a race between 5 people on a circular track. The track has an inside radius of 50 m. Each lane of the track is 1 m wide. The lanes are numbered 1 to 5, as shown. The start and finish line is also shown.

1. Suppose all 5 runners begin at the start line and run once around the track. Calculate the distance that each runner runs. Assume that $\pi = 3.14$.

2. To have all runners run the same distance, the start line for each lane must be staggered. Make the necessary calculations and mark a different start line for each lane. Each of the other runners must cover the same distance as the runner in lane 1 covers in 1 lap of the track from the start to the finish line.

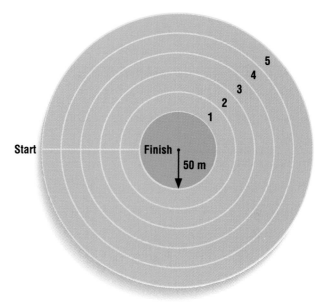

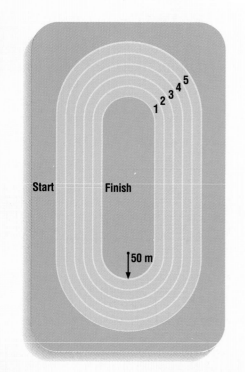

Activity ❸ Designing an Oval Track

1. Design an oval track like the one used in the Olympic Games. The ends of the track have an inside radius of 50 m. The sides of the track are straight. There are 5 lanes and the width of each lane is 1 m. The runner in lane 1 must run 400 m in 1 lap from the start to the finish.

2. Calculate the distance each runner would run if all the runners started at the same start line and finished after 1 lap of the track.

3. Make the necessary calculations and mark the start line for each lane. Each runner must run 400 m in a lane, and the finish line is the same for all runners.

Review

1. Write the GCF of each pair.

a) $35, 40$ **b)** $21, 28$

c) $34, 51$ **d)** $120, 96$

e) $10a^2, 5a$ **f)** $16xy, 12xz$

g) $10ab^2, 18ab$ **h)** $15xy, 25x^2y^2$

2. Write the GCF of each set.

a) $21x^2y, 15xy^2, 9x^2y^2$

b) $24x^2, -16xy, 32y^2$

c) $18xy^2, -27x^2y^2, 36x^2y$

Factor.

3. $5x - 15$ **4.** $6x^2 - 18x$

5. $5ab + 10ac$ **6.** $7a^2 + 35a^3$

7. $8abc - 12bc$ **8.** $3x^2 + 9y^2$

9. $3a^2 - 6ab + a$ **10.** $2x + 6y - 10z$

Expand and simplify.

11. $2(3x + 1) + 3(x + 4)$

12. $4(a + 5) + 3(a - 2)$

13. $3y(2y - 7) + 2(y - 5)$

14. $2(m + 1) - m(m + 1)$

15. $-z(2z + 3) - (z - 5)$

16. $5x(2x - 7) - 3x(3x - 5)$

Expand.

17. $2y(-y^2 + 3y - 7)$

18. $-3t(1 - 2t - t^2)$

19. $4m(m^2 + 2m - 3)$

20. $-3x(2x^2 - 4x + 2)$

Divide.

21. $\dfrac{8a^3b^5 - 16a^4b^4 + 4a^5b^3}{4a^3b^3}$

22. $\dfrac{6a^4b^5z^5 - 12a^4b^5z^4}{-3a^3b^4z^2}$

Expand.

23. $(x + 2)(x - 3)$ **24.** $(x - 4)(x + 7)$

25. $(x + 5)(x + 2)$ **26.** $(x - 2)(x - 3)$

27. $(x + 10)(x - 2)$ **28.** $(2x - 5)(3x - 2)$

29. $(-2a - 3)(5a + 2)$ **30.** $(4x - 7)(-3x + 2)$

31. $(3x - 5)(-7x + 6)$ **32.** $(-5a - b)(2a + 3b)$

Factor.

33. $x^2 + 8x + 7$ **34.** $x^2 - 6x + 5$

35. $y^2 + 8y + 15$ **36.** $a^2 + 8a + 12$

37. $b^2 + 10b + 24$ **38.** $x^2 - 7x + 6$

39. $x^2 - 11x + 28$ **40.** $a^2 - 7a + 12$

Factor.

41. $a^2 - a - 20$ **42.** $x^2 - x - 30$

43. $x^2 - 5x - 14$ **44.** $m^2 - 6m - 40$

45. $x^2 + 4x - 21$ **46.** $x^2 + 10x - 24$

47. $x^2 + 2x - 35$ **48.** $x^2 - 2x - 15$

Factor fully.

49. $2x^2 + 24x + 40$ **50.** $5a^2 - 40a + 80$

51. $4w^2 - 4w - 120$ **52.** $3r^2 - 21r + 30$

53. $2j^2 - 6j + 8$ **54.** $3t^2 + 18t - 21$

55. $7y^2 + 7y - 140$ **56.** $3z^2 - 39z + 126$

Factor.

57. $x^2 - 1$ **58.** $y^2 - 4$ **59.** $4a^2 - 9$

60. $a^2 - 4b^2$ **61.** $4x^2 - y^2$ **62.** $4a^2 - 9b^2$

63. $9 - x^2$ **64.** $25 - 49x^2$ **65.** $2a^2 - 50$

66. $5x^2 - 20$ **67.** $4x^2 - 36$ **68.** $16a^2 - 36$

Identify the expressions that are perfect squares.

69. $x^2 - 2x + 1$ **70.** $x^2 + 9x + 3$

71. $x^2 - 8x - 16$ **72.** $x^2 + 10x + 25$

Expand.

73. $(x + 2)^2$

74. $(x - 3)^2$

75. $(y + 6)^2$

76. $(m - 5)^2$

Expand.

77. $(x - 2)(x^2 - 3x + 2)$

78. $(x - 3)(x^2 - 5x - 3)$

79. $(x + 1)(2x^2 - 2x + 1)$

80. $(x + 5)(3x^2 - x - 1)$

81. $(x^2 - x + 1)(x + 1)$

82. $(x^2 + 2x + 3)(x - 1)$

83. $(5x^2 - 5x - 3)(x - 4)$

84. $(4x^2 - 3x - 7)(x + 2)$

Simplify.

85. $\dfrac{x - 1}{2} + \dfrac{x - 4}{3}$

86. $\dfrac{x - 2}{3} + \dfrac{1 - x}{5}$

87. $\dfrac{3 - x}{3} + \dfrac{2(x - 2)}{4}$

88. $\dfrac{x - 5}{6} + \dfrac{2(x + 3)}{7}$

89. $\dfrac{1}{x^2} + \dfrac{1 - x}{x^2}$

90. $\dfrac{3x + 1}{7x^2} + \dfrac{2 - x}{7x^2}$

Simplify.

91. $\dfrac{x - 5}{2} - \dfrac{x + 1}{3}$

92. $\dfrac{x + 2}{3} - \dfrac{x - 3}{4}$

93. $\dfrac{2(x + 3)}{2} - \dfrac{x - 1}{7}$

94. $\dfrac{x - 1}{6} - \dfrac{2 - x}{7}$

95. $\dfrac{1 - x}{7} - \dfrac{2 - x}{5}$

96. $\dfrac{x - 2}{4} - \dfrac{x - 3}{7}$

97. $\dfrac{2x + 1}{2x} - \dfrac{x - 1}{2x}$

98. $\dfrac{7 - x}{x^2} - \dfrac{2 - x}{x^2}$

99. The area of a rectangle is represented by the expression $x^2 + 10x + 16$.

a) Factor the expression.

b) A larger rectangle is 2 units longer on each side. Write a factored expression for the area of the larger rectangle.

c) Expand and simplify the expression for the area of the larger rectangle.

Group Decision Making
Mirror, Mirror on the Wall

Solve this problem in home groups.

| 1 2 3 4 | 1 2 3 4 | 1 2 3 4 |

Home Groups

| 1 2 3 4 | 1 2 3 4 | 1 2 3 4 |

The problem is this: When you are standing in front of a mirror and you want to see more of yourself, should you move forward or backward?

1. As a group, discuss the solution to the problem. Try to find a solution that everyone agrees with. Use a mirror to test your group's solution.

2. Next, make a drawing of the problem. Use a stick figure for the person in front of the mirror and a point on the figure for the person's eyes. Remember that the reflection appears at the same distance behind the mirror as the person is in front of the mirror.

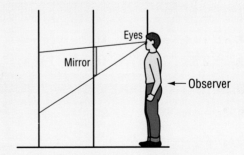

3. Make other drawings on top of the first one, with the stick figure moved forward and backward. Discuss the results.

4. Does a change in the size of the mirror change the problem?

5. Meet as a class. Present your group's solution to the problem.

Chapter Check

Factor fully.

1. $3xy - 6xz$ **2.** $24xy^2 + 12x^2y$

Expand and simplify.

3. $2x(x - 2) + 3(x + 3)$

4. $4x(x + 1) - 5x(x - 1)$

5. $-3x(x^2 - 2x + 1)$

6. $2m(2m^2 - 6m - 10)$

Divide.

7. $\dfrac{5y^4 - 10y^5 + 15y^6}{5y^4}$

8. $\dfrac{12a^5b^3 - 8a^4b^3 + 4a^3b^3}{4a^3b^3}$

Expand.

9. $(x - 2)(x + 4)$

10. $(x - 3)(2x + 7)$

11. $(4a - 3b)(2a - 3b)$

12. $(y + 3)(-2y + 1)$

Factor.

13. $x^2 + 7x + 10$ **14.** $x^2 - 9x + 18$

15. $x^2 - 3x - 10$ **16.** $x^2 + 2x - 35$

17. $x^2 + 8x + 16$ **18.** $x^2 - 18x + 17$

Factor fully.

19. $2x^2 - 8x + 8$ **20.** $5x^2 - 5x - 100$

Expand.

21. $(x - 2)^2$ **22.** $(w + 7)^2$

Factor.

23. $a^2 - 4$ **24.** $4x^2 - 25$

25. $81 - x^2$ **26.** $1 - 4b^2$

Factor.

27. $2t^2 - 200$ **28.** $3x^2 - 12$

29. $100 - 16t^2$ **30.** $2 - 18y^2$

State whether each trinomial is a perfect square.

31. $x^2 - 10x + 25$ **32.** $a^2 - 14a - 49$

33. $x^2 - 12x + 36$ **34.** $y^2 - 16y - 64$

Simplify.

35. $\dfrac{25xy}{5y} \times \dfrac{2x^2y^3}{2y}$ **36.** $\dfrac{10a^2b^3}{5ab^4} \div \dfrac{2ab}{5a^2b^2}$

Simplify.

37. $\dfrac{x + 3}{2} + \dfrac{5 + x}{3}$ **38.** $\dfrac{2(x - 3)}{5} - \dfrac{x - 1}{7}$

39. A rectangle has an area of $x^2 + 13x + 30$.
a) Express the area as a product of 2 binomials.

b) The length of a second rectangle is 2 units more than the length of the first rectangle. The width of the second rectangle is 1 unit less than the width of the first rectangle. Write an expression in factored form for the area of the second rectangle.

c) Expand and simplify your expression from part b).

BENT OFFERINGS by Don Addis.
By permission of Don Addis and Creators Syndicate.

214

Using the Strategies

1. Using different fractions with 10s as denominators, fill in the 3-by-3 grid below so that the sum vertically, horizontally, and diagonally is $1\frac{1}{2}$.

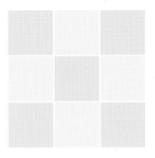

2. a) Write any 2-digit number.
b) Keep summing the digits in your number until you obtain a single digit. For example, for 67 the sum of the digits is $6 + 7$ or 13. The sum of the digits for 13 is $1 + 3$ or 4.
c) Divide the 2-digit number you wrote by 9 and note the remainder. What do you notice?
d) Repeat parts a) to c) for other 2-digit numbers. Describe your results.
e) Do the results for numbers with more than 2 digits follow the same pattern?

3. In the following division problem, a and b represent missing single-digit numbers. Find values for a and b.

$$\begin{array}{r} 2b7 \\ a21\overline{)79287} \end{array}$$

4. The greatest common factor of 2 numbers, m and n, is 14. If $m = 2 \times 5 \times 7^2$, name 3 numbers that could be n.

5. Kim has 2 chores at home. Every 4 days, she must clean the gerbil cage. Every 6 days, she must clean the canary cage. Last Monday, she did both jobs. On what day of the week will she next do both jobs?

6. To hang a picture on a bulletin board, Masao uses 4 thumbtacks, 1 in each corner. For 2 pictures of the same size, Masao can overlap the corners and hang 2 pictures with only 6 tacks.

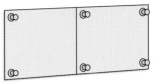

a) What is the minimum number of tacks Masao needs to hang 6 pictures of the same size in a row?
b) Write an expression for finding the number of tacks needed to hang any number of pictures in a row.

7. The graph shows the speed of a car for 10 min. Write a story to explain the graph.

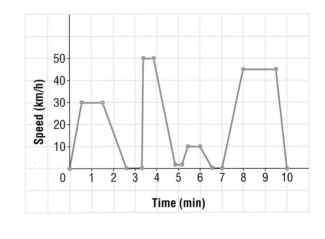

DATA BANK

1. Ontario and Quebec are Canada's 2 largest provinces. What percent of the total area of Canada's provinces is covered by these 2 provinces combined?

2. Use information from the Data Bank on pages 364 to 369 to write a problem. Have a classmate solve your problem.

215

CHAPTER 6

Measurement

The construction of the Alexander Graham Bell Museum in Baddeck, Nova Scotia, uses a common geometric shape. Name the shape.

The photographs below show an experiment in which a ball is supported by a strip of Bristol board. Explain how the result of this experiment is related to the construction of the museum.

List 5 other examples of how the shape you identified above is used for strength.

Alexander Graham Bell Museum

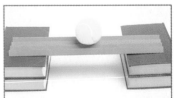

Seeing Shapes

Some of the information that we receive comes from pictures that can create illusions.

The spoon looks broken because light rays bend as they pass from one material into another. For example, they bend when they pass from air into water.

Activity ❶ Length

1. Horizontal and vertical lines can create an illusion involving length. In the diagram, does the horizontal or the vertical line seem longer?

2. Measure the lines and compare their lengths.

3. Draw a similar diagram in which the horizontal and vertical lines appear to be equal in length. Then, measure them to find the difference in their lengths.

Activity ❸ Reversing

1. Focus on this box until you see it change position.

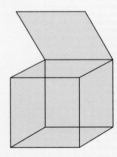

2. Describe the second position as you perceive it. Compare your description with your classmates'.

Activity ❷ Perspective

1. Do the sides of the triangle appear to be straight or bent?

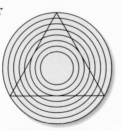

2. Describe the effect the circles have on the sides of the triangle.

Activity ❹ Impossible Figures

1. Focus on the figure and describe what you see.

2. Is this figure possible in the real world? Why?

Warm Up

1. State the sum of the interior angles of a triangle.

Determine the unknown angle measures in each triangle.

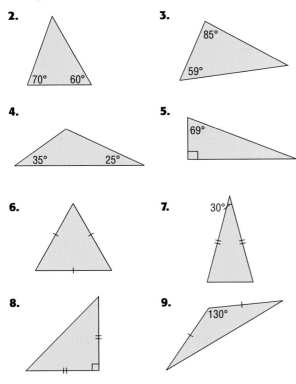

2.

70° 60°

3.

85° 59°

4.

35° 25°

5.

69°

6.

7.

30°

8.

9.

130°

Explain the meaning of each term.

10. enlargement

11. reduction

12. image

13. scale factor

14. What is the scale factor of this enlargement?

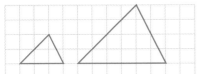

15. What is the scale factor of this reduction?

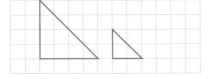

Mental Math

Calculate the perimeter of each figure.

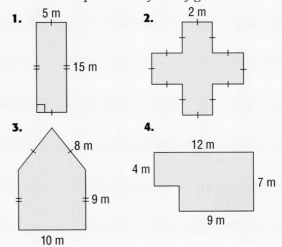

1. 5 m 15 m

2. 2 m

3. 8 m 9 m 10 m

4. 12 m 4 m 7 m 9 m

Calculate the area of each figure.

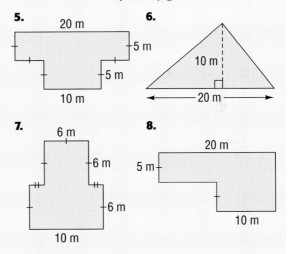

5. 20 m 5 m 5 m 10 m

6. 10 m 20 m

7. 6 m 6 m 6 m 10 m

8. 20 m 5 m 10 m

Calculate.

9. $37 + 23 + 20 + 10$

10. $52 - 12 + 30 - 20$

11. $84 + 16 - 25 + 5$

12. $61 - 31 + 47 - 7$

13. $92 - 12 - 35 - 15$

14. $73 + 17 - 30 - 20$

15. $56 + 44 - 80 + 20$

Congruent Triangles

Congruent triangles are triangles that have the same size and shape.

Activity ❶

1. Follow these steps to construct △ABC where AB = 7 cm, BC = 8 cm, and AC = 10 cm.

a) Draw line segment AB = 7 cm.

b) Set your compasses to a radius of 8 cm. Then, use B as a centre and draw an arc.

c) Set your compasses to a radius of 10 cm. Then, use A as a centre and draw an arc to intersect the first arc. Label the point of intersection C.

d) Draw BC and AC.

2. Is it possible to construct △DEF where DE = 7 cm, EF = 8 cm, and DF = 10 cm so that the size and shape of △DEF are different from the size and shape of △ABC? Explain.

Activity ❷

1. Construct △GHI so that GH = 5 cm and GI = 7 cm.

2. Is it possible to construct △JKL with JK = 5 cm and JL = 7 cm so that the size and shape of △JKL are different from the size and shape of △GHI? Explain.

Activity ❸

1. Construct △MNO so that ∠M = 35°, ∠N = 65°, and ∠O = 80°.

2. Is it possible to construct △PQR with ∠P = 35°, ∠Q = 65°, and ∠R = 80° so that the size and shape of △PQR are different from the size and shape of △MNO? Explain.

Activity ❹

1. Construct △RST so that ∠R = 70°, RS = 6 cm, and RT = 7 cm.

2. Is it possible to construct △XYZ with ∠X = 70°, XY = 6 cm, and XZ = 7 cm so that the size and shape of △XYZ are different from the size and shape of △RST? Explain.

Activity ❺

1. Construct △ABC so that ∠A = 40°, AB = 7 cm, and ∠B = 55°.

2. Is it possible to construct △DEF with ∠D = 40°, DE = 7 cm, and ∠E = 55° so that the size and shape of △DEF are different from the size and shape of △ABC? Explain.

Activity ❻

1. Construct △PQR so that ∠P = 35° and PQ = 7 cm.

2. Is it possible to construct △XYZ with ∠X = 35° and XY = 7 cm so that the size and shape of △XYZ are different from the size and shape of △PQR? Explain.

Activity ❼

1. Use the results of the first 6 activities to decide which sets of 3 facts need to be given so that only 1 triangle can be constructed.

6.1 Congruent Triangles

Many beautiful and unusual structures are built using congruent triangles. One such structure is shown in this photograph of Katimavik, built for Expo 67 in Montreal.

Activity: Use the Diagrams

Each of these 4 triangles is positioned differently but they all have the same size and shape. Copy or trace them into your notebook.

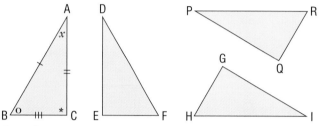

Inquire

1. Mark AB with a single tick as shown in the diagram above. Then, in the other 3 triangles, use a single tick to mark the sides that are the same length as AB.

2. Mark AC with 2 ticks. Then, in the other 3 triangles, use two ticks to mark the sides that are the same length as AC.

3. Use 3 ticks to mark each of the remaining equal sides.

4. Mark ∠A with an x. Then, in the other 3 triangles, use an x to mark the angles that have the same measure as ∠A.

5. Mark ∠B with an o. Then, in the other 3 triangles, use an o to mark the angles that have the same measure as ∠B.

6. Use an asterisk, * , to mark the remaining equal angles.

A triangle has 6 parts, 3 angles and 3 sides. Two triangles are **congruent** if you can match up their vertices so that all pairs of corresponding angles and corresponding sides are equal.
In △ABC and △DEF, the following corresponding parts are equal.

∠A = ∠D   AB = DE

∠B = ∠E   BC = EF

∠C = ∠F   AC = DF

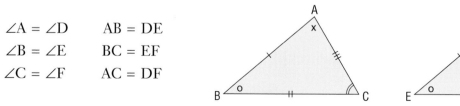

We say △ABC ≅ △DEF. The symbol for congruence, ≅, is read "is congruent to." Note that the vertices of each triangle are listed in the same order as their corresponding angles.

You do not need to know that all 6 parts of 1 triangle are equal to the 6 corresponding parts of another triangle to prove congruency. Knowing that 3 parts of one triangle are equal to 3 corresponding parts of another triangle may be sufficient to say that the triangles are congruent.

The chart gives you 3 ways to state that 2 triangles are congruent.

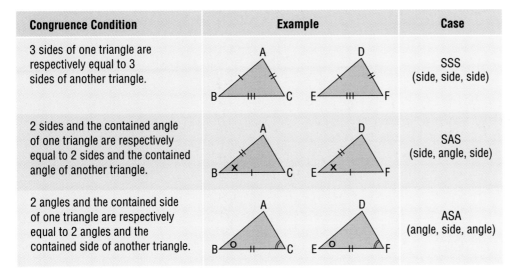

Congruence Condition	Example	Case
3 sides of one triangle are respectively equal to 3 sides of another triangle.		SSS (side, side, side)
2 sides and the contained angle of one triangle are respectively equal to 2 sides and the contained angle of another triangle.		SAS (side, angle, side)
2 angles and the contained side of one triangle are respectively equal to 2 angles and the contained side of another triangle.		ASA (angle, side, angle)

Example 1

a) State why △RST ≅ △LMN.
b) List the other equal sides and angles.

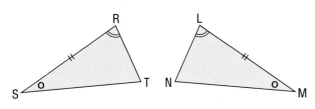

Solution

a) In △RST and △LMN,

$$\angle R = \angle L$$
$$RS = LM$$
$$\angle S = \angle M$$

Therefore, △RST ≅ △LMN **(ASA)**

b) $RT = LN$
$ST = MN$
$\angle T = \angle N$

Example 2

a) State why △PQR ≅ △BCA.
b) List the other equal parts.

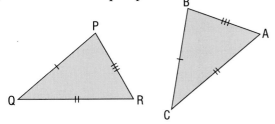

Solution

a) In △PQR and △BCA,

$$PQ = BC$$
$$QR = CA$$
$$PR = BA$$

Therefore, △PQR ≅ △BCA **(SSS)**

b) $\angle P = \angle B$
$\angle Q = \angle C$
$\angle R = \angle A$

CONTINUED ➤

Example 3

a) State why △PQR ≅ △STR.
b) List the other corresponding equal parts.

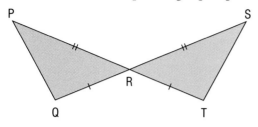

Solution

a) In △PQR and △STR,
  PR = SR
  ∠PRQ = ∠SRT (opposite angles)
  QR = TR
Therefore, △PQR ≅ △STR **(SAS)**

b) PQ = ST
  ∠P = ∠S
  ∠Q = ∠T

Practice

Name the equal sides and angles for these pairs of congruent triangles.

1.

△BIG ≅ △CAT

2.

△HOT ≅ △CAR

Is each pair of triangles congruent in questions 3–9? If they are, what case did you use?

3.

4.

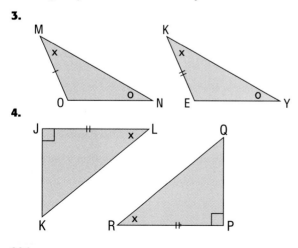

5.

6.

7.

8.

9.

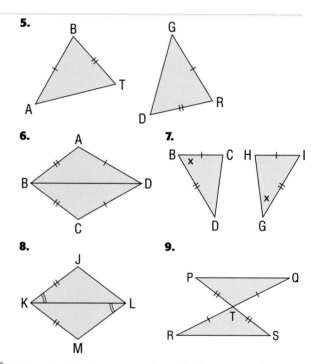

What is the fewest number of other parts that must be equal before you can state that the following pairs of triangles are congruent? Explain.

10.

11.

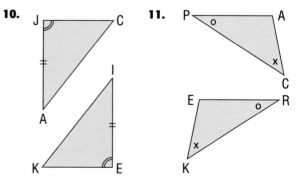

Are these pairs of triangles congruent? If they are, give the case and list all the corresponding equal parts.

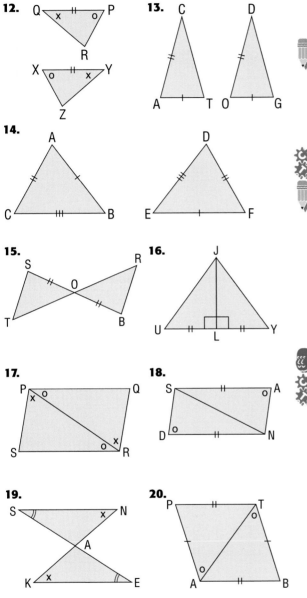

12.

13.

14.

15.

16.

17.

18.

19.

20.

Problems and Applications

21. Alexi thinks that two triangles look congruent. Find two different ways he could find out if they are congruent without cutting the triangles out. Explain your reasoning.

22. How many pairs of congruent triangles are there on the flag of Newfoundland and Labrador?

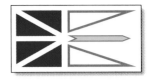

23. Do the gables on these 2 roofs form congruent triangles? Explain.

24. a) Triangles are used in construction because they hold their shape. To change the shape of this triangle, you have to change the length of at least 1 of the sides. Why?

4 cm 6 cm 5 cm

b) To change the shape of this figure, you do not have to change the length of a side. Why not?

5 cm 3 cm

25. Work with a classmate to decide which of the following are always congruent, sometimes congruent, or never congruent. Illustrate your answer with diagrams.

a) 2 triangles with the same perimeter
b) 2 rectangles with the same area
c) 2 squares with the same perimeter
d) 2 rectangles with the same perimeter

WORD POWER

a) Louisiana is 1 of 6 American states in which the name contains the consecutive letters IS. What are the other 5 states?
b) Which 2 Canadian provinces also contain the consecutive letters IS?

Investigating Similar Triangles

Activity ❶ Constructing Similar Triangles

1. a) Construct a triangle with side lengths of 3 cm, 4 cm, and 5 cm. Measure each angle in the triangle to the nearest degree.

b) Repeat part a) for a triangle with side lengths of 6 cm, 8 cm, and 10 cm.

c) Compare the angles in the two triangles.

d) Compare the side lengths in the two triangles.

2. Repeat step 1 for a triangle with side lengths of 4 cm, 5 cm, and 6 cm, and a triangle with side lengths of 6 cm, 7.5 cm, and 9 cm.

3. The two triangles in step 1 are said to be **similar triangles**. So are the two triangles in step 2. Write a rule for identifying similar triangles.

4. How do the shapes of the similar triangles compare?

5. How do the sizes of the similar triangles compare?

Activity ❷ Identifying Similar Triangles

Draw the triangles on grid paper. State whether the triangles in each pair are similar. Justify your answers.

1.

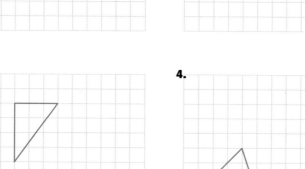

2.

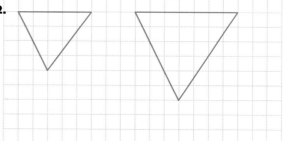

3.

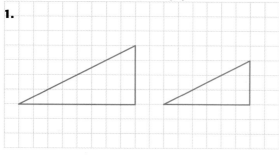

4.

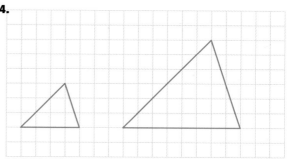

Right Triangles

Activity ❶ Naming the Legs of Right Triangles

The legs of right triangles are named in relation to the acute angle being considered.

1. Study the two right triangles shown. Describe how the legs are named in relation to the marked angle.

2. Copy the following triangles into your notebook. Label the sides of each triangle as the hypotenuse, the opposite leg, and the adjacent leg in relation to each marked angle.

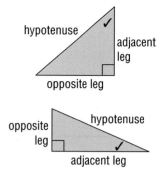

a)

b)

c)

d)

e)

f)

Activity ❷ The Pythagorean Theorem

1. Write the Pythagorean Theorem in words.

2. Use the letters in the diagram to write the Pythagorean Theorem.

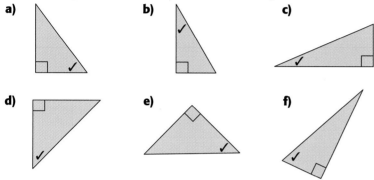

3. Use the Pythagorean Theorem to calculate the unknown side of each triangle.

a)

b)

c)

d)

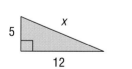
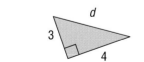
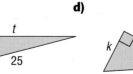

4. Use the Pythagorean Theorem to calculate the unknown side to the nearest tenth of a centimetre.

a)

b)

c)

d)

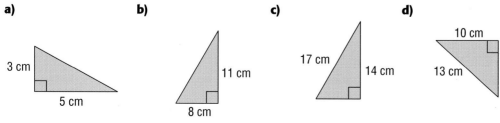

6.2 Similar Triangles

Before constructing a new plane, aeronautical engineers build and test a model. The model plane is the same shape as, or is similar to, the real plane. **Similar figures** have the same shape but not necessarily the same size.

Activity: Construct the Triangles

Draw △ABC and △DEF on grid paper. Measure the angles and sides in each triangle and complete the table.

Model Aircraft of 767 in old Air Canada livery.

Inquire

1. How do the measures of the corresponding angles compare?

2. Find the ratios of the lengths of the corresponding sides, AB:DE, BC:EF, and AC:DF.

3. How do the ratios of the corresponding sides compare?

4. a) In what way are △ABC and △DEF the same as congruent triangles?
b) In what way are they different from congruent triangles?

5. What is the ratio of the lengths of corresponding sides in congruent triangles?

6. a) △DEF is an enlargement of △ABC. Explain why.
b) What is the scale factor?

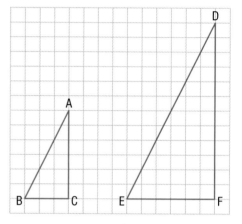

△ABC		△DEF	
∠A =	AB =	∠D =	DE =
∠B =	BC =	∠E =	EF =
∠C =	AC =	∠F =	DF =

△PQR and △WXY are similar. This means that
• The corresponding angles are equal.

$$\angle P = \angle W \qquad \angle Q = \angle X \qquad \angle R = \angle Y$$

• The ratios of the corresponding sides are equal.
$$\frac{PQ}{WX} = \frac{QR}{XY} = \frac{PR}{WY} \qquad \text{or} \qquad \frac{r}{y} = \frac{p}{w} = \frac{q}{x}$$

We write △PQR ~ △WXY.

~ means "is similar to"

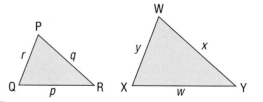

You can state that 2 triangles, △ABC and △DEF, are similar if you know that the corresponding pairs of angles are equal.

$$\angle A = \angle D \qquad \angle B = \angle E \qquad \angle C = \angle F$$

You can state that 2 triangles, △ABC and △DEF, are similar if you know that the ratios of the corresponding sides are equal.

$$\frac{AB}{DE} = \frac{BC}{EF} = \frac{AC}{DF} \qquad \text{or} \qquad \frac{c}{f} = \frac{a}{d} = \frac{b}{e}$$

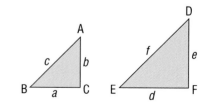

228

Example 1

△DEF ~ △RST. Find the values of r and e.

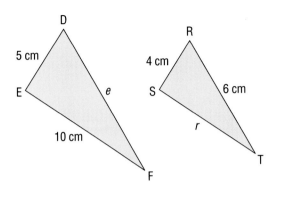

Solution

Since the triangles are similar, the ratios of the corresponding sides are equal.

$$\frac{DE}{RS} = \frac{EF}{ST} = \frac{DF}{RT}$$

Substitute. $\frac{5}{4} = \frac{10}{r} = \frac{e}{6}$

Take the ratios 2 at a time.

$$\frac{5}{4} = \frac{10}{r} \qquad\qquad \frac{5}{4} = \frac{e}{6}$$

Use the cross-product rule.

$$5 \times r = 10 \times 4 \qquad 5 \times 6 = e \times 4$$
$$5r = 40 \qquad\qquad 30 = 4e$$
$$r = 8 \qquad\qquad 7.5 = e$$

So, r is 8 cm, and e is 7.5 cm.

Similar triangles can be used to find distances that are difficult to measure directly.

Example 2

The diagram shows how surveyors can lay out 2 triangles to find the width of the Bow River near Banff, Alberta. Use the triangles to calculate the width of the river, DE.

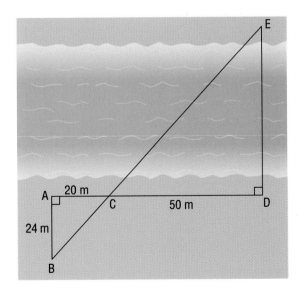

Solution

If △ABC is similar to △DEC, you can write ratios of corresponding sides to find DE.

In △ABC and △DEC,
∠CAB = ∠CDE   (both 90°)
∠ACB = ∠DCE   (opposite angles)

If 2 angles in one triangle are equal to 2 angles in another triangle, the third angles in each triangle must be equal.
∠ABC = ∠DEC

Since corresponding angles are equal,
△ABC ~ △DEC.

Since the triangles are similar, the ratios of corresponding sides are equal.

$$\frac{AC}{DC} = \frac{AB}{DE}$$
$$\frac{20}{50} = \frac{24}{DE}$$
$$20 \times DE = 24 \times 50$$
$$20 \times DE = 1200$$
$$DE = 60$$

The width of the river is 60 m.

CONTINUED ▶

Practice

Use grid paper to make a figure similar to, but not congruent to, each of the following figures.

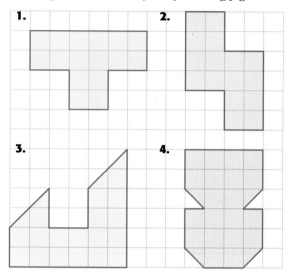

1.

2.

3.

4.

The triangles in each pair are similar. Find the unknown side lengths.

5.

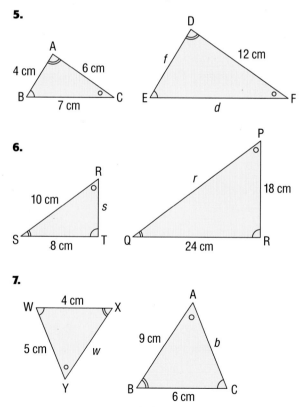

A

4 cm   6 cm

B
7 cm   C

D

f   12 cm

E
d   F

6.

R

10 cm   s

S   8 cm   T

P

r   18 cm

Q   24 cm   R

7.

W   4 cm   X

5 cm   w

Y

A

9 cm   b

B   6 cm   C

8.

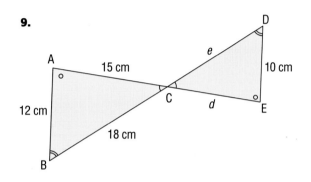

D

8 cm   9 cm

E   10 cm   F

P

r   6 cm

Q   p   R

9.

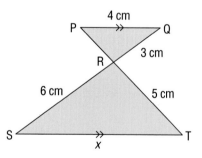

A   15 cm

12 cm

B   18 cm

e

C   10 cm

d   E

D

10. Find *x*.

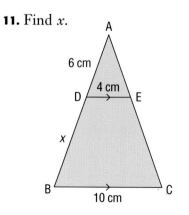

4 cm

P   Q

R   3 cm

6 cm   5 cm

S   x   T

11. Find *x*.

A

6 cm

D   4 cm   E

x

B   10 cm   C

230

Problems and Applications

12. The 5-m flagpole casts a 4-m shadow at the same time of day as a building casts a 30-m shadow. How tall is the building?

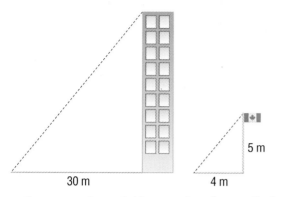

13. Surveyors have laid out triangles to find the length of the lake. Calculate this length.

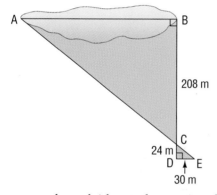

14. Surveyors have laid out these triangles to calculate the width of a canyon. Find this width to the nearest metre.

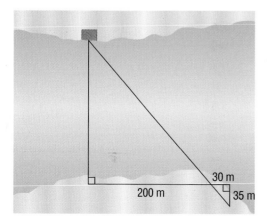

15. Pierre thinks that two triangles on a page look similar. Describe two different methods he could use to find out if the triangles are similar. Explain your reasoning.

16. Serena made a scale drawing of her triangular flower garden. Two sides of her garden are 5 m and 6 m long, and form an angle of 40°. Serena drew a 40° angle on paper, marked points at 10 cm and 12 cm on the arms, and joined these points. She measured the third side to be 9.5 cm. How long is the third side of the garden?

17. Is each of the following statements true or false? Use examples to explain your reasoning.
a) All similar triangles are congruent.
b) All congruent triangles are similar.

18. Decide on 3 outdoor objects whose heights you want to calculate. Your choices might include a street lamp, a flagpole, and the school. At the same time of day, find the length of the shadow cast by a metre-stick and the length of the shadow of each chosen object. Calculate the height of each object.

LOGIC POWER

Use your knowledge of geography to identify the province these towns are in. Then, check by finding this area on a map.

Comparing Triangles Using Geometry Software

Use a geometry software package to complete the following activities. If geometry software is unavailable, use a ruler and protractor.

Activity ❶

1. Construct a right triangle ABC. Make ∠A the right angle. Make ∠B and ∠C different from each other.

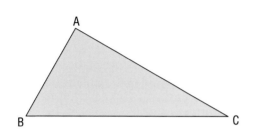

2. Measure ∠B and ∠C.

3. Construct the perpendicular AD to side BC.

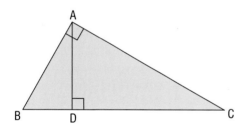

4. Measure ∠DAB and ∠DAC.

5. Using all the angle measures you know, decide how △ABC, △DBA, and △DAC are related.

6. Use your result from step 5 to predict as many equal ratios of side lengths of the triangles as possible.

7. Measure the side lengths you included in step 6. Calculate the ratios to check your predictions. Compare your findings with a classmate's.

Activity ❷

Refer to the triangles in Activity 1. Assume that ∠A remains a right angle and that AD remains perpendicular to BC.

1. What would have to be true about △ABC to make △ABD and △ACD congruent? Explain.

2. If △ABD and △ACD are congruent, how is each of these triangles related to △ABC?

Ratios of Side Lengths in Right Triangles

Use a geometry software package to complete the following activities. If geometry software is unavailable, use a ruler and protractor.

Activity ❶

1. Construct the right triangle XYZ with the angles shown and with side lengths of your choice.

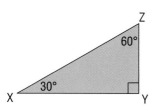

2. Measure
a) XY **b)** XZ **c)** YZ

3. Determine each of the following ratios to 2 decimal places.
a) $\dfrac{YZ}{XY}$ **b)** $\dfrac{YZ}{XZ}$ **c)** $\dfrac{XY}{XZ}$

4. Construct a similar triangle PQR in which the side lengths are different from those in △XYZ.

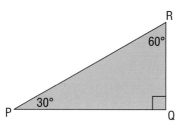

5. Measure
a) PQ **b)** PR **c)** QR

6. Determine each of the following ratios to 2 decimal places.
a) $\dfrac{QR}{PQ}$ **b)** $\dfrac{QR}{PR}$ **c)** $\dfrac{PQ}{PR}$

7. a) Compare your results from steps 3 and 6.
b) Compare your results with those of your classmates.

8. What can you conclude about the ratios of the side lengths in a right triangle with fixed angle measures?

Activity ❷

Check your conclusion from Activity 1, step 8, by repeating steps 1 to 6 for two different triangles with angles of 40°, 50°, and 90°.

Staging Rock Concerts

One of the most exciting aspects of a rock concert is the integration of the music and the lighting. The lights around the stage are held in place by lighting pipes. The process of suspending the lights is known as "flying the pipes."

Before the pipes are flown, the lighting designer must find the proper angles for the lights. To do this, the designer uses a ruler and protractor.

In the following example, the stage has a depth of 8 m. The support for the 3 pipes is to be 1 m from the back of the stage. The 3 pipes, A, B, and C, are to be 9 m, 7 m, and 5 m above the stage floor. To find the angle at which each pipe must be pointed, the designer uses the following steps.

Draw the stage floor, GE, letting 1 cm represent 1 m.

Find $\frac{1}{4}$ of the stage depth. $\frac{1}{4} \times 8 = 2$

Mark the lights' *focal point*, F, $\frac{1}{4}$ of the stage depth or 2 m from the front of the stage.

Mark a point, D, on the pipe support 1 m from the back of the stage.

Draw the pipe support and mark the lighting pipes, A, B, and C, 9 m, 7 m, and 5 m from the stage floor.

Join AF, BF, and CF to make ∠FAD, ∠FBD, and ∠FCD. Measure these 3 angles.

∠FAD = 38°, ∠FBD = 45°, and ∠FCD = 54°.

Lighting technicians set the pipes to these angles on the pipe support before raising the support.

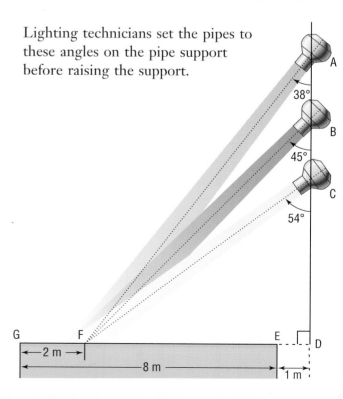

Activity ❶

These questions refer to the example on the opposite page.

1. a) Another way to determine ∠FAD is to measure ∠AFD and use the angle properties of a triangle. What is the relationship between the measures of ∠FAD and ∠AFD? Explain.

b) Why might a designer choose to measure ∠AFD, ∠BFD, and ∠CFD and to calculate ∠FAD, ∠FBD, and ∠FCD from them?

2. The measure of ∠FBD could be determined without the use of a protractor. Explain how.

Activity ❷

The lighting designer adjusts the angles of the lighting pipes for stages of different sizes. Use the table to find the angles needed for pipes A, B, and C at each venue.

Venue	Stage Width (m)	Stage Depth (m)	Pipe Height (m) A	B	C	Distance of Pipe Support from Stage (m)
Maple Leaf Gardens	12	8	11	10	9	3
B.C. Place	16	12	12	10	7	1
O'Keefe Centre	8	6	9	7	6	0
Lansdowne Park	12	10	10	8	6	2

Activity ❸

For some lighting designs, it is important to use the same lighting angles throughout a tour. In these cases, the height of each lighting pipe is the variable that the designer must determine.

1. Choose one of the venues in Activity 2. Use the stage depth and the distance of the pipe support from the stage to determine the heights of the pipes for angles of 35°, 45°, and 50°.

2. Describe how the problem solving process differs from the process used in the example.

Activity ❹

Very few concerts have lighting equipment only behind the performers. For variety and visibility, most designers also hang lighting pipes on both sides of the stage.

1. Using the data from Activity 2, add pipes A, B, and C on stage left, and pipes X, Y, and Z on stage right for one of the venues.

2. How are the triangles you drew for stage left and the triangles you drew for stage right related?

Activity ❺

1. With a partner, choose a performer or group for whom you would like to do a lighting design. Also, choose one of the venues in Activity 2.

2. Decide how many pipes to use
a) at the back of the stage
b) on each side of the stage

3. Decide how far from the stage to place the pipe supports.

4. Choose the colours of the lights.

5. Use the stage dimensions to determine the angles of the lighting pipes.

6.3 Right Triangles and the Tangent Ratio

Early Canadian pioneers faced long, harsh winters. Many of their normal household needs, such as warm quilts, were handmade. The quilts are still prized for their intricate needlework. This quilt, called the *Prairie Queen*, shows different-sized, similar right triangles.

Activity: Compare the Ratios

Draw this set of nested triangles on grid paper. Then, copy and complete the table. Express each ratio in decimal form.

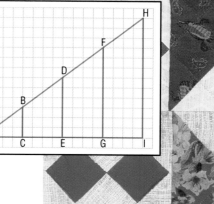

Triangle	△ ABC	△ ADE	△ AFG	△ AHI
Ratio	$\frac{BC}{AC} =$	$\frac{DE}{AE} =$	$\frac{FG}{AG} =$	$\frac{HI}{AI} =$

How do the ratios compare?

Inquire

1. Why are △ABC, △ADE, △AFG, and △AHI similar?

2. Which angle is common to all 4 triangles?

3. The ratio you found is called the **tangent ratio** for the common angle. Explain the meaning of the tangent ratio by describing the positions of the 2 sides in each ratio in relation to the common angle.

4. Measure the common angle to the nearest degree.

5. The tangent ratio for an angle can be determined with the [TAN] key on a scientific calculator. Set your calculator to [DEG] mode, enter the measure of the common angle, and press the [TAN] key. Record the display to 2 decimal places.

6. The ratio from the Activity and the value from your calculator both represent the tangent ratio for the common angle. Compare the two values. If they are different, explain.

Trigonometry is the study of the relationships among the sides and angles of triangles. One such relationship is the tangent ratio, which is an example of a **trigonometric ratio**.

Example 1

Find the tangent ratio, to 3 decimal places, for each angle.
  a) 40°   **b)** 55°   **c)** 73°   **d)** 89°

Solution

a) $\tan 40° \doteq 0.839$ C **40** [TAN] ⎰ 0.8390996 ⎱

b) $\tan 55° \doteq 1.428$ **c)** $\tan 73° \doteq 3.271$ **d)** $\tan 89° \doteq 57.290$

$\doteq$ means "approximately equal"

236

Example 2

Find each angle measure, to the nearest degree, for each tangent ratio.

a) $\tan A = 1.782$ **b)** $\tan B = 0.509$ **c)** $\tan C = 6.895$ **d)** $\tan D = 0.063$

Solution

a) If $\tan A = 1.782$ C 1.782 INV TAN $\boxed{60.700287}$ or C 1.782 2ND TAN⁻¹ $\boxed{60.700287}$

     $\angle A \doteq 61°$

b) If $\tan B = 0.509$, $\angle B \doteq 27°$ **c)** If $\tan C = 6.895$, $\angle C \doteq 82°$ **d)** If $\tan D = 0.063$, $\angle D \doteq 4°$

Example 3

a) Find $\tan C$ in $\triangle ABC$. **b)** Calculate $\angle C$ to the nearest degree.

Solution

a) The tangent ratio may be found for either acute angle in a right triangle. For $\angle C$, the tangent ratio is found as follows:

$$\tan C = \frac{\text{length of the leg opposite } \angle C}{\text{length of the leg adjacent to } \angle C}$$

Think: $\tan = \dfrac{\text{opposite}}{\text{adjacent}}$

$$= \frac{4}{3}$$

$$\doteq 1.333$$

b) Using a calculator, $\angle C \doteq 53°$.   C 4 ÷ 3 = INV TAN $\boxed{53.130102}$

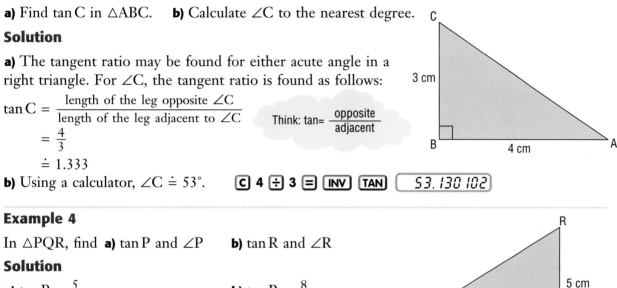

Example 4

In $\triangle PQR$, find **a)** $\tan P$ and $\angle P$ **b)** $\tan R$ and $\angle R$

Solution

a) $\tan P = \dfrac{5}{8}$ **b)** $\tan R = \dfrac{8}{5}$

     $= 0.625$ $= 1.6$

     $\angle P \doteq 32°$ $\angle R \doteq 58°$

Example 5

In $\triangle JKL$, find the length of KL, to the nearest metre.

Solution

$$\tan K = \frac{10}{KL}$$

$$\tan 30° = \frac{10}{KL}$$

$$0.577 \doteq \frac{10}{KL}$$

$$KL \times 0.577 \doteq 10$$

$$KL \doteq \frac{10}{0.577}$$

$$KL \doteq 17.3$$

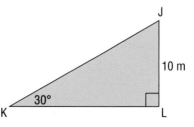

The length of KL is 17 m, to the nearest metre.

CONTINUED ➤

Practice

Find the following to 3 decimal places.

1. tan 15° **2.** tan 62° **3.** tan 5°

4. tan 30° **5.** tan 82° **6.** tan 45°

Find ∠B to the nearest degree.

7. tan B = 0.600 **8.** tan B = 0.833

9. tan B = 3.025 **10.** tan B = 5.050

Find ∠W to the nearest degree.

11. $\tan W = \frac{4}{5}$ **12.** $\tan W = \frac{6}{7}$

13. $\tan W = \frac{7}{4}$ **14.** $\tan W = \frac{15}{9}$

Calculate tan C in each triangle.

15.

16.

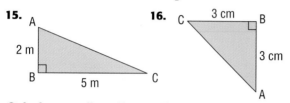

Calculate tan D, ∠D, tan E, and ∠E. Round each angle measure to the nearest degree.

17.

18.

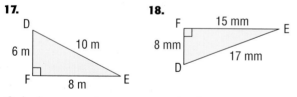

Calculate x to the nearest tenth of a metre.

19. **20.**

21. **22.**

23. **24.**

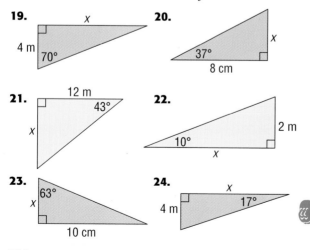

Problems and Applications

25. In a right triangle, the leg adjacent to an angle of 23° is 12 cm long. How long is the leg opposite the 23° angle, to the nearest tenth of a centimetre?

26. In a right triangle, the leg opposite the 53° angle is 4 cm long. How long is the leg adjacent to the 53° angle, to the nearest centimetre?

27. When a ladder is rested against a tree, the foot of the ladder is 1 m from the base of the tree and forms an angle of 64° with the ground. How far up the tree does the ladder reach, to the nearest tenth of a metre?

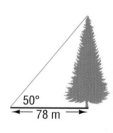

28. One of Canada's tallest trees is a Douglas fir on Vancouver Island. The angle of elevation measured by an observer who is 78 m from the base of the tree is 50°. How tall is this tree, to the nearest metre?

29. The angle of inclination of the rafters of the roof of a house is 26°. The roof support is 3 m high. How wide is the house, to the nearest metre?

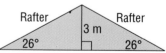

30. Pietra walked diagonally across a rectangular school yard 45 m by 65 m. To the nearest degree, at what angle with respect to the longer side did she walk?

31. Calculate the acute angle, to the nearest degree, formed by these lines.

32. Write a problem similar to questions 25 and 26. Have a classmate solve it.

6.4 Right Triangles and the Sine Ratio

The flagpole in front of the provincial parliament buildings in Victoria, British Columbia, is a single Douglas fir. With a height of 42.3 m, the flagpole must be supported by guy wires. There are two sets of guy wires, one set attached at an elevation of 24.7 m, the other at an elevation of 37.0 m.

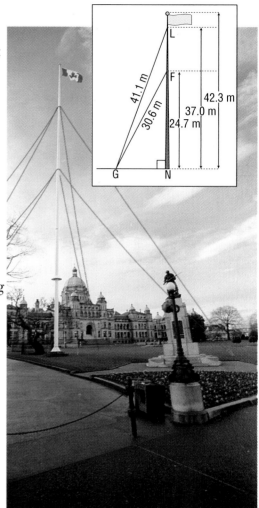

Activity: Use the Diagram

Complete the ratios in the table. Express them in decimal form to 2 decimal places.

Triangle	△ FGN	△ LGN
Ratio	$\frac{FN}{FG}=$	$\frac{LN}{LG}=$

Inquire

1. Each ratio you found is called a **sine ratio**. In △FGN, you found the sine ratio for ∠FGN.
a) Explain the meaning of the sine ratio for ∠FGN by describing the positions of the 2 sides in the ratio in relation to ∠FGN.
b) Test your explanation by checking the positions of the sides used to calculate the sine ratio for ∠LGN in △LGN.

2. With a protractor, measure to the nearest degree
a) ∠FGN   **b)** ∠LGN

3. The sine ratio for an angle can be determined with the [SIN] key on a scientific calculator.
a) Set your calculator to [DEG] mode, enter the measure of ∠FGN, and press the [SIN] key. Record the display to 2 decimal places.
b) Repeat part a) for ∠LGN.

4. Compare the ratio from the Activity with the ratio from question 3 and explain any differences for
a) ∠FGN   **b)** ∠LGN

Example 1

Find the sine ratio, to 3 decimal places, for each angle.
a) 75°   **b)** 52°   **c)** 17°   **d)** 90°

Solution

a) $\sin 75° \doteq 0.966$ [C] 75 [SIN] 0.9659258
b) $\sin 52° \doteq 0.788$ **c)** $\sin 17° \doteq 0.292$ **d)** $\sin 90° = 1.000$

Example 2

a) Find sin R in △RST.
b) Calculate ∠R to the nearest degree.

S
17 cm
8 cm
R   T

CONTINUED

239

Solution

a) The sine ratio may be found for either acute angle in a right triangle.

$$\sin R = \frac{\text{length of the leg opposite } \angle R}{\text{length of the hypotenuse}}$$

$$= \frac{8}{17}$$

$$\doteq 0.471$$

Think: $\sin = \frac{\text{opposite}}{\text{hypotenuse}}$

b) Using a calculator, $\angle R \doteq 28°$. [C] **8** [÷] **17** [=] [INV] [SIN]   `28.072487`

or [C] **8** [÷] **17** [=] [2ND] [SIN⁻¹]   `28.072487`

Example 3

In $\triangle JKL$, find the length of JK, to the nearest tenth of a centimetre.

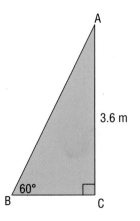

Solution 1

Using the sine ratio,

$$\sin J = \frac{17}{25}$$

$$= 0.68$$

$$\angle J \doteq 43°$$

Therefore, $\angle L = 180° - 43° - 90°$

$$= 47°$$

$$\sin L = \frac{JK}{25}$$

$$\sin 47° = \frac{JK}{25}$$

$$0.731 \doteq \frac{JK}{25}$$

$$0.731 \times 25 \doteq JK$$

$$18.275 \doteq JK$$

EST $0.7 \times 30 = 21$

Solution 2

Using the Pythagorean Theorem,

$$JK^2 + LK^2 = JL^2$$

$$JK^2 + 17^2 = 25^2$$

$$JK^2 = 25^2 - 17^2$$

$$= 625 - 289$$

$$= 336$$

$$JK = \sqrt{336}$$

$$\doteq 18.33$$

The length of JK is 18.3 cm, to the nearest tenth of a centimetre.

Example 4

In $\triangle ABC$, find the length of AB, to the nearest tenth of a metre.

Solution

$$\sin 60° = \frac{3.6}{AB}$$

$$0.866 \doteq \frac{3.6}{AB}$$

$$0.866 \times AB \doteq 3.6$$

$$AB \doteq \frac{3.6}{0.866}$$

$$\doteq 4.16$$

EST $4 \div 1 = 4$

The length of AB is 4.2 m, to the nearest tenth of a metre.

Practice

Find the following to 3 decimal places.

1. sin 45°   **2.** sin 60°   **3.** sin 37°

4. sin 25°   **5.** sin 0°   **6.** sin 89°

Find ∠J to the nearest degree.

7. sin J = 0.503   **8.** sin J = 0.952

9. sin J = 0.712   **10.** sin J = 0.303

11. sin J = 0.998   **12.** sin J = 0.101

Find ∠B to the nearest degree.

13. $\sin B = \frac{2}{3}$ **14.** $\sin B = \frac{3}{4}$ **15.** $\sin B = \frac{1}{2}$

16. $\sin B = \frac{2}{5}$ **17.** $\sin B = \frac{1}{8}$ **18.** $\sin B = \frac{7}{9}$

Calculate sin T. Then, find ∠T to the nearest degree.

19.

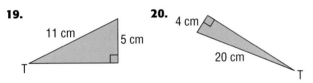

20.

Find the value of x to the nearest tenth of a centimetre.

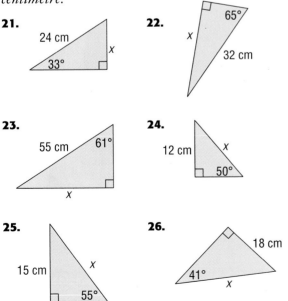

21.

22.

23.

24.

25.

26.

Problems and Applications

27. In △PQR, ∠Q = 90° and PR = 20 cm. Find PQ to the nearest tenth of a centimetre if ∠R = 41°.

28. In △DEF, find ∠F to the nearest degree if DE = 15 cm, DF = 18 cm, and ∠E = 90°.

29. In △ABC, ∠B = 90°. If AB = 10 cm and ∠C = 38°, find the length of AC, to the nearest tenth of a centimetre.

30. A 1.5-m hoe rests against the side of a garden shed. The angle the handle of the hoe forms with the ground is 71°. How far up the wall of the shed does the hoe reach, to the nearest tenth of a metre?

31. △ABC is an isosceles triangle. The height of the triangle is 3 cm, and the two acute angles at its base are each 56°. How long are the two equal sides, to the nearest tenth of a centimetre?

32. A tree is splintered by lightning 2 m up its trunk, so that the top part of the tree touches the ground. The angle the top of the tree forms with the ground is 70°. How tall is the tree, to the nearest tenth of a metre?

33. a) Evaluate sin 39° with a calculator. Round your answer to the nearest thousandth.
b) Use the diagram to write the ratio represented by your answer to part a).
c) What is the length of *a* in terms of *c*?
d) What is the length of *c* in terms of *a*? Explain.

34. Write a problem similar to question 27, 28, or 29. Have a classmate solve it.

6.5 Right Triangles and the Cosine Ratio

To mark the fifteenth Commonwealth Games held in Victoria, the world's tallest totem pole *The Spirit of Nations* was erected at Songhees Point on Victoria Harbour. Unlike most totem poles, which are stabilized by sinking them into the ground, *The Spirit of Nations* requires anchor lines because it sits on rock.

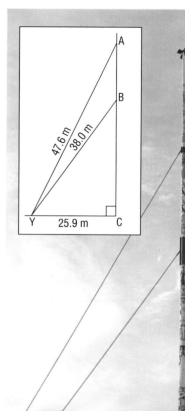

Activity: Use the Diagram

Complete the ratios in the table and express them in decimal form to 2 decimal places.

Triangle	△ ACY	△ BCY
Ratio	$\frac{CY}{AY}=$	$\frac{CY}{BY}=$

Inquire

1. Each ratio you found is called a **cosine ratio**. In △BCY, you found the cosine ratio for ∠BYC.

a) Explain the meaning of the cosine ratio for ∠BYC by describing the positions of the 2 sides in the ratio in relation to ∠BYC.

b) Test your explanation by checking the positions of the sides used to calculate the cosine ratio for ∠AYC in △ACY.

2. With a protractor, measure to the nearest degree
a) ∠BYC   **b)** ∠AYC

3. The cosine ratio for an angle can be determined with the
[COS] key on a scientific calculator.

a) Set your calculator to [DEG] mode, enter the measure of ∠BYC, and press the [COS] key. Record the display to 2 decimal places.
b) Repeat part a) for ∠AYC.

4. Compare the ratio from the Activity with the ratio from question 3 and explain any differences for
a) ∠BYC   **b)** ∠AYC

Example 1

Find the cosine ratio, to 3 decimal places, for each angle.
a) 42°   **b)** 9°   **c)** 20°   **d)** 90°

Solution

a) $\cos 42° \doteq 0.743$ [C] **42** [COS] $\boxed{0.7431448}$
b) $\cos 9° \doteq 0.988$ **c)** $\cos 20° \doteq 0.940$ **d)** $\cos 90° = 0.000$

Example 2

a) Calculate $\cos B$ in △BDE.
b) Calculate ∠B to the nearest degree.

Solution

a) The cosine ratio may be found for either acute angle in a right triangle.

$$\cos B = \frac{\text{length of the leg adjacent to } \angle B}{\text{length of the hypotenuse}}$$

$$= \frac{5}{13}$$

$$\doteq 0.385$$

Think: $\cos = \dfrac{\text{adjacent}}{\text{hypotenuse}}$

b) Using a calculator, $\angle B = 67°$.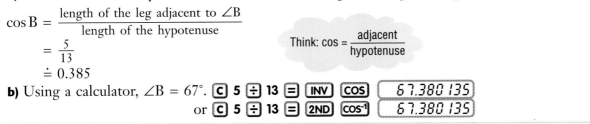

Example 3

In $\triangle WXY$, find the length of XY, to the nearest centimetre.

Solution 1

Using the cosine ratio,

$$\cos W = \frac{11}{24}$$

$$\doteq 0.458$$

$$\angle W \doteq 63°$$

Since $\angle W = 63°$ and $\angle X = 90°$, $\angle Y = 27°$.

$$\cos Y = \frac{XY}{24}$$

$$\cos 27° = \frac{XY}{24}$$

$$0.891 \doteq \frac{XY}{24}$$

$$0.891 \times 24 \doteq XY$$

$$21.384 \doteq XY$$

EST $1 \times 20 = 20$

Solution 2

Using the Pythagorean Theorem,

$$WX^2 + XY^2 = WY^2$$

$$11^2 + XY^2 = 24^2$$

$$XY^2 = 24^2 - 11^2$$

$$= 576 - 121$$

$$= 455$$

$$XY = \sqrt{455}$$

$$\doteq 21.33$$

The length of XY is 21 cm, to the nearest centimetre.

Example 4

A ladder leans against a vertical wall and makes an angle of 65° with the ground. The foot of the ladder is 2 m from the base of the wall. Calculate the length of the ladder, to the nearest tenth of a metre.

Solution

The cosine ratio can be used to calculate the length of the ladder.

$$\cos 65° = \frac{2}{x}$$

$$0.423 \doteq \frac{2}{x}$$

$$0.423 \times x \doteq 2$$

$$x \doteq \frac{2}{0.423}$$

$$\doteq 4.728$$

EST $2 \div 0.4 = 5$

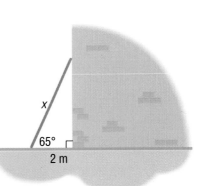

The length of the ladder is 4.7 m, to the nearest tenth of a metre.

CONTINUED ▶

Practice

Find the following to 3 decimal places.

1. cos 30°   **2.** cos 45°   **3.** cos 60°   **4.** cos 89°

5. cos 0°   **6.** cos 5°   **7.** cos 19°   **8.** cos 83°

Find ∠P to the nearest degree.

9. cos P = 0.343   **10.** cos P = 0.887

11. cos P = 0.621   **12.** cos P = 0.019

13. cos P = 0.731   **14.** cos P = 0.524

Find ∠Q to the nearest degree.

15. $\cos Q = \frac{1}{6}$ **16.** $\cos Q = \frac{5}{11}$ **17.** $\cos Q = \frac{5}{9}$

18. $\cos Q = \frac{7}{8}$ **19.** $\cos Q = \frac{15}{16}$ **20.** $\cos Q = \frac{3}{14}$

Calculate cos T. Then, find ∠T to the nearest degree.

21.   **22.**

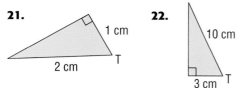

Find x to the nearest tenth of a centimetre.

23. **24.** **25.** **26.** **27.** **28.** **29.** **30.**

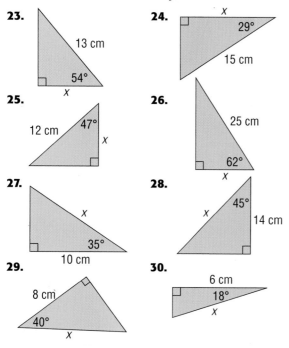

Problems and Applications

31. The leg adjacent to the 74° angle in a right triangle is 6 cm long. How long is the hypotenuse, to the nearest tenth of a centimetre?

32. The hypotenuse of a right triangle is 10 cm long. How long is the leg adjacent to the 21° angle, to the nearest tenth of a centimetre?

33. A kite string is 350 m long. The angle the string makes with the ground is 50°. How far from the person holding the string is a person standing directly under the kite?

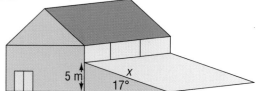

34. A graded ramp is to be built to a barn loft. The ramp is to be inclined at an angle of 17°. The floor of the loft is 5 m above ground level. Use the sine ratio to find the length of the ramp, to the nearest tenth of a metre.

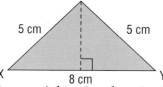

35. Find all the angles in △WXY, to the nearest degree.

W, 5 cm, 5 cm, X, 8 cm, Y

36. a) Does a right triangle exist in which the sine and cosine ratios of the same acute angle are equal?

b) If such a triangle exists, explain why the ratios are equal.

37. Write a problem similar to questions 31 and 32. Have a classmate solve it.

6 Solving Right Triangles

Activity: Study the Diagram

The diagram shows some approximate measurements for the Leaning Tower of Pisa. Name the unknown angles and the unknown side in the triangle.

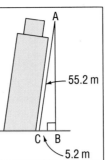

Inquire

1. a) Describe two different methods you could use to calculate the angle that the tower makes with the ground.
b) Use a method of your choice to complete the calculations. Round your answer to the nearest degree.

2. a) Describe two different methods you could use to calculate the vertical height of the top of the tower above the ground.
b) Use a method of your choice to complete the calculations. Round your answer to the nearest tenth of a metre.

3. Of the unknown angles and sides you listed in the Activity, which one have you not yet found? Determine its value.

To **solve** a right triangle means to find all the unknown sides and unknown angles.

Example 1

Solve △ABC. Find lengths to the nearest tenth of a centimetre and angles to the nearest degree.

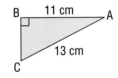

Solution

The cosine ratio can be used to calculate ∠A.

$\cos A = \frac{11}{13}$

$\doteq 0.846$

$\angle A \doteq 32°$

$\angle C = 180° - 32° - 90°$

$= 58°$

The Pythagorean Theorem can be used to calculate the length of BC.

$BC^2 = 13^2 - 11^2$

$= 169 - 121$

$= 48$

$BC = \sqrt{48}$

$\doteq 6.928$

EST $\sqrt{49} = 7$

The length of BC is 6.9 cm, to the nearest tenth of a centimetre. ∠A is 32° and ∠C is 58°, to the nearest degree.

If you stand outside a building and look at an upstairs window, the angle that your line of sight makes with the horizontal is known as the **angle of elevation**.

If someone is standing at the window and looking down at you, the angle that the person's line of sight makes with the horizontal is known as the **angle of depression**.

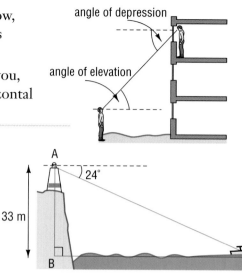

Example 2

A lighthouse sits at the top of a sheer cliff. The top of the lighthouse is 33 m above sea level. The angle of depression to sight a small fishing boat at sea is 24°. How far from the base of the cliff is the fishing boat, to the nearest metre?

Solution

In △ABC, ∠BAC = 90° − 24°
= 66°
The length of BC can be found from the tangent ratio.

$$\tan 66° = \frac{BC}{33}$$
$$2.246 \doteq \frac{BC}{33}$$
$$2.246 \times 33 \doteq BC$$
$$74.12 \doteq BC$$

The fishing boat is 74 m from the base of the cliff, to the nearest metre.

Example 3

Ropes are used to pull a totem pole upright. Then, the ropes are anchored in the ground to hold the pole until the hole is filled. The rope holding this totem pole is 18 m long and forms an angle of 48° with the ground. Find, to the nearest metre,
a) the height of the totem pole
b) how far the anchor point is from the base of the totem pole

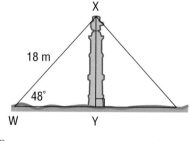

Solution

The height of the pole can be found using the sine ratio. Once two sides of the right triangle are known, the third side may be found using the Pythagorean Theorem.

a)
$$\sin 48° = \frac{XY}{18}$$
$$0.743 \doteq \frac{XY}{18}$$
$$0.743 \times 18 \doteq XY$$
$$13.374 \doteq XY$$

EST 0.7 × 20 = 14

The height of the totem pole is 13 m, to the nearest metre.

b) Using the Pythagorean Theorem,
$$WY^2 = 18^2 - 13^2$$
$$= 324 - 169$$
$$WY = \sqrt{155}$$
$$\doteq 12.450$$

EST √144 = 12

The anchor point is 12 m from the pole, to the nearest metre.

Practice

Find all the unknown angles to the nearest degree and all the unknown sides to the nearest tenth of a unit.

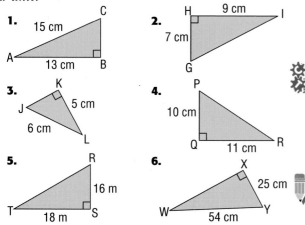

1. C, 15 cm, A, 13 cm, B

2. H, 9 cm, I, 7 cm, G

3. K, 5 cm, J, 6 cm, L

4. P, 10 cm, Q, 11 cm, R

5. R, 16 m, T, 18 m, S

6. X, 25 cm, W, 54 cm, Y

Solve each triangle. Round each side length to the nearest tenth of a unit and each angle to the nearest degree.

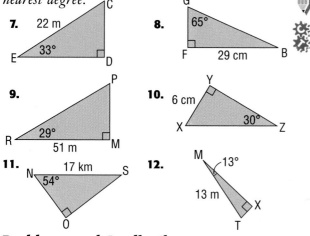

7. 22 m, C, 33°, E, D

8. G, 65°, F, 29 cm, B

9. P, 29°, R, 51 m, M

10. Y, 6 cm, X, 30°, Z

11. N, 17 km, S, 54°, O

12. M, 13°, 13 m, X, T

Problems and Applications

13. A kite is 32 m above the ground. The angle the kite string makes with the ground is 39°. How long is the kite string, to the nearest metre?

14. The two guy wires supporting a flagpole are each anchored 7 m from the flagpole and form an angle of 52° with the ground. What is the total length of guy wire, to the nearest metre, needed to support this flagpole?

15. Calgary's Bankers Hall building is 197 m tall. From a point level with, and 48 m from, the base of the building, what is the angle of elevation of the top of the building, to the nearest degree?

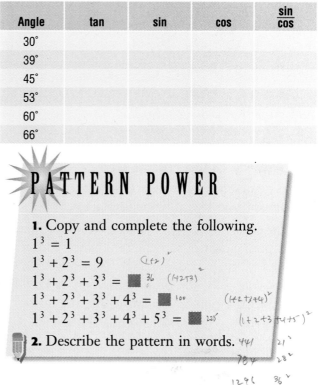

16. a) When you are standing without shoes on, what is the height of your eyes above the ground, to the nearest centimetre?
b) Calculate the angle of depression, to the nearest degree, you would use to look at a point on the ground 5 m in front of you.
c) Would the answer to part b) be greater or less for a person taller than you? Explain.

17. a) Copy and complete this table. Write each ratio as a decimal to 3 decimal places.
b) Compare each tangent value to each value in the last column. What do you notice?
c) Explain your results in part b).

Angle	tan	sin	cos	$\frac{sin}{cos}$
30°				
39°				
45°				
53°				
60°				
66°				

PATTERN POWER

1. Copy and complete the following.
$$1^3 = 1$$
$$1^3 + 2^3 = 9 \quad (1+2)^2$$
$$1^3 + 2^3 + 3^3 = \blacksquare \quad 36 \quad (1+2+3)^2$$
$$1^3 + 2^3 + 3^3 + 4^3 = \blacksquare \quad 100 \quad (1+2+3+4)^2$$
$$1^3 + 2^3 + 3^3 + 4^3 + 5^3 = \blacksquare \quad 225 \quad (1+2+3+4+5)^2$$

2. Describe the pattern in words. 441 21²
784 28²
1296 36²

247

Fractal Geometry

One of the newest branches of mathematics is **fractal geometry**. The word "fractal" comes from the Latin verb *frangere*, which means to break. The study of fractals has led to the development of new computer graphics programs and may give scientists a way to describe complex things in nature.

Activity ❶ The H Fractal

The diagrams show the first 3 stages of an H Fractal with a reduction factor of $\frac{1}{2}$.

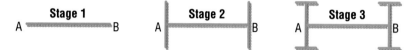

In stage 1, begin with a horizontal line segment AB of length 1 unit. In stage 2, add 2 vertical line segments, each of length $\frac{1}{2}$, perpendicular to AB at A and B. In stage 3, add 4 horizontal line segments, each of length $\frac{1}{4}$, perpendicular to the 2 vertical line segments. This H fractal has a reduction factor of $\frac{1}{2}$ because each new set of line segments is half as long as the previous set.

1. On grid paper, draw the first 4 stages of an H fractal with a reduction factor of $\frac{1}{2}$.

2. On grid paper, draw the first 4 stages of an H fractal with a reduction factor of $\frac{3}{4}$.

Activity ❷ The Fractal Tree

The diagrams show the first 3 stages of a fractal tree with a reduction factor of 0.7.

To produce the second stage from the first, 2 perpendicular branches are added to the end of the previous branch. Notice that if we continued the previous branch, it would bisect the right angle formed by the new branches. We can construct a third stage from the second in the same way.

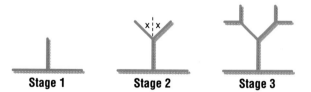

Draw the first 4 stages of a fractal tree using a reduction factor of your choice.

Activity ❸ The Binary Tree

The diagrams show the first 3 stages of a binary tree with a reduction factor of $\frac{1}{2}$.

Begin with a vertical branch of length 1. Each horizontal branch is twice the length of the vertical branch above it. Each vertical branch is $\frac{1}{2}$ the length of the vertical branch above it.

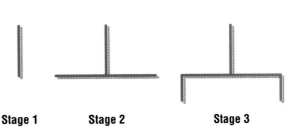

Stage 1   **Stage 2**   **Stage 3**

Draw the first 6 stages of a binary tree using a reduction factor of your choice.

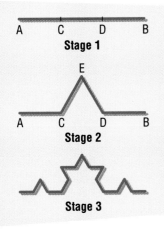

Activity ❹ The "Snowflake" Fractal

This is the most famous fractal. The first 3 stages are shown.

Begin with a line segment AB and divide it into 3 equal parts. In stage 2, an equilateral triangle CED is constructed on the middle line segment. The middle segment CD is then removed. The process can be repeated as many times as you wish.

Construct a fractal curve by drawing squares instead of triangles.

Activity ❺ Sierpinski's Sieve

The diagrams show the first 3 stages of Sierpinski's Sieve.

Begin with an equilateral triangle. Divide the triangle into 4 smaller congruent equilateral triangles, and remove the inner triangle. At each stage, a triangle is removed from the centre of each triangular region.

Draw the first 4 stages of Sierpinski's Sieve.

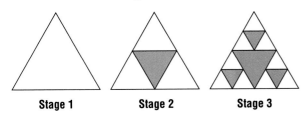

Stage 1   **Stage 2**   **Stage 3**

Activity ❻ Uses of Fractals

1. Use your research skills to find out how computer graphics programs based on fractal geometry are used in movies such as *Star Trek II*.

2. Can you find any other applications of fractals? If so, describe them.

249

Automobiles

Automobiles are designed to be visually appealing to potential buyers. They are also designed so that there will be less air resistance at high speeds.

Activity ❶

1. Draw 3 reference points on a blank piece of paper, as shown below.

2. Join your 3 reference points using curved lines.

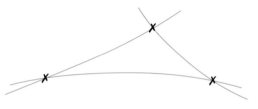

3. Draw the shape of an automobile within the curved lines.

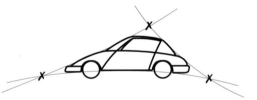

4. How would you locate the reference points to design a low sportscar? a family sedan?

5. Compare your answers to question 4 with your classmates'.

Activity ❷

1. Trace the automobile on the right onto a sheet of blank paper.

2. Draw its 3 reference points and the curved lines.

3. Trace the 3 reference points onto another sheet of blank paper and trade them for a classmate's.

4. Design a new automobile with your classmate's reference points.

5. How similar are your designs to each other's and to the original design?

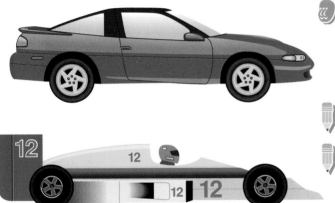

Activity ❸

1. Examine the pictures of the sportscar, racing car, and van shown on the left.

2. Rank these 3 vehicles in terms of their maximum speed, from lowest to highest.

3. Which of the vehicles is the most air resistant? Explain.

4. What shapes offer the least air resistance? Explain why this is so.

5. Trace each picture onto a blank sheet of paper.

6. Locate the 3 reference points for each type of vehicle.

7. Trade your 3 sets of reference points for a classmate's.

8. Design 3 new vehicles from your classmate's reference points.

9. Compare your designs with the original designs.

Activity ❹

1. Experiment with the design of an automobile using 4 and 5 reference points. Compare your results with your classmates'.

2. Research computer programs that are available to design automobiles.

Review

1. State why these triangles are congruent and list all the corresponding equal parts.

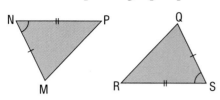

Explain why the pairs of triangles are congruent.

2.

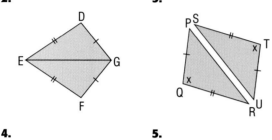

3.

4.

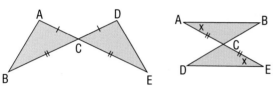

5.

The pairs of triangles are similar. Find the unknown sides.

6.

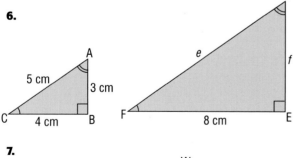

7.

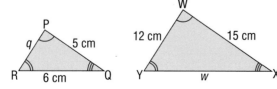

8.

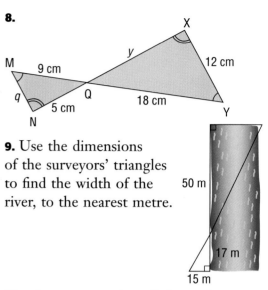

9. Use the dimensions of the surveyors' triangles to find the width of the river, to the nearest metre.

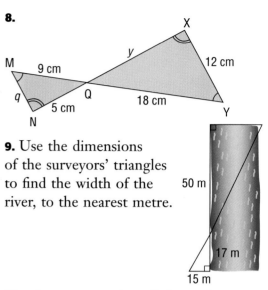

Use the tangent ratio to find x to the nearest tenth of a centimetre.

10.

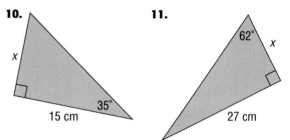

11.

Use the sine ratio to find x to the nearest tenth of a metre.

12.

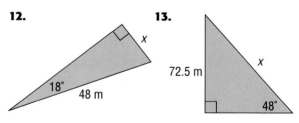

13.

Use the cosine ratio to find x to the nearest unit.

14.

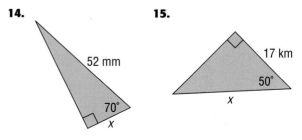

15.

252

Solve each triangle. Round each side length to the nearest tenth of a unit and each angle to the nearest degree.

16.

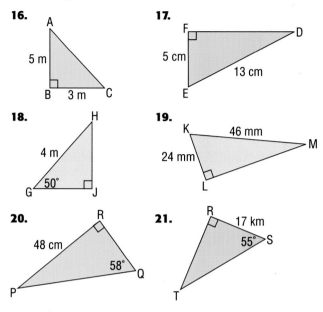

A, 5 m, B, 3 m, C

17.

F, 5 cm, E, 13 cm, D

18.

H, 4 m, G, 50°, J

19.

K, 46 mm, M, 24 mm, L

20.

R, 48 cm, P, 58°, Q

21.

R, 17 km, 55°, S, T

22. When a road has a 10% gradient, it means that the road rises 10 m for every 100 m of horizontal distance travelled. What is the angle of inclination of the road, to the nearest degree?

x, 100 m, 10 m

23. The Commodity Exchange Tower in Winnipeg is 117 m tall. When the sun's rays make an angle of 68° with the ground, what is the length of the building's shadow on level ground, to the nearest metre?

117 m, 68°

24. If you were in a hot air balloon 500 m above Selkirk, Manitoba, at what angle of depression would you look at a point on the ground 800 m horizontally from the balloon?

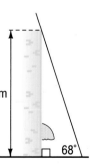

500 m, 800 m

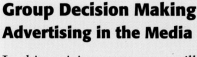

Chapter Check

Which pairs of triangles are congruent? Explain.

1.

2.

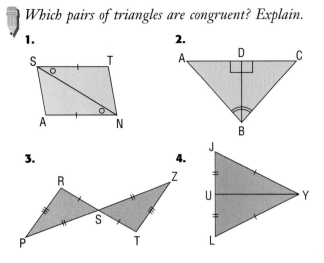

3.

4.

The pairs of triangles are similar. Find the unknown side lengths.

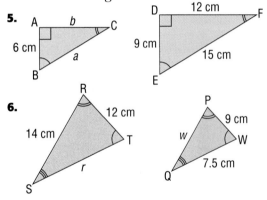

5.

6.

Are the triangles similar? Are the triangles congruent? Explain.

7.

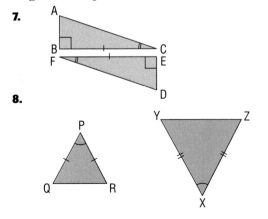

8.

Use the tangent ratio to find p to the nearest tenth of a unit.

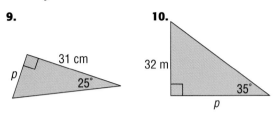

9.

10.

Use the sine ratio to find m to the nearest unit.

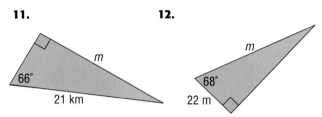

11.

12.

Use the cosine ratio to find w to the nearest tenth of a unit.

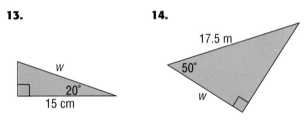

13.

14.

Solve the triangles for the unknown sides and angles. Round each side length to the nearest tenth of a unit and each angle to the nearest degree.

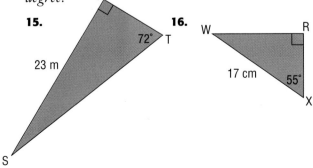

15.

16.

Using the Strategies

1. How many squares are in this diagram?

2. The number in each large square is found by adding the numbers in the 2 small squares connected to it. What are the numbers in the small squares?

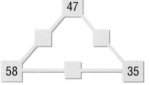

3. The Beach bus leaves every 20 min and the Sand bus leaves every 45 min. If they leave together at noon, when is the next time that they will leave together?

4. The amount of a purchase is $12.43. How can the exact amount be paid without using a $10.00 bill, but using the smallest number of bills and coins?

5. This is a 4-by-4 square.

One way to separate it into 2 congruent shapes, made up of smaller squares, is shown.

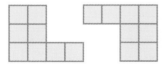

Find at least 5 other ways.

6. Six consecutive even numbers are written on a piece of paper. If the sum of the first 3 numbers is 60, what is the sum of the last 3?

7. Which of these pizzas is the best buy? Why?

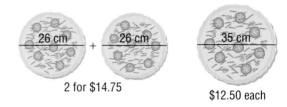

8. Six water glasses are in a row. The first 3 are full, and the last 3 are empty. How can 1 glass be moved so that full glasses and empty glasses alternate?

9. What is the minimum number of mass comparisons an inspector needs to make to find 1 counterfeit coin in a collection of 40 coins. Assume that the counterfeit coin is lighter than the others.

10. You fill a glass half full of water from the tap. Then, you add enough ice cubes to the water to fill the glass. Sketch a graph of temperature versus time from the moment you add the ice to the water until the moment when the ice has all melted.

DATA BANK

1. A bathtub can hold 142 L of water up to the overflow. How many bathtubs can the world's largest reservoir fill when it is full?

2. Which 2 provinces are closest to each other in surface area? Which province is larger and by how much?

CHAPTER 7

Shape and Space

The average number of people per square metre on a Tokyo train filled to capacity is officially 4. In fact, the average number of people per square metre on Tokyo trains in rush hour is 10. Can 10 people in your class stand on 1 m² of floor?

Estimate the area of your classroom floor in square metres. About how many people are there per square metre in your classroom?

If your classroom were as crowded as a Tokyo train in rush hour, about how many people would be in the room?

Tangrams

A tangram is a 7-piece puzzle that comes from China. The origin of the word "tangram" is itself interesting. The ending of the word, *gram*, refers to something drawn, such as a diagram. The beginning of the word, *tan*, dates back to the Tang dynasty, A.D. 618-906, the greatest dynasty in Chinese history. The 7 tangram pieces are shown assembled as a square.

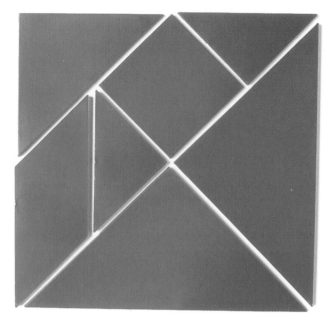

Activity ❶ Convex and Concave Figures

Polygons are closed geometric figures with line segments as sides. You are already familiar with triangles (3 sides), quadrilaterals (4 sides), pentagons (5 sides), and hexagons (6 sides).

Polygons can be convex or concave. If you wrap a piece of string around the perimeter of a convex polygon and pull the string tight, the string makes contact with every point of the polygon. On the other hand, if you wrap a piece of string around a **concave polygon**, the string does not make contact with every point of the polygon. A concave polygon bends in at some point or points, leaving gaps.

Using all 7 tangram pieces, it is possible to construct 9 different convex quadrilaterals without holes in the middle. One of them is the square shown at the top of this page. The others are 2 rectangles, 2 parallelograms, and 4 trapezoids. Use your 7 tangram pieces to construct these 8 quadrilaterals. Sketch your solutions on grid paper.

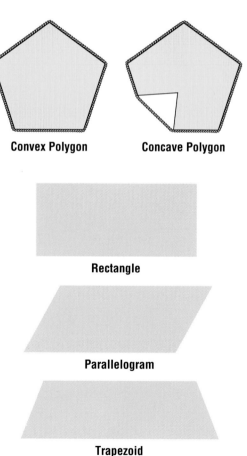

Convex Polygon   **Concave Polygon**

Rectangle

Parallelogram

Trapezoid

Activity ❷ Quadrilaterals

1. From a tangram, select the 4 triangles shown. Use the 4 triangles to make the following quadrilaterals. Sketch your solutions on grid paper.

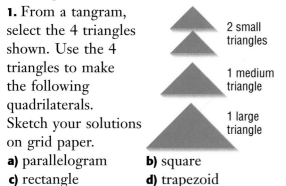

2 small triangles

1 medium triangle

1 large triangle

a) parallelogram   **b)** square
c) rectangle   **d)** trapezoid

2. Are any of these quadrilaterals regular polygons? Explain.

Activity ❸ More Convex Figures

1. There are 7 other convex polygons without holes in the middle that can be constructed. Use the 7 tangram pieces to construct these polygons.

a) 1 triangle   **b)** 3 pentagons   **c)** 3 hexagons

2. Are any of these polygons regular polygons? Explain.

Activity ❹ Area with Tangrams

Let the area of the smallest tangram piece be 1 square unit. Calculate the areas of the other tangram pieces, and record the areas in a chart.

Mental Math

Calculate.

1. 3.14×10 **2.** 3.14×100 **3.** 3.14×1000 **4.** $3.14 \times 10\ 000$

5. $3.14 \div 10$ **6.** $3.14 \div 100$ **7.** $3.14 \div 1000$ **8.** $3.14 \div 10\ 000$

Calculate.

9. $5 \times 25 \div 1000$ **10.** 12×8 **11.** 14×7 **12.** 2.5×6

13. $8 \times 5 \times 3$ **14.** $10 \times 7 \times 9$ **15.** $4(7 + 6)$ **16.** $15.5 \div 5$

Estimate.

17. $(3.14)(1.2)$ **18.** $(3.14)(1.8)$ **19.** $(3.14)(5.8)$ **20.** $(3.14)(0.9)$

Estimate, then calculate.

21. $\frac{1}{2}(6.2 + 4.8)$ **22.** $\frac{1}{2}(2.2 + 5.8)$ **23.** $\frac{1}{2}(3.9 + 8.1)$ **24.** $\frac{1}{2}(10.2 + 9.8)$

Estimate.

25. $(3.14)(2.2)^2$ **26.** $(3.14)(3.3)^2$ **27.** $(3.14)(5.4)^2$ **28.** $(3.14)(4.9)^2$

Estimate.

29. $(3.14)(2.1)(3.2)$ **30.** $(3.14)(5.2)(2.4)$ **31.** $(3.14)(5.6)(5.1)$ **32.** $(3.14)(7.2)(10.4)$

Estimate.

33. $(3.14)(2.4)^3$ **34.** $(3.14)(4.3)^3$ **35.** $(3.14)(9.8)^3$ **36.** $(3.14)(5.1)^3$

7.1 Areas of Rectangles, Squares, and Circles

Activity: Use the Information

Precision figure skating teams perform routines set to music. Teams may be made up of 20 or 24 skaters.

Several times in a routine, the full team lines up across the ice. When the team rotates around the centre spot on the ice, the skaters cover a complete circle. When the skaters sweep the ice from one end or one side to the other, they cover a rectangle.

Inquire

1. On an ice surface 30 m by 56 m, what is the area of the largest rectangle the skaters could cover? the area of the largest square? the area of the largest circle?

2. If the skaters split into 2 groups to practise, they could divide the ice into 2 congruent rectangles in 2 ways. Use diagrams to show the 2 ways and calculate the area that each group would have.

3. a) Which of the 2 ways of dividing the ice surface would allow each group to cover the largest possible circle? Explain.
b) Find the area of the largest possible circle in part a).

Example 1

The Canadian flag has 2 red rectangles, with a square in the middle. Calculate the area of 1 red rectangle.

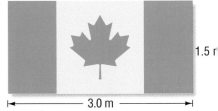

1.5 m

3.0 m

Solution

The formula for the area of the rectangular flag is $A = lw$.

$$A = lw$$
$$= (3.0)(1.5)$$
$$= 4.5$$

The formula for the area of the white square is $A = s^2$.

$$A = s^2$$
$$= (1.5)^2$$
$$= 2.25$$

Area of 2 red rectangles is $4.5 - 2.25 = 2.25$
Area of 1 red rectangle is $\frac{2.25}{2} = 1.125$
The area of 1 red rectangle is 1.125 m².

Example 2

There are 5 circles marked on a hockey rink. Each circle has a radius of 4.5 m. For the rink shown, calculate the area of the ice that lies outside the circles and between the goal lines. Round your answer to the nearest tenth of a square metre.

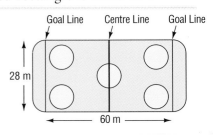

Goal Line   Centre Line   Goal Line

28 m

60 m

Solution

The ice between the goal lines is rectangular.

$A = lw$
$= 60 \times 28$ **EST** $60 \times 30 = 1800$
$= 1680$

The area of each circle is given by the formula

$A = \pi r^2$
$= 3.14(4.5)^2$ **EST** $3 \times 5 \times 5 = 75$
$= 63.585$

For 5 circles, $A = 5 \times 63.585$ **EST** $5 \times 60 = 300$
$= 317.925$

Area of rectangle less total area of circles $= 1680 - 317.925$ **EST** $1700 - 300 = 1400$
$= 1362.075$

The area of the ice outside the circles and between the goal lines is 1362.1 m², to the nearest tenth of a square metre.

Practice

Determine each area.

1.

2.

4.2 cm

8.6 cm

6.3 m

Calculate the area of each circle, to the nearest square centimetre.

3.

6 cm

4.

10.6 cm

Problems and Applications

Calculate the area of each patio.

5.

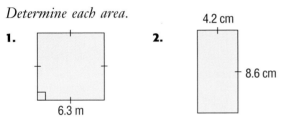

8 m
4 m
8 m
3 m

6.

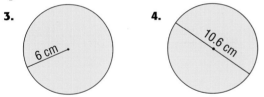

4.1 m
5.2 m
2.1 m

7. Calculate each area to the nearest square unit.

a)

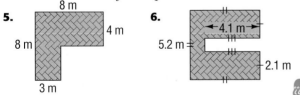

9 m

b)

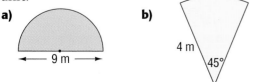

4 m
45°

8. a) Calculate the area of the glass in this window to the nearest tenth of a square metre.

b) A protective storm window for this window costs $19.99/m². What is the cost of the storm window?

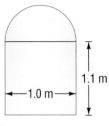

1.1 m
1.0 m

9. A rectangular lot measures 66 m by 107 m. A sidewalk surrounds the lot. The sidewalk is 2 m wide. What is the area of the sidewalk?

10. You want to plant a 16-m² rectangular garden and build the shortest possible fence around it. What shape should you make the garden?

11. A gardener wants to rope off a rectangular area of grass. The gardener has 10 m of rope to block off 2 sides of the area and will use a wall of the garage and a wall of the house for the other 2 sides. What is the largest area that can be roped off?

12. The area of the circle is 153.86 m². Work with a partner to calculate the area of the shaded region. Use $\pi = 3.14$.

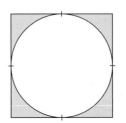

261

7.2 Areas of Parallelograms, Triangles, and Trapezoids

Some of the most distinctive architecture is composed of parallelograms, triangles, and trapezoids.
This photograph of the ceiling in the Hockey Hall of Fame is an example.

Activity: Determine the Formula

Copy the parallelogram onto grid paper. Cut a right triangle from the parallelogram along the height, h. Then, fit the right triangle onto the opposite end of the remainder of the parallelogram so that the two pieces form a rectangle.

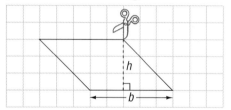

1. What is the area of the rectangle in square units?

2. Write a formula for the area of the rectangle in terms of the variables b and h.

3. What is the area of the parallelogram in square units?

4. Write a formula for the area of the parallelogram in terms of b and h.

Example 1

Many Canadian heritage quilts are made from simple geometric shapes such as identical parallelograms. If the side of each square on the grid is 5 cm, what is the area of each parallelogram in this section of a quilt?

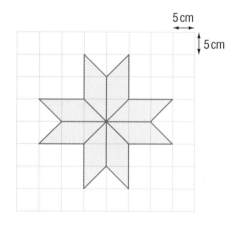

Solution

The formula for the area of a parallelogram is $A = bh$. The base of each parallelogram in this quilt is 10 cm and each height is 5 cm.

$$A = bh$$
$$= (10)(5)$$
$$= 50$$

The area of each parallelogram in the quilt is 50 cm².

Activity: Determine the Formula

Copy this triangle and trapezoid onto grid paper.

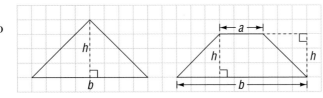

Inquire

1. Along one side of the triangle, draw another identical triangle to form a parallelogram similar to the one shown.

2. Write a formula for the area of the parallelogram in terms of b and h.

3. How is the area of the triangle related to the area of the parallelogram?

4. Write a formula for the area of the triangle in terms of b and h.

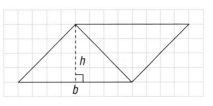

5. In the trapezoid, draw a diagonal to form 2 triangles as shown. Then, write the area of each triangle in terms of its base and height.

6. What is the sum of the areas of both triangles in terms of a, b, and h?

7. Factor the sum you found in question 6, and write a formula for the area of a trapezoid in terms of a, b, and h.

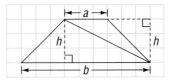

Example 2

Calculate the area of each figure to the nearest tenth of a square centimetre.

a)

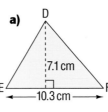

b)

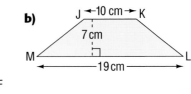

Solution

a) The formula for the **area of a triangle** is $A = \frac{1}{2}bh$.

$A = \frac{1}{2}bh$

$= \frac{1}{2}(10.3)(7.1)$ **EST** $(0.5)(10)(7) = 35$

$= \frac{1}{2}(73.13)$

$= 36.565$

The area of $\triangle DEF$ is about 36.6 cm².

b) The formula for the **area of a trapezoid** is $A = \frac{1}{2}(a + b)h$.

$A = \frac{1}{2}(a + b)h$

$= \frac{1}{2}(10 + 19)(7)$

$= \frac{1}{2}(29)(7)$ **EST** $(0.5)(30)(7) = 105$

$= \frac{1}{2}(203)$

$= 101.5$

The area of trapezoid JKLM is 101.5 cm².

CONTINUED

263

Practice

Calculate the area of each figure.

1.

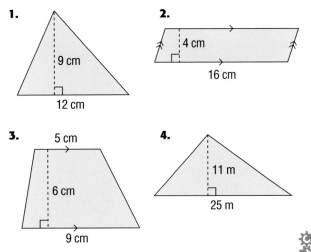

9 cm

12 cm

2.

4 cm

16 cm

3.

5 cm

6 cm

9 cm

4.

11 m

25 m

Estimate each area. Then, calculate it to the nearest square centimetre or square metre.

5.

11.2 m

8.3 m

6.

26.3 cm

14.6 cm

7.

10.6 cm

7.4 cm

8.

2.5 cm

Problems and Applications

9. Calculate the area of the shaded region in each diagram.

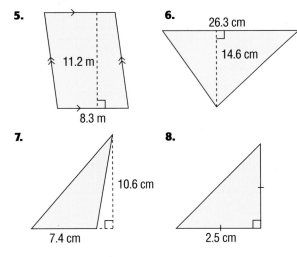

a)

12 cm

8 cm

10 cm   10 cm

12 cm

b)

8 cm

10 cm

14 cm

10. The area of a parallelogram is 8400 cm². Its height is 60 cm. What length is its base?

11. Many Canadian cities use the Blue Box for recycling. The sides, the front, and the back of the Blue Box are trapezoids. What is the area of a side and a front or back?

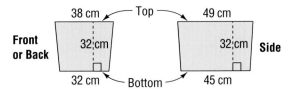

Front or Back

38 cm — Top

32 cm

32 cm — Bottom

49 cm

32 cm   Side

45 cm

12. The area of a triangle is 14.4 cm², and the length of its base is 6.4 cm. What is its height?

13. Without calculating any areas, decide how the areas of the triangles, parallelogram, and trapezoid compare. Explain.

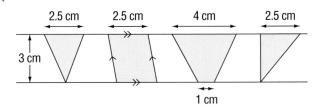

2.5 cm   2.5 cm   4 cm   2.5 cm

3 cm

1 cm

14. The area of trapezoid PQRS is 26 cm². Work with a partner to calculate *a* when *b* = 8 cm and *h* = 4 cm.

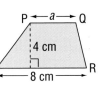

P ← *a* → Q

4 cm

S   8 cm   R

WORD POWER

Change the word SLOW to the word FAST by changing 1 letter at a time. Each time you change a letter, you must form a real word. The best solution requires the fewest steps. Compare your list of words with a classmate's.

Areas of Irregular Figures

Look at the figure of the arrow. It has been drawn on a grid with each square equal to 1 square unit.

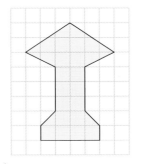

The area of the arrow can be estimated by counting the number of whole and part squares that it covers.

The number of whole squares is 16. The number of part squares is 14.

Total Area = (Number of whole squares) + $\frac{1}{2}$(Number of part squares)

$$= 16 + 0.5(14)$$
$$= 16 + 7$$
$$= 23$$

The total area of the arrow is about 23 square units.

Why do you think you calculate one-half of the part squares?

Activity

1. Trace your hand on a sheet of 1-cm grid paper.

2. Estimate the area of your hand by counting whole squares and part squares.

3. Measure your arm length in centimetres.

4. Collect a class set of arm lengths in centimetres and hand areas in square centimetres.

5. Graph the data on a grid with arm length along the horizontal axis and hand area along the vertical axis. Can you make a general conclusion about arm length and hand area from the data? If you can, what is it?

265

Volumes

Volume is the amount of space occupied by an object.

Activity ❶ Volume of a Prism

1. Cut the top from an empty 250-mL milk carton to form a prism.

2. What type of prism have you made?

3. Fill the prism with layers of 1-cm cubes.

4. How many 1-cm cubes just fill the prism?

5. What is the volume of the prism?

Activity ❷ Volume of a Pyramid

1. Draw the net of a pyramid that has the same base area and height as the prism you made in Activity 1.

2. Cut out the net, tape it, and place the pyramid inside the prism.

3. Estimate how many times greater the volume of the prism is than the volume of the pyramid.

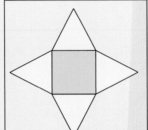

4. Cut along 3 sides of the pyramid's base. Then, fill the pyramid with sand and empty it into the prism. Repeat until the prism is full.

a) How many pyramids full of sand does it take to fill the prism?

b) How close was your estimate in step 3?

5. From your results, what fraction of the volume of the prism is the volume of the pyramid?

6. Construct the net of a triangular prism and the net of a triangular pyramid, so that the prism and the pyramid have congruent bases and equal heights.

7. Cut out and tape the prism and the pyramid. Estimate how many times greater the volume of the prism is than the volume of the pyramid.

8. Check your estimate by using the pyramid to fill the prism with sand.

9. Are your results from step 8 consistent with the fraction you found in step 5?

Activity ❸ Volume of a Cylinder

1. Obtain an empty cylindrical tin can. Make sure that there are no sharp edges where the lid was removed.

2. a) Cover the bottom of the can as completely as possible with a layer of 1-cm cubes. Add more layers to fill the can as completely as possible.
b) Use the number of cubes in the can to estimate its volume.
c) Is your estimated volume an underestimate or an overestimate? Explain.

3. Empty the can, then fill it with water. Use a graduated cylinder to measure the volume of water in the can.

4. What is the volume of the can in cubic centimetres? Explain.

5. Compare the volume you stated in step 4 with your estimate in step 2.

Activity ❹ Volume of a Cone

1. Use a piece of construction paper to form a cone whose tip just touches the bottom of the tin can you used in Activity 3. The curved surface of the cone should touch the inside circumference of the top of the can.

2. Tape your cone and cut it so that its height is the same as the height of the cylinder.

3. Estimate how many times greater the volume of the cylinder is than the volume of the cone.

4. Fill the cone with sand and empty it into the cylinder. Repeat until the cylinder is full.
a) How many cones full of sand does it take to fill the cylinder?
b) How close was your estimate in step 3?

5. From your results, what fraction of the volume of the cylinder is the volume of the cone?

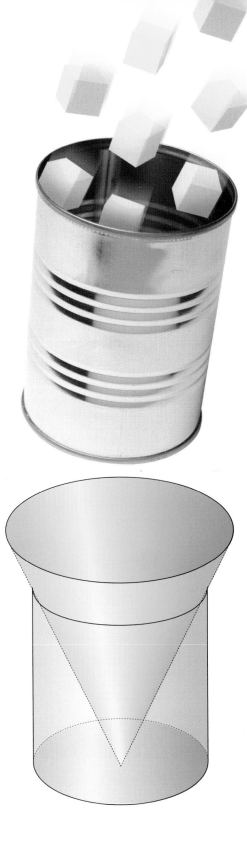

7.3 Surface Area and Volume of a Prism

Activity: Solve the Problem

Mark has to wrap a gift for his friend.
The gift box measures 40 cm by
20 cm by 20 cm. Mark has 16 000 cm²
of wrapping paper. Mark wants
to know if he has enough paper.

Inquire

1. What type of prism is the box?

2. What types of figures are the faces of the box?

3. Calculate the area of each face.

4. What is the sum of all the areas?

5. Does Mark have enough paper? What
assumptions did you make?

Example 1

Fort York was built next to Lake Ontario during the War of 1812.
The 2.1 m high parapet that surrounds it forms a triangle with
sides of 309 m, 153 m, and 324 m, as shown. The shape of the
Fort resembles a triangular prism, but without a top. Find the
interior surface area of the Fort to the nearest square metre.

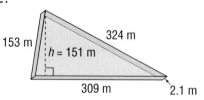

153 m   324 m
$h = 151$ m
309 m   2.1 m

Solution

The surface area of a prism is the sum of the areas of the faces.
In this case, the faces are the triangular base of the Fort and the
3 rectangular walls. The area of the triangular base is given by

$A = \frac{1}{2}bh$

$= \frac{1}{2}(309 \times 151)$ **EST** $\frac{1}{2}(300)(150) = 22\ 500$

$= \frac{1}{2}(46\ 659)$ [C] 0 [·] 5 [×] 309 [×] 151 [=] 23329.5

$= 23\ 329.5$

The area of the 3 rectangular faces is

$2.1(309) + 2.1(153) + 2.1(324)$ **EST** $2(300) + 2(200) + 2(300) = 1600$

$= 648.9 + 321.3 + 680.4$

$= 1650.6$ [C] 2 [·] 1 [×] [(] 309 [+] 153 [+] 324 [)] [=] 1650.6

The surface area is

$23\ 329.5 + 1650.6 = 24\ 980.1$ **EST** $23\ 000 + 2000 = 25\ 000$

The interior surface area of Fort York is 24 980 m² to the
nearest square metre.

Activity: Investigate Volume

Build this rectangular prism with interlocking cubes.

Inquire

1. How many cubes represent the amount of space occupied by the prism?

2. Let the side of 1 cube be 1 unit of length.
a) What is the height of the prism?
b) What is the area of the base of the prism in square units?

3. Multiply the area of the base by the height, and compare the result with the amount of space you calculated in question 1.

4. The amount of space occupied by a prism is called the **volume**. Write a formula to calculate the volume of this prism. Use the variables V, B, and h, where B is the area of the base and h is the height.

Example 2

Calculate each volume.

a)

b)

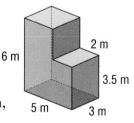

Solution

The volume of a prism is the area of its base times its height.

a) The cereal box is a rectangular prism.
$V = B \times h$

$= [(19)(5)](25)$ $\boxed{\text{EST}}$ $(20)(5)(25) = 2500$

$= 2375$

The volume of the box is 2375 cm³.

b) The cheese box is a triangular prism. The base and height of the triangle are 10 cm each.

$$V = B \times h$$
$$= [\tfrac{1}{2}(10)(10)](2)$$
$$= (50)(2)$$
$$= 100$$

The volume of the box is 100 cm³.

Example 3

A **composite solid** is made up of 2 or more prisms joined together. Find the volume of this composite solid.

Solution

The solid is composed of a smaller prism, where $l = 3$ m, $w = 2$ m, and $h = 3.5$ m, and a larger prism, where $l = 3$ m, $w = 3$ m, and $h = 6$ m. The volume of the smaller prism is (3)(2)(3.5) or 21 m³. The volume of the larger prism is (3)(3)(6) or 54 m³.

Total volume $= 21 + 54$

$= 75$

The volume of the composite solid is 75 m³.

CONTINUED ▶

269

Practice

Name each prism.

1.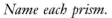

2.

3.

4.

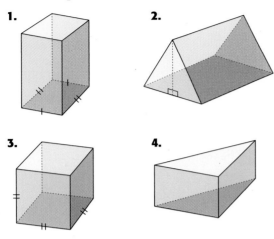

Which prism can be formed from each net?

5.

6.

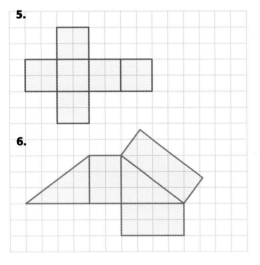

Estimate the surface area of each prism. Then, calculate it to the nearest square centimetre or square metre.

7.

6 m
13 m
5 m

8.

5.2 cm
2.2 cm
1.4 cm

Calculate each surface area.

9.

5 cm

10.

11 m
9 m
25 m
12 m

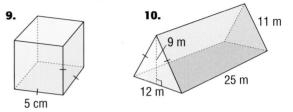

Estimate, then calculate the volume of each rectangular prism.

11.

2 m
3 m
4 m

12.

5 cm
12 cm
3 cm

13.

13 cm
12 cm
11 cm

14.

9 m
6 m
2 m

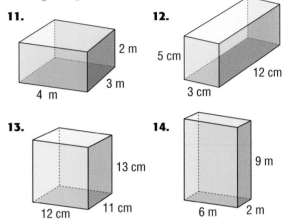

Calculate the surface area and volume of each prism to the nearest square or cubic unit.

15.

11 m
9 m
2 m

16.

10 m
8.5 m
10 m
20 m
10 m

17.

130 cm
20 cm
50 cm
120 cm

18.

3.2 cm
8.5 cm
4.1 cm

19.

230 m
120 m
110 m

20.

23.9 m
15.2 m
18.4 m
23.6 m

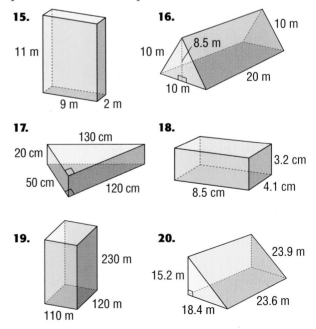

Problems and Applications

21. A covered garbage bin is to be built so that it measures 1.5 m by 1.2 m by 1.0 m.
a) How much plywood will it take to build the garbage bin?

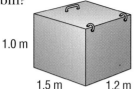

1.0 m
1.5 m   1.2 m

b) How many cubic metres of garbage will it hold?

22. a) Calculate the surface area of this room.

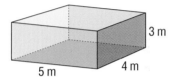

3 m
5 m   4 m

b) One 4-L can of paint will cover 36 m². If you want to give the ceiling and walls of the room 2 coats of paint, how many 4-L cans will you need? What assumptions have you made?

23. a) The dimensions of the base of a composter are 1 m by 1 m. Its height is 0.65 m. It is a prism with a top, a bottom, and 4 sides. Calculate its surface area.
b) The cost of material to build this composter is $9.98/m². What is the total cost of the material?
c) If a town has set aside $1 250 000 for the materials to build these composters, how many composters can be built?

24. The surface area of a cube is 216 cm². What are the dimensions of this cube?

25. a) A prism has a height of 10 cm. Find its surface area if the dimensions of the base are 8 cm by 2 cm.
b) Draw and label a diagram of the prism on dot paper or centimetre grid paper.
c) What is the name of the prism?

26. How many cubic metres of air does the tent contain?

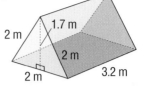

1.7 m
2 m
2 m
2 m   3.2 m

27. Canada's Anik E1 is a domestic communications satellite. Launched in September, 1991, it is a rectangular prism with $l = 23$ m, $w = 8.5$ m, and $h = 4.3$ m. Calculate the surface area and volume of Anik E1 to the nearest square or cubic unit.

28. The diagram shows the side view of a pool.

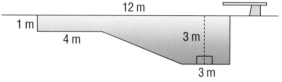

12 m
1 m
4 m   3 m
3 m

a) The pool is 5 m wide. Calculate its volume.
b) A pump can drain water from the pool at 0.3 m³/min. How long does it take to drain the pool?

29. A garden storage shed is to be built in the shape of a rectangular prism before the roof is added. The volume of the shed before the roof is put on is 24 m³. What are the most appropriate dimensions for the rectangular prism?

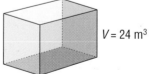

$V = 24$ m³

30. Work with a partner to calculate the surface area and volume of the interior of your classroom.

31. Write a problem that requires the calculation of the surface area and volume of a prism. Have another classmate solve your problem.

7.4 Surface Area and Volume of a Pyramid

The Great Pyramid of Khufu is shown in this photograph. It was built by an ancient Egyptian civilization around 2500 B.C. In spite of its age, its sophisticated design continues to amaze people.

Inquire

1. Name the different geometric figures the Great Pyramid is made up of.

2. What is the name of this type of pyramid?

3. The area of the square base of Khufu is 53 058 m². What is the length of each side of the base to the nearest metre?

4. The **slant height** of the pyramid, or the height of each triangular face, is 187 m. What is the surface area of each face?

5. What is the total amount of exposed surface area on this pyramid?

Example 1

Calculate the surface area of this square-based pyramid.

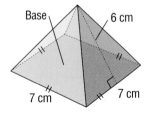

Solution

The **surface area of a pyramid** is the sum of the area of the base and the areas of the triangular faces.

The base of the pyramid is a square.
Base Area $= (7)(7)$
$\qquad = 49$

The 4 triangular faces are identical.
Face Area $= 4[\frac{1}{2}(7)(6)]$
$\qquad = 4(21)$
$\qquad = 84$

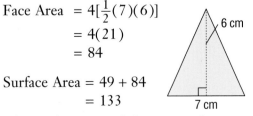

Surface Area $= 49 + 84$
$\qquad\quad = 133$

The surface area of the pyramid is 133 cm².

Example 2

Calculate the volume of this pyramid.

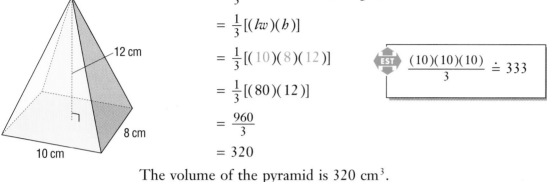

12 cm

8 cm

10 cm

Solution

The **volume of a pyramid** is one-third the product of the area of the base and the height.

$$V = \frac{1}{3}(\text{Area of Base})(\text{Height})$$

$$= \frac{1}{3}[(lw)(h)]$$

$$= \frac{1}{3}[(10)(8)(12)]$$

$$= \frac{1}{3}[(80)(12)]$$

$$= \frac{960}{3}$$

$$= 320$$

EST $\dfrac{(10)(10)(10)}{3} \doteq 333$

The volume of the pyramid is 320 cm^3.

Example 3

a) What is the volume of this prism?
b) What is the maximum volume of a pyramid that can fit upright inside this prism?

Solution

a) The volume of the prism is

$$V = B \times h$$
$$= [(6)(5)](8)$$
$$= 240$$

The volume of the prism is 240 cm^3.

b) The biggest pyramid that can fit upright inside this prism has the same base and height as the prism.

The volume of the pyramid is

$$V = \frac{1}{3} \times B \times h$$
$$= \frac{1}{3}(240)$$
$$= 80$$

The maximum volume of the pyramid is 80 cm^3.

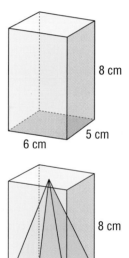

8 cm

6 cm

5 cm

8 cm

6 cm

5 cm

CONTINUED

Practice

Calculate each surface area.

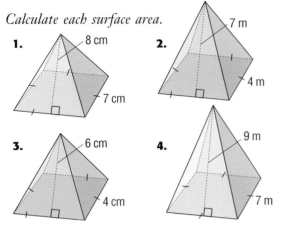

1. 8 cm, 7 cm

2. 7 m, 4 m

3. 6 cm, 4 cm

4. 9 m, 7 m

Estimate, then calculate each volume to the nearest cubic unit.

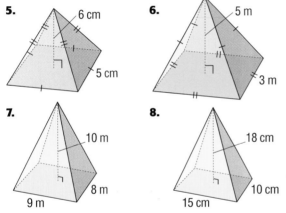

5. 6 cm, 5 cm

6. 5 m, 3 m

7. 10 m, 8 m, 9 m

8. 18 cm, 10 cm, 15 cm

Problems and Applications

9. The rectangular base of a pyramid measures 10 cm × 9 cm. The height of the pyramid is 12 cm. Calculate its volume.

10. The length of one side of the base of the Great Pyramid is 230 m, and the height of the pyramid is 146 m. What is its volume?

11. What happens to the volume of a square pyramid under these conditions?
a) The base is unchanged and the height is doubled.
b) The base is unchanged and the height is tripled.

c) The height is unchanged and the area of the base is doubled.

12. The slant height of a pyramid is about 120 m and each side of its base measures about 180 m. Calculate the surface area to the nearest thousand square metres.

13. A pyramid sits inside a cube so that the base of the pyramid is a face of the cube. What is the maximum volume of the pyramid if the side length of the cube is 24 cm?

14. A pyramid and a prism have congruent square bases and equal volumes. How do their heights compare? Explain.

LOGIC POWER

The cubes are identical. Each face has a ○, □, ■, or ● on it.

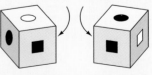

What symbol is on each of the faces indicated by the arrows?

274

Virtual Reality

Virtual reality is the use of computers and graphics software to create sights and sounds from real-world data. The result is an impression of the real world. Soon, even touch and smell will be included in the "world" created by virtual reality.

Virtual reality is seen as a powerful training tool for people who take hazardous jobs or who must learn to use expensive equipment.

A Canadian company uses virtual reality in the systems it designs to train air traffic controllers in several countries. The controllers practise on a virtual reality system before tackling the real job at an airport.

Activity ❶

Virtual reality may be used to train doctors.

1. List 5 skills that trainee doctors might practise on a virtual reality system.

2. Describe the advantages of having doctors train in this way.

3. Describe any disadvantages of having doctors train in this way.

Activity ❷

Firefighters may be trained on a virtual reality system. What could the system simulate for a firefighter?

Activity ❸

Choose a situation in which you think a virtual system could be used for training. Describe what your system would do.

Activity ❹

Describe a computer game that could be played with a virtual reality system.

7.5 Surface Area and Volume of a Cylinder and a Cone

Nearly perfect cylindrical shapes can be found in nature. An example is this part of the trunk of one of Canada's biggest trees. It is a Douglas fir that grows near Port Renfrew on Vancouver Island.

Activity: Develop a Formula

Join the shorter edges of a sheet of paper to form a cylinder. Do not crease the paper.

Inquire

1. a) Name the shapes of the top and bottom of your cylinder.
b) Write a formula for the combined area of these shapes.

2. a) What name is given to the distance around the top of the cylinder?
b) Write a formula for this distance in terms of r.

3. a) What was the original shape of the sheet of paper?
b) How does the length of this shape compare with the distance around the top of the cylinder?
c) What is the length of this shape in terms of r?

4. How does the height, h, of the cylinder compare with the width of the sheet of paper?

5. Write the formula for the area of the sheet of paper in terms of r and h.

6. Use the results of questions 1 b) and 5 to write a formula for the surface area of a cylinder that has a top and a bottom.

Example 1

The cylindrical can of juice has a diameter of 6 cm and a height of 13 cm. Find the surface area to the nearest tenth of a square centimetre.

Solution

The area of the curved surface is the area of a rectangle. The top and bottom are circles. The formula for the **surface area of a closed cylinder**, a cylinder with a top and bottom, is $2\pi r^2 + 2\pi rh$.

$$\begin{aligned} \text{Surface Area} &= 2\pi r^2 + 2\pi rh \\ &= 2(3.14)(3)^2 + 2(3.14)(3)(13) \\ &= 56.52 + 244.92 \\ &= 301.44 \end{aligned}$$

> EST
> $(2)(3)(10) + (2)(3)(3)(10)$
> $= 60 + 180$
> $= 240$

The surface area of the juice can is 301.4 cm² to the nearest tenth of a square centimetre.

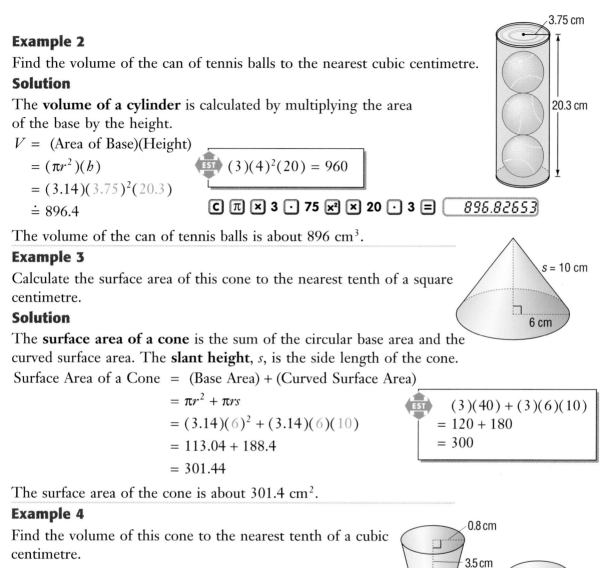

Example 2

Find the volume of the can of tennis balls to the nearest cubic centimetre.

Solution

The **volume of a cylinder** is calculated by multiplying the area of the base by the height.

V = (Area of Base)(Height)

$\quad = (\pi r^2)(h)$

$\quad = (3.14)(3.75)^2(20.3)$

$\quad \doteq 896.4$

EST $(3)(4)^2(20) = 960$

C π × 3 · 75 x² × 20 · 3 = 896.82653

The volume of the can of tennis balls is about 896 cm³.

Example 3

Calculate the surface area of this cone to the nearest tenth of a square centimetre.

Solution

The **surface area of a cone** is the sum of the circular base area and the curved surface area. The **slant height**, s, is the side length of the cone.

Surface Area of a Cone = (Base Area) + (Curved Surface Area)

$\quad = \pi r^2 + \pi rs$

$\quad = (3.14)(6)^2 + (3.14)(6)(10)$

$\quad = 113.04 + 188.4$

$\quad = 301.44$

EST $(3)(40) + (3)(6)(10)$
$= 120 + 180$
$= 300$

The surface area of the cone is about 301.4 cm².

Example 4

Find the volume of this cone to the nearest tenth of a cubic centimetre.

Solution

The **volume of a cone** is equal to one-third the volume of a cylinder with the same base and height.

Volume of a Cone $= \frac{1}{3}$(Base Area)(Height)

$\quad = \frac{1}{3}(\pi r^2)(h)$

$\quad = \frac{(3.14)(0.8)^2(3.5)}{3}$

$\quad = \frac{7.0336}{3}$

$\quad \doteq 2.3$

EST $\frac{(3)(1^2)(3)}{3} = 3$

C π × · 8 x² × 3 · 5 ÷ 3 = 2.3457225

The volume of the cone is about 2.3 cm³.

CONTINUED ▶

Practice

Calculate each surface area to the nearest square centimetre.

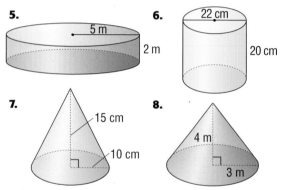

1. 6 cm, 11 cm

2. 2.7 cm, 5.8 cm

3. 13 cm, 5 cm

4. 25 cm, 7 cm

Estimate, then calculate each volume.

5. 5 m, 2 m

6. 22 cm, 20 cm

7. 15 cm, 10 cm

8. 4 m, 3 m

Calculate the surface area and volume of the following.

9. 4 m, 6 m

10. 3 cm, 4 cm, 5 cm

Problems and Applications

11. A paper cup at a water dispenser has a conical shape. The radius of the cup is 3 cm, and its height is 6 cm.

a) Find the slant height of the cup to the nearest tenth of a centimetre.

b) Calculate how much paper, to the nearest square centimetre, is required to make the cup.

12. The Canadarm used on the space shuttle is a cylinder that is 15.2 m long with a diameter of 38 cm. What is its surface area to the nearest tenth of a square unit?

13. A cone-shaped container has a diameter of 20 cm and a height of 20 cm. How many litres of water will the cone hold to the nearest litre?

14. A hobby club runs remote-controlled boats in a tank that is shaped as shown.

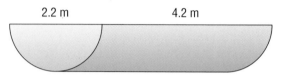

2.2 m   4.2 m

What volume of water can this tank hold to the nearest cubic metre?

15. Paper towels are sold in packages of 2 rolls. Each roll is a cylinder with a height of 30 cm and an outer diameter of 12 cm.
a) Design a shipping carton that will contain 12 packages of paper towels.
b) The inner diameter of each roll is 4 cm. How much wasted space is there in the carton?

16. Write a problem that requires the calculation of the surface area and volume of a cone. Have a classmate solve your problem.

NUMBER POWER

Place the digits from 1 to 9 in the circles so that the consecutive sums of the four numbers on each side differ by 1.

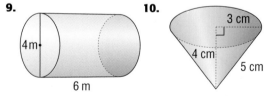

278

Programming Formulas in BASIC

Work with a partner to examine the following computer programs, and describe what each line of the program does or asks you to do.

1. NEW
```
10 PRINT"SURFACE AREA OF A"
20 PRINT"RECTANGULAR PRISM"
30 INPUT"LENGTH IS";L
40 INPUT"WIDTH IS";W
50 INPUT"HEIGHT IS";H
60 A=2*L*W+2*L*H+2*W*H
70 PRINT"SURFACE AREA IS";A
80 END
```

2. NEW
```
10 PRINT"VOLUME OF A"
20 PRINT"RECTANGULAR PRISM"
30 INPUT"LENGTH IS";L
40 INPUT"WIDTH IS";W
50 INPUT"HEIGHT IS";H
60 V=L*W*H
70 PRINT"VOLUME IS";V
80 END
```

3. NEW
```
10 PRINT"SURFACE AREA OF A"
20 PRINT"SQUARE PYRAMID"
30 INPUT"LENGTH IS";L
40 INPUT"SLANT HEIGHT IS";S
50 A=4*1/2*L*S + L^2
60 PRINT"AREA IS";A
70 END
```

4. NEW
```
10 PRINT"VOLUME OF A"
20 INPUT"SQUARE PYRAMID"
30 INPUT"LENGTH IS";L
40 INPUT"HEIGHT IS";H
50 V=1/3*L^2*H
60 PRINT"VOLUME IS";V
70 END
```

5. NEW
```
10 PRINT"SURFACE AREA"
20 PRINT"OF A CYLINDER"
30 INPUT"RADIUS IS";R
40 INPUT"HEIGHT IS";H
50 A=2*3.14*R^2+2*3.14*R*H
60 PRINT"THE SURFACE AREA IS";A
70 END
```

6. NEW
```
10 PRINT"VOLUME OF A CYLINDER"
20 INPUT"RADIUS IS";R
30 INPUT"HEIGHT IS";H
40 V=3.14*R^2*H
50 PRINT"VOLUME IS";V
60 END
```

7. NEW
```
10 PRINT"SURFACE AREA OF A CONE"
20 INPUT"RADIUS IS";R
30 INPUT"SLANT HEIGHT IS";S
40 A=3.14*R^2+3.14*R*S
50 PRINT"THE SURFACE AREA IS";A
60 END
```

8. NEW
```
10 PRINT"VOLUME OF A CONE"
20 INPUT"RADIUS OF BASE IS";R
30 INPUT"HEIGHT IS";H
40 V=1/3*3.14*R^2*H
50 PRINT"VOLUME IS";V
60 END
```

Estimate, then use a program to calculate the surface area and volume of each of the following.

9. rectangular prism with L = 3.5 cm, W = 4.5 cm, H = 6.2 cm

10. square pyramid with L = 1 m, H = 1.2 m, S = 1.3 m

11. cylinder with R = 2 cm, H = 3.5 cm

12. cone with R = 3 m, H = 4 m, S = 5 m

13. What advantages are there in using a computer program to perform these types of computations?

Design Problems in Three Dimensions

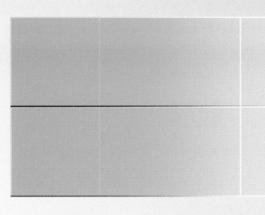
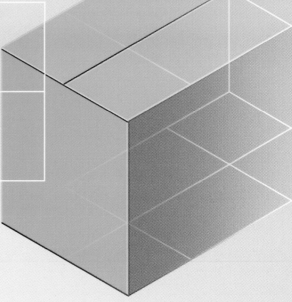

Activity ❶ Designing Boxes

Many cardboard boxes are made in the shape of a rectangular prism. Suppose you are an industrial designer who must decide what dimensions to use for a box to hold 12 objects, each the size of a one-centimetre cube.

1. Use 12 one-centimetre cubes to make a rectangular prism. Record its dimensions.

2. Repeat step 1 three times, making a different rectangular prism each time.

3. Copy and complete the table.

Prism	Dimensions (cm)	Volume (cm³)	Surface Area (cm²)
1			
2			
3			
4			

4. The most cost-effective, or cheapest, container of a given volume is the one that uses the least material. To package 12 cm³ of product in a box with sides that are whole numbers of centimetres, what dimensions would give the most cost-effective box? Explain.

5. a) For each prism, calculate the rate $\frac{\text{volume}}{\text{surface area}}$, to 2 decimal places.
b) What happens to this rate as a box becomes more cost-effective?

6. Many boxes do not have whole-number dimensions. Suppose you had to design a box to hold 8 m³ of product. Possible dimensions of the box would include 8 m × 1 m × 1 m, 2 m × 2 m × 2 m, 1.6 m × 2 m × 2.5 m, and 1 m × 1.25 m × 6.4 m. For these sets of dimensions, and any others you choose, complete a table like the one in step 3.

7. Use the rate $\frac{\text{volume}}{\text{surface area}}$ to choose the most cost-effective box. What shape is this box?

8. Why are many products not packed in the shape of box you found in step 7?

Activity ❷ Boxes Within Boxes

Many shipping boxes hold smaller boxes.

1. What is the maximum number of 6 cm × 6 cm × 6 cm boxes you can pack in shipping boxes with the following dimensions?
a) 24 cm × 24 cm × 24 cm
b) 48 cm × 48 cm × 48 cm

2. Of the two shipping boxes in step 1, which is the more cost-effective?

3. a) Do shipping boxes become more cost-effective as they get larger or smaller?

b) What other factors do you think are used to decide the size of a shipping box?

4. What is the maximum number of boxes measuring 5 cm × 4 cm × 3 cm that can be packed into a shipping box that is 24 cm × 20 cm × 18 cm?

5. What is the maximum number of boxes measuring 10 cm × 6 cm × 5 cm that can be packed into a shipping box that is 30 cm × 20 cm × 11 cm?

Activity ❸ Designing Cans

Industrial designers must also decide what height and radius to use for a cylindrical container.

1. The table shows the radii and heights of 4 possible cylindrical cans. Copy and complete the table. Round each volume and surface area to the nearest whole number.

Can	Radius (cm)	Height (cm)	Volume (cm³)	Surface Area (cm²)
1	1	36		
2	2	9		
3	3	4		
4	6	1		

2. Which are the two most cost-effective cans? Explain.

3. a) What general shape of cylinder is the most cost-effective choice for a can?

b) Why do you think cylindrical cans are not all made with this general shape?

4. Think about food products that come in cylindrical cans. Give possible reasons why each shape of cylinder is used for each can.

Activity ❹ Variations in Cans

1. Make up the dimensions of 4 cans with the same radius but different heights. Calculate the volume and surface area of each can. Record the results in a table similar to the one in Activity 3.

2. Use the table to draw separate graphs.
a) volume versus height
b) surface area versus height

3. How are the two graphs similar? How are they different?

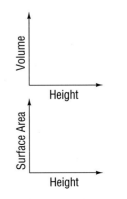

281

Vanishing Points and Perspective

Many artists from the 14th to 16th century, a period known as the Renaissance, studied mathematics and engineering. The artists used geometry to help them show the three-dimensional world on a two-dimensional surface. They used the concepts of perspective and vanishing points to help create great works of art.

Activity ❶ One Vanishing Point

1. a) To sketch a cube using 1 vanishing point, draw a square for the front face of the cube.
b) Draw a horizontal line parallel to the horizontal edges of the square. This line is called the **eye level.**
c) Mark a vanishing point above the top edge of the square on the eye level line.

2. Draw a line from each corner of the square to the vanishing point. These lines are called **vanishing lines**.

3. Complete the sketch of the cube using the vanishing lines as edges of the cube.

4. Erase the eye level line and any unnecessary parts of the vanishing lines. The viewer sees the cube from above and in front.

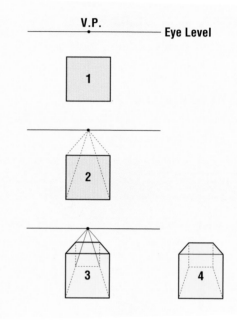

Activity ❷ Perspectives I

1. Sketch a cube where the eye level line is below the cube and the vanishing point is to the right of the cube. How does the viewer see the cube?

2. Sketch a cube where the eye level line is through the centre of the cube and the vanishing point is to the right of the cube. How does the viewer see the cube?

3. Sketch a cube where the eye level line is below the cube and the vanishing point is directly below the cube. How does the viewer see the cube?

Activity ❸ Two Vanishing Points

1. a) To sketch a cube using 2 vanishing points, draw the front edge of the cube.
b) Draw an eye level line above the front edge of the cube, and mark 2 vanishing points on the line.

2. Draw vanishing lines from each end of the front edge of the cube to the vanishing points.

3. a) To form the remaining front vertical edges, draw vertical line segments, parallel to the front edge. Draw these lines to intersect the vanishing lines.
b) Draw more vanishing lines to these new edges to determine the back edges of the cube.

4. Erase the eye level line and any unnecessary parts of the vanishing lines.

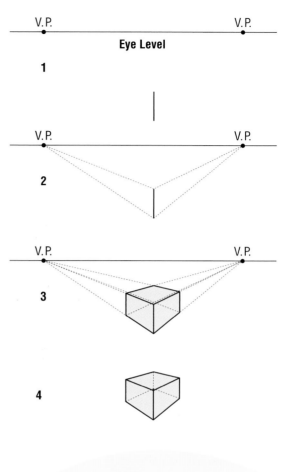

Activity ❹ Perspectives II

1. Use 2 vanishing points to sketch a cube with the eye level line above the cube.

2. Use 2 vanishing points to sketch a cube with the eye level line passing through the cube.

Activity ❺ Sketching Letters in Perspective

1. Sketch the letter M using 1 vanishing point.

2. Sketch the letter T using 2 vanishing points.

3. Sketch your initials using 1 or 2 vanishing points.

283

Different Views

Knowing how to represent 3-dimensional objects in 2 dimensions is an important skill. Taking 2-dimensional drawings of an object and building the 3-dimensional figure is also useful.

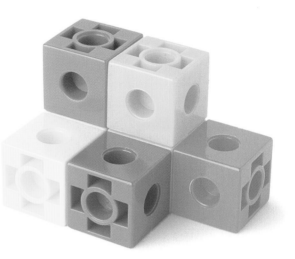

Activity ❶ Front, Side, and Top Views

This 3-dimensional shape was built using 7 cubes. The front view, right-side view, top view, and base design are shown. The base design is the top view with numbers giving the number of cubes in each position.

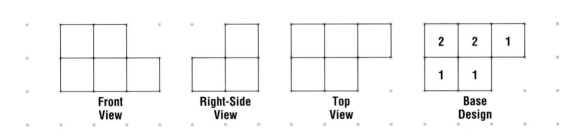

Front View	Right-Side View	Top View	Base Design

Base Design:

2	2	1
1	1	

On grid paper, sketch the front view, right-side view, top view, and base design for each of the following shapes.

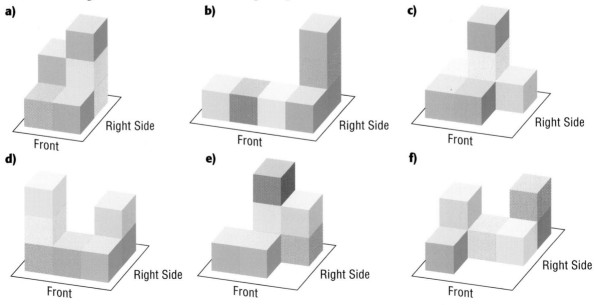

a)

Right Side
Front

b)

Right Side
Front

c)

Right Side
Front

d)

Right Side
Front

e)

Right Side
Front

f)

Right Side
Front

Activity ❷ Build the Model

Use these 2-dimensional drawings of 3 views to build the
3-dimensional shape. Draw the base design on grid paper.

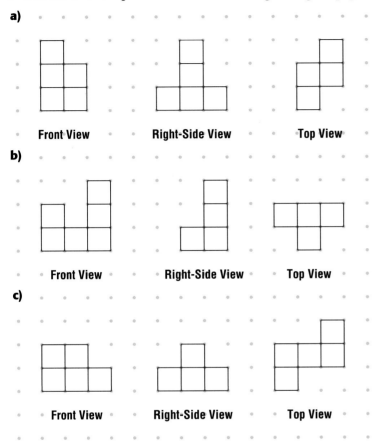

a)

Front View Right-Side View Top View

b)

Front View Right-Side View Top View

c)

Front View Right-Side View Top View

Activity ❸ Build the Model

The front and top views of models built with 7 cubes are shown.

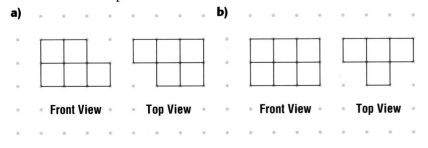

a)

Front View Top View

b)

Front View Top View

Build the model. On grid paper, draw the right-side view and
the base design. Is there more than 1 solution? Compare with
a classmate's solution.

CONTINUED

Activity ❹ Perspective Drawings

Instead of drawing two-dimensional views of a three-dimensional shape, you can draw a perspective view of the whole shape on isometric dot paper. For example, the shape built from interlocking cubes at the top of page 284 looks like this when it is represented on isometric dot paper.

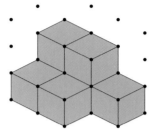

1. Use isometric dot paper to represent each of the three-dimensional shapes in parts a) to f) of Activity 1 on page 284.

2. Use the following perspective drawings to draw the front view, right-side view, and top view of each shape.

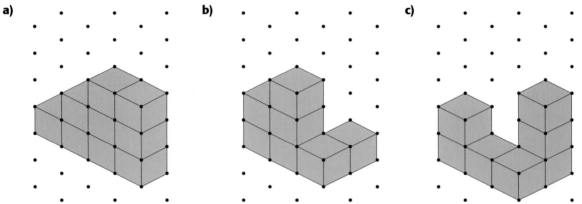

a)   b)   c)

3. Use the views shown in parts a), b), and c) of Activity 2 on page 285 to complete a perspective drawing of each object on isometric dot paper.

Activity ❺ Views of Everyday Objects

1. The objects are viewed from above. Name each object.

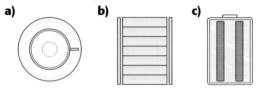

a)   b)   c)

2. Sketch the house as it would look from each view.

a) front
b) side
c) top

3. Draw the front view, side view, and top view of each object.

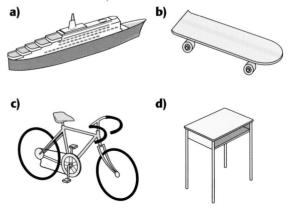

a)   b)

c)   d)

Computer-Assisted Design

The diagram shows a computer-generated design for a simple threaded bolt.

The computer allows us to rotate the design to inspect different views. We can also sketch the design in any direction to observe the effect.

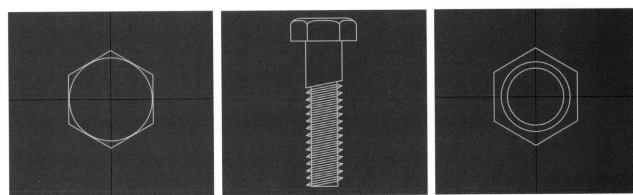

| Top View | Side View | Bottom View |

Activity ❶

1. What are the advantages of computer-assisted design over drawing by hand?

2. Describe any advantages that drafting has over computer-assisted design.

3. Compare your opinions with your classmates'.

Activity ❷

1. Research the uses of computer-assisted design. What mathematics does the designer need to know?

2. Describe any uses that you did not expect.

3. Describe your findings to your group.

Locus

A **locus** in a plane is the set of all points in the plane that satisfy a given condition. Suppose a locus is defined as the set of all points in the plane that are equidistant from parallel lines *l* and *m*.

> *Equidistant from means the same distance from.*

We can identify examples of points that satisfy the condition.

All points in the plane that satisfy the condition lie on a third line that is parallel to lines *l* and *m* and midway between them.

If lines *l* and *m* are 2 cm apart, we can describe the locus as the line parallel to lines *l* and *m* and 1 cm from each of them.

Activity ❶ Identifying a Locus

1. For each condition, sketch the locus in the plane. Describe the locus fully in words.
a) all points that are 3 cm from point A
b) all points equidistant from the endpoints of line segment AB
c) all points equidistant from the arms of ∠DEF
d) all points that are 4 cm from line *n*
e) all points equidistant from all 4 sides of square ABCD

2. State whether it is possible to sketch the complete locus. Explain.
a) all points 4 cm or less from point K
b) all points more than 4 cm from point K

Activity ❷ Applications

1. Sketch and describe each locus in the plane.
a) all points equidistant from the goal lines on a hockey rink
b) all points on a dart board that triple the score when a dart lands on them
c) all points equidistant from the edges of a city street
d) all points that can receive a signal from a radio transmitter with a range of 80 km
e) all points that can be wiped by a car's windshield wiper

Activity ❸ Problem Solving

In questions 1 to 3, sketch and describe each locus in the plane.

1. all points traced by a point on the outside of a car tire as the car is driven down the highway

2. all points traced by a point on the outside of a small wheel, N, rolling clockwise around a large drive wheel, M

3. all points traced by the centre of the smaller wheel in question 2

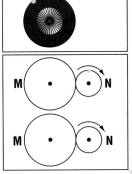

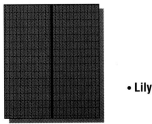

4. Lily and Katerina are playing hide and seek. Lily is hiding behind a garden shed. The diagram shows her location from above. For each of the following conditions, sketch the locus of all points in the plane. If it is not possible to sketch the complete locus, explain why.

a) all points from which Katerina would not be able to see Lily

b) all points from which Katerina would be able to see Lily

• Lily

5. A circular fountain has a radius of 2 m. A circular flower bed surrounds the fountain. There is no gap between the flower bed and the fountain. The outside circumference of the flower bed is the locus of points in the plane that are 3 m from the centre of the fountain. Sketch the flower bed and calculate its area.

6. A horse grazing in a rectangular field is tethered to the fence at the midpoint of the longer side. The field is 50 m by 40 m, and the tether is 20 m long.

a) Sketch the locus that shows the area in which the horse can graze.

b) Calculate the area of grass that the horse cannot reach.

Activity ❹ Using Geometry Software

Some geometry software programs will draw a locus.

1. Explore a suitable program to discover how to draw each locus described in question 1 of Activity 1.

2. Use the program to draw a locus of your own. Describe your locus to a classmate and challenge your classmate to draw it with the software.

Sight

Even though a horse's eyes are twice as large as a human's, the horse cannot see an area directly in front of it. This area is called the **blind spot**. When horses, such as Canada's Big Ben, compete in jumping competitions they actually jump the barriers blind.

Peripheral vision in humans and animals is the range or angle through which vision is possible. The angle of peripheral vision for a horse is 170° on one side and 170° on the other side. A horse cannot see an area within an angle of 10° directly in front of it or 10° directly behind it.

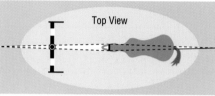

Top View

Activity ❶ The Blind Spot

1. To locate your blind spot, mark 2 black dots 5 cm apart on a blank piece of paper as shown.

●   ●

2. Hold the paper in front of you with your arm extended.

3. Cover your left eye with your hand and look at the left dot with your right eye.

4. Continue looking at the left dot and move the paper toward you slowly until the right dot disappears. The point at which this happens is called the blind spot for your right eye.

5. Have a classmate measure the distance from your eye to the paper.

6. Repeat the experiment to find the blind spot for your left eye by covering your right eye and looking at the right dot.

7. Are the blind spot distances the same for both eyes?

Activity ❷ Peripheral Vision

1. To determine your angle of peripheral vision, you will need a blank index card and an index card with a black dot drawn on it that has a diameter of 1 cm.

2. Use chalk to draw a circle with a radius of 1 m on a large piece of paper placed on the floor.

3. Stand on the centre of the circle and have 1 classmate stand in front of you at the edge of the circle holding the card with the black dot on it. Have another classmate hold the blank card beside the card with the black dot on it. The blank card should be to your left of the card with the dot on it.

4. Stare at the black dot while the classmate with the blank card moves slowly to your left, along the edge of the circle. Say, "Stop" when you can no longer see the blank card.

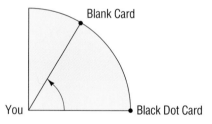

5. Have another classmate draw a line from you to the person holding the card with the dot and a line from you to the person holding the blank card.

6. Measure and record the angle between the 2 lines drawn in step 5.

7. Repeat the procedure with the blank card moving to your right.

8. Add the 2 angles you have found and record them. The sum of these 2 angles is your angle of peripheral vision.

9. Find the average angle of peripheral vision for your class.

291

Review

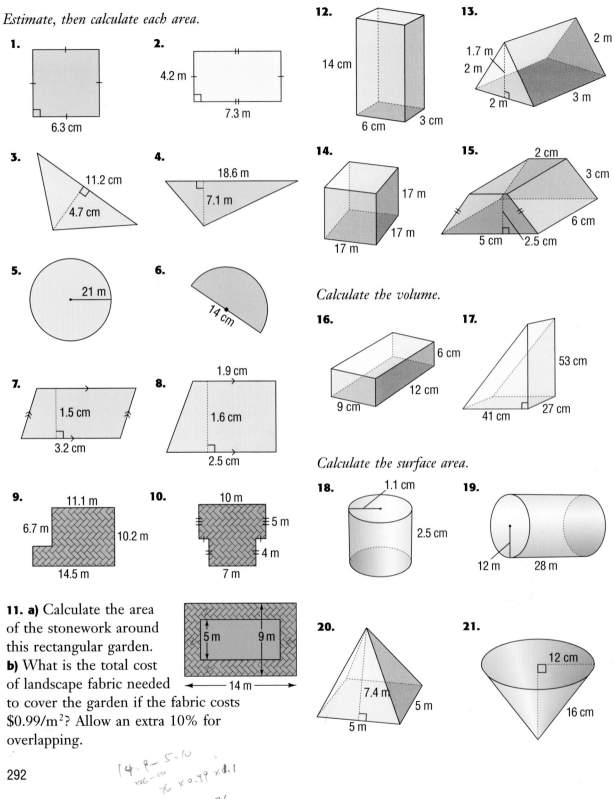

Estimate, then calculate each area.

1.

6.3 cm

2.

4.2 m

7.3 m

3.

11.2 cm

4.7 cm

4.

18.6 m

7.1 m

5.

21 m

6.

14 cm

7.

1.5 cm

3.2 cm

8.

1.9 cm

1.6 cm

2.5 cm

9.

11.1 m

6.7 m

10.2 m

14.5 m

10.

10 m

5 m

4 m

7 m

11. a) Calculate the area of the stonework around this rectangular garden.
b) What is the total cost of landscape fabric needed to cover the garden if the fabric costs $0.99/m²? Allow an extra 10% for overlapping.

5 m   9 m

14 m

Calculate the surface area.

12.

14 cm

6 cm   3 cm

13.

1.7 m
2 m

2 m

2 m

3 m

14.

17 m

17 m

17 m

15.

2 cm

3 cm

6 cm

5 cm   2.5 cm

Calculate the volume.

16.

6 cm

12 cm

9 cm

17.

53 cm

41 cm   27 cm

Calculate the surface area.

18.

1.1 cm

2.5 cm

19.

12 m   28 m

20.

7.4 m

5 m

5 m

21.

12 cm

16 cm

292

14 · 8 − 5 · 10
126 − 50
76 × 0.99 × 0.1

82.76

Calculate the volume to the nearest unit.

22.

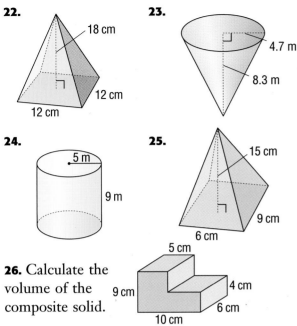

18 cm
12 cm
12 cm

23.

4.7 m
8.3 m

24.

.5 m
9 m

25.

15 cm
9 cm
6 cm

26. Calculate the volume of the composite solid.

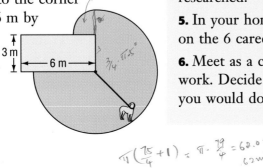

5 cm
9 cm
4 cm
6 cm
10 cm

27. A foam container has the shape of a rectangular prism. Its inside dimensions are 12 cm by 10 cm by 15 cm. Its outside dimensions are 14 cm by 12 cm by 17 cm.
a) Find the outside surface area.
b) Find the inside surface area.
c) Find the volume of foam in the container.

28. A 4 m by 4 m square is removed from the centre of a 15 m by 30 m rectangle. What is the area of the remaining part?

29. A pizza with a diameter of 45 cm has a circular ring of tomato sauce with a radius of 20 cm. Find the area of the bare crust around the edge of the pizza, to the nearest square centimetre.

30. Suneel tied his dog to the corner of a shed. The shed is 6 m by 3 m. The rope is 5 m long. Calculate the area within the dog's reach to the nearest square metre.

$\frac{1}{4} \cdot \pi \cdot 2^2$

3 m
6 m

$\frac{3}{4} \cdot \pi \cdot 5^2$

$\pi \left(\frac{75}{4} + 1 \right) = \pi \cdot \frac{79}{4} = 62.0 \, m^2$
$62 \, m^2$

Group Decision Making
Researching Construction Careers

1. Meet as a class to choose 6 careers in the construction industry. Your choices might include a plumber, an electrician, a crane operator, an architect, or a building contractor.

2. Go to home groups. Assign one career to each home group member.

Home Groups

3. Form an expert group of 4 with students who have the same career as you to research. Decide on the questions you want to answer about your career. One of the questions should be: "How is math used in this career?" Research your assigned career in your expert group.

Expert Groups

4. Return to your home group and share your findings about the career you researched.

5. In your home group, prepare a report on the 6 careers.

6. Meet as a class to discuss your group work. Decide what went well and what you would do differently next time.

Chapter Check

Calculate the area.

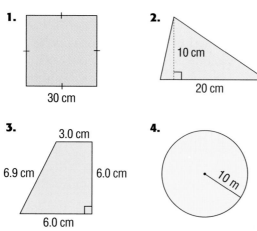

1.
30 cm

2.
10 cm
20 cm

3.
3.0 cm
6.9 cm   6.0 cm
6.0 cm

4.
10 m

Calculate the surface area.

5.
10 cm
5 cm   4 cm

6.
10 cm
30 cm

7.
1 m
1.2 m
1.2 m

8.
8 cm
15 cm

Calculate the volume to the nearest unit.

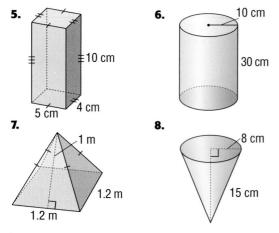

9.
8 m
4 m

10.
16.4 m
8 m

11.
6.1 m
3.3 m
3.3 m

12.
150 cm
280 cm   310 cm

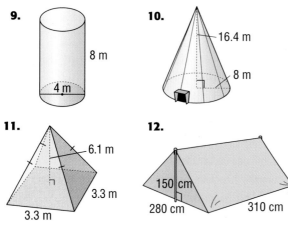

Determine the area of each patio.

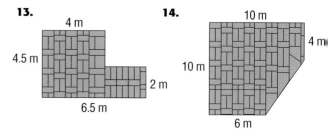

13.
4 m
4.5 m
2 m
6.5 m

14.
10 m
4 m
10 m
6 m

15. Circular patio stones are placed as shown to make a walkway that is 7.2 m long.

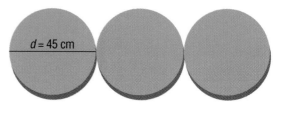

d = 45 cm

a) How many patio stones are used?
b) The patio stones do not cover the entire width of the walkway, which is filled with gravel. If the walkway is 0.6 m wide, what area is covered with gravel?

16. A juice box measures 10 cm × 6 cm × 3 cm.
a) What is its surface area?
b) What is its volume?

17. A block is a rectangular prism of volume 600 cm³. What is the height of the block if its length is 20 cm and its width is 10 cm?

18. Determine the volume of the composite solid.

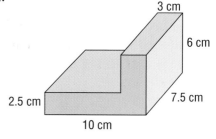

3 cm
6 cm
2.5 cm
7.5 cm
10 cm

sing the Strategies

1. What is the sum of these numbers?
a) first 3 odd numbers
b) first 4 odd numbers
c) first 5 odd numbers
d) first 6 odd numbers
e) first 25 odd numbers
f) first 105 odd numbers

2. If a year has 2 months in a row with Friday the 13th, what months are they?

3. The area of the large square is 64 cm^2.

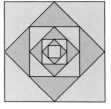

Each smaller square is formed by joining the midpoints of the sides of the next larger square. What is the area of the smallest square?

4. How many pieces of string each 8.5 cm long can be cut from a spool of string 400 cm long? What assumptions have you made?

5. The number 2601 is a 4-digit number that is a perfect square because $51^2 = 2601$. What is the smallest 4-digit number that is a perfect square and that has all even digits?

6. The average of two numbers is 21. When a third number is included, the average of the three numbers is 23. What is the third number?

7. Justine, Chris, and Meelang plan to travel together in a van. They will all sit in the front seat. In how many different arrangements can they sit in each of the following situations?
a) all three can drive
b) only Chris and Meelang can drive
c) only Justine can drive

8. List the different ways you can make change for a dollar using only quarters and nickels.

9. Starting at the letter A, how many different pathways can you follow to spell ANGLE?

10. A square piece of paper is folded in half as shown. The perimeter of each new rectangle formed is 24 cm. What is the perimeter of the original square?

11. The ship will leave the harbour at 08:30. You have to be on board 20 min before departure. It takes 25 min to drive to the ship from your hotel. You must allow 15 min to check out of the hotel. It will take you 20 min to pack. You need half an hour to eat breakfast and at least 45 min to shower and dress. For what time should you place your wake-up call?

DATA BANK

1. How many times will Mercury orbit the sun in the time it takes Jupiter to orbit the sun once?

2. Use the DATA BANK to make up your own problem. Have a classmate solve your problem. Check your classmate's solution.

CHAPTER 8

Transformations

Can you pass your body through a baseball card? You can if you change the card's shape with some scissors.

Fold the card lengthwise.

Starting at one end of the card, make the first cut from the fold, the second from the open side, and so on. Never cut all the way across from either side. Make as many cuts as possible. Begin the last cut from the fold.

Unfold the card and cut along the fold as shown, stopping before the ends.

Now stretch the card into a large circle and pass your body through it.

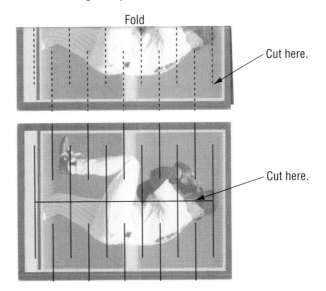

Fold

Cut here.

Cut here.

Activity ❶ Slides, Flips, and Turns

An elevator slides up and down in the elevator shaft. The elevator on the second floor can be called a slide image of the elevator on the ground floor.

The reflection of a mountain in a still lake is a flip image of the mountain.

When a chair on a Ferris wheel moves from the bottom to the top, the chair at the top can be called a turn image of the chair at the bottom.

Find 3 more examples of each of the following and sketch the original figure and its image.

1. slides **2.** flips **3.** turns

Activity ❷ Patterns

1. Identify each pattern as a slide, flip, or turn.

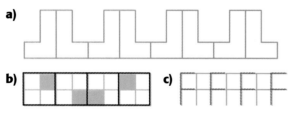

2. Draw a slide pattern, a flip pattern, and a turn pattern.

Activity ❸ The Square

Write the slide, flip, or turn that gives each image.

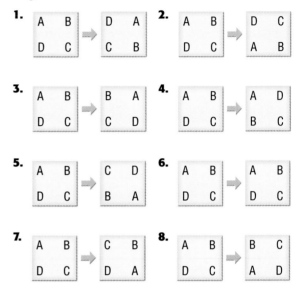

Activity ❹

Identify each figure as a slide, flip, or turn of the red figure.

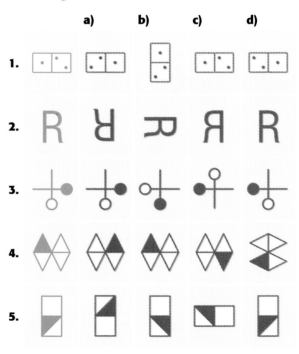

298

Activity ❺ Tile Patterns

In mathematics, tiling the plane means to cover an area with shapes so that there are no gaps and the shapes do not overlap.

Select 1 or more of these shapes and tile the plane to make an interesting design.

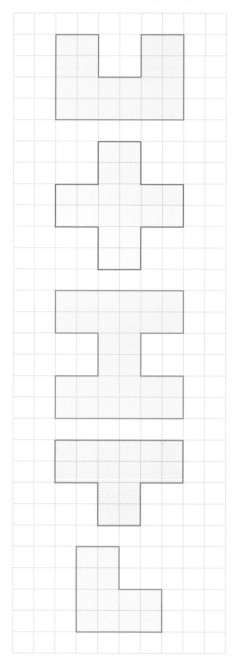

Mental Math

Calculate.

1. 220×0.1 **2.** 2000×0.01

3. $300 \div 100$ **4.** 4500×0.001

5. $0.2 \div 10$ **6.** $600 \div 0.01$

7. 0.003×1000 **8.** $0.01 \div 0.01$

Add.

9. $\$3.99 + \$4.99$ **10.** $\$3.50 + \$4.25$

11. $\$3.98 + \$4.98$ **12.** $\$7.99 + \$2.95$

13. $\$5.90 + \$2.95$ **14.** $\$0.99 + \$2.45$

15. $\$1.95 + \$2.95$ **16.** $\$4.60 + \$3.60$

Simplify.

17. $-7 - (-3)$ **18.** $-12 \div (-6)$

19. $-4 \times (-5)$ **20.** $-6 - 4 - 2$

21. $-6 + 3 - 8$ **22.** $20 \div (-5)$

23. $9 - 8 - 7$ **24.** $5 \times (-2) \times (-1)$

Calculate.

25. 2 at $\$2.99$ **26.** 4 at $\$2.98$

27. 5 at $\$0.99$ **28.** 3 at $\$19.98$

29. 4 at $\$3.95$ **30.** 6 at $\$4.98$

31. 3 at $\$2.95$ **32.** 5 at $\$1.98$

Calculate.

33. $\frac{5}{6} - \frac{2}{3}$ **34.** $\frac{3}{4} + \frac{1}{8}$ **35.** $\frac{2}{5} \div \frac{2}{3}$

36. $\frac{1}{2} \times \frac{3}{5}$ **37.** $\frac{1}{3}$ of 72   **38.** $\frac{1}{4}$ of 84

Simplify.

39. $6^2 - 24 + 3$ **40.** $100 - 8^2 - 6^2$

41. $500 \div 10 + 47$ **42.** $200 - 12^2$

43. $3^3 + 40 + 10$ **44.** $2^2 + 3^2 + 4^2$

45. $4 \times 50 + 23 - 1$ **46.** $7 + 20 \times 3 + 2$

47. $3^2 \times 100 + 47$ **48.** $29 + 29 + 29$

49. $19 \times 3 - 4$ **50.** $10^2 + 7^2 - 4$

8.1 Translations

A **translation**, or slide, is a motion that is described by length and direction.

A helicopter can go straight up and down, or back and forth, or some combination of these two motions. If a helicopter goes down 30 m, then goes west 60 m, we say that the helicopter is "translated down 30 m," then "translated west 60 m." The description of each translation includes the direction and the distance.

Activity: Draw a Translation Image

Plot △ABC with coordinates A(1, 1), B(5, 1), and C(5, 4). Translate each point 6 units to the right and 4 units up. Label the new points A′, B′, and C′. Join A′, B′, and C′ to form a triangle.

Inquire

1. What are the coordinates of the vertices of △A′B′C′?

2. △A′B′C′ is called the **translation image** of △ABC. How do the lengths of the sides of △A′B′C′ compare with the lengths of the sides of △ABC?

3. Are the two triangles congruent? Explain.

4. What is true about the measures of the angles after a translation?

5. What number do you add to the *x*-coordinate of each vertex of △ABC to give the *x*-coordinate of each vertex of △A′B′C′?

6. What number do you add to the *y*-coordinate of each vertex of △ABC to give the *y*-coordinate of each vertex of △A′B′C′?

7. Describe a translation in your own words.

△DEF has been translated 5 units to the left and 3 units up (5L, 3U). △D′E′F′ is the image of △DEF. Notice that D–E–F and D′–E′–F′ read in the same direction; in this case it is counterclockwise (ccw). We say that:

"△DEF and △D′E′F′ have the same **sense**."

The translation arrow shows the distance the triangle is translated and the direction of the translation.

The translation can be described mathematically as the ordered pair [−5, 3] or as the following **mapping**.

$(x, y) \rightarrow (x - 5, y + 3)$

The lengths of line segments and the sizes of angles do not change in a translation. The original figure and its image have the same sense.

Example

△RST has vertices R(−3, −2), S(1, −3), and T(0, 4). Use the mapping $(x,y) \rightarrow (x-2, y+4)$ to draw the translation image of △RST.

Solution

Plot △RST and find the coordinates of the vertices of its image.

$$(x,y) \rightarrow (x-2, y+4)$$

For R: $(-3,-2) \rightarrow (-3-2, -2+4)$ so R′ is (−5, 2)
For S: $(1,-3) \rightarrow (1-2, -3+4)$ so S′ is (−1, 1)
For T: $(0,4) \rightarrow (0-2, 4+4)$ so T′ is (−2, 8)

Plot R′, S′, and T′ and join them.
△R′S′T′ is the translation image of △RST.

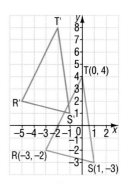

Practice

1. Which of the lettered figures are translation images of the green figure? Give reasons for your answers.

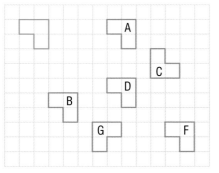

2. Plot each set of figures on a grid. Graph the image of each figure under the given translation.

a) 4 units right and 3 units up

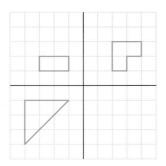

b) 2 units left and 5 units down

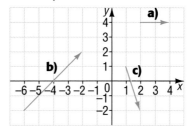

3. State the translation described by each arrow. Write your answers in the form [x,y].

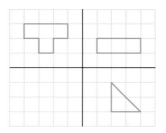

Describe each translation in words.

4. $(x,y) \rightarrow (x+3, y+2)$

5. $(x,y) \rightarrow (x-1, y+4)$

6. $(x,y) \rightarrow (x-2, y-3)$

7. $(x,y) \rightarrow (x+5, y-1)$

8. $(x,y) \rightarrow (x, y+6)$ **9.** $(x,y) \rightarrow (x-3, y)$

10. [2,−3]   **11.** [−3,5]   **12.** [−4,2]   **13.** [1,−6]

CONTINUED ▶

Draw an arrow on grid paper to show each translation.

14. $[2, -3]$ **15.** $[-1, -5]$ **16.** $[1, -5]$ **17.** $[5, 0]$

18. $[3, -2]$ **19.** $[-2, 3]$ **20.** $[0, -5]$ **21.** $[5, -4]$

Name the translation that maps each green figure onto its purple image.

22.   **23.**

Find the coordinates of each point after the translation.

	Point	Translation
24.	(2, 3)	[3, 4]
25.	(−3, −1)	[2, −2]
26.	(5, −2)	[−1, 5]
27.	(−5, 7)	[−2, −6]

Express each translation as an ordered pair.

28. A(3, 5) to A′(7, 9)

29. C(2, 1) to C′(3, 0)

30. X(−2, −4) to X′(−3, −5)

31. M(0, −1) to M′(4, −6)

32. T(−1, −3) to T′(−6, 5)

33. P(0, 4) to P′(−1, −2)

Draw each triangle on grid paper. Then, draw the translation image.

34. A(3, 2), B(−1, 4), C(−3, −5)
$(x, y) \rightarrow (x − 4, y + 2)$

35. D(−2, 0), E(4, −1), F(2, −5)
$(x, y) \rightarrow (x + 3, y − 3)$

36. R(0, 0), S(−4, 0), T(−3, −5)
$(x, y) \rightarrow (x + 2, y + 3)$

Problems and Applications

37. The translation [2, 3] translates △ABC so that the coordinates of the vertices of the image, △A′B′C′, are A′(3, 4), B′(0, 7), and C′(−2, −1). What are the coordinates of A, B, and C?

38. a) △RST has vertices R(3, 0), S(−1, 5), and T(−3, 1). Draw △RST on grid paper.
b) Determine the coordinates of the vertices of △R′S′T′ under the translation $(x, y) \rightarrow (x + 4, y + 2)$. Draw △R′S′T′.
c) Apply the translation $(x, y) \rightarrow (x + 1, y − 5)$ to △R′S′T′ and find the coordinates of the vertices of the image, △R″S″T″. Draw △R″S″T″.
d) Determine the translation that maps △RST onto △R″S″T″.

39. a) Draw the line $y = 2x + 1$ on grid paper.
b) Draw the image of the line after the translation $(x, y) \rightarrow (x + 2, y + 5)$.

40. What translations are needed to get a robot at point A to move an object from point B to point A?

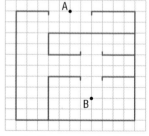

41. a) Draw △XYZ so that it lies entirely in the first quadrant. Name the coordinates of X, Y, and Z.
b) Name a translation that gives an image, △X′Y′Z′, that lies entirely in the fourth quadrant.
c) Name a translation of △X′Y′Z′ that gives an image, △X″Y″Z″, that lies entirely in the second quadrant.
d) Give a classmate the coordinates of X, Y, and Z, and the names of both translations. Have your classmate find the coordinates of X″, Y″, and Z″.

3.2 Reflections

When you stand in front of a mirror, you see an image of yourself, your reflection. If you move closer to the mirror, the image moves closer. If you move back, the image moves back. The image is always the same distance from the mirror as you are. In mathematics, a **reflection** is a transformation in which a figure is reflected or flipped over a **mirror line** or **reflection line**.

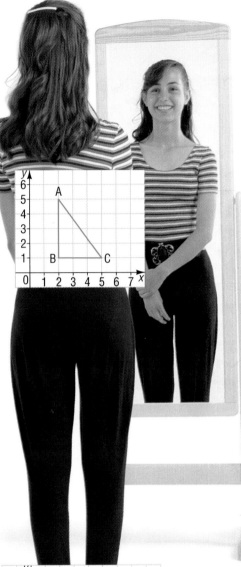

Activity: Draw a Reflection Image

Plot △ABC with coordinates A(2, 5), B(2, 1), and C(5, 1). Reflect point A in the *y*-axis to locate point A′ so that A and A′ are the same perpendicular distance from the *y*-axis. Reflect points B and C in the *y*-axis to locate B′ and C′. Join A′, B′, and C′ to form a triangle.

Inquire

1. What are the coordinates of A′, B′, and C′?

2. △A′B′C′ is the **reflection image** of △ABC. How do the side lengths in △A′B′C′ compare with the side lengths in △ABC?

3. Are the two triangles congruent? Explain.

4. What is true about the measures of the angles after a reflection?

5. Do △ABC and △A′B′C′ have the same sense? Explain.

6. Describe a reflection in your own words.

Example

△DEF has vertices D(2, 6), E(4, 1), and F(7, 4). Draw the image of △DEF after a reflection in the *x*-axis.

Solution

Draw △DEF.
Locate D′ so that the perpendicular distance from D′ to the *x*-axis equals the perpendicular distance from D to the *x*-axis. The coordinates of D′ are (2, −6). Locate E′ and F′ in the same way.

$$D(2, 6) \rightarrow D'(2, -6)$$
$$E(4, 1) \rightarrow E'(4, -1)$$
$$F(7, 4) \rightarrow F'(7, -4)$$

Join points D′, E′, and F′. △D′E′F′ is the image of △DEF after a reflection in the *x*-axis.

The lengths of line segments and the sizes of angles do not change in a reflection. The sense of a reflection image is the reverse of the sense of the original figure.

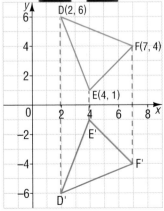

CONTINUED

303

Practice

1. Which of the lettered figures are reflections of the green figure? Give reasons for your answer.

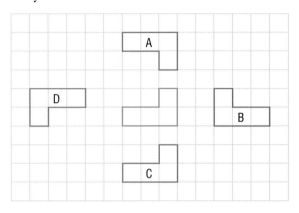

Trace each diagram. Use a Mira or paper folding to locate the reflection line.

2.

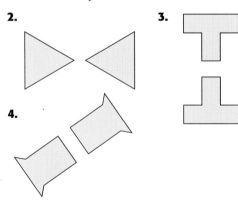

3.

4.

In each diagram, the reflection line is l. Trace each diagram and use a Mira or paper folding to draw the reflection image.

5.

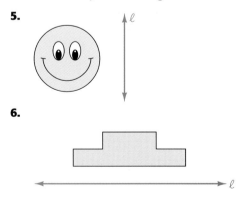

6.

7.

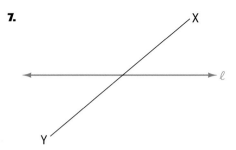

Copy each figure onto a grid and draw its reflection image in the x-axis.

8.

9.

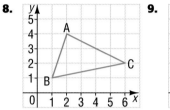
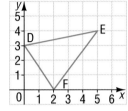

10.

11.

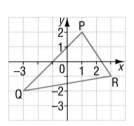

Draw each triangle on a grid. Draw the image after a reflection in the y-axis.

12.

13.

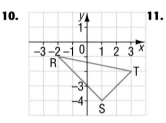

14.

15.

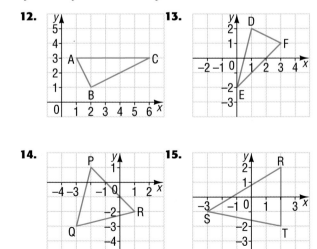

16. Find the coordinates of the image of each point after a reflection in each axis.

		Reflection Line	
	Point	**x-axis**	**y-axis**
a)	(1, 4)		
b)	(2, 3)		
c)	(−1, −2)		
d)	(−3, −2)		
e)	(−3, 2)		
f)	(4, 0)		

17. △ABC has vertices A(1, 1), B(5, 2), and C(3, 6). Draw the image of △ABC after a reflection in the y-axis.

18. △RST has vertices R(2, 5), S(−2, 4), and T(−1, −2). Draw the image of △RST after a reflection in the x-axis.

Problems and Applications

19. The letter M is a reflection of itself through the vertical red reflection line.

a) What other letters are reflections of themselves through vertical reflection lines?
b) What letters are reflections of themselves through horizontal reflection lines?
c) What letters are reflections of themselves through horizontal and vertical reflection lines?
d) Which of the ten digits are reflections of themselves?
e) Are you a reflection of yourself through a vertical reflection line? Explain.

Draw the triangles on a grid. Draw the image after a reflection in the given reflection line.

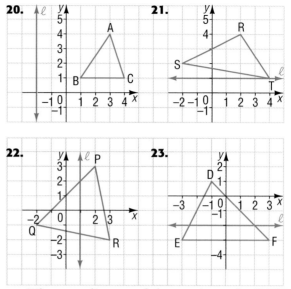

24. The coordinates of the vertices of △DEF are D(1, 5), E(−2, −2), and F(5, 1). Draw △DEF and its image after a reflection in the line y = −1.

25. a) △PQR has vertices P(−5, 6), Q(−7, 2), and R(−1, 1). Draw △PQR on grid paper.
b) Reflect △PQR in the y-axis and draw the image △P′Q′R′.
c) Reflect △P′Q′R′ in the x-axis and draw the image △P″Q″R″.

26. Which coordinate of a point does not change when the point is reflected
a) in the x-axis?   **b)** in the y-axis?

27. a) Draw a graph of the line x + y = 4.
b) Reflect the line in the x-axis.
c) Reflect the line in the y-axis.

28. △A″B″C″ has vertices A″(3, 4), B″(2, 1), and C″(1, 3). △A″B″C″ is an image obtained from the translation (x, y) → (x + 1, y − 2) on △ABC, followed by a reflection in the y-axis. Work with a classmate to find the coordinates of the vertices of the original triangle, △ABC.

305

8.3 Rotations

The hands of this antique clock turn or rotate about a point. This point is the centre of the clock face.

In mathematics, a **rotation** is a transformation in which a figure is turned or rotated about a point.

Activity: Draw a Rotation Image

Plot △ABC with coordinates A(0, 0), B(3, 0), and C(3, 4). Use tracing paper to rotate △ABC 90° counterclockwise (ccw) about the origin. Draw the **rotation image** of △ABC and name it △A′B′C′.

Inquire

1. What are the coordinates of A′, B′, and C′?

2. How do the lengths of the sides of △ABC compare with the lengths of the sides of △A′B′C′?

3. Are the two triangles congruent? Explain.

4. What is true about the measures of the angles after a rotation?

5. Do △ABC and △A′B′C′ have the same sense? Explain.

6. A 90° rotation is called a $\frac{1}{4}$ turn.
  a) What is a 180° rotation called?
  b) What is a 270° rotation called?

7. Describe a rotation in your own words.

To rotate an object and find its image, you need to know the amount and direction of the rotation. You also need to know the **centre of rotation** or **turn centre**.

Example

△RST has vertices R(−5, 0), S(−1, 0), and T(−2, −3). Draw the image of △RST after a rotation of 180° clockwise (cw) about the origin.

Solution

Draw △RST. Find the rotation image of each vertex.
R(−5, 0) → R′(5, 0)
S(−1, 0) → S′(1, 0)
T(−2, −3) → T′(2, 3)
Join points R′, S′, and T′.
△R′S′T′ is the rotation image of △RST.

⊙ marks the turn centre

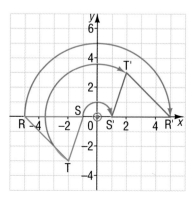

The lengths of line segments and the sizes of angles do not change in a rotation. The original figure and its image have the same sense.

Practice

The green flag has been rotated about the origin. The purple flag is the image. Name the rotation.

1. **2.** **3.**

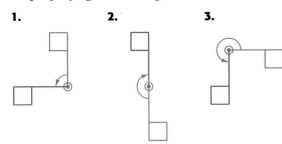

The green flag has been rotated about the origin. The purple flag is the image. Name 2 rotations for each case.

4. **5.** **6.**

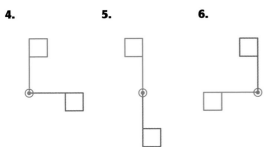

Copy each figure onto grid paper and draw the image after the given rotation about the red turn centre.

7. **8.**

180° cw **90° ccw**

9. **10.**

90° cw **180° cw**

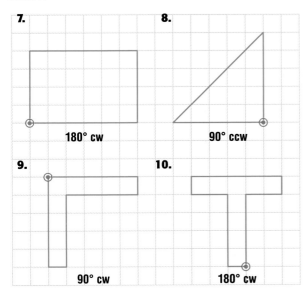

Draw the image of each figure after a 90° clockwise rotation about the origin.

11. **12.**

13. **14.**

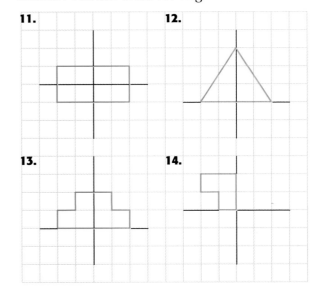

Draw the image of each figure after a 180° counterclockwise rotation about the origin.

15. **16.**

17. **18.**

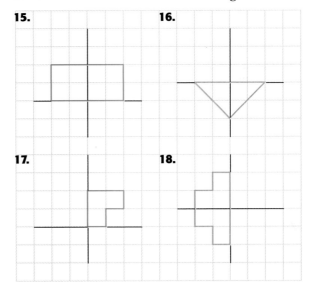

19. △DEF has vertices D(0, 0), E(–4, 2), and F(0, 6). Draw the image of △DEF after a 90° counterclockwise rotation about the origin.

20. △ABC has vertices A(1, 0), B(3, 4), and C(3, 0). Draw the image of △ABC after a 90° clockwise rotation about the origin.

CONTINUED ▶

Copy each figure and find the image after the given rotation about the red turn centre.

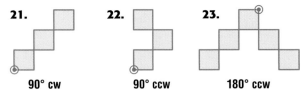

21. 90° cw **22.** 90° ccw **23.** 180° ccw

Copy and complete the table with the image of each rotation about the origin.

| | Rotation | | |
Point	90° ccw	180° cw	270° ccw
24. (0, 6)			
25. (–4, 0)			
26. (0, –3)			
27. (3, 4)			
28. (–4, 3)			

Problems and Applications

29. Rectangle ABCD has vertices A(1, 0), B(1, 2), C(6, 2), and D(6, 0). Draw the image of the rectangle after a 180° counterclockwise rotation about the origin.

30. Parallelogram ABCD has vertices A(–1, 0), B(–2, 2), C(–6, 2), and D(–5, 0). Draw the image of the parallelogram after a 90° clockwise rotation about the origin.

31. Copy the figure onto grid paper and rotate it 90° clockwise about
a) point P   **b)** the origin

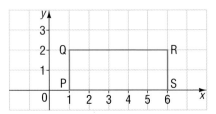

32. The parallelogram PQRS has vertices P(1, 0), Q(3, 3), R(8, 3), and S(6, 0). Draw the image of the parallelogram after a 90° clockwise rotation about S. What sort of figure is the image?

33. Rotate each letter by a $\frac{1}{2}$ turn clockwise about the indicated point. Which ones make readable letters when rotated?

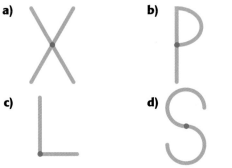

a)   **b)**

c)   **d)**

34. This figure is to be rotated so that its image lies exactly on top of the original figure. Which point(s) named in the figure could be the turn centre if

a) a 180° rotation is used?
b) a 360° rotation is used?

35. Plot the line $x + y = 2$ on a grid and rotate it 90° clockwise about the origin. At what angle do the line and its image intersect?

36. a) Plot the line $y = x - 3$ on a grid. Rotate the line 180° about the origin. How are the line and its image related?
b) Repeat part a) for the line $y = x$.
c) Explain why your findings in parts a) and b) are different.

37. a) Name another clockwise rotation that will give the same image of a figure as a 90° clockwise rotation about the origin.
b) Name a counterclockwise rotation that will give the same image of the figure as in part a).

38. The stars in the sky appear to rotate 360° about a point every day. What is that point?

39. List 3 examples of real objects that rotate about a turn centre. Compare your list with a classmate's. Choose objects that have not been mentioned in this section.

8.4 Dilatations

Lewis Carroll's *Alice's Adventures in Wonderland* and *Through the Looking Glass* are considered the most famous children's books written in English. In both books, the story is a dream in which Alice changes size and encounters fantastic creatures.

A transformation that changes the size of an object is called a **dilatation**. Dilatations are called **enlargements** or **reductions**, depending on the way in which the size is changed.

Activity: Draw a Dilatation Image

Plot rectangle ABCD with coordinates A(4, 2), B(−2, 2), C(−2, −2), and D(4, −2). Multiply the coordinates of A by 2 to give its image A′(8, 4). Multiply the coordinates of the other vertices by 2 to give B′, C′, and D′. Join A′, B′, C′, and D′ to make rectangle A′B′C′D′, which is the dilatation image of rectangle ABCD.

Inquire

1. How do the side lengths of rectangle A′B′C′D′ compare with the side lengths of rectangle ABCD?

2. How do the ratios $\dfrac{AB}{A'B'}$, $\dfrac{BC}{B'C'}$, $\dfrac{CD}{C'D'}$, and $\dfrac{AD}{A'D'}$ compare?

3. How do the angles of rectangle A′B′C′D′ compare with the angles of rectangle ABCD?

4. Calculate the area of each rectangle. How do the areas compare?

5. Do rectangle ABCD and its image, rectangle A′B′C′D′, have the same sense?

6. a) Draw a line from the origin, (0, 0), through A and extend it. Does it pass through A′?
b) Does a straight line pass through the origin, B, and B′? the origin, C, and C′? the origin, D, and D′?

7. We say that rectangle ABCD has been enlarged by a dilatation with **centre** (0, 0) and a **scale factor** of 2. Describe a dilatation of this type in your own words.

8. Repeat this activity by dividing each coordinate of rectangle ABCD by 2 to give the coordinates of the image rectangle A″B″C″D″. How do the lengths of the sides, the sizes of the angles, and the area compare with those of rectangle ABCD?

The dilatation with centre (0, 0) and scale factor k can be described mathematically as a mapping.

$(x,y) \rightarrow (kx, ky)$

When $k > 1$, the mapping gives an enlargement.
When $k < 1$, the mapping gives a reduction.
The image and the original figure are **similar**.
They have the same shape, but not the same size.

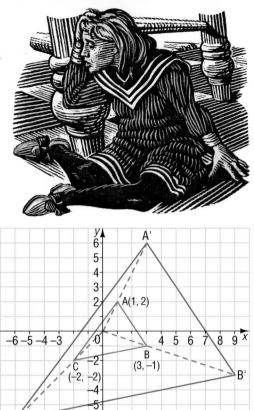

Example

△ABC has vertices A(1, 2), B(3, −1), and C(−2, −2). Find the image of △ABC under the mapping $(x,y) \rightarrow (3x, 3y)$.

Solution

Draw △ABC.

For $(x,y) \rightarrow (3x, 3y)$

$A(1,2) \rightarrow A'(3,6)$
$B(3,-1) \rightarrow B'(9,-3)$
$C(-2,-2) \rightarrow C'(-6,-6)$

Plot A', B', and C' and join them.
△A'B'C' is the image of △ABC.

Practice

A figure is shown with its image to the right. What is the scale factor?

1.

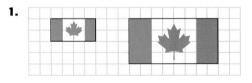

2.

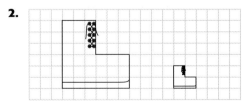

3. Copy the figure onto grid paper and enlarge it by a scale factor of 2.

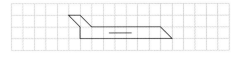

4. Copy the figure onto grid paper and reduce it by a scale factor of $\frac{1}{2}$.

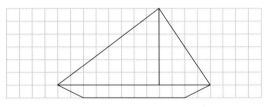

Draw the dilatation image of each line segment under the given mapping.

	Line Segment	Mapping
5.	A(3, 2), B(1, 4)	$(x, y) \rightarrow (2x, 2y)$
6.	C(6, 4), D(−2, 2)	$(x, y) \rightarrow (\frac{1}{2}x, \frac{1}{2}y)$
7.	E(−1, −1), F(1, 2)	$(x, y) \rightarrow (3x, 3y)$
8.	G(9, 3), H(−6, 0)	$(x, y) \rightarrow (\frac{1}{3}x, \frac{1}{3}y)$

9. △RST has vertices R(2, 3), S(−1, 4), and T(−3, −2). Find the image of △RST under the mapping $(x,y) \rightarrow (3x, 3y)$.

10. Quadrilateral DEFG has vertices D(6, 4), E(–2, 6), F(–4, –4), and G(4, –6). Find the image of quadrilateral DEFG under the mapping $(x,y) \rightarrow \left(\frac{1}{2}x, \frac{1}{2}y\right)$.

Problems and Applications

11. Copy this piece of an impossible chessboard onto grid paper and enlarge it by a scale factor of 2.

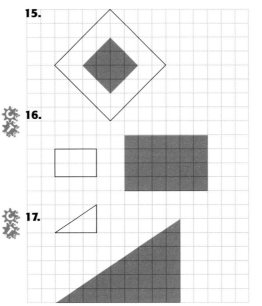

12. Copy this disappearing block puzzle onto grid paper and reduce it by a scale factor of $\frac{1}{2}$.

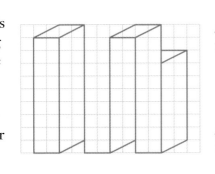

13. △PQR has vertices P(–2, 2), Q(–2, –2), and R(2, –2).
a) Draw △PQR on grid paper.
b) Calculate the area of △PQR.
c) Find the image of △PQR, △P′Q′R′, under the mapping $(x,y) \rightarrow (3x, 3y)$.
d) Calculate the area of △P′Q′R′.
e) Find the image of △PQR, △P″Q″R″, under the mapping $(x,y) \rightarrow \left(\frac{1}{2}x, \frac{1}{2}y\right)$.
f) Calculate the area of △P″Q″R″.
g) Write the following ratios.
area △P′Q′R′ : area △PQR
area △P″Q″R″ : area △PQR
h) How is each ratio related to the scale factor that produced the image?

14. a) State the types of dilatations you see in:
- a map of a province
- a movie screen
- a television screen
- a blueprint of a house

b) Find 2 other examples of enlargements or reductions in real-world objects. Estimate the scale factors involved.

In questions 15–17, copy the figure and its red image onto grid paper. Find the dilatation centre and state the scale factor.

15.

16.

17.

18. What would the image of a triangle look like under this mapping?
$(x,y) \rightarrow (1x, 1y)$

19. △ABC has vertices A(4, 2), B(1, –2), and C(8, –3).
a) Draw △ABC on grid paper.
b) Find the image of △ABC for a dilatation with centre (4, 0) and a scale factor of 2.

20. Use a figure of your choice and investigate these mappings. Describe your findings.
a) $(x,y) \rightarrow (2x, 4y)$
b) $(x,y) \rightarrow (-2x, -2y)$

311

Transformations with Geometry Software

Complete the following activities with a geometry software package. If you do not have suitable software, use grid paper.

Activity ❶ Reflections and Coordinates

1. Draw △ABC with vertices A(2, 3), B(4, 1), and C(1, 2).

2. Reflect △ABC in the x-axis and determine the coordinates of the vertices of its image.

3. Reflect △ABC in the y-axis and determine the coordinates of the vertices of its image.

4. Copy and complete the table for reflections of △ABC and the other triangles in each axis.

Triangle	Original Coordinates	Coordinates after Reflection	
		in x-axis	in y-axis
△ ABC	A(2, 3), B(4, 1), C(1, 2)		
△ DEF	D(–1, 4), E(–4, 3), F(–2, 1)		
△ PQR	P(–2, –3), Q(–1, –4), R(–3, –5)		
△ XYZ	X(3, –1), Y(2, –4), Z(4, –3)		

5. Write a rule for finding the coordinates of the point (x, y) after a reflection in
a) the x-axis   **b)** the y-axis

6. Are any x- and y-values exceptions to your rule? Explain.

7. Rectangle ABCD has vertices A(0, 3), B(–4, 3), C(–4, –2), and D(0, –2). Predict the coordinates of the vertices of its image after a reflection in
a) the x-axis   **b)** the y-axis

8. Carry out the reflections to check your predictions.

Activity ② Combined Reflections

1. For each triangle in Activity 1, carry out a reflection in the *x*-axis, then reflect the image in the *y*-axis. Determine the coordinates of the final image. Tabulate your findings.

Triangle	Original Coordinates	Coordinates after Combined Reflection in Both Axes
△ ABC	A(2, 3), B(4, 1), C(1, 2)	
△ DEF	D(−1, 4), E(−4, 3), F(−2, 1)	
△ PQR	P(−2, −3), Q(−1, −4), R(−3, −5)	
△ XYZ	X(3, −1), Y(2, −4), Z(4, −3)	

2. Write a rule for finding the coordinates of the point (*x*, *y*) after a combined reflection in both axes.

3. Are any *x*- and *y*-values exceptions to your rule? Explain.

4. Is your rule affected by the order in which the two reflections are carried out? Explain.

5. Quadrilateral WXYZ has vertices W(1, 3), X(−5, 0), Y(−3, −2), and Z(0, −2). Predict the coordinates of the vertices of its image after a combined reflection in both axes. Then, carry out the combined reflection to check your predictions.

Activity ③ 180° Rotations

1. For each of the triangles in Activity 1, carry out a 180° rotation, clockwise or counterclockwise, about the origin. Determine the coordinates of the final image. Tabulate your findings.

Triangle	Original Coordinates	Coordinates after 180° Rotation about the Origin
△ ABC	A(2, 3), B(4, 1), C(1, 2)	
△ DEF	D(−1, 4), E(−4, 3), F(−2, 1)	
△ PQR	P(−2, −3), Q(−1, −4), R(−3, −5)	
△ XYZ	X(3, −1), Y(2, −4), Z(4, −3)	

2. How do the results of a 180° rotation about the origin compare with the results of a combined reflection in both axes?

3. Quadrilateral PQRS has vertices P(0, 0), Q(3, 4), R(−2, 5), and S(−4, −1). Predict the coordinates of the vertices of its image after a 180° rotation about the origin. Then, carry out the rotation to check your predictions.

Activity ④ Using the Results

1. Without carrying out the transformations, predict the coordinates of the vertices of the following images.

a) △KLM with vertices K(1, −4), L(−2, −5), M(3, 2), following a reflection in the *y*-axis

b) △FGH with vertices F(4, 0), G(3, −3), H(−1, 5), following a reflection in the *x*-axis

c) △STU with vertices S(3, −5), T(2, 2), U(−4, −1), following a combined reflection in both axes

d) △QRS with vertices Q(−2, −2), R(−4, 3), S(0, 0), following a 180° rotation about the origin

2. State the coordinates of the vertices of a rectangle whose image after a combined reflection in both axes lies exactly on the original rectangle. Compare your rectangle with that of a classmate.

8.5 Symmetry

A **line of symmetry** is a mirror line that reflects an object onto itself. Line symmetry is also called **reflectional symmetry** or **mirror symmetry**. Insects, flowers, and many other natural objects have lines of symmetry.

Describe where the line of symmetry is on the ladybug.

Activity: Draw Lines of Symmetry

When water drops are sprinkled onto a dry, hot skillet, the drops dance across the skillet. The drops take many different shapes. A few of them are shown. Trace the water drops and draw all their lines of symmetry. You may want to use a Mira.

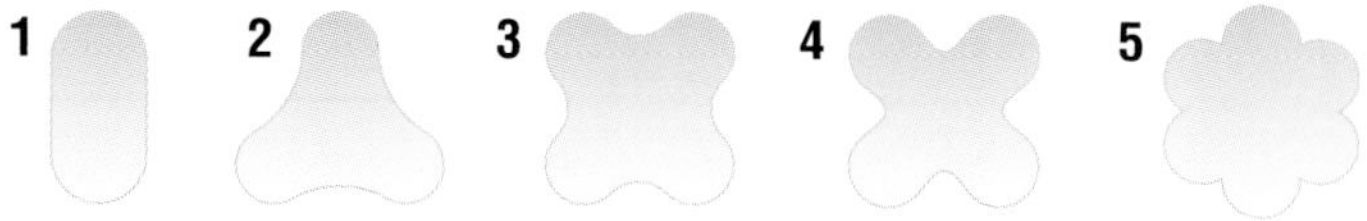

1 2 3 4 5

Inquire

1. How many lines of symmetry does each water drop have?

2. How many lines of symmetry does a square have?

3. How many lines of symmetry does an isosceles triangle have? an equilateral triangle?

4. List some objects in the classroom that have several lines of symmetry.

A figure that can be mapped onto itself with a turn of less than one complete rotation has **rotational symmetry** or **turn symmetry**. The number of times the figure matches with itself in a turn of 360° is the **order** of rotational symmetry. Rotational symmetry of order 2 is also called **point symmetry**.

Example

Determine the order of turn symmetry of water drop 2.

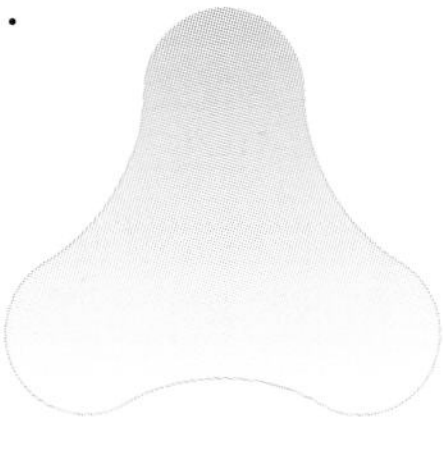

Solution

Trace the water drop and put the tracing on top of the original. Put a pencil point or pen point on the centre and turn the tracing. Count the number of times the tracing matches the original in a 360° turn. The tracing matches 3 times.

The water drop has turn symmetry of order 3.

Practice

How many lines of symmetry does each figure have?

1. **2.**

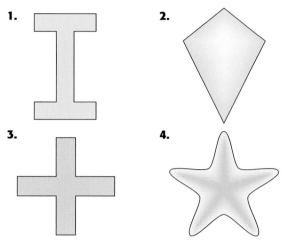

3. **4.**

What is the order of turn symmetry for each figure?

5. **6.**

7. **8.**

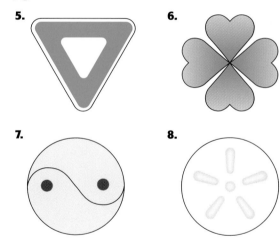

Problems and Applications

9. Print the capital letters of the alphabet.
a) Which letters have a vertical line of symmetry?
b) Which letters have a horizontal line of symmetry?
c) Which letters have both a vertical and a horizontal line of symmetry?
d) Which of the letters have point symmetry?

Trace each figure. Then, add enough parts so that it is symmetric about the red line.

10. **11.**

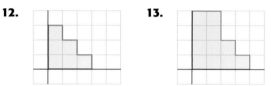

Trace each figure. Then, add parts to each of the other 3 quadrants so that the figure has
a) *1 line of symmetry*
b) *2 lines of symmetry*
c) *no lines of symmetry*
d) *rotational symmetry of order 4*
e) *rotational symmetry of order 2*

12. **13.**

14. A double six set of dominoes uses seven patterns from "blank" to six. The set starts with the double blank domino and goes to the double six domino.

In a double six domino set, how many dominoes have
a) no lines of symmetry?
b) 1 line of symmetry?
c) 2 lines of symmetry?
d) rotational symmetry of order 2?

15. Many company logos have lines of symmetry and rotational symmetry. Find examples of company logos with symmetry. Copy them into your notebook and record the type of symmetry they have. Why do logo designers use symmetry?

16. Work with a classmate to find flags of the world that have lines of symmetry. Sketch the flags.

Distortions on a Grid

When you stand in front of a mirror in a fun house, your image is distorted. When you distort a figure in mathematics, you may stretch, shrink, and turn it in many directions.

Activity ❶

1. Draw the arrow on grid paper.

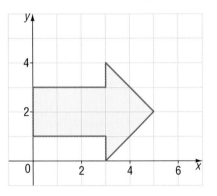

Find the image of the arrow under the following mappings.
a) $(x,y) \rightarrow (2x,y)$
b) $(x,y) \rightarrow (x,2y)$

Describe how each image has been distorted from the original arrow.

2. A kite ABCD has vertices A(0, 0), B(2, 4), C(0, 6), and D(–2, 4). Draw the kite on grid paper, then draw the images of the kite under the following mappings.
a) $(x,y) \rightarrow (3x,y)$
b) $(x,y) \rightarrow (x,2y)$
c) $(x,y) \rightarrow \left(x,\frac{y}{2}\right)$
d) $(x,y) \rightarrow (2x,2y)$

Does each distortion give an image that is also a kite?

3. Draw a square with vertices (3, 3), (–3, 3), (–3, –3), and (3, –3). If you draw the square under each of the mappings you used for the kite in question 2, is the image always a square?

Activity ❷

Draw the T on grid paper.

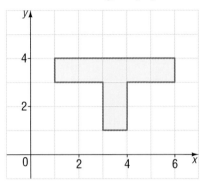

Draw the images of the T under the following mappings.
a) $(x,y) \rightarrow (-x,2y)$
b) $(x,y) \rightarrow (2x,-y)$

Describe how each image has been distorted from the original T-shape.

Activity ❸

Draw the figure on grid paper.

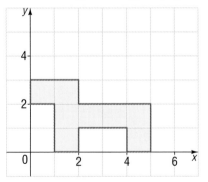

Draw the images of the figure under the following mappings.
a) $(x,y) \rightarrow \left(\frac{x}{2},3y\right)$
b) $(x,y) \rightarrow \left(3x,\frac{y}{2}\right)$

Describe how each image has been distorted from the original figure.

Activity ❹

The rectangle ABCD has been transformed under the mapping $(x,y) \rightarrow \left(2x, \frac{x+y}{2}\right)$.

$$(x,y) \rightarrow \left(2x, \frac{x+y}{2}\right)$$
$$A(0,0) \rightarrow A'(0,0)$$
$$B(4,0) \rightarrow B'(8,2)$$
$$C(4,3) \rightarrow C'(8,3.5)$$
$$D(0,3) \rightarrow D'(0,1.5)$$

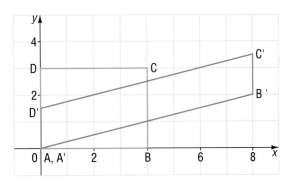

1. Draw the following figure on grid paper.

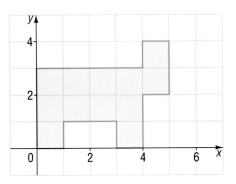

Draw the image of the figure under this mapping.

$$(x,y) \rightarrow \left(2x, \frac{x+y}{2}\right)$$

2. Draw the image of the same figure under this mapping.

$$(x,y) \rightarrow \left(\frac{x+y}{2}, 2y\right)$$

3. Redraw the figure away from the axes and apply the mappings from steps 1 and 2 of this activity to the figure.

Activity ❺

1. With any combinations of the mappings you have used, write your own mapping that will distort a figure in an unusual way.

2. Have a classmate use your mapping to distort a figure.

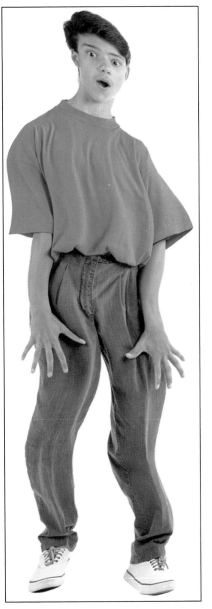

Escher Drawings

Islamic artists use tessellations in much of their work. A **tessellation** or tiling is an arrangement of shapes that completely covers the plane without overlapping or leaving gaps. The Dutch artist M.C. Escher became fascinated with tile patterns he found in Spain. Escher used translations, rotations, and reflections to make tessellations of animals and humans. This Escher tessellation is based on translations in parallelograms.

Activity ❶ Geometric Figures that Tessellate

Only 3 regular polygons will tile the plane: an equilateral triangle, a square, and a regular hexagon. However, many irregular figures will tile the plane.

1. Use grid paper to show how an irregular triangle tiles the plane.

2. Draw an example of an irregular quadrilateral that tiles the plane.

3. The diagram shows one example of an irregular hexagon that tiles the plane. Draw another example.

Activity ❷ Tessellations Using Translations

1. You can alter the opposite sides of a square and use translations to tile the plane.

a) Make an alteration to one side.

b) Translate the alteration to the opposite side.

c) Alter the other sides in a similar way.

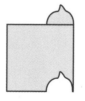

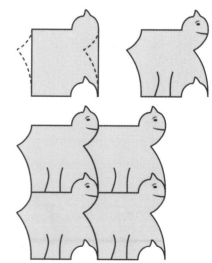

d) Use the new figure to tile the plane.

2. Alter the opposite sides of a parallelogram and use translations to tile the plane.

3. Alter the opposite sides of a hexagon and use translations to tile the plane.

318

Activity ❸ Tessellations Using Rotations

This Escher tessellation is based on rotations in regular hexagons.

1. You can alter the sides of a square and use rotations to tile the plane.

a) Make an alteration to one side.

b) Rotate the alteration.

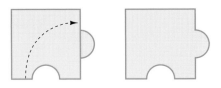

c) Use the new figure to tile the plane.

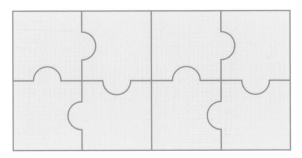

2. Alter the sides of a rhombus and use rotations to tile the plane.

3. Alter the sides of a triangle and use rotations to tile the plane.

Activity ❹ Impossible Figures

Escher also used impossible geometric figures, such as the one to the right, in his art.

1. What are impossible figures?

2. Research other examples of Escher's art that include these figures.

319

Review

State each translation arrow as an ordered pair.

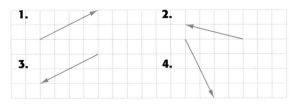

Describe each translation in words.

5. $(x, y) \rightarrow (x + 2, y + 3)$

6. $(x, y) \rightarrow (x - 3, y - 1)$

7. $[-4, 5]$ **8.** $[0, 6]$

Express each translation as an ordered pair.

9. $A(5, 4) \rightarrow A'(6, 2)$

10. $B(3, -1) \rightarrow B'(-1, 5)$

11. $C(0, -3) \rightarrow C'(2, -6)$

12. △ABC has vertices A(3, 2), B(4, −1), and C(−2, 1). Find the coordinates of the image of △ABC under this mapping.
$(x, y) \rightarrow (x + 4, y + 3)$

13. △RIK has vertices R(−2, 3), I(3, 0), and K(2, −3). Find the image of △RIK under the mapping $(x, y) \rightarrow (x - 3, y - 2)$.

Find the coordinates of the image after a reflection in each axis.

	Point	x–axis	y–axis
14.	(4, 5)		
15.	(5, −2)		
16.	(−3, 6)		
17.	(−3, −2)		

Copy each figure onto a grid and draw its reflection image in the x-axis.

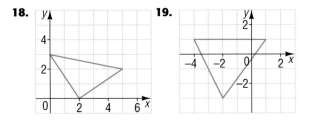

Copy each figure onto a grid and draw its reflection image in the y-axis.

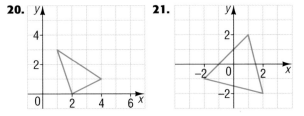

22. △DEF has vertices D(2, 3), E(5, 1), and F(4, 6). Find the coordinates of the image of △DEF after a reflection in the x-axis.

23. △RST has vertices R(3, −1), S(−3, 2), and T(−4, −3). Find the coordinates of the image of △RST after a reflection in the y-axis.

Draw the image of each figure after a 90° counterclockwise rotation about the origin.

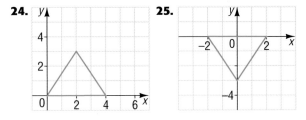

Draw the image of each figure after a 180° clockwise rotation about the origin.

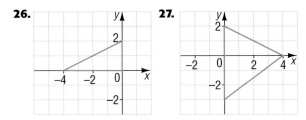

28. △DEF has vertices D(3, 0), E(3, −4), and F(0, −4). Draw the image of △DEF after a 180° counterclockwise rotation about the origin.

29. △ABC has vertices A(3, 0), B(3, 5), and C(6, 0). Draw the image of △ABC after a 90° clockwise rotation about the origin.

30. △PQR has vertices P(2, 1), Q(2, −2), and R(−1, −1). △PQR undergoes the translation [1, 2], followed by the translation [−3, 1], to give the image △P″Q″R″.
a) Find the coordinates of P″, Q″, and R″.
b) Name the single translation that maps △PQR onto △P″Q″R″.

31. △XYZ has vertices X(−2, 2), Y(1, 4), and Z(2, 1). △XYZ is reflected in the *y*-axis and then in the *x*-axis to give the image △X″Y″Z″.
a) Find the coordinates of X″, Y″, and Z″.
b) Name a single transformation that maps △XYZ onto △X″Y″Z″.

Draw the dilatation image of each line segment under the given mapping.

	Line Segment	Mapping
32.	A(2, 3), B(5, 0)	$(x, y) \rightarrow (2x, 2y)$
33.	C(−1, 2), D(3, −3)	$(x, y) \rightarrow (3x, 3y)$
34.	E(4, 6), F(−6, −2)	$(x, y) \rightarrow (\frac{1}{2}x, \frac{1}{2}y)$
35.	G(−6, 0), H(0, 6)	$(x, y) \rightarrow (\frac{1}{3}x, \frac{1}{3}y)$

36. △PQR has vertices P(3, 2), Q(3, −1), and R(2, −2). Find the image of △PQR under the mapping $(x, y) \rightarrow (2x, 2y)$.

37. Quadrilateral ABCD has vertices A(−6, 2), B(−4, −6), C(2, −8), and D(6, 10). Find the image of quadrilateral ABCD under the mapping $(x, y) \rightarrow \left(\frac{1}{2}x, \frac{1}{2}y\right)$.

How many lines of symmetry does each figure have?

38. **39.** **40.**

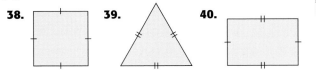

What is the order of turn symmetry for each figure?

41. **42.** **43.**

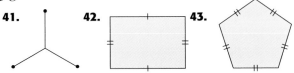

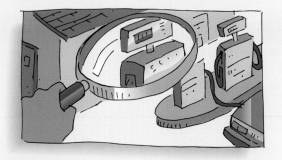

Chapter Check

1. △ABC has vertices A(−2, 0), B(0, −3), and C(3, −2). Find the coordinates of the image of △ABC under the mapping $(x,y) \rightarrow (x+5, y+4)$.

2. △PQR has vertices P(2, −1), Q(0, 2), and R(−3, −2). Draw the image of △PQR under the mapping $(x,y) \rightarrow (x-4, y+3)$.

3. △RST has vertices R(−1, 1), S(−3, 4), and T(−6, 3). Draw the image of △RST after a reflection in the x-axis.

4. △DEF has vertices D(2, 4), E(−4, 1), and F(−1, −3). Draw the image of △DEF after a reflection in the y-axis.

5. △JKL has vertices J(−4, 0), K(−3, 5), and L(0, −3). Draw the image of △JKL after a 180° clockwise rotation about the origin.

6. △GHI has vertices G(4, 0), H(4, −3), and I(0, −2). Draw the image of △GHI after a 90° counterclockwise rotation about the origin.

7. △STU has vertices S(0, 1), T(−3, 3), and U(4, −3). Draw the image of △STU under the mapping $(x,y) \rightarrow (2x, 2y)$.

8. Quadrilateral PQRS has vertices P(−2, 2), Q(2, 4), R(3, 1), and S(1, −1).
a) Draw quadrilateral PQRS on grid paper.
b) Quadrilateral P′Q′R′S′ is the image of quadrilateral PQRS under the mapping $(x,y) \rightarrow (3x, 3y)$. Find the coordinates of P′, Q′, R′, and S′, and draw quadrilateral P′Q′R′S′.

9. △XYZ has vertices X(2, 1), Y(−2, 1), and Z(−1, 3). △XYZ is reflected in the x-axis and then in the y-axis to give the image △X″Y″Z″. Find the coordinates of X″, Y″, and Z″.

How many lines of symmetry does each figure have?

10.

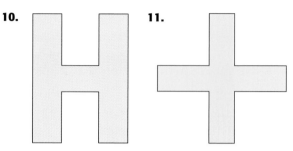

11.

What is the order of turn symmetry for each figure?

12.

13.

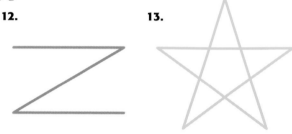

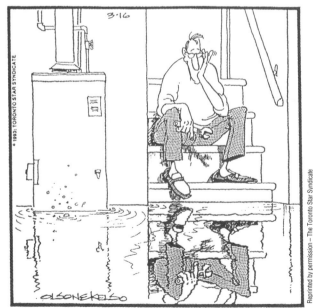

This will be a wonderful day for self reflection.

Using the Strategies

1. How many different-sized squares can be constructed on a 5-by-5 geoboard?

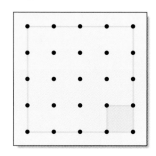

2. Find 2 multiples of 13 that are also multiples of 17.

3. Find 3 consecutive integers whose product is 1716.

4. When you write the whole numbers in words, "one," "two," "three," and so on, what is the first word that has the letters in alphabetical order?

5. The squares are exactly the same size. The total area of the figure is 384 cm². What is the perimeter of the figure?

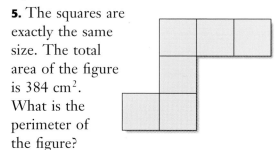

6. On a "prime day," both the month and the day are prime. March 13 is a prime day because March is month 3, which is prime, and so is 13. How many prime days are there this year?

7. The diagram shows one way of covering a 5 cm by 2 cm rectangle with 5 rectangles measuring 2 cm by 1 cm.

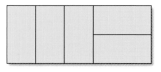

In how many other ways can you cover this rectangle with the smaller rectangles?

8. How many triangles are in the 1st row? the 2nd? the 3rd? the 4th? If the pattern continues, how many triangles are in the 10th row? the 20th row? the 100th row? the *n*th row?

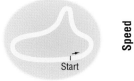

9. You spend $2.75 in a store and receive $7.25 change from $10.00. Notice that the arrangement of the digits in the amount you spent is a rearrangement of the digits in your change. Find 4 other pairs of amounts spent and change from $10.00 that share this property.

10. A car is racing around this track.

Sketch a graph of speed versus distance travelled for 1 lap of the track.

DATA BANK

1. Write the ratio of the speed of the strongest strong breeze to the speed of the strongest moderate breeze. Express your answer in lowest terms.

2. The longest covered bridge is in Hartland, New Brunswick. The longest cable suspension bridge is under construction in Akashi Kaikyo, Japan. How many times longer is the Japanese bridge than the bridge in New Brunswick?

Chapter 5

Find the GCF of each pair.

1. 42, 56   **2.** $10t^2, 2t$ **3.** $14xy, 35x^2y^2$

Factor.

4. $3x - 21$ **5.** $5x^2y + 15xy^2$

Expand.

6. $(4x)(5y)$ **7.** $-2x(3 - x)$ **8.** $3x(2x - 3)$

Divide.

9. $45x \div 9$ **10.** $\dfrac{-32xy}{8y}$ **11.** $\dfrac{4x - 8x^2 + 12x^3}{4x}$

Expand.

12. $(x - 3)(x + 1)$ **13.** $(2x - 1)(3x - 2)$

Factor.

14. $x^2 - 7x - 8$ **15.** $a^2 + 10a - 11$

16. $b^2 - 2b + 1$ **17.** $y^2 - 10y - 56$

Factor fully.

18. $2x^2 - 20x + 50$ **19.** $3x^2 + 3x - 36$

20. $4a^2 - 4a - 80$ **21.** $5a^2 - 25a + 30$

Expand.

22. $(x + 7)(x - 7)$ **23.** $(3 - t)(3 + t)$

24. $(5p - 1)(5p + 1)$ **25.** $(6 - 9y)(6 + 9y)$

Factor.

26. $x^2 - 4$ **27.** $4p^2 - 49$ **28.** $8x^2 - 72$

Simplify.

29. $\dfrac{25x^2y}{5} \times \dfrac{2x^4y^2}{5x^3y^3}$ **30.** $\dfrac{2 + x}{2} + \dfrac{5 - x}{5}$

Expand.

31. $(2x - 1)^2$ **32.** $(3 - 2y)^2$ **33.** $(p - 3q)^2$

Factor.

34. $m^2 + 10m + 25$ **35.** $4w^2 - 12w + 9$

Expand and simplify.

36. $(y + 3)(2y^2 + 7y - 4y)$

Chapter 6

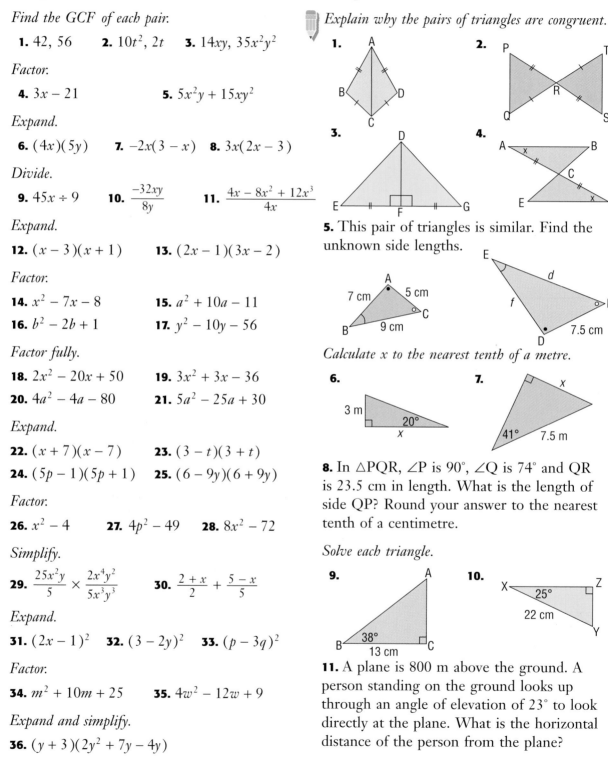

Explain why the pairs of triangles are congruent.

1.   **2.**

3.   **4.**

5. This pair of triangles is similar. Find the unknown side lengths.

Calculate x to the nearest tenth of a metre.

6.   **7.**

8. In $\triangle PQR$, $\angle P$ is $90°$, $\angle Q$ is $74°$ and QR is 23.5 cm in length. What is the length of side QP? Round your answer to the nearest tenth of a centimetre.

Solve each triangle.

9.   **10.**

11. A plane is 800 m above the ground. A person standing on the ground looks up through an angle of elevation of $23°$ to look directly at the plane. What is the horizontal distance of the person from the plane?

Chapter 7

Estimate, then calculate the area of each figure.

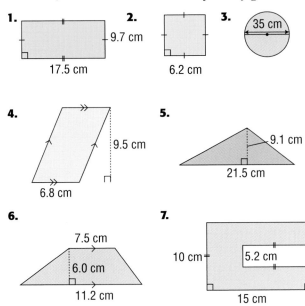

1. 17.5 cm, 9.7 cm

2. 6.2 cm

3. 35 cm

4. 9.5 cm, 6.8 cm

5. 9.1 cm, 21.5 cm

6. 7.5 cm, 6.0 cm, 11.2 cm

7. 10 cm, 5.2 cm, 15 cm

Calculate the volume and surface area of each solid.

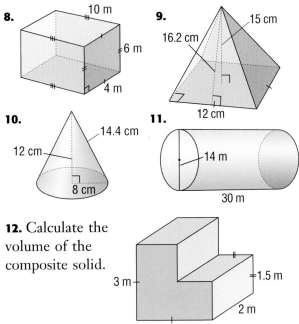

8. 10 m, 6 m, 4 m

9. 16.2 cm, 15 cm, 12 cm

10. 14.4 cm, 12 cm, 8 cm

11. 14 m, 30 m

12. Calculate the volume of the composite solid. 3 m, 1.5 m, 2 m

13. How many boxes 1 m by 1 m by 0.5 m will fit into a storage container 3 m by 4 m by 10 m?

Chapter 8

1. Draw the triangle on grid paper. Then, draw its translation image.
W(−1, 4), Y(−3, 1), Z(−1, 1)
$(x, y) \rightarrow (x + 2, y − 3)$

2. △K′L′M′ is the image of △KLM under the translation [−3, 2]. The coordinates of the vertices of △K′L′M′ are K′(2, 1), L′(2, −3), and M′(7, 1). What are the coordinates of the vertices of △KLM?

Draw each triangle on a grid. Draw its image after a reflection in
a) *the x-axis.* **b)** *the y-axis.*

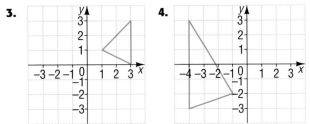

3.

4.

Copy the figure onto grid paper. Draw the image after the given rotation about the given turn centre.

5. 90° turn clockwise about the turn centre A

6. 180° turn counterclockwise about the origin

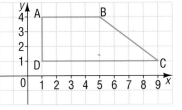

7. Square ABCD has vertices A(3, 3), B(3, −3), C(−3, −3) and D(−3, 3). Draw the image of square ABCD under each mapping.
a) $(x, y) \rightarrow (2x, 2y)$ **b)** $(x, y) \rightarrow \left(\frac{1}{3}x, \frac{1}{3}y\right)$

Copy each figure.
a) *Draw the lines of symmetry.*
b) *State the order of turn symmetry.*

8.

9.

Data Analysis and Probability

The graph shows the world's projected population growth.

Suppose you hold a concert on Vancouver Island in the year 2010. The area of Vancouver Island is 31 285 km^2. If each person needs an area of 1 m^2, could the whole world attend your concert? Could the whole world attend in the year 2060?

Estimate the first year in which the whole world could not attend the concert. What assumptions have you made? Are your assumptions reasonable?

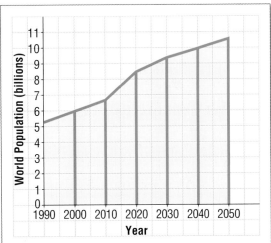

Canadian Weather Facts

The table shows the percent chance of different types of weather in some Canadian cities.

Type of Weather	City							
	Vancouver	Edmonton	Regina	Winnipeg	Toronto	Montreal	Halifax	St. John's
January Thaw	100	96	84	54	98	98	100	100
10-cm Snowfall in January	38	17	3	27	49	81	72	84
Temperature of –20°C or Lower in Winter	0	100	100	100	89	100	76	23
April Gale	8	0	35	19	27	12	10	68
May Snowfall	0	58	43	53	9	21	44	79
June Frost	0	21	43	30	0	0	0	60
June Fog	23	41	58	50	85	69	100	100
At Least 10 Wet Days in July	21	96	51	72	40	77	68	84
Temperature of 35°C or more in Summer	0	0	64	43	32	9	0	0
September Frost	2	92	97	87	40	30	8	14
December Thunderstorm	7	0	0	7	21	11	13	11
Hail During the Year	69	83	89	82	64	68	36	25

Activity ❶

Use the table to answer these questions.

1. Which cities have the same chance of a January thaw?

2. Which city has the highest chance of a temperature of 35°C or more in summer?

3. Which city has the lowest chance of an April gale?

4. Is the chance of a December thunderstorm higher in Toronto or in Montreal?

5. Which 2 cities always get a January thaw and a June fog?

6. How many times higher is the chance of

a) a June frost in St. John's than a June frost in Winnipeg?

b) a September frost in Edmonton than a September frost in Vancouver?

c) a 10-cm snowfall in January in St. John's than a 10-cm snowfall in January in Regina?

Activity ❷

Use the data in the table to write 3 more problems. Have a classmate solve your problems.

Warm Up

1. This circle graph shows data on volumes of natural gas produced in different provinces.

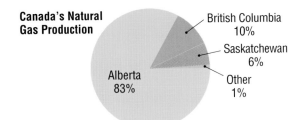

Canada's Natural Gas Production

British Columbia 10%

Saskatchewan 6%

Alberta 83%

Other 1%

a) Rank the provinces in decreasing order of natural gas production.

b) If approximately 100 000 000 000 m³ of natural gas are produced in Canada each year, how much is produced in Alberta? How much is produced in British Columbia and Saskatchewan together?

2. This table gives approximate distances a cheetah can run for certain lengths of time. A cheetah is able to keep up this pace for only a few hundred metres.

Time (s)	Distance (m)
1	30
2	60
3	90
4	120
5	150
6	180

a) Display the data on a line graph.
b) Describe the pattern in the graph.
c) Explain the pattern.

Multiply. Write each answer in simplest form.

3. $\frac{1}{4} \times \frac{3}{4}$ **4.** $\frac{1}{2} \times \frac{1}{6}$ **5.** $\frac{3}{8} \times \frac{1}{3}$

6. $\frac{5}{6} \times \frac{1}{4}$ **7.** $\frac{1}{2} \times \frac{1}{2} \times \frac{1}{2}$ **8.** $\frac{1}{3} \times \frac{3}{4} \times \frac{9}{10}$

9. $\frac{1}{10} \times \frac{3}{10} \times \frac{9}{10}$ **10.** $\frac{1}{2} \times \frac{5}{6} \times \frac{2}{3}$

Write each fraction as a percent. Round each answer to the nearest tenth, if necessary.

11. $\frac{1}{4}$ **12.** $\frac{4}{5}$ **13.** $\frac{1}{3}$ **14.** $\frac{3}{8}$ **15.** $\frac{2}{3}$ **16.** $\frac{1}{6}$

Mental Math

Calculate each product. Look for easy combinations.

1. $5 \times 2 \times 8$ **2.** $25 \times 4 \times 7$

3. $7 \times 5 \times 2$ **4.** $12 \times 4 \times 25$

5. $4 \times 6 \times 25$ **6.** $5 \times 18 \times 2$

Find each sum. Think quarters.

7. $12.75 + $8.25

8. $3.25 + $4.50

9. $2.75 + $4.50

10. $5.00 + $2.50 + $3.50

11. $6.25 + $2.75 + $5.50

12. $8.50 + $3.75 + $2.75

Find each sum. Look for sums of 50.

13. $21 + 34 + 16 + 19$

14. $27 + 35 + 23 + 10$

15. $42 + 19 + 6 + 31$

Estimate the total bill.

16. $0.69 + $1.89 + $1.49 + $0.87

17. $0.87 + $2.69 + $1.34 + $2.45

18. $2.59 + $1.89 + $5.99 + $3.49

19. $2.29 + $1.89 + $1.49 + $4.69

Estimate each product.

20. 6.02×4.07 **21.** 3.1×12.6

22. 42.8×9.8 **23.** 312×4.9

Estimate each sum.

24. $3\frac{1}{3} + 4\frac{1}{4}$ **25.** $8\frac{2}{3} + 16\frac{1}{4}$

26. $5\frac{1}{3} + 2\frac{1}{2}$ **27.** $12\frac{3}{4} + 3\frac{3}{8}$

9.1 Reading Scatter Plots

A **scatter plot** can be used to show whether a relationship exists between two variables.

Activity: Interpret the Graph

The scatter plot shows the relationship between the lengths and wingspreads of 22 birds.

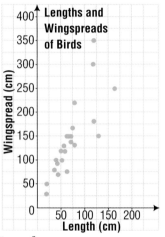

Inquire

1. a) Estimate the least wingspread shown.
b) Estimate the length of the bird with this wingspread.

2. a) Estimate the length of the bird with a wingspread close to 220 cm; 180 cm.
b) Estimate the wingspread of most birds that are about 50 cm long; 75 cm long.

3. a) Describe the pattern made by the points.
b) Describe any relationship you see between the lengths of birds and their wingspreads.
c) How does the scatter plot show this relationship?

Problems and Applications

1. The scatter plot shows the winning times for 5 races at the 1992 Olympics.
a) What was the approximate winning time for the 400-m race?
b) About how many times greater was the winning time for the 800-m race than for the 100-m race?
c) If there had been a 1000-m race, what winning time would you estimate for it?
d) Estimate how far a top male athlete can run in 3 min.

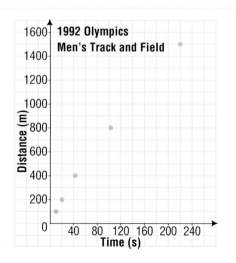

330

2. This scatter plot compares the masses and lengths of different kinds of bears.

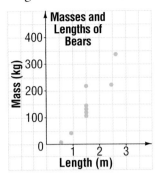

a) Estimate the length of the kind of bear that has the greatest mass.

b) What is the approximate length of the kind of bear with a mass of about 45 kg?

c) If a kind of bear had a mass of about 300 kg, about what length would you expect it to have?

d) What relationship between mass and length does the scatter plot suggest?

3. The scatter plot shows how the average temperature of the ocean changes with latitude in the southern hemisphere.

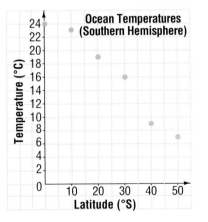

a) Describe the relationship between average ocean temperature and latitude in the southern hemisphere.

b) Estimate the average ocean temperature at a latitude of 35°S; 22°S.

c) Would you expect to see a similar relationship for the northern hemisphere? Explain.

d) At what latitude is the border between the United States and Canada's Western Provinces?

e) What do you think is the average ocean temperature at this latitude? Explain.

4. The scatter plot shows the lengths of lizards, not including their tails, and the lengths of their tails.

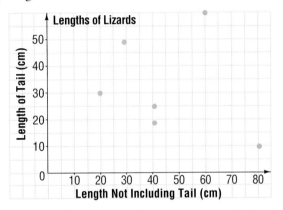

a) Does the scatter plot suggest a relationship between the lengths of lizards and the lengths of their tails? Explain.

b) Do all scatter plots show a relationship? Explain.

5. a) How does a scatter plot show whether there is a relationship between two variables?

b) Refer to the scatter plot in question 2. Consider only the 5 points that represent kinds of bears with lengths of about 1.5 m. What relationship do these 5 points suggest between the lengths and masses of bears?

c) Is it possible for a scatter plot to mislead you about whether a relationship exists? Explain.

9.2 Drawing Scatter Plots

Activity: Study the Example

The table gives the prices of certain books in Canada and in the United States. To draw the scatter plot:

1. Draw and label the axes. Choose a scale that allows you to plot all the data.

2. Plot a point to represent the data for each book.

3. Give the graph a title.

Book	Price	
	In Canada (Canadian $)	In the U.S (U.S. $)
World's Most Amazing Puzzles	6.95	4.95
Jurassic Park	7.99	6.99
Card Games Around the World	10.50	4.95
The Big Four	4.75	3.50
Graphic and Op-Art Mazes	5.95	3.95
The Human Factor	6.99	5.99
1001 Wonders of Science	12.95	10.95
Mind-Boggling Mazes	5.75	3.50
Gold & Silver, Silver & Gold	11.95	8.95
Ransom	4.50	3.50
Solv-A-Crime Puzzles	1.50	1.00
A Brief History of Time	16.95	13.95
Sports Almanac	11.95	9.95
Great Adventures of Sherlock Holmes	3.99	2.99

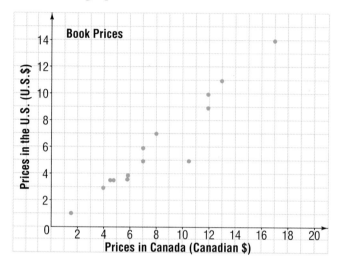

Inquire

1. Do the data in the table suggest a relationship between the prices of the books in Canadian dollars and in U.S. dollars? Explain.

2. Describe any pattern you see in the points on the scatter plot.

3. Does the scatter plot suggest a relationship between the prices of the books in Canadian dollars and in U.S. dollars? Explain.

4. Do you find it easier to look for a relationship between variables on a scatter plot or in a table? Explain.

5. To compare the U.S. and Canadian prices for just one book, is it easier to use the scatter plot or the table? Explain.

6. You could label each point on the scatter plot with the name of the book it describes. What are the advantages and disadvantages of doing this?

7. If you see a relationship between the prices of the books in Canadian dollars and in U.S. dollars, give possible reasons why the relationship exists.

Problems and Applications

1. The table shows the speeds of the winners and the year of the Blue Riband Award for the fastest Atlantic crossing by a liner.

Year	Winner	Speed (km/h)
1840	*Britannia*	19.6
1863	*Scotia*	25.9
1882	*Alaska*	31.9
1897	*Kaiser Wilhelm der Grosse*	41.5
1909	*Mauretania*	48.0
1929	*Bremen*	51.7
1938	*Queen Mary*	58.7
1952	*United States*	66.0

Draw a scatter plot of speed versus year. Describe any relationship you see.

2. The table shows the lengths, from the nose to the end of the tail, and the masses of different types of cats.

Type of Cat	Length (cm)	Mass (kg)
Lion	300	180
Lioness	270	140
Cheetah	180	45
Mountain Lion	240	90
Jaguar	260	140
Leopard	265	70
Tiger	270	190
Tigress	240	135
Lynx	90	30

Display the data on a scatter plot of mass versus length. Describe any relationship you see.

3. The table shows the number of countries represented at the Summer Olympics in different years.

Year	1920	1924	1928	1932	1936	1948
Number of Countries	29	44	46	37	49	59

Year	1952	1956	1960	1964	1968	1972
Number of Countries	69	67	83	93	112	122

a) Draw a scatter plot of the number of countries versus the year. Describe any relationship you see.

b) Use your scatter plot to estimate the numbers of countries represented in 1976 and in 1984.

c) Research the actual numbers of countries represented in 1976 and 1984.

d) Compare your estimates from part b) with your findings from part c). Research the reasons for any differences.

4. The table shows the percent of Canadians under 20 years of age in different years.

Year	Percent of Canadians Under 20
1966	42
1971	39
1976	36
1981	32
1986	29
1991	27

a) Display the data on a scatter plot of percent versus year. Describe any relationship you see.

b) What does the scatter plot tell you about changes in the average age of Canadians from 1966 to 1991? Explain.

5. a) Different students travel to school in different ways — by car, on foot, and so on. Ask 10 students who travel to school in the same way as you to estimate the distance, in kilometres, from their home to the school. Also, ask them the average time, in minutes, the trip takes.

b) Use your data to draw a scatter plot of distance versus time. Describe any relationship you see.

c) Aside from the way in which a student travels and the distance from home to school, what factors can affect the length of time for the trip?

333

9.3 Lines of Best Fit

Activity: Use the Graph

The scatter plot shows the relationship between the areas and greatest depths of seas.

The line shown on the graph is called the **line of best fit**. This line is as close as possible to the points. There are about as many points above the line as there are below the line.

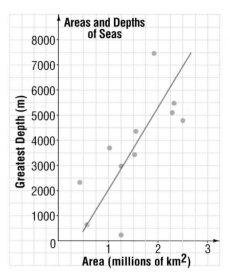

Inquire

1. a) Describe the relationship between the areas and greatest depths of seas.

b) How does the line of best fit help to show this relationship?

2. a) How well does the line of best fit match the points on the scatter plot?

b) In what ways does the line of best fit not match the points?

3. Is it possible to draw a different line of best fit for this scatter plot? Explain.

4. When you **interpolate**, you estimate values within the range of given values. Use the line of best fit to interpolate the greatest depth of a sea with an area of about 1 400 000 km².

5. When you **extrapolate**, you extend a line to estimate values outside the range of given values. Use the line of best fit to extrapolate the area of a sea with a greatest depth of about 9000 m.

Example

The table shows winning times in the women's 400-m track and field event at the Olympics.

Year	Winner	Winning Time (s)
1964	Cuthbert (Australia)	52.0
1968	Besson (France)	52.03
1972	Zehrt (East Germany)	51.08
1976	Szewinska (Poland)	49.29
1980	Koch (East Germany)	48.88
1984	Brisco-Hooks (U.S.)	48.83
1988	Bryzguina (USSR)	48.65
1992	Perec (France)	48.83

Display the data on a scatter plot of winning time versus year. Draw a line of best fit.

Solution

Draw the scatter plot. Then, draw a straight line that is as close as possible to the points plotted on the grid.

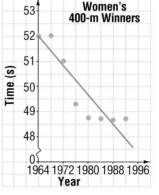

Problems and Applications

1. The table shows some winning times in the men's 110-m hurdles at the Olympics Games.

Year	Winner	Winning Time (s)
1956	Calhoun (U.S.)	13.5
1960	Calhoun (U.S.)	13.8
1964	Jones (U.S.)	13.6
1968	Davenport (U.S.)	13.3
1972	Milburn (U.S.)	13.24
1976	Drut (France)	13.30
1980	Munkelt (East Germany)	13.39
1984	Kingdom (U.S.)	13.20
1988	Kingdom (U.S.)	12.98
1992	McKoy (Canada)	13.12

a) Draw a scatter plot of winning time versus year. Draw a line of best fit.

b) Canada's Earl Thomson won the event in 1920. Extrapolate to estimate his winning time.

c) Earl Thomson's actual winning time was 14.8 s. Compare this time with your estimate.

d) Estimate the winning time in 2020; in 2060.

e) Are your estimates in part d) reasonable? Explain.

f) Display the data in the table on a broken-line graph. Does a line of best fit or a broken-line graph show more clearly the relationship between the winning time and the year? Explain.

2. The table shows, for a major video chain, the number of rentals of a particular video in each week the video has been available.

Week	Number of Rentals
1	642
2	635
3	762
4	695
5	564
6	508
7	455
8	293
9	215
10	160

a) Draw a scatter plot of number of rentals versus the week. Draw a line of best fit for the data.

b) Describe the relationship.

c) Estimate the number of rentals of the video in the 15th week.

3. The table shows the height and the circumference of a tree at different ages.

Age (years)	Height (m)	Circumference (cm)
1	1.1	15.2
2	1.1	18.2
3	2.4	20.7
4	2.5	23.2
5	3.1	27.0
6	4.3	29.5
7	4.5	32.0
8	5.3	33.9

a) Draw a scatter plot of height versus circumference. Draw a line of best fit.

b) Describe the relationship.

c) Estimate the circumference for a height of 2 m; 6 m.

d) Estimate the height for a circumference of 25 cm; 10 cm.

e) What other scatter plots could you construct from the data in the table?

f) Draw another scatter plot and use it to write 2 problems. Have a classmate solve your problems.

4. a) How can you decide whether interpolations based on a line of best fit are reasonable?

b) How can you decide whether extrapolations based on a line of best fit are reasonable?

5. a) Your arm stretch is the distance between your fingertips when your arms are fully extended. Measure the height and the arm stretch for 12 classmates. Record your results.

b) Draw a scatter plot of arm stretch versus height. Draw a line of best fit.

c) Describe the relationship between the arm stretch and the height. Does the relationship seem reasonable? Explain.

Scatter Plots

Activity ❶ Using a Computer Spreadsheet

A computer spreadsheet program can be used to draw a scatter plot.

1. The table shows forecasts for a September day. Open a spreadsheet and enter the data.

	A	B	C
1	**City**	**Low (°C)**	**High (°C)**
2	Amsterdam, Holland	10	19
3	Ankara, Turkey	5	21
4	Athens, Greece	23	30

b) Select the cells containing the data you want to display on the scatter plot. Choose the chart option. Select the scatter plot icon. Follow the instructions to create a scatter plot.

c) Format to make the changes you want to the type, labels, gridlines, and scales.

d) Draw a line of best fit for your scatter plot. You might use a draw feature on a toolbar or copy your chart into a word processing program and use its drawing feature. If you cannot draw the line of best fit with your computer, print the scatter plot and draw it with a pencil.

2. The table shows the average high or low in September for 6 cities in Western Canada. Use your line of best fit to complete the table.

City	Low (°C)	High (°C)
Edmonton, Alberta		17
Penticton, British Columbia	8	
Prince Rupert, British Columbia		15
Regina, Saskatchewan		19
Whitehorse, Yukon	3	
Winnipeg, Manitoba	6	

3. a) The highest temperature ever recorded in Regina in September was 37°C. Estimate the low temperature that day.

b) The lowest temperature ever recorded in Vancouver in September was 0°C. Estimate the high temperature that day.

City	Temperature Forecasts	
	Low (°C)	High (°C)
Amsterdam, Holland	10	19
Ankara, Turkey	5	21
Athens, Greece	23	30
Beijing, China	15	26
Berlin, Germany	4	19
Brussels, Belgium	9	19
Cairo, Egypt	21	33
Calgary, Canada	2	18
Geneva, Switzerland	9	18
Kingston, Jamaica	25	34
Lima, Peru	12	19
Lisbon, Portugal	14	22
London, England	11	21
Mexico City, Mexico	14	24
Miami, United States	25	33
New Delhi, India	23	34
Oslo, Norway	5	16
Rio de Janeiro, Brazil	20	25
Rome, Italy	15	22
Sydney, Australia	13	22
Stockholm, Sweden	4	16
Tokyo, Japan	18	25
Vancouver, Canada	12	21
Vienna, Austria	10	16
Yellowknife, Canada	5	17

4. a) Think of weather statistics that might be related. Examples might include data on temperatures or precipitation. Research the data. You might use an almanac, an encyclopedia, a CD-ROM, the Internet, the weather section of a newspaper, or a television weather report.

b) Draw a scatter plot. If a relationship exists, draw a line of best fit.

c) Write 2 problems based on your scatter plot. Have a classmate solve your problems.

Activity ❷ Using a Graphing Calculator

To use a graphing calculator to draw a scatter plot and a line of best fit, follow these steps.

• Specify the mode for graphing.

• Set the range for the coordinate plane. Xmin and Xmax are the minimum and maximum values of the x-axis. Ymin and Ymax are the minimum and maximum values of the y-axis.

• Set the scales on the axes. Xscl and Yscl are the scales on the x-axis and the y-axis.

• Clear the statistical memories.

• Input the x and y data.

• Draw the scatter plot and the line of best fit.

1. Use a set of at least 6 hockey cards issued in the same year. Draw a scatter plot of goals versus assists for the last year shown on each card. Draw a line of best fit.

2. a) Interpolate a value from your data. Make up a statement involving your value.

b) Extrapolate a value from your data. Make up a statement involving your value.

3. a) For the cards, select other data that you think might be related. You might choose all the data from one card or use different cards.

b) Create a scatter plot and line of best fit with your graphing calculator for these data. Is there a relationship? Explain.

4. Research sports statistics to be used for a scatter plot and line of best fit. Consider sports cards, an almanac, or a CD-ROM. Repeat steps 1 and 2 for your data.

5. a) What other kinds of graphs would be appropriate for displaying the data from steps 1, 3, or 4? Explain.

b) Can you create the kinds of graphs from part a) with your graphing calculator?

c) What kinds of graphs would not be appropriate for displaying these data? Explain.

Activity ❸ Making Comparisons

1. What are the advantages and disadvantages of drawing a scatter plot with

a) a spreadsheet program?   **b)** a graphing calculator?

2. Do you prefer to draw a scatter plot using a spreadsheet program, a graphing calculator, or grid paper? Explain.

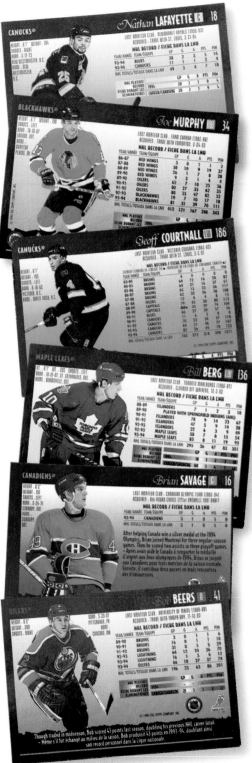

Estimating with a Line of Best Fit

Activity ❶ Mass and Volume

You will need a material, such as Plasticine, that can be made into pieces of different sizes. An alternative is a set of rubber stoppers of different sizes. Make sure that the material you use sinks in water. Also, make sure that the material does not soak up water, like a sponge or paper towel.

1. a) Measure the mass of a piece of the material.

b) Measure the volume of the same piece of material by using it to displace water in a graduated cylinder.

2. Repeat step 1 for 7 more different-sized pieces of the same material. Record your data in a table.

3. a) Draw a scatter plot of mass versus volume. Draw a line of best fit.

b) What relationship does the scatter plot suggest?

4. Choose a mass within the range of masses you measured. Interpolate to estimate the volume of a piece of the material with this mass.

5. Choose a volume greater than any of the volumes you measured. Extrapolate to estimate the mass of a piece of the material with this volume.

6. a) If you used a material that floats in water, the volume measurements would be misleading. Explain why.

b) If you used a material that floats in water, how could you change the way the volume is measured to get accurate values?

Activity ❸ Temperature

1. Record the outside temperature every hour on the hour as many times as possible over a two-day period.

2. Construct a scatter plot of temperature versus time of day for the two-day period. Draw a line of best fit.

3. a) What relationship does the line of best fit suggest between temperature and time of day?

b) Do you think that the relationship you described in part a) is reasonable? Explain.

4. a) Use the line of best fit to estimate the temperature in the middle of the night between the first and second days.

b) Do you think that your estimate from part a) is reasonable? Explain.

5. a) Describe some situations in which you can use a line of best fit to make reasonable estimates.

b) Do lines of best fit always give reasonable estimates? Explain.

c) What assumptions do you make when you use a line of best fit to make estimates?

Activity ❷ Basketball Shots

1. Use masking tape to mark a horizontal distance of 2 m from a basketball hoop. Have each member of your group shoot 10 baskets from this distance. Record the total number of successful shots for your group.

2. Repeat step 1 for 5 other distances from the basket. Use distances of 3 m, 4 m, 5 m, and so on.

3. Display the data on a scatter plot of successful shots versus distance. Draw the line of best fit.

4. Use the line of best fit to interpolate the number of successful shots from a distance of

a) 4.5 m   **b)** 6.5 m

5. Use the line of best fit to extrapolate the number of successful shots from a distance of

a) 1 m   **b)** 8 m

6. a) Compare your estimates from steps 4 and 5 with your classmates'.

b) Do you think that your estimates are reasonable? Explain.

7. a) Have each member of your group try 10 shots from each of the distances in steps 4 and 5.

b) Compare the results with your estimates. Explain any differences.

339

Misleading Statistics

Activity ❶ Data-Gathering Methods

If you gather your own data, you are using a **primary data-gathering method**. If you use someone else's data, you are using a **secondary data-gathering method**.

1. State whether each of the following is a primary or secondary source of data.
a) conducting a telephone survey
b) using a CD-ROM
c) performing an experiment
d) reading an opinion poll
e) using an almanac
f) interviewing people on the street

2. Explain one way data from a primary source could be misleading.

3. Explain one way data from a secondary source could be misleading.

Activity ❷ Populations and Samples

The entire set of items from which data are taken is the **population**. When a population is large, data might be gathered from a **sample** of the population. If you wanted to know the most popular car among grade 9 students in your school, you might survey a sample from among the whole population of grade 9 students.

Data are often used to draw conclusions about a population. For these conclusions to be reliable, a **representative sample** is needed. If you were trying to predict the results of the next student election in your school, you might survey a sample of students. Your representative sample would not include teachers, because teachers cannot vote in the election.

A magazine is doing a survey to present opinions of Canadians about whether they agree that federal government spending is appropriate.

1. If you were doing the survey, what population would you choose?

2. Describe 4 possible samples of the population.

3. How could a sample that is not representative result in misleading data?

Activity ❸ Bias

A sample should be random and unbiased. In a **random sample**, each member of the population has an equal chance of being chosen. In an **unbiased sample**, all groups in the population are fairly represented.

1. Describe 3 ways in which you could choose a random sample of grade 9 students in your school.

2. If you wanted to know the most popular sport at your school, why would you not just survey members of the swim team?

3. To avoid a biased result, what sample would you survey to find out
a) what brand of CD player is best?
b) the hours that video arcades should be open for business?

4. A **stratified sample** considers the different groups in a population. If there are 300 males and 350 females in grade 9, a stratified sample might include 30 males and 35 females. Would you use a random sample or a stratified sample for each of the following surveys? Explain.
a) What music should be played at a shopping mall?
b) Should pets be allowed in an apartment building?

Activity ❹ Misleading Presentations

1. A scatter plot can be used to misrepresent data. These 2 scatter plots display the same data in different ways.

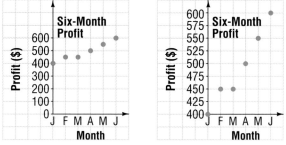

a) How are the scatter plots the same?

b) How are they different?

c) What impression is the second scatter plot intended to create?

2. In a newspaper, magazine, or computer source, find an example of a scatter plot or a different kind of graph that presents data in a misleading way. Write a report on how it is misleading.

3. Statements that distort the meaning of data may create news headlines. Find examples and report them to the class.

4. Why might a newspaper or other news medium present a misleading report?

5. Find examples of advertisers who use before-and-after pictures or graphs. Describe any examples that attempt to mislead.

6. How do commercials try to convince you to buy a product? Describe any techniques that are misleading. How could you change the commercials so that they are not misleading?

Activity ❺ Effective Statistics

Statistics are used to highlight the significance of events and to clarify their meaning. This headline

WORST STORM IN 100 YEARS

is more effective than this headline.

STORM CLOSES CITY

1. Find and describe examples of the effective use of statistics in the media.

2. How is the relationship between the headlines and the statistics made clear?

3. Explain how the statistics justify the headlines.

4. Are any important data missing from the story?

5. How might the data have been collected?

Collecting Data

Technology provides many methods for finding and organizing data.

Activity ❶ Databases

A database is a collection of data. Some databases, such as the Data Bank on pages 364 to 369 of this book, are not computerized. Computer databases are commonly found on computer discs and CD-ROMs.

1. Find an example of a database on a computer disc. Write a few sentences about the data on the disc.

2. Find an example of a database on a CD-ROM. Write a few sentences about the data on the CD-ROM.

3. CD-ROMs can use sounds and moving pictures that are not possible in books. How do these features of CD-ROMs help you to understand the data?

4. Compare CD-ROMs and computer discs for the storage of data. Describe the advantages and disadvantages of each.

5. Compare computerized and non-computerized databases for the storage of data. What are the advantages and disadvantages of each?

6. Give an example of a database that you would like for your own use. Explain why you would like it.

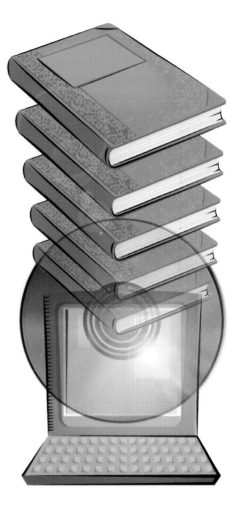

Activity ❷ Database Managers

A database manager organizes data so that it can be retrieved easily. In a printed encyclopedia, the information on each subject makes up the database. The encyclopedia itself is the database manager. A library computer system that allows you to call up information about the resources in the library is a computerized database manager.

Features of database managers may include the following.

Find: Records can be located for viewing or updating.

Sort: Data can be sorted in different ways.

Copy: Data can be copied and pasted into other programs.

Calculate: Formulas can be used to make calculations with the data.

1. For a computer database of your choice, select a way to sort some data. What are the advantages and disadvantages of sorting data
a) electronically?   **b)** manually?

2. Describe how a computerized database manager might be used by
a) a firefighter   **b)** a doctor   **c)** a teacher
d) someone in a career of your choice

Activity ❸ The Internet

The Internet, or the net, is an electronic medium that gives access to people and databases around the world.

1. Research information about the Internet. Write a few sentences to describe your findings. Compare your findings with a classmate's.

2. Describe the advantages and disadvantages of using the Internet to collect data.

3. The Internet is constantly changing. Describe a recent change that improved the Internet as a way to collect data.

4. Predict a future change to the Internet. Describe an advantage or disadvantage of this possible change.

Activity ❹ Biased Data

1. Suppose you were doing research to find out who are the most popular world leaders.
a) If your data came from a CD-ROM database of surveys conducted in North America, do you think that your data could be biased? Explain.
b) Could you reduce any bias in the data by using the Internet to access databases in different countries? Explain why or why not.

2. If you used the data recorded by supermarket scanners to identify the most popular food products in Canada, could there be any bias in your data? Explain.

3. a) Choose a subject that interests you and describe how you could use technology to access information in databases.
b) Describe how you would try to obtain unbiased data.

4. Is there any way to be sure that data collected from databases are unbiased? Explain.

5. Compare your opinions with your classmates'.

Stylometry

Did Sir Francis Bacon write some of the plays attributed to Shakespeare? This is one of the questions a stylometer tries to answer. **Stylometry** is the science of measuring written words. It is used to show that one particular person has written something.

Authors, like burglars, leave "fingerprints." The "fingerprints" of an author are verbal. From year to year, a certain author uses roughly the same proportion of 5-letter words in written pieces. The same is true for words of any other length. But the proportion of 5-letter words will likely differ from one author to another. When analyzing writing, the first task of a stylometer is to graph how someone writes.

The following excerpt is from a piece by Canadian humorist Stephen Leacock (1869–1944).

"I've been reading some very interesting statistics," he was saying to the other thinker.

"Ah, statistics!" said the other; "wonderful things, sir, statistics; very fond of them myself."

"I find, for instance," the first man went on, "that a drop of water is filled with little…with little…I forget just what you call them…little — er — things, every cubic inch containing — er — containing…let me see…"

"Say a million," said the other thinker, encouragingly.

"Yes, a million, or possibly a billion…but at any rate, ever so many of them."

"Is it possible?" said the other. "But really, you know, there are wonderful things in the world. Now, coal…take coal…."

"Very good," said his friend, "let us take coal," settling back in his seat with the air of an intellect about to feed itself.

"Do you know that every ton of coal burnt in an engine will drag a train of cars as long as…I forget the exact length, but say a train of cars of such and such a length, and weighing, say so much…from…from…hum! for the moment the exact distance escapes me…drag it from…"

"From here to the moon," suggested the other.

"Ah, very likely; yes, from here to the moon. Wonderful, isn't it?"

"But the most stupendous calculation of all, sir, is in regard to the distance from the earth to the sun. Positively, sir, a cannon-ball — er — fired at the sun…"

"Fired at the sun," nodded the other, approvingly, as if he had often seen it done.

"And travelling at the rate of…of…"

"Of three cents a mile," hinted the listener.

"No, no, you misunderstand me — but travelling at a fearful rate, simply fearful, sir, would take a hundred million — no, a hundred billion — in short would take a scandalously long time in getting there — "

Activity ❶

1. To draw the graph of how Stephen Leacock wrote, copy and complete the following table for the excerpt.

Word Length in Letters	Frequency	
	Number of Words	Percent of Total
1		
2		
3		
4		
5		
6		
7		
8		
9		
10		
11		
12		
13+		

2. Graph the percent of total values versus the word length values.

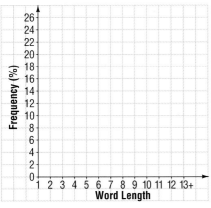

Activity ❷

1. Construct the graph for a newspaper article. Do not count any proper names.

2. Compare the graph with the graph you drew for Stephen Leacock.

Activity ❸

1. Construct the graph for something you have written. Do not count any proper names.

2. Compare your graph with Stephen Leacock's.

3. Compare your graph with your classmates'.

4. Why might the graphs for Stephen Leacock's writing and your writing not be as accurate as they could be?

Making Decisions

Activity ❶ Choosing Numbers

1. Choose a kind of lottery or a game in which people select numbers. Describe how you think people use calculations, experiments, guesswork, experience, or other methods to select numbers.

2. Answer the following questions to plan a survey to find out how people choose the numbers. Give reasons for your answers.

a) Will you use a primary data-gathering method or a secondary data-gathering method?

b) What is the population?

c) Will you survey the whole population or a sample?

d) If you plan to survey a sample, how will you find a representative sample of the population?

e) How can you ensure that your sample is unbiased?

f) Should the sample be random or stratified?

3. a) Write the questions you will ask. Include questions on how people choose numbers and what people think of the methods they use.

b) Carry out your survey. Record the results in a suitable way.

4. Organize your results. Use your results to make conclusions. Include answers to the following questions.

a) What methods do people use to choose numbers?

b) What do people think of their own methods for choosing numbers?

c) Did you introduce any biases into your survey? Explain.

d) If you did introduce biases, do you think that they are important? Explain.

5. Present your conclusions orally, in writing, or in a combination of these two ways.

Activity ❷ Other Decisions

1. How do you decide where to sit? Describe how your decision varies with the place. Consider, for example, a theatre, a classroom, a stadium, and your home. Describe how your decision is influenced by other people. What other factors affect your decision? Find out how other people decide where to sit.

2. Describe to a classmate the effect that the weather forecast has on the activities you plan for a summer weekend. Are your decisions affected by the source of the weather forecast or by how many days before the weekend you hear the forecast? How do your past experiences influence your decisions? What other factors influence your decisions?

Activity ❸ The Game Show

Gerry was the contestant on a television game show called *It's Your Move*. Gerry answered all the questions correctly. He then had the chance to win the big prize, a new car.

The host led Gerry to three doors on the stage. The doors were numbered 1, 2, and 3. The host explained that there was a new car behind one of the doors and nothing behind the other two. The host said that she knew which door hid the car.

The host asked Gerry to pick a door. Gerry chose door number 2. The host then walked over to the doors and opened door number 3. There was nothing behind door number 3. Then the host asked Gerry if he would like to change his mind about door number 2 and take door number 1.

Gerry thought for a minute and said, "I will take door number 1."

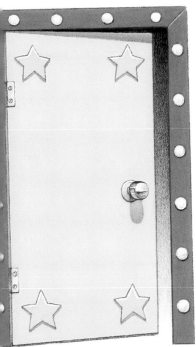

1. a) Did Gerry make the choice that gave him the best chance to win the car? Explain why you think Gerry should or should not have changed his mind.

b) Compare your decision with your classmates'.

2. Test whether Gerry was right to change his mind. Work in groups and set up the game. You could use cups for the doors and a piece of chalk for the car. Choose a host, a contestant, and a recorder. Play the game and have the recorder write the result in a table, like the one shown.

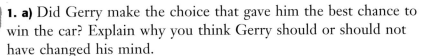

Gerry should have changed his mind.	Gerry should not have changed his mind.

3. Take turns at being the host, the contestant, and the recorder. Play the game a total of 20 times. Record all the results. Use the results to decide whether Gerry was right.

9.4 The Probability Formula

Activity: Use the Pattern

The possible outcomes of an experiment are often called the **sample space**. When you roll a die, the sample space is 1, 2, 3, 4, 5, and 6. Each of the 6 outcomes has an equal chance of happening or is **equally likely**. So, the chance or **probability** of rolling a 3, $P(3)$, is 1 out of 6.

$P(3) = \frac{1}{6}$ Number of ways to get a 3

Total number of possible outcomes

Inquire

1. What is the probability of each of the following outcomes?

a) $P(6)$ **b)** $P(\text{even number})$
c) $P(\text{prime number})$ **d)** $P(\text{number divisible by 3})$
e) $P(\text{number divisible by 7})$ **f)** $P(\text{number less than 3})$

2. a) What is the sample space for the toss of a coin?
b) What is the probability of each outcome?

When all the outcomes are known and equally likely, the probability of a single outcome is given by the **probability formula**.

$$\text{Probability of an outcome} = \frac{\text{number of favourable outcomes}}{\text{total number of possible outcomes}}$$

Example

Find the probability of each of the following outcomes for this spinner. Express each answer as a percent.

a) a 4
b) an odd number
c) a 4 or a 7
d) a 9
e) a number from 1 to 8
f) the colour green

Solution

There are 8 equal sectors on the spinner.

a) There is one 4.
So, $P(4) = \frac{1}{8}$ or 12.5%

b) There are 4 odd numbers.
So, $P(\text{odd}) = \frac{4}{8}$ or $\frac{1}{2}$ or 50%

c) There is one 4 and one 7.
So, $P(4 \text{ or } 7) = \frac{2}{8}$ or $\frac{1}{4}$ or 25%

d) There is no 9.
So, $P(9) = \frac{0}{8}$ or 0 or 0%

e) There are 8 numbers from 1 to 8.
So, $P(1 \text{ to } 8) = \frac{8}{8}$ or 1 or 100%

f) There are 4 green sectors.
So, $P(\text{green}) = \frac{4}{8}$ or $\frac{1}{2}$ or 50%

You can see from the above example that an impossible outcome has a probability of 0, and a certain outcome has a probability of 1. Outcomes that are neither impossible nor certain have probabilities between 0 and 1 or between 0% and 100%.

Practice

1. What is the probability of spinning each of the following numbers with this spinner?
a) 1
b) a prime number
c) 1, 2, 3, or 4
d) 6

2. Which number or numbers have these probabilities for the spinner in question 1?
a) 0   **b)** $\frac{1}{5}$ **c)** 1

3. What is the probability of rolling each of these numbers with a die? Express each answer as a percent.
a) 2   **b)** an odd number
c) 4, 5, or 6   **d)** a number from 1 to 6

Problems and Applications

4. a) On this spinner, what is $P(\text{blue})$?
b) What is $P(\text{red})$?
c) How many times more likely is the spinner to land on blue than on red?

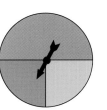

5. There are 4 green, 15 red, 6 yellow, and 5 black marbles in a bag. You remove 1 marble without looking. State the probability that it is
a) red   **b)** black   **c)** purple
d) green, yellow, red, or black

6. Each letter of the word IMPOSSIBLE is on a different card. All the cards are the same size. The cards are placed face down and shuffled. State the probability that you will randomly draw each of the following letters. Write each answer as a decimal.
a) I   **b)** N   **c)** S   **d)** L

7. State the probability of drawing these cards from a standard deck of 52 playing cards.
a) the 2 of clubs   **b)** a black card
c) a heart   **d)** a red jack

8. If you add the probabilities of all the possible outcomes for a spinner or die, what is the result? Explain.

9. If the probability of spinning a 1 on a spinner is 0.2, what is the probability of not spinning a 1?

10. A driving instructor says that the probability of her students passing their driving test on the first try is 0.80.
a) If the instructor now has 25 students, how many do you expect to pass on the first try?
b) If you take lessons from this instructor, what is your chance of passing on the first try? Explain.

11. a) Draw a spinner that gives the following probabilities.
$P(\text{red}) = \frac{1}{8}$ $P(\text{blue}) = \frac{3}{8}$
$P(\text{green}) = \frac{1}{2}$ $P(\text{yellow}) = 0$
b) Describe your method and compare it with a classmate's.
c) Predict the outcomes from spinning the spinner 1200 times.

12. Design your own spinner and write a problem to be answered with it. Have a classmate solve your problem.

13. a) In a weather forecast on TV, how are the probabilities of different types of weather reported?
b) How accurate are the probabilities? Explain.
c) List other examples of the use of probabilities in the media. Compare your list with your classmates'.

9.5 Independent Events

Activity: Conduct an Experiment

Work with a partner and toss a penny and a nickel at the same time. Repeat another 19 times. Record the results of the 20 trials and calculate the probability of each outcome. Collect data from the rest of the class and calculate each probability using all the data.

Inquire

1. How many different outcomes are possible when 2 coins are tossed at the same time?

2. What is the sample space when 2 coins are tossed at the same time?

3. What is the probability of throwing
a) 2 heads?   **b)** 2 tails?
c) a head and a tail?   **d)** 2 heads or 2 tails?

4. Write each probability from question 3 as a percent.

When 2 coins are tossed simultaneously, the outcome for one coin has no effect on the outcome for the other. The events are said to be **independent** of each other.

In the Activity, you found probabilities by performing an experiment. A probability found in this way is called an **experimental probability**. In Example 1, below, no experiment is performed. The probability calculated in this example is called a **theoretical probability**.

Example 1

A coin is tossed and a die is rolled at the same time. What is the probability of getting a head and a 6?

Solution 1

Construct a **tree diagram** to show the sample space. There is only 1 favourable outcome out of 12 equally likely outcomes.
$P(\text{H}, 6) = \frac{1}{12}$

Solution 2

For a toss of a coin, $P(\text{H}) = \frac{1}{2}$
For a roll of a die, $P(6) = \frac{1}{6}$
$P(\text{H}, 6)$ is $\frac{1}{2}$ of $\frac{1}{6} = \frac{1}{2} \times \frac{1}{6}$
$\qquad\qquad\qquad = \frac{1}{12}$

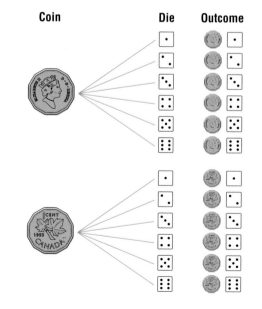

Coin   **Die**   **Outcome**

Note from Example 1 that the probability of a set of independent events is the product of the probabilities of the individual outcomes.

$$P(A \text{ and } B) = P(A) \times P(B)$$

Example 2

Without looking, Tibor took one card from each of 3 decks. What is the probability that the 3 cards he took are the jack of clubs, the ace of spades, and the 7 of diamonds?

Solution

Tibor chose each card from a different deck of cards, so his choices were independent. There are 52 cards in a deck.

There is only one jack of clubs, so $P(J\clubsuit) = \frac{1}{52}$.

There is only one ace of spades, so $P(A\spadesuit) = \frac{1}{52}$.

There is only one 7 of diamonds, so $P(7\diamondsuit) = \frac{1}{52}$.

$$P(J\clubsuit \text{ and } A\spadesuit \text{ and } 7\diamondsuit) = \frac{1}{52} \times \frac{1}{52} \times \frac{1}{52}$$
$$= \frac{1}{140\ 608}$$

The probability that Tibor took the jack of clubs, the ace of spades, and the 7 of diamonds is $\frac{1}{140\ 608}$ or about 0.0007%.

Problems and Applications

1. The spinner and the die are used for an experiment. Estimate each probability.

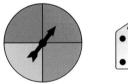

a) spinning red
b) rolling a 5
c) spinning red and rolling a 5
d) rolling an odd number and spinning green
e) rolling an even number and not spinning blue

2. A red die and a green die are rolled. What is the probability of each outcome?
a) 6 on the red die and 1 on the green die
b) 6 on each die
c) an even number on the red die and an odd number on the green die

3. A bag contains 3 red and 2 blue cubes. Each cube is replaced after it is drawn. What is each probability?
a) a red cube then a blue cube
b) 2 red cubes

4. For the spinners, which game would you rather play? Why?

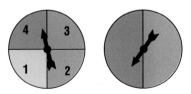

a) If you play on the numbered spinner, you win if you spin a 1.
b) You win on the second spinner if, in 2 turns, you spin red then blue.

5. A nickel, a dime, and a penny are tossed.
a) What is the sample space?
b) Are all the outcomes equally likely?
c) What is the probability of tossing 3 heads?
d) What is the probability of tossing 2 heads and a tail?

CONTINUED

351

6. A red die, a blue die, and a white die are rolled.

Calculate each probability.
a) a number greater than 3 on the red die, an even number on the blue die, and a prime number on the white die
b) a 5 on all 3 dice
c) a different number on each die

7. What is the probability of choosing a club from each set of cards from a 52-card deck?
a) the full deck
b) all the black cards
c) all the red cards

8. Three cards are chosen from a deck. Each card is replaced before the next card is chosen. What is each probability?
a) 3 aces   **b)** 3 hearts
c) a diamond, a club, and a spade
d) 4♠, 3♦, and king♥   **e)** 9♦, jack♣, and 9♦

9. A bag contains a red marble, a blue marble, and a yellow marble. Each marble is replaced before the next one is drawn. What is each probability?
a) 3 draws that give a red marble, a blue marble, and a yellow marble
b) 2 draws that give 2 yellow marbles
c) 3 draws that give 3 yellow marbles
d) 4 draws that give 4 yellow marbles

10. Beans are drawn from a bag containing 3 red beans, 2 blue beans, and 1 yellow bean. Each bean is replaced before the next one is drawn. What is each probability?
a) blue, then red
b) blue, then another blue
c) red, then blue, then red
d) yellow, then blue, then red

e) red, then blue, then yellow
f) 5 blue beans in a row
g) green

11. In questions 9 and 10, each object was replaced before the next one was drawn. Explain why.

12. Find each theoretical probability.
a) a child being female for any birth in a family
b) in a family with 2 children, both are girls
c) in a family with 3 children, all 3 are boys

13. The activity involves picking a card from a bag, spinning the spinner, and tossing a coin.

 A B B C C C D D D D

What is each probability?
a) D and 3 and a head
b) C and 2 and a tail
c) A and 3 and a head
d) D and 2 and a head
e) B and 1 and a tail
f) A and 1 and a head

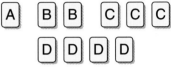

14. If you toss a coin and it shows a head, what is the probability of tossing a tail on the next toss? Explain.

15. Design a spinner so that, when you toss a coin then spin the spinner, the probability of "a head then red" is
a) $\frac{1}{10}$ **b)** $\frac{1}{6}$ **c)** 0

16. a) Design an experiment that involves finding the probability of independent events. Have a classmate perform your experiment.
b) Is the probability from part a) a theoretical probability or an experimental probability? Explain.

Simulation Experiments

A **simulation** is an experiment that acts like another experiment. Suppose you do not have a die but you want to find the experimental probability of rolling a 4. A simulation experiment might involve six cards, numbered 1 to 6, in a bag. You could draw a card, record the outcome, and return the card to the bag. The outcomes from a number of draws could be used to calculate the experimental probability of drawing or rolling a 4.

One way to simulate experiments is to use random numbers. Research how to generate random numbers with a graphing calculator and with a computer.

Activity ❶ Coin Tosses

1. a) List the possible outcomes when 3 coins are tossed.
b) Calculate the theoretical probability of each outcome.

2. To simulate the experiment, set up your graphing calculator to generate the digits 1 and 2 randomly.

3. Let 1 represent a head and 2 represent a tail. Generate a set of three random digits and record how many heads it represents. Carry out the simulation a total of 40 times. Tabulate your results.

4. Use your data to calculate the experimental probability of each outcome. Compare your results with the theoretical probabilities.

Number of Heads	Tally	Frequency
0		
1		
2		
3		

Activity ❷ A Combination Lock

A lock on a briefcase has three independent dials, each numbered from 0 to 9.

1. How many possible combinations are there for the lock?

2. If you forgot the combination, what would be the probability of guessing the combination and opening the lock? Explain.

3. Describe how you could use a graphing calculator to determine the experimental probability of guessing the combination.

4. Do you see any difficulties in carrying out the method you described in step 3? Explain.

5. How might a computer help you to overcome any difficulties you described in step 4?

Experimental Probability

For some events, such as tossing a coin or rolling a die, you can determine the probability of an outcome mathematically, without doing the experiment. For other events, you must determine the probability of an outcome by experiment.

Activity ❶ The Paper Cup

When you throw a paper cup, there are 3 ways it can land: on its side, on its top, and on its bottom.

1. Estimate the probability of a tossed cup landing in each of the 3 positions.

2. Toss a paper cup 25 times and record your results in a table, like the one shown.

Outcome	Tally
Side	
Top	
Bottom	

3. Combine your results with your classmates'.

4. Use the class results to find the experimental probability of a cup landing in each of the 3 positions.

5. Compare the experimental results with your estimates.

Activity ❷ Dropping Cubes

Set up an experiment to determine the probability of dropping a plastic cube into a container, such as a paper bag. To perform the experiment, stand with the container behind you at your feet. Hold the cube over your shoulder and face forward. Each group in the class should use the same size of container.

1. Estimate the probability of your group dropping the cube into the container.

2. Have each member of the group try the experiment 10 times. Combine the results.

3. Use the results to find the experimental probability of your group dropping the cube into the container.

4. Compare the probability for your group with the probabilities found by other groups.

Activity ❸ Thumbtacks

When you roll a thumbtack, there are 2 ways it can stop: point down or point up.

1. Estimate the probability of a rolled thumbtack stopping in each position.

2. Roll 10 thumbtacks 10 times and record your results.

3. Combine your results with the results of your classmates.

4. Use the class results to find the experimental probability of a rolled thumbtack stopping in each position.

5. Compare the experimental results with your estimates.

Activity ❹ Other Experimental Probabilities

A sports commentator knows the probability of a certain baseball player getting a hit because of the number of "experiments" the hitter has conducted. List 5 other events for which the probability is found by experiment or on the basis of actual happenings.

Review

1. The scatter plot shows the winning times in the women's 200-m run at the Olympic Games in different years.

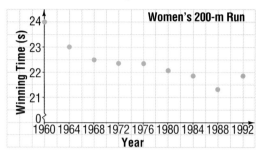

a) Describe the relationship between the winning time and the year.

b) What was the approximate winning time in 1976, when the Olympics were held in Montreal?

c) In what year was the winning time closest to 22.5 s?

d) About how many seconds longer did the race take in 1960 than it did in 1988?

2. The table shows the total population of Canada's four Western Provinces in different years.

Year	Population (nearest 0.1 million)
1941	3.2
1951	3.7
1961	4.8
1971	5.7
1981	7.0
1991	7.9

a) Display the data on a scatter plot of population versus year. Draw a line of best fit.

b) Describe the relationship between the population and the year.

c) Estimate the total population of the four Western Provinces in 1966; in 2001.

3. The table shows the wingspans and lengths of airplanes.

Plane (Year built)	Length (m)	Wingspan (m)
Flyer (1903)	6.43	12.29
June Bug (1908)	9.1	13.89
Demoiselle (1909)	6.1	5.5
Blériot XI (1909)	8	7.8
Deperdussin Racer (1912)	6.1	6.65
Grand (1913)	20.02	28.02
Junkers J-1 (1915)	9.04	16.8
Fokker DVII (1918)	7.01	8.94
Ford Trimotor (1926)	15.19	22.6
Lockheed Vega (1927)	8.38	12.5

a) Display the data on a scatter plot of wingspan versus length.

b) Draw a line of best fit.

c) Interpolate the wingspan of an airplane with a length of 10 m.

d) Extrapolate the length of an airplane with a wingspan of 30 m.

4. Find each probability.

a) $P(H)$

b) $P(H \text{ or } I)$

c) $P(\text{blue})$

d) $P(\text{yellow})$

e) $P(\text{blue or green})$

f) $P(G, H, \text{ or } I)$

g) $P(G, H, I, J, K, \text{ or } L)$

5. A bag contains 3 red cubes, 5 blue cubes, and 2 green cubes. What is the probability of drawing each of the following if each cube is replaced before the next draw?

a) a red cube, then another red cube

b) a yellow cube

c) a blue cube, then a red cube, then a green cube

6. This spinner is used for an experiment in which you toss a dime, roll a die, and spin the spinner.

a) How many possible outcomes are there?

b) What is the probability of tossing a head, rolling a 4, and spinning a 4?

c) What is the probability of tossing a tail, rolling an odd number, and spinning an odd number?

d) What is the probability of tossing a tail, rolling an even number, and spinning an even number?

7. Three cards are drawn from a 52-card deck of playing cards. What is the probability of drawing the following if each card is replaced before the next draw?

a) 3 kings   **b)** 3 clubs

c) a queen, then a jack, then an ace

d) a heart, then a diamond, then a club

e) 1♥, then 2♣, then a red card

f) ace♠, then 5♥, then queen♠

g) 6♦, then 6♦, then 6♦

Group Decision Making
The SCAMPER Technique

The writer B. Eberle used the mnemonic SCAMPER to help people expand their thinking during brainstorming sessions. The letters in SCAMPER each represent a different idea to think about.

S : Substitute – What if a thing or a person takes another's place?

C : Combine – What if you put things together or combine purposes?

A : Adapt – What if you adjust something? What else is this?

M : Modify, Magnify, Minify – What if you change the purpose? the size? the colour? the sound? the speed?

P : Put to Other Uses – What other uses are there?

E : Eliminate – What if you get rid of a part? a whole?

R : Rearrange – What if you change the order? turn something around? backwards? upside down?

Suppose you were designing a home entertainment centre. You might consider the following questions.

a) What if you *substitute* 8 television screens for 1?

b) What if you *combine* the entertainment room and a gym so you can be actively involved in the music or movies?

c) What if you *adapt* the ceiling to become television screens?

d) What if you *modify* the roof of your house so that it holds 4 satellite dishes?

e) What if you *eliminate* the walls of one room in the house?

f) What if you *rearrange* the floors in the house so that the top floor becomes the bottom floor?

1. In home groups, use this technique to design a classroom or a movie theatre.

2. Present your design to the class and explain how you used the SCAMPER technique.

3. Evaluate the technique.

Chapter Check

1. The scatter plot shows how the world's annual fresh water consumption changed over 50 years.

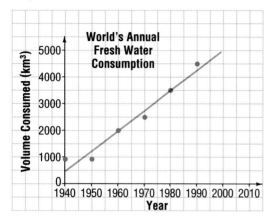

a) About how much fresh water was used in 1940? 1965? 1980? 1995?

b) During which year was about 3000 km³ of water used?

c) About how many times more fresh water was used in 1990 than in 1940?

d) Estimate the world's fresh water consumption in 2015.

e) What relationship does the scatter plot show?

2. The table shows the percent of the world's land and the percent of the world's population on each continent.

Continent	Percent of Land	Percent of Population
Africa	20	12
Antarctica	9	0
Asia	30	60
Australia	5	0.3
Europe	7	14
N. America	16	8
S. America	12	5

a) Display the data on a scatter plot of percent of population versus percent of land.

b) Is there a relationship between the percent of population and the percent of land? Explain.

c) Which continents have a greater percent of the world's population than they have of the world's land?

d) Which are the 2 least crowded continents? Explain.

3. Find the number of possible outcomes when you roll a die, spin the spinner, and toss a coin.

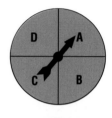

4. Find each probability.

a) $P(1)$

b) $P(\text{yellow})$

c) $P(1 \text{ or } 2)$

d) $P(\text{white})$

e) $P(5 \text{ or } 6)$

f) $P(\text{red, green, or yellow})$

g) $P(1, 2, 3, 4, 5, \text{ or } 6)$

h) $P(\text{odd number})$

5. A box contains 4 white marbles, 5 green marbles, and 3 blue marbles. Each marble is replaced before the next draw. What is the probability of drawing each of the following?

a) a white marble

b) a green marble, then a blue marble

c) 3 blue marbles

d) a blue marble, then a green marble, then a white marble

Using the Strategies

1. Copy the diagram. Place the numbers from 1 to 10 in the circles so that the numbers on each side of the pentagon total 14. The 5 has been placed for you.

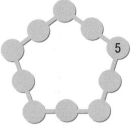

2. A block of cheese, covered with wax, measures 12 cm by 12 cm by 10 cm. The block is cut into 2-cm cubes.
a) How many cubes are there?
b) How many cubes have wax on 3 faces?
c) How many cubes have wax on 2 faces?
d) How many cubes have no wax on them?

3. The diagram shows how 20 sheep have been placed in 8 pens so that there are 6 sheep in each row of 3 pens.

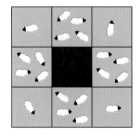

Rearrange the sheep so that there are 7 sheep in each row of 3 pens.

4. You are standing in line at the cafeteria. You are seventh from the front and eighth from the end. How many people are in the line?

5. The number 9 has 3 different factors, 1, 3, and 9. Find all the positive integers less than 50 that have an odd number of different factors.

6. A team gets 2 points for a win, 1 point for a tie, and no points for a loss. The Bears have played 28 games. They have 27 points and 7 losses. How many wins do they have?

7. The perimeter of the figure is 12 units.

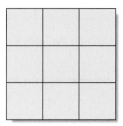

Sketch your answers to the following.
a) Remove 1 square and keep the perimeter the same.
b) Remove 2 squares and keep the perimeter the same.
c) Remove 1 square and increase the perimeter by 2.
d) Remove 2 squares and increase the perimeter by 2.
e) Remove 2 squares and increase the perimeter by 4.

8. Sketch a graph of the time needed to decorate the gym for a graduation dance versus the number of people who volunteer to help.

9. If 2 months in a row have a Friday the 13th, what months are they? Explain.

DATA BANK

1. A plane left Calgary at 16:00 and flew to Montreal at a speed of 700 km/h. At what time did it land in Montreal?

2. When you travel from east to west across the International Date Line, do you lose a day or gain a day?

Estimate, then calculate to the nearest tenth.

1. $\sqrt{50}$ **2.** $4\sqrt{18}$ **3.** $\sqrt{5} + 2\sqrt{10}$

4. The area of a triangle, whose base and height are the same, is 60 cm². What is the base, to the nearest centimetre?

Evaluate each expression for $m = -1$, $n = 2$.

5. $3m^2 - 2mn$ **6.** $m^3 + 3n^2$

Evaluate.

7. $9^2 - 2^3$ **8.** $2^8 \div 4^2$ **9.** $5^2 \times 2^4$

Simplify.

10. $b^7 \times b^2$ **11.** $3^6 \div 3^3$ **12.** $(n^2)^5$

Find the value of x.

13. $5^3 \times 5^x = 5^8$ **14.** $(10^3)^x = 10^9$

15. $w^x \times w^4 = w^{10}$ **16.** $b^5 \div b^x = b^3$

Estimate, then calculate. Write each answer in scientific notation.

17. $(5.2 \times 10^2) \times (1.9 \times 10^4)$

18. $(9.12 \times 10^3) \div (4.8 \times 10^5)$

19. $(1.4 \times 10^{-2}) \times (8 \times 10^{-3})$

20. $(8.2 \times 10^{-5}) \div (4.1 \times 10^{-3})$

Evaluate.

21. $(-2.5)^2(-2.5)^4$ **22.** $(-6)^5 \div (-6)^3$

23. $3^4 + 3^0$ **24.** 2^{-1} **25.** $3^{-1} - 3^{-2}$

26. $4^{-2} \times 4^0$ **27.** $(2^3)^2$ **28.** $(-1)^{21}$

Simplify.

29. $m^{-2} \times m^3$ **30.** $x^{-3} \div x^{-4}$ **31.** $(2m^2)^4$

32. $\left(\dfrac{-2x}{y}\right)^3$ **33.** $\dfrac{w^{-4} \times w^{-3}}{w^{-9}}$ **34.** $(3xy)^2(-xy)^3$

Evaluate for $x = 3$.

35. $5x$ **36.** $3x + 1$

Simplify.

37. $2m - 6m + 5m$ **38.** $2w + 5z - 3w + z$

39. The diagonal of a square can be found using the formula
$$d = \sqrt{2A},$$
where A is the area of the square. Determine the diagonals of squares with the following areas. Round each answer to the nearest tenth of a unit.

a) 38 cm²   **b)** 150 m²   **c)** 14.5 cm²

Write an equation for each statement.

40. A number multiplied by four is twelve.

41. A number increased by two is eight.

42. A number decreased by five and then multiplied by four is eight.

Solve.

43. $m - 5 = 2$ **44.** $1 = x - 6$

45. $a + 2 = 5$ **46.** $m + 3 = 7$

Solve.

47. $5n = 25$ **48.** $4m = 8$ **49.** $2b = 2.4$

50. $\dfrac{x}{3} = 4$ **51.** $\dfrac{y}{5} = 4$ **52.** $\dfrac{a}{11} = -3$

Solve.

53. $3x + 4 = 7$ **54.** $3m + 2.4 = 3.9$

55. $1.2n - 3.2 = 1.6$ **56.** $2x + 4.3 = -2.1$

Solve and check.

57. $4y + 22 = 2y$ **58.** $3x - 12 = 5x + 2x$

59. $4y = 12.7 - y + 2.8$

Expand and simplify.

60. $3(4m + 5n - 7)$ **61.** $3(x + 4) - (x - 9)$

Solve.

62. $3(x - 5) - 6 = 4 - 2x$

63. $2(x + 1) + 3x - 7 = 3(x + 4) - 2$

64. $2.5x + 1.5 = 10.75$ **65.** $\dfrac{x}{7} - 5 = 3 - 1$

66. $\dfrac{3x}{5} - 4 = \dfrac{x}{5} + 6$ **67.** $\dfrac{x - 2}{3} = \dfrac{x - 2}{4}$

68. Toni, Bianca, and Gemma have three consecutive whole numbers of dollars. The total amount of money they have is $66. How much money does each person have?

69. The table shows the distances covered by a grey fox at top speed in different lengths of time.

Distance (m)	18.5	37	55.5		
Time (s)	1	2	3	4	5

a) Copy and complete the table.
b) Write a formula to calculate the distance covered, d, from the time, t.

70. The total rainfall in Victoria and Edmonton in June is about 107 mm. Edmonton has 53 mm more rainfall than Victoria in June. How much rainfall does each city have in June?

71. Sophia can paint a room in 3 h. Kuhiko can paint the same room in 2 h. How long will it take them to paint the room if they paint it together?

Solve each inequality and graph the solution on a number line.

72. $5x - 4 \geq 3x - 2$ **73.** $7x - 4 < 4x - 13$

74. $6x - 5 > 4x + 1$ **75.** $3x - 1 \leq 5x + 3$

State the degree of each polynomial.

76. $3xy + 2x$ **77.** $2y^3 + 3y - 2$

Arrange the terms in each polynomial in ascending powers of x.

78. $3x - 2x^3 + 7x^4 + 5$ **79.** $2x^3 + 3xy - x^4y^5 + y^2$

Simplify.

80. $(5x^2 + 3x - 4) + (-x^2 + x + 2)$
81. $(4x^2 - 2x - 1) - (2x^2 - x + 5)$

Add.

82. $2x^2 + 4x - 2$ **83.** $x^2 - 6x - 1$
    $\underline{3x^2 - 2x + 1}$ $\underline{5x^2 + x - 4}$

Subtract.

84. $2x^2 - 7x + 4$ **85.** $5x^2 + x - 7$
    $\underline{x^2 + 3x + 1}$ $\underline{-4x^2 - 2x + 3}$

Multiply.

86. $(3x)(5y)$ **87.** $(-6s)(2t)$
88. $(2m^3)(3y^2)$ **89.** $-3y^4(-5x^2y^3)$

Divide.

90. $\dfrac{49x^5y^3}{14x^3y}$ **91.** $10a^2b^5c^4 \div (-5ab^2c^2)$

Find the GCF.

92. 12, 30   **93.** 25, 45
94. $8y^2, 20y^3$ **95.** $6mn^3, 18m^3n^4$

Factor.

96. $7y + 14$ **97.** $3p^2q - 12p^2q^2$
98. $10a^2b + 35ab^2$ **99.** $14x^2y - 7xy^2 + 28x^3y^3$

Simplify.

100. $2y(y - 3)$ **101.** $2m(m - 1) + 3(m + 2)$
102. $-2x(x^2 + 2x + 5)$

Divide.

103. $\dfrac{4pq^3 - 6p^2q^2 + 2p^3q^4}{-2pq^2}$

104. $\dfrac{-22y^2z + 66y^4z^3 - 11y^3z}{22yz}$

Expand.

105. $(a - 4)(a + 2)$ **106.** $(3m + 2)(2m + 5)$
107. $(y + 1)(y - 1.5)$ **108.** $1.5(n + 1)(n - 2)$

Factor.

109. $x^2 + 18x + 32$ **110.** $x^2 - 2x - 35$

Factor fully.

111. $2x^2 - 4x - 12$ **112.** $4x^2 + 28x + 40$

Expand.

113. $(m + 5)(m - 5)$ **114.** $(3y - 2)(3y + 2)$

CONTINUED ▶

Factor.

115. $y^2 - 16$ **116.** $100w^2 - 4z^2$

Square.

117. $(w - 3)^2$ **118.** $(2x + 5)^2$

119. $(3z + a)^2$ **120.** $(2p - 3q)^2$

Expand and simplify.

121. $(x - 2)(x^2 + 3x + 1)$

122. $(3w^2 - 4w + 2)(2w + 1)$

123. Determine the area of the figure.

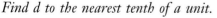

Simplify.

124. $\dfrac{x^2 y}{y^2} \times \dfrac{xy}{x}$ **125.** $\dfrac{w^5 z^3}{9} \div \dfrac{w^2 z^2}{15}$

126. $\dfrac{3}{x} + \dfrac{5 + x}{x}$ **127.** $\dfrac{2(y + 2)}{3} - \dfrac{y - 1}{4}$

Are these pairs of triangles congruent? If so, give the case and list all the corresponding equal parts.

128. **129.**

130. **131.**

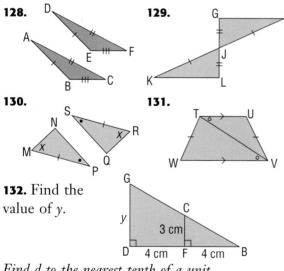

132. Find the value of y.

Find d to the nearest tenth of a unit.

133. **134.**

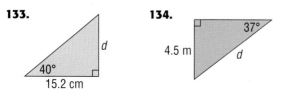

Find the measure of $\angle A$ to the nearest degree.

135. **136.**

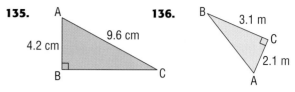

Solve each triangle. Round each side length to the nearest tenth of a unit and each angle to the nearest degree.

137. **138.**

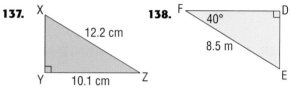

Calculate each area to the nearest tenth of a square unit.

139. **140.**

141. **142.**

143. **144.**

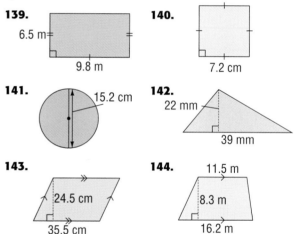

Calculate the area of each shaded region to the nearest tenth of a square unit.

145. **146.**

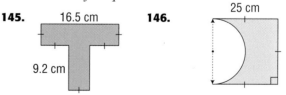

Estimate, then calculate the surface area and volume of each solid to the nearest square or cubic unit.

147. **148.**

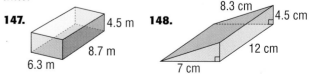

149.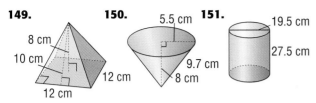

150. 5.5 cm

151. 19.5 cm

27.5 cm

8 cm
10 cm
12 cm

9.7 cm
8 cm

12 cm

Describe each translation in words.

152. $(x, y) \rightarrow (x - 2, y + 5)$ **153.** $[-4, -4]$

154. $(x, y) \rightarrow (x + 7, y + 3)$ **155.** $[3, -5]$

156. The vertices of △MNP are M(−3, 5), N(5, 5), and P(−3, −4). The vertices of △M′N′P′, the translation image of △MNP, are M′(1, 4), N′(9, 4), and P′(1, −5). Find the translation that maps △MNP onto △M′N′P′.

Draw each triangle on grid paper. Draw the image after the reflection in the reflection line m.

157.

158.

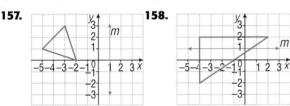

159. a) Draw the graph of the line $x - y = -3$.
b) Reflect the line in the x-axis.
c) Reflect the line in the y-axis.

160. Parallelogram WXYZ has vertices W(−2, 2), X(3, 2), Y(1, −4), and Z(−4, −4). Draw the image of the parallelogram after a 90° turn counterclockwise about the origin.

161. Rectangle KLMN has vertices K(−1, 1), L(3, 1), M(3, −1), and N(−1, −1). Find the image of rectangle KLMN under the mapping $(x, y) \rightarrow (2x, 2y)$.

162. Copy the figure onto grid paper and reduce it by a scale factor of $\frac{1}{3}$.

163. How many lines of symmetry does this figure have?

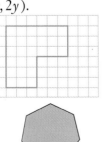

164. Draw the figure on grid paper. Add parts to each of the other 3 quadrants so that the figure has

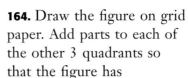

a) 1 line of symmetry
b) 0 lines of symmetry
c) rotational symmetry of order 4

165. What is the order of turn symmetry of this figure?

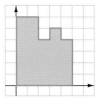

166. Portage La Prairie, Manitoba, lies at a latitude of 50°N. The table shows the sunset times in April and May one year in Portage La Prairie.

Date	Time
April 15	19:53
April 22	20:04
April 29	20:15
May 6	20:26
May 13	20:36
May 20	20:46
May 27	20:55

a) Display the data on a scatter plot of sunset times versus date. Draw a line of best fit.
b) Interpolate the sunset times in Portage La Prairie on April 18 and May 25.
c) Extrapolate the sunset times in Portage La Prairie on March 3 and June 19. What assumptions have you made?
d) Could you use your line of best fit to extrapolate the sunset time in Portage La Prairie on August 30? Explain.

167. A card is drawn from a deck of playing cards. What is each probability?

a) a spade   **b)** an ace   **c)** queen of hearts

168. A coin is tossed and a die is rolled. Calculate each probability.

a) $P(6, \text{head})$ **b)** $P(\text{even number, tail})$

169. A box contains 3 blue cubes, 2 red cubes and 1 black cube. A cube is replaced after each choice. If you choose 3 cubes from the box, what is each probability?

a) $P(2 \text{ red cubes, 1 blue cube})$ **b)** $P(3 \text{ blue cubes})$
c) $P(1 \text{ red cube, 1 blue cube, 1 black cube})$

TIME ZONES

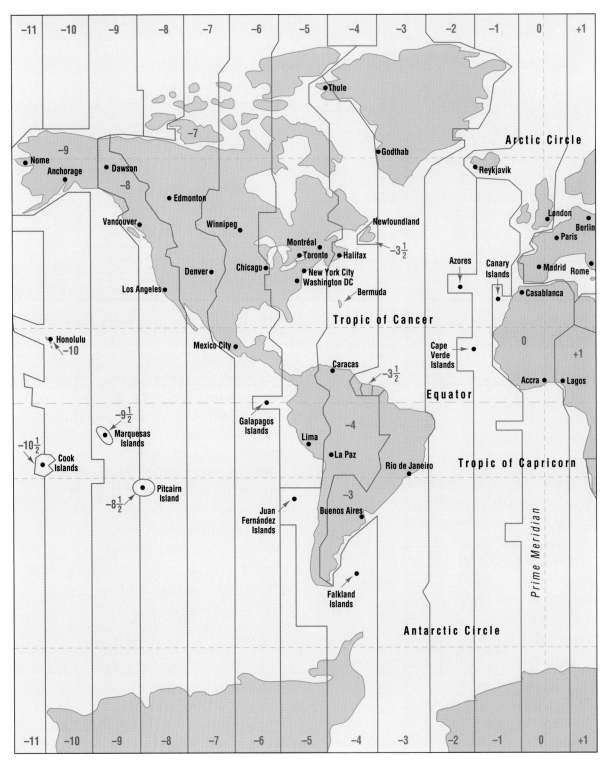

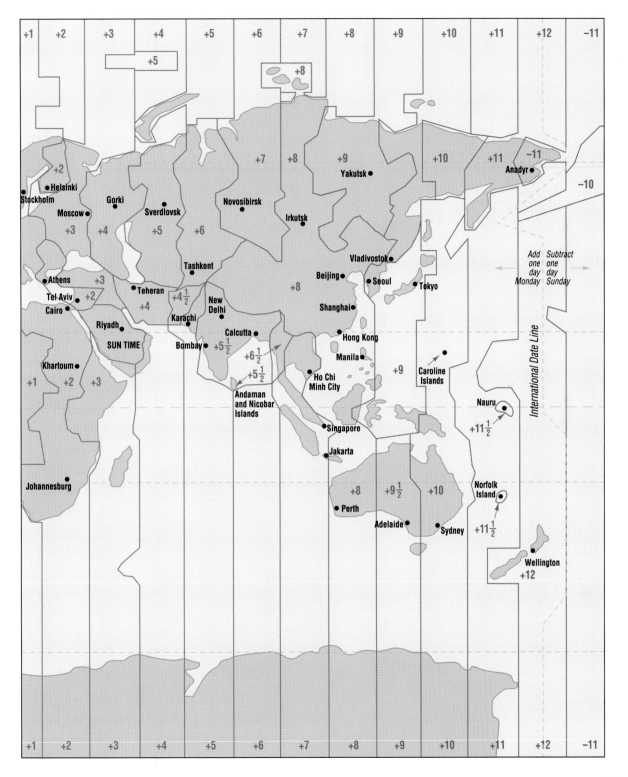

FLYING DISTANCES BETWEEN CANADIAN CITIES

From	To	(km)
Calgary	Edmonton	248
	Montreal	3003
	Ottawa	2877
	Regina	661
	Saskatoon	520
	Toronto	2686
	Vancouver	685
	Victoria	725
	Winnipeg	1191
Charlottetown	Ottawa	976
	Toronto	1326
Edmonton	Calgary	248
	Ottawa	2848
	Regina	698
	Saskatoon	484
	Toronto	2687
	Vancouver	826
	Winnipeg	1187
Halifax	Montreal	803
	Ottawa	958
	Saint John	192
	St. John's	880
	Sydney	306
	Toronto	1287
Montreal	Calgary	3003
	Fredericton	562
	Halifax	803
	Moncton	707
	Ottawa	151
	Saint John	614
	St. John's	1618
	Toronto	508
	Vancouver	3679
	Winnipeg	1816
Ottawa	Calgary	2877
	Charlottetown	976
	Edmonton	2848
	Halifax	958
	Montreal	151
	Toronto	363
	Vancouver	3550
	Winnipeg	1687
Regina	Calgary	661
	Edmonton	698
	Saskatoon	239
	Toronto	2026
	Vancouver	1330
	Winnipeg	533
St. John's	Halifax	880
	Montreal	1618
	Toronto	2122

From	To	(km)
Toronto	Calgary	2686
	Charlottetown	1326
	Edmonton	2687
	Halifax	1287
	Montreal	508
	Ottawa	363
	Regina	2026
	St. John's	2122
	Vancouver	3342
	Windsor	314
	Winnipeg	1502
Victoria	Calgary	725
	Vancouver	62
Windsor	Toronto	314
Winnipeg	Calgary	1191
	Edmonton	1187
	Montreal	1816
	Ottawa	1687
	Regina	533
	Saskatoon	707
	Toronto	1502
	Vancouver	1862

DRIVING DISTANCES BETWEEN CANADIAN CITIES

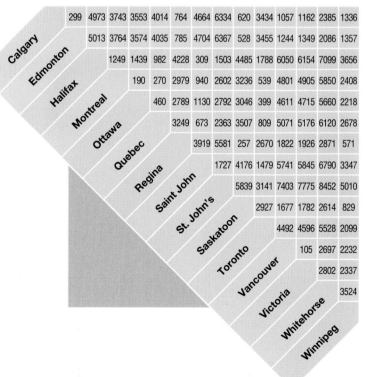

	Calgary	Edmonton	Halifax	Montreal	Ottawa	Quebec	Regina	Saint John	St. John's	Saskatoon	Toronto	Vancouver	Victoria	Whitehorse	Winnipeg
Calgary	299	4973	3743	3553	4014	764	4664	6334	620	3434	1057	1162	2385	1336
Edmonton		5013	3764	3574	4035	785	4704	6367	528	3455	1244	1349	2086	1357
Halifax			1249	1439	982	4228	309	1503	4485	1788	6050	6154	7099	3656
Montreal				190	270	2979	940	2602	3236	539	4801	4905	5850	2408
Ottawa					460	2789	1130	2792	3046	399	4611	4715	5660	2218
Quebec						3249	673	2363	3507	809	5071	5176	6120	2678
Regina							3919	5581	257	2670	1822	1926	2871	571
Saint John								1727	4176	1479	5741	5845	6790	3347
St. John's									5839	3141	7403	7775	8452	5010
Saskatoon										2927	1677	1782	2614	829
Toronto											4492	4596	5528	2099
Vancouver												105	2697	2232
Victoria													2802	2337
Whitehorse														3524

AREAS AND POPULATIONS OF CANADIAN PROVINCES

Province	Area (km²)	Population
Newfoundland and Labrador	405 720	568 474
New Brunswick	73 440	723 900
Nova Scotia	55 491	899 942
Prince Edward Island	5660	129 765
Quebec	1 540 680	6 895 963
Ontario	1 068 582	10 084 885
Manitoba	649 950	1 091 942
Saskatchewan	652 330	988 928
Alberta	661 190	2 545 553
British Columbia	947 800	3 282 061

WORLD BRIDGE RECORDS

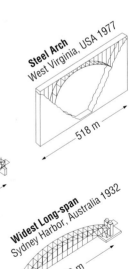

Cable Suspension
Akashi Kaikyo, Japan (under construction)
890 m
1780 m

Cable Suspension
Humber, United Kingdom 1980
890 m
1410 m

Stone Arch
Pennsylvania, USA 1901
1161 m

Cantilever
Quebec, Canada 1917
549 m

Covered
New Brunswick, Canada 1899
391 m

Steel Arch
West Virginia, USA 1977
518 m

Widest Long-span
Sydney Harbor, Australia 1932
503 m

(Bridge widths are exaggerated for the purpose of this diagram.)

367

PLANETS: DISTANCES, ORBITS, MOONS

Mercury

Distance from the sun: 58 000 000 km

Time to orbit sun: 88 d

Number of moons: 0

Venus

Distance from the sun: 108 000 000 km

Time to orbit sun: 225 d

Number of moons: 0

Earth

Distance from the sun: 150 000 000 km

Time to orbit sun: 1 year

Number of moons: 1

Mars

Distance from the sun: 228 000 000 km

Time to orbit sun: 687 d

Number of moons: 2

Jupiter

Distance from the sun: 779 000 000 km

Time to orbit sun: 12 years

Number of moons: 16

Saturn

Distance from the sun: 1 425 000 000 km

Time to orbit sun: 29.5 years

Number of moons: 18

Uranus

Distance from the sun: 2 870 000 000 km

Time to orbit sun: 84 years

Number of moons: 15

Neptune

Distance from the sun: 4 497 000 000 km

Time to orbit sun: 165 years

Number of moons: 8

Pluto

Distance from the sun: 5 866 000 000 km

Time to orbit sun: 248 years

Number of moons: 1

ELEVATIONS OF THE TEN HIGHEST CITIES

City	Elevation (m)
Bogotá, Colombia	2 639
Addis Ababa, Ethiopia	2 450
Mexico City, Mexico	2 309
Nairobi, Kenya	1 820
Johannesburg, South Africa	1 734
Calgary, Canada	1 045
São Paulo, Brazil	776
Ankara, Turkey	686
Edmonton, Canada	666
Madrid, Spain	655

WORLD'S TOP TEN GOLD PRODUCERS

Country	Annual Production (t)
South Africa	621
United States	205
Australia	152
Canada	128
Brazil	100
Philippines	43
Colombia	33
Papua New Guinea	33
Chile	23
Venezuela	16

WORLD'S LARGEST RESERVOIRS

Location	Capacity (million kL)
Owem Falls, Uganda	2 700 000
Kariba, Zambia	180 600
Bratsk, Russian Federation	169 270
Aswan, Egypt	168 900
Akosombo, Ghana	148 000
Daniel Johnson, Canada	141 852
Guri, Venezuela	138 000
Krasnoyarsk, Russian Federation	73 300
Bennett, WAC, Canada	70 309
Zeya, Russian Federation	68 400

BEAUFORT WIND SCALE

Beaufort Number	Name	Speed (km/h)	Effect on Land
0	Calm	less than 1	Calm; smoke rises vertically.
1	Light air	1-5	Weather vanes inactive; smoke drifts with air.
2	Light breeze	6-11	Weather vanes active; wind felt on face; leaves rustle.
3	Gentle breeze	12-19	Leaves and small twigs move; light flags extend.
4	Moderate breeze	20-28	Small branches sway; dust and loose paper blow about.
5	Fresh breeze	29-38	Small trees sway; waves break on inland waters.
6	Strong breeze	39-49	Large branches sway; umbrellas difficult to use.
7	Moderate gale	50-61	Whole trees sway; difficult to walk against wind.
8	Fresh gale	62-74	Twigs broken off trees; walking against wind very difficult.
9	Strong gale	75-88	Slight damage to buildings; shingles blown off roof.
10	Whole gale	89-102	Trees uprooted; considerable damage to buildings.
11	Storm	103-117	Widespread damage; very rare occurrence.
12-17	Hurricane	more than 117	Violent destruction.

WIND CHILL CHART

Wind Speed	Thermometer Reading (degrees Celsius)														
	4	2	−1	−4	−7	−9	−12	−15	−18	−21	−23	−26	−29	−32	−34
Calm	4	2	−1	−4	−7	−9	−12	−15	−18	−21	−23	−26	−29	−32	−34
8 km/h	3	1	−3	−6	−9	−11	−14	−17	−21	−24	−26	−29	−32	−36	−37
16 km/h	−2	−6	−9	−13	−17	−19	−23	−26	−30	−33	−36	−39	−43	−47	−50
24 km/h	−6	−9	−12	−17	−21	−24	−28	−32	−36	−40	−43	−46	−51	−54	−57
32 km/h	−8	−11	−16	−20	−23	−27	−31	−36	−40	−43	−47	−51	−56	−60	−63
40 km/h	−9	−14	−18	−22	−26	−30	−34	−38	−43	−47	−50	−55	−59	−64	−67
48 km/h	−11	−15	−19	−24	−28	−32	−36	−41	−45	−49	−53	−57	−61	−66	−70
56 km/h	−12	−16	−20	−25	−29	−33	−37	−42	−47	−51	−55	−58	−64	−68	−72
64 km/h	−13	−17	−21	−26	−30	−34	−38	−43	−48	−52	−56	−60	−66	−70	−74

Legend: Cold | Very Cold | Bitterly Cold | Extremely Cold

Answers

Exploring Math

Problem Solving p. xii

1. 12   **2.** 14   **3.** 8 more, not counting rotations of the square   **4.** 8   **6.** 4

Mathematics as Communication p. xiii

Activity 1:   **1.** 12 km, 12 km, 12 km, 12 km, 12 km
2. Anywhere on the line segment joining A and B.
Activity 2:   **1.** 16 km, 14 km, 16 km, 12 km, 20 km
2. At the camp located at B.   **Activity 3:**
1. Anywhere on the line segment joining B and C.
2. At the camp located at C.   **Activity 4:**
1. Anywhere on the line segment joining the middle two camps.   **2.** At the middle camp.

Mathematics as Reasoning p. xiv

Activity 1:   **1.** $4 \times 5 + 8 \div 2$ **2.** $(7 - 4) \times (4 + 4)$
3. $(7 - 4 \div 4) \times 4$ **Activity 2:**   **1.** Sari: blue
MATHPOWER; Terri: green
COMPUTERPOWER; Dmitri: black
SCIENCEPOWER

Algebra p. xvi

Activity 1:   **1. a)** 2, 4; 3, 6; 4, 8   **b)** The square
must represent a number twice that of the triangle.
2. a) 1, 3; 2, 6; 3, 9   **b)** 1, 1; 2, 2; 3, 3   **c)** 2, 2; 4, 3;
6, 4   **d)** 3, 2; 6, 4; 9, 6   **e)** 0, 0; 2, 2; no other whole
number pairs   **f)** 0, 0; no other whole number pairs
Activity 2:   **1.** 7   **2.** 12   **3.** 2   **4.** 6   **5.** 20   **6.** 2
Activity 3:   **1.** 10   **2.** 3   **3.** 3   **4.** 4   **5.** 0

Functions p. xvii

Activity 1:   **1. b)** 4, 8, 12, 16, 20, 40, 400   **c)** The
perimeter equals 4 times the figure number.
2. a) 4, 6, 8, 10, 12, 22, 202; the perimeter equals 2
times the figure number, plus 2.   **b)** 8, 12, 16, 20,
24, 44, 404; the perimeter equals 4 times the figure
number, plus 4.   **c)** 8, 10, 12, 14, 16, 26, 206; the
perimeter equals 2 times the figure number, plus 6.
Activity 2:   **1.** y equals x less 8; x equals y plus 8
2. y equals x divided by 2; x equals 2 times y
3. y equals 20 less x; x equals 20 less y **4.** y equals 2
times x plus 1; x equals the quantity y less 1, divided
by 2

Trigonometry p. xx

Activity :   **2. a)** 1.96   **b)** equal   **3.** 11.2 m

Probability p. xxii

Activity 1:   **1. a)** This is the ratio of the number of
red marbles to the total number of marbles.   **b)** $\frac{2}{10}, \frac{5}{10}$
2. 50%   **3.** 50   **Activity 3:** $\frac{1}{8}, \frac{1}{16}, \frac{1}{256}$

Mathematics and Counting p. xxiii

Activity 1:   **1.** 12   **Activity 2:** 8   **Activity 3:** 12
Activity 4:   **1.** 18, 22, 26   **2.** 63, 127, 255
3. 6, 2, $\frac{2}{3}$ **4.** 29, 47, 76

Investigating Limits p. xxiv

Activity 1:   **2.** 1   **Activity 2:**   **5.** 78.5 cm^2
7. Yes; the errors in the approximations would
decrease.

Mathematical Structure p. xxv

Activity 1:   **1.** 05:00   **2.** 20 h   **3. a)** 8   **b)** 6   **c)** 4
d) 1   **e)** 6   **f)** 4   **g)** 10   **h)** 7   **Activity 2:**   **1. a)** yes
b) no   **c)** yes   **d)** no   **2. a)** 2   **b)** 3   **c)** 0   **d)** 2   **e)** 0
3. a) yes   **b)** no

Chapter 1

Getting Started pp. 2–3

Activity 1:   **1.** 3, 5; 5, 7; 11, 13; 17, 19; 29, 31;
41, 43; 59, 61; 71, 73   **2.** 3, 5, 7   **3. a)** $24 = 11 + 13$
b) $30 = 7 + 23$ **c)** $42 = 19 + 23$ **d)** $100 = 41 + 59$
Mental Math   **1.** 115   **2.** 144   **3.** 49   **4.** 121
5. 330   **6.** 80   **7.** 133   **8.** 412   **9.** 1600   **10.** 6969
11. 17   **12.** 12.3   **13.** 31   **14.** 61   **15.** 3342   **16.** 50
17. 0.95   **18.** 60   **19.** 30   **20.** 32   **21.** 578   **22.** 695
23. 498   **24.** 821   **25.** 210   **26.** 705   **27.** 165
28. −82   **29.** 149   **30.** −895   **31.** 32   **32.** −2   **33.** 79
34. 19   **35.** 9   **36.** −7   **37.** 20   **38.** 37   **39.** 48
40. −26   **41.** 50   **42.** 10   **43.** 80   **44.** 38   **45.** 196
46. 34   **47.** 36   **48.** 36   **49.** 150   **50.** −20

Learning Together pp. 4–5

Activity 1:   **1.** c   **2. a)** yes   **b)** yes   **3.** Integers are
made up of positive and negative whole numbers.
Whole numbers are made up of the natural numbers
plus 0.   **Activity 2:**   **1.** $\frac{1}{2}, \frac{1}{4}, \frac{5}{8}, -\frac{1}{5}, -\frac{3}{4}, -\frac{17}{20}$
2. terminating decimal   **3. a)** No; often the result is

another fraction or decimal number. **b)** No; integers do not include decimal numbers. **Activity 3:**
1. 0.666..., –0.6363..., 0.1666..., –0.555... **2. a)** no
b) a bar over the repeating digits **3.** $0.\overline{6}$, $-0.\overline{63}$,
$0.1\overline{6}$, $-0.\overline{5}$ **4.** Natural numbers inside the whole numbers, which are inside the integers, which are inside the rational numbers. **5.** Rational numbers can be written in the form $\frac{a}{b}$, where a is any integer and b is any integer except 0. **Activity 4:**
1. a) true **b)** false. Integers do not include decimal numbers. **c)** false. Natural numbers do not include negative digits. **d)** false **e)** true **f)** false. It is a non-terminating, non-repeating decimal. **2.** 2 can be written as the fraction $\frac{2}{1}$, is positive, and is greater than 0. **3.** –10 can be written as the fraction $-\left(\frac{10}{1}\right)$. Since it is a negative integer, it cannot be a whole number. **4.** All negative integers. **5.** No; it is a non-terminating, non-repeating decimal.
Activity 5: **1. a)** $\frac{1}{3}$ **b)** $\frac{1}{8}$ **c)** $-\frac{1}{10}$ **d)** $-\frac{1}{7}$ **2. a)** $\frac{1}{2}$
b) $\frac{1}{3}$ **c)** $-\frac{1}{5}$ **d)** $-\frac{1}{8}$

Learning Together pp. 6–7

Activity 1: **1. a)** 64 **b)** 100 **c)** 1 000 000
Activity 2: **1.** 15, 21, 28 **3.** a square number
Activity 3: The locker doors that are closed are numbered by perfect squares: 1, 4, 9, 16,..., 900, 961
Activity 4: Answers may vary. **1. a)** $33 = 5^2 + 2^2 + 2^2$
b) $42 = 5^2 + 4^2 + 1$ **c)** $77 = 6^2 + 5^2 + 4^2$ **d)** $88 = 8^2 + 4^2 + 2^2 + 2^2$ **e)** $153 = 12^2 + 3^2$ **f)** $212 = 14^2 + 4^2$
g) $208 = 12^2 + 8^2$ **h)** $903 = 23^2 + 19^2 + 3^2 + 2^2$

Section 1.1 pp. 10–11

Practice **1.** –7, 7 **2.** –9, 9 **3.** –11, 11 **4.** –25, 25
5. –0.8, 0.8 **6.** –0.1, 0.1 **7.** –1.4, 1.4 **8.** –0.5, 0.5
9. 5 **10.** 10 **11.** 15 **12.** 16 **13.** 13 **14.** 0.6
15. 0.2 **16.** 1.1 **17.** 0.9 **18.** 5 **19.** 8 **20.** 10
21. 30 **22.** 30 **23.** 60 **24.** 90 **25.** 200 **26.** 900
27. 0.9 **28.** 0.9 **29.** 0.2 **30.** 0.2 **31.** 0.2
32. 0.05 **33.** 0.09 **34.** 0.02 **35.** 0.01 **36.** 0.02
37. 6, 5.6 **38.** 7, 6.6 **39.** 8, 7.9 **40.** 9, 8.9
41. 10, 10.0 **42.** 10, 14.4 **43.** 30, 33.5
44. 100, 142.1 **45.** 300, 293.3 **46.** 400, 449.6
47. 4.4 **48.** 0.9 **49.** 9.9 **50.** 28.8 **51.** 2.4
52. 18.2 **53.** 1.7 **54.** 0.2 **Problems and Applications** **55. a)** 4 **b)** 5 **c)** 6 **d)** 7 **e)** –10 **f)** 8
g) 20 **h)** –9 **i)** 51.1 **56. a)** 20.8 cm **b)** 14.1 m
57. a) 16.2 cm² **b)** 113.9 cm² **58. a)** 6.0 cm
b) 10.1 m **c)** 28.4 mm **d)** 45.1 cm **59.** 629 m
60. c) Results are equal since $\sqrt{8} = \sqrt{4 \times 2} = 2\sqrt{2}$

61. They are opposites. **62.** 6.5 cm – half the side length of the square **63.** An error. Negative numbers do not have square roots. **64.** One possible answer is (0, 7) and (7, 0). **65. a)** 17, 24, 28, 33 **b)** The sum of the first n odd numbers is n^2.

Section 1.2 p. 13

Practice **1.** 7, 6.8 **2.** 20, 17.4 **3.** –9, –9.5
4. 40, 40.6 **5.** –63, –65.7 **6.** 13, 12.5 **7.** 69, 65.2
8. 100, 106.5 **9.** 4.7, 4.5 **10.** 11, 10.8 **11.** 1.4, 1.4
12. 2.8, 2.9 **Problems and Applications**
13. a) 5.0 cm **b)** 20.0 cm **14. a)** 15.0 m **b)** 60.0 m
15. a) 7.4 m **b)** 29.6 m **16. a)** 9.5 cm **b)** 38 cm
17. a) 14.1 m **b)** 56.4 m **18. a)** 28.3 cm **b)** 113.2 cm
19. a) 100 m by 100 m **b)** 50 m by 50 m
20. a) 7.3 km/h, 10.1 km/h **b)** 18.5 km/h, 15.6 km/h
21. a) 340 m/s **b)** 330 m/s **c)** 324 m/s
22. Approximately 11 000 km/h

Section 1.3 p. 15

Problems and Applications **1.** 6 **2.** 9 **3.** 78, 79,
80 **4.** 46, 48, 50, 52 **5.** 55 **6.** 4 **7.** 2 **8.** 17 m
× 13 m **9.** 25 m, 31 m **10.** 16 **11.** 7 **12.** 8 cm
× 7 cm × 6 cm **13.** 6 kg cashews, 18 kg peanuts
14. Companion–15, Officer–46, Member–92

Section 1.4 pp. 17–18

Practice **1.** 5; 3 **2.** 10; 7 **3.** x; 5 **4.** t; 2
5. 2 **6.** –7 **7.** 13 **8.** –1 **9.** 4^6 **10.** 6^4 **11.** m^5
12. r^3 **13.** 5×5 **14.** $1 \times 1 \times 1 \times 1 \times 1 \times 1$
15. $2 \times 2 \times 2 \times 2 \times 2$ **16.** $10 \times 10 \times 10 \times 10$
17. $0 \times 0 \times 0$ **18.** $y \times y \times y \times y$ **19.** $5 \times x \times x \times x$
20. $2m \times 2m \times 2m$ **21.** $x \times x \times x \times y$ **22.** $x \times y \times y \times y$
23. $xy \times xy \times xy$ **24.** $ab \times ab \times ab \times ab$ **25.** 8 **26.** 81
27. 125 **28.** 100 000 **29.** 2^2 **30.** 4^3 **31.** x^3
32. y^2 **33.** 10^2 **34.** 10^3 **35.** 10^5 **36.** 10^6 **37.** 10^8
38. 10^7 **39.** 32 **40.** 125 **41.** 256 **42.** 343
43. 10 000 000 **44.** 729 **45.** 0.25 **46.** 1.331
47. 0.0001 **48.** 2^2 **49.** 3^3 **50.** 2^4 **51.** 5^3 **52.** 5^2
53. equal **54.** 2^3 **55.** 58 **56.** 48 **57.** 24 **58.** 8
59. 0.1 **60.** 0.005 12 **61.** 1.6 **62.** 0.001 **63.** 76
64. 60 **65.** 32 **66.** 4 **67. a)** –64 **b)** 11 **c)** 73
d) 64 **68. a)** 13 **b)** –1 **c)** –35 **d)** 14 **e)** –150 **f)** 105
Problems and Applications **69. a)** 2000 **b)** 8000
c) 64 000 **70. a)** 2^7 **b)** 2^{10} **71. a)** 25 m, 45 m, 40 m
b) 6 s **72. a)** Each number may be written as a power with the same number base and exponent.
b) 5^5, 10^{10} **73.** $4a$ **74.** $6a$ **75. a)** 49 **b)** 301 **c)** 1
76. a) sometimes true **b)** always true **c)** never true
77. a) 8, 16, 32, 64 **b)** approx. 1.8×10^{13} km

Section 1.5 p. 21

Practice **1.** 5^7 **2.** 2^{10} **3.** 7^{10} **4.** 10^7 **5.** 4^{11} **6.** 3^7
7. y^6 **8.** x^9 **9.** a^7 **10.** 4 **11.** 2 **12.** 6 **13.** 1
14. 3 **15.** 2 **16.** 3 **17.** 1 **18.** 4^2 **19.** 3^1 or 3
20. 9^0 or 1 **21.** 10^1 or 10 **22.** 4^6 **23.** 5^0 or 1
24. m^1 or m **25.** x^2 **26.** 4 **27.** 2 **28.** 7 **29.** 10
30. 1 **31.** 9 **32.** 4 **33.** 5 **34.** 2^{12} **35.** 3^{10} **36.** 4^{14}
37. 10^{15} **38.** 5^{16} **39.** x^{20} **40.** y^9 **41.** t^{42} **42.** m^5
43. 2 **44.** 3 **45.** 4 **46.** 2 **47.** 3 **48.** 3 **49.** 5
50. 1 **Problems and Applications** **51.** 10^5 or
100 000 **52. a)** multiplied bases; added exponents
when bases were not equal **b)** 72 **53. a)** divided
bases; subtracted exponents when bases were not
equal **b)** 54 **54.** smallest is 1^{23456}

Section 1.6 p. 23

Problems and Applications **1.** \$2589.00; assuming
\$215.75/month **2.** 860; assuming 20 cases per
member **3.** 200; assuming equal proportions
4. 75 km; assuming average speed of 15 km/h **5.** A
reduction of 0.1 s per week training **6.** Assuming
a representative survey **7.** 26 m **8. a)** 2 **b)** 3
9. 2 419 200 s; assuming 28 days **10. a)** 7 h;
assuming driving at the speed limit **b)** 23:45
11. a) 12.5, 6.25, 3.125 **b)** 32, 39, 47 **c)** 63, 127, 255
12. 31.5 s **13.** \$33 554 432.00; assuming an initial
price of \$0.50. Alternative solution is to expand 2^{25}.

Section 1.7 p. 25

Practice **1.** $4.5 \times 10\ 000$, 4.5×10^4; 85 000,
8.5×10^4; 110 000, 1.1×10^5; 978 000 000,
$9.78 \times 100\ 000\ 000$; 20 300 000, $2.03 \times 10\ 000\ 000$
2. 3 **3.** 6 **4.** 4 **5.** 7 **6.** 5 **7.** 8 **8.** 770 000
9. 67 000 **10.** 7.6×10^6 **11.** 9.8×10^8 **12.** 35
13. 2.3×10^4 **14.** 6.7×10^3 **15.** 130 000
16. 1.7×10^{10} **17.** 4.8×10^{15} **18.** 5.963×10^{14}
19. 6×10^{12} **20.** 6.3×10^{14} **21.** 1.5×10^3
22. 1×10^2 **Problems and Applications**
23. a) 9.1×10^4 **b)** 8×10^{23} **c)** 9.5×10^7
24. a) 2.2×10^{16} **b)** 2325.4 years **25.** Since 56 is
larger than 10.

Section 1.8 pp. 28–29

Practice **1.** $\frac{1}{2}$ **2.** −5 **3.** 1 **4.** −9 **5.** 5 **6.** 2
7. 0 **8.** 1 **9.** $\left(\frac{1}{4}\right)^3$ **10.** $(-3)^5$ **11.** p^5 **12.** $(-n)^4$
13. $3^4 \times (-2)^3$ **14.** $(-2)(-2)(-2)(-2)(-2)$
15. $-2 \times 2 \times 2 \times 2 \times 2$ **16.** $\left(-\frac{1}{x}\right)\left(-\frac{1}{x}\right)\left(-\frac{1}{x}\right)$ **17.** 9
18. 9 **19.** 1 **20.** −1 **21.** −125 **22.** −125
23. −0.125 **24.** 1.4641 **25.** 6.25 **26.** 5^9 **27.** $(-8)^5$

28. $(-2)^7$ **29.** $\left(\frac{1}{2}\right)^7$ **30.** $(-2.1)^8$ **31.** $(-0.2)^5$ **32.** 5^1
33. 6^6 **34.** $(-0.4)^2$ **35.** $(-9)^5$ **36.** 2^6 **37.** $(-3)^{28}$
38. $\left(-\frac{1}{5}\right)^6$ **39.** $(-6)^{15}$ **40.** $(-4)^{42}$ **41.** $(-2.3)^{12}$ **42.** x^6
43. $\left(\frac{1}{y}\right)^7$ **44.** z^7 **45.** $(-m)^{10}$ **46.** s^8 **47.** $(-r)^6$
48. $(-5)^5$, −3125 **49.** 6^7, 279 936 **50.** $(-2)^{10}$, 1024
51. $(-1)^{12}$, 1 **52.** $(-3.1)^8$, 8528.9 **53.** $(-3)^2$, 9
54. $(-10)^4$, 10 000 **55.** $(-4)^1$, −4 **56.** 16 **57.** 729
58. −3125 **59.** 729 **60.** −64 **61.** 256 **62.** 256
63. −243 **64.** 64 **65.** 36 **66.** 64 **67.** −384
68. 324 **69.** 26 **70.** 781 **71.** −2592 **72.** −10.125
73. 6400 **74.** 27.04 **75.** −0.018 **76. a)** $0.0\overline{2}$ **b)** −4.5
c) 1702 **d)** 9 **77. a)** −8 **b)** 405 **c)** 5 **d)** −72 **e)** −125
f) 25 **g)** −13.5 **h)** −47 **i)** −216 **Problems and
Applications** **78. a)** 4 **b)** 9 **c)** 4 **d)** 10 **e)** 4 **f)** −1.3
or 1.3 **g)** 4 **h)** −0.6 **79. a)** 2 **b)** 3 **c)** 6 **d)** 64 **e)** 3
f) 2 **80.** 10 cm, 8 cm; 125 cm³, 343 cm³, 74.088 cm³
81. a) 160, 320, 640, 1280, 2560 **b)** 163 840
c) 10×2^{40} **82.** positive **83.** negative **84.** Length
must be positive. **85. a)** yes **b)** no **c)** yes

Learning Together pp. 30–31

Activity 1: **1.** The digits 2, 4, 8, 6 repeat in this
order. **2.** 6 **3. a)** 6 **b)** 2 **c)** 4 **4.** 8 **Activity 2:**
1. The digits 3, 9, 7, 1 repeat in this order. **2.** 1
Activity 3: 3 **Activity 4:** **1.** 6 **2.** constant
3. Any base whose ones digit is a 6, for example,
16 **Activity 5:** **1. a)** 6 **b)** 4 **2.** The digits 4, 6
repeat in this order **3.** Any base whose ones digit is
a 4, for example, 34 **Activity 6:** **1.** Use the table
method but this time draw the graph of the last two
digits.

Section 1.9 p. 34

Practice **1.** x^2 **2.** a^3 **3.** p^5 **4.** n^4 **5.** t^6 **6.** $-y^6$
7. x^6 **8.** y^6 **9.** m^4 **10.** n^{12} **11.** x^9 **12.** y^6
13. z^{12} **14.** m^{20} **15.** p^{36} **16.** s^{20} **17.** $-x^{31}$ **18.** 1
19. x^2y^2 **20.** a^3b^3 **21.** x^2y^2 **22.** m^4n^4 **23.** p^3q^3
24. $4x^2t^2$ **25.** $16x^2y^2$ **26.** $-8a^3x^3$ **27.** $-27r^3s^3$
28. x^6y^6 **29.** x^4y^6 **30.** a^6b^3 **31.** a^2b^6 **32.** m^3n^3
33. a^2b^4 **34.** j^6k^8 **35.** x^4y^2 **36.** −1 **37.** $8x^6$ **38.** $9y^6$
39. $16x^8$ **40.** $25y^4$ **41.** m^4 **42.** $-n^6$ **43.** $-8n^6$
44. $9y^4$ **45.** $9p^2q^2r^2$ **46.** $-27y^3z^3$ **47.** $-64x^6y^9$
48. $-9x^2$ **49.** $\frac{m^4}{16}$ **50.** $\frac{r^8}{t^8}$ **51.** $-\frac{d^5}{p^5}$ **52.** $\frac{8b^3}{125c^3}$
53. $-\frac{8x^3}{y^6}$ **54.** $\frac{9s^8}{4q^6}$ **55.** $4x^6y^7$ **56.** $-12x^3y^3$ **57.** $24x^5y^8$
58. $-200a^4b^3c^3$ **59.** $-540a^9b^8$ **Problems and
Applications** **60. a)** $4x^2y^2$ **b)** $16x^4y^6$ **61. a)** $27x^6y^3$
b) $125y^6$ **62.** 157 464 **63. a)** no **b)** yes

Section 1.10 p. 35
Problems and Applications **1.** 10 **2.** 10 000 000
3. 12.25 days, or during the 13th day

Section 1.11 pp. 38–39
Practice **1. a)** $\frac{1}{9^8}$ **b)** $\frac{1}{1^4}$ **c)** $\frac{1}{0.5^6}$ **d)** $\frac{1}{-7^6}$ **e)** 5^4
f) $(-3)^5$ **2. a)** 8^{-2} **b)** 7^{-3} **c)** 9^{-4} **d)** 2^{-2} **e)** 3^{-3} **f)** 2^{-6} or 4^{-3} **g)** 3^{-5} **3.** 1 **4.** 64 **5.** $\frac{1}{3}$ **6.** $\frac{-1}{1000}$ **7.** 1000
8. $\frac{1}{729}$ **9.** 3 **10.** 16 **11.** −3 **12.** 7^9 **13.** 9^2
14. 8^{-8} **15.** 6^4 **16.** 5^{-5} **17.** 4^{-8} **18.** 3^{12} **19.** 9^{-8}
20. 8^5 **21.** -2^6 **22.** 2^3 **23.** 3^{-6} **24.** 5^{-2} **25.** 8^1
26. $(-2)^{-6}$ **27.** $(-3)^0$ **28.** 81 **29.** 16 **30.** $\frac{1}{25}$
31. $\frac{1}{36}$ **32.** 7 **33.** 1 **34.** 10 000 **35.** 100 **36.** $\frac{1}{2}$
37. 1 **38.** 28 **39.** 15.5 **40.** 134 **41.** $\frac{5}{4}$ **42.** 9
43. $\frac{1}{9}$ **44.** $\frac{1}{2}$ **45.** 7 **46.** $\frac{3}{2}$ **47.** $\frac{-4}{9}$ **48.** 3 **49.** $\frac{1}{25}$
50. 1 **51.** 100 **52.** $-\frac{27}{8}$ **53.** $\frac{16}{9}$ **54.** x^7 **55.** x
56. y^{-4} **57.** t^4 **58.** m^8 **59.** b^2 **60.** m^8 **61.** t^{-8}
62. y^{10} **63.** m^5 **64.** a^{-8} **65.** t^{-2} **66.** y^{-1} **67.** t^8

71. a) 6 **b)** $\frac{45}{256}$ **72. a)** $\frac{2}{x^6 y}$ **b)** $\frac{3x^{11}}{y^2}$ **73. a)** 8 **b)** 81
c) 1 **d)** $\frac{1}{8}$ **e)** $\frac{1}{9}$ **f)** $\frac{1}{16}$ **g)** $\frac{1}{36}$ **h)** −1 **i)** $\frac{1}{25}$ **74.** 2^{-3} is greater **75. a)** 3 **b)** 4 **c)** 0 **d)** −2 **e)** −3 **f)** 3
g) 2 **h)** 10 **76. a)** 1 **b)** $\frac{27}{8}$ **c)** $\frac{-8}{9}$ **d)** $\frac{7}{16}$ **e)** $\frac{25}{16}$
f) $\frac{9}{25}$ **77. a)** $\frac{1}{32}$ **b)** 2^{-5} **c)** $\frac{1}{2^5}$ **d)** 39 900 years
78. a) sometimes true **b)** sometimes true **c)** always true **79. b)** $\frac{1}{4}$

Technology pp. 40–41
Activity 1: 0, 1, 10, 11, 100, 101, 110, 111, 1000, 1001, 1010, 1011, 1100, 1101, 1110, 1111
Activity 2: **1.** 1, 10, 100, 1000, 10000, 100000, 1000000, 10000000 **2.** equal **Activity 3:**
1. 10100 **2.** 100101 **3.** 111000 **4.** 1001110
5. 10010011 **Activity 4:** **1.** 21 **2.** 25 **3.** 42
4. 51 **Activity 5:** **1.** 8, 16, 32
2. $7.205\ 759\ 4 \times 10^{16}$ codes, 197 418 066 years

Section 1.12 pp. 42–43
Practice **1.** 4.5×10^6 **2.** 8.9×10^{-2} **3.** 2.0×10^{-1}
4. 5.5×10^{-5} **5.** 4.5×10^8 **6.** 3.4×10^5
7. 3.3×10^{-7} **8.** 1.0×10^{-8} **9.** 6.0×10^{-9}
10. 1.0×10^{-12} **11.** 230 000 000 **12.** 0.000 004 7
13. 0.000 000 007 **14.** 0.000 001 **15.** 2.3×10^7
16. 4.5×10^{-8} **17.** 5×10^{-6} **18.** 10^{-10} **19.** 7.8×10^8
20. 6.8×10^{-7} **21.** 8×10^{-11} **22.** 10^{-8} **23.** 1.25×10^{-6}
24. 9.6×10^{-6} **25.** 1.312×10^{-4} **26.** 2.6×10^5
27. 5.0×10^{-2} **Problems and Applications**
28. a) 4.35×10^{-3}, 4.3×10^{-3}, 10^{-3}, 8.4×10^{-4} **b)** 5.6×10^{-8}, $\frac{1}{10^8}$, 5.6×10^{-9}, 10^{-9} **c)** 10^{-2}, 2.12×10^{-3}, 2.1×10^{-3}, $\frac{1}{1000}$ **29.** 4.0×10^{41} **30. a)** 2.0×10^6 J
b) 8.0×10^{-4} J **c)** 1.5×10^6 J **31.** 0.23 is not larger than 1 **32.** 5×10^0 **33. a)** 1×10^{-14}, 1×10^9

Technology pp. 44–45
Activity 1: **1. b)** in order of appearance
Activity 2: **1. b)** no **2. b)** brackets first, then exponents **3.** brackets exponents division multiplication addition subtraction **7.** −116

Section 1.13 p. 47
Problems and Applications **1. a)** 25 m **b)** 44.8 m
c) 60 m **d)** 76.8 m **2.** $v = 5.5h$ **3. a)** $c = 3.5 + 1.4d$, (d in km) **b)** $14.00 **4.** $30.80 **5.** $5.90 **6.** 4.4 s
7. a) 11.9 years **b)** 0.2 years **c)** 84.1 years

Section 1.14 p. 49
Problems and Applications **1. a)** 1330 km
b) 1822 km **c)** 492 km **3.** 21:45 **4.** −47°C
5. 18:00 on July 1 **6. a)** 6050 km **b)** 67 h **7.** 1.4
8. Prince Edward Island, Nova Scotia, New Brunswick, Ontario, Quebec, Alberta, British Columbia, Manitoba, Saskatchewan, Newfoundland, and Labrador.

Connecting Math and Archaeology
pp. 50–51
Activity 1: Percent of C-14 remaining: 100, 50, 25, 12.5, 6.25, 3.13, 1.56, 0.78 **Activity 2:**
1. about 23 000 years **2.** about 13 200 years
3. about 12 800 years **4.** about 24 600 years
5. about 18 900 years

Review pp. 52–53
1. 25 **2.** 49 **3.** 144 **4.** 961 **5.** 0.4 **6.** 9 **7.** 11
8. 20 **9.** 36 **10.** 74 **11.** −56 **12.** 11 **13.** 5, −5
14. 6, −6 **15.** 8, −8 **16.** 12, −12 **17.** 7.7 **18.** 19.3
19. 35.7 **20.** 202.7 **21.** 2.2 **22.** 0.1 **23.** −0.4
24. 12.4 **25.** 0.4 **26.** 13.6 **27.** 1.9 **28.** 0.6 **29.** 2^8
30. 5^4 **31.** 2^8 **32.** 7^{12} **33.** 3^9 **34.** 6^4 **35. a)** 1
b) −138 **c)** 61 **36.** 2.73×10^7 **37.** 1.93×10^{-8}
38. 25 300 000 **39.** 0.000 971 **40.** 7.75×10^8
41. 2.294×10^{-1} **42.** 3.44×10^{14} **43.** 243 **44.** 144
45. −125 **46.** 160 **47.** 1 **48.** 1 **49.** 0.5 **50.** $0.\overline{1}$
51. $0.2\overline{96}$ **52.** $2.\overline{7}$ **53.** 9 **54.** 40 **55.** $-0.\overline{6}$

56. 0.375 **57.** 2^{-2} **58.** n^2 **59.** 3^{-8} **60.** $-x^{-5}$
61. 0.4^{-8} **62.** 4^{-2} **63.** $15\,625$ **64.** 8 **65.** 36
66. 4096 **67.** 0.5 **68.** 16 **69.** $0.031\,25$ **70.** $0.\overline{1}$
71. a) 36 **b)** -32 **c)** 36 **d)** 125 **e)** 172 **f)** 36
72. 471.6 **73.** $16\,930$ **74.** 0.063 **75.** $0.123\,94$
76. $-8x^6y^9$ **77.** $25x^4y^4$ **78.** $-8a^3b^3c^{12}$ **79.** $2x^8y^7z^8$

80. $-27a^{12}b^4x^4$ **81.** $\dfrac{f^3}{27}$ **82.** $-\dfrac{r^7}{q^7}$ **83.** $\dfrac{25m^2}{49n^2}$

84. a) 20 cm by 20 cm **b)** $10\,000$ cm^2 **c)** 400 cm
85. a) 0.5×10^{-2} km^2 per person **b)** 71 m **86. a)** The
decimal point should be after the digit 4.
b) 4.5×10^6 **87. a)** 341 m/s **b)** 348 m/s **c)** 305 m/s
assuming a temperature of $-40°$C **88.** $3.20

Chapter Check p. 54

1. 6 **2.** 20 **3.** -11 **4.** 9.6 **5.** 17.7 **6.** 0 **7.** -35
8. 7.5 **9.** 5 **10.** 16 **11.** 81 **12.** 125 **13.** 3^9
14. 2^4 **15.** 5^8 **16.** 4.5×10^7 **17.** 2.13×10^5 **18.** 81
19. 1 **20.** 1 **21.** 0.2 **22.** $0.\overline{012345679}$ **23.** $0.\overline{1}$
24. -8 **25.** 0.49 **26.** -4 **27.** 0.2 **28.** 0.75
29. 16 **30.** 4.0×10^{-4} **31.** 2.31×10^{-12} **32.** 0.0046
33. $0.000\,003\,21$ **34.** 4.845×10^{-7} **35.** 3.3×10^3
36. $(-3)^{-1}$ **37.** s^{-3} **38.** 2^3 **39.** 3^{-2} **40. a)** 48
b) -27 **41.** 231 km by 231 km **42.** $-27x^{12}y^9$

43. $9x^8y^8$ **44.** $\dfrac{g^2}{64}$ **45.** $-\dfrac{b^9}{d^9}$ **46.** $\dfrac{16y^4}{81k^4}$ **47. a)** $237.50

b) $512.50

Using the Strategies p. 55

1. 253×14 or 154×23 **2.** 7 cm, assuming the
cardboard has dimensions 21 cm by 14 cm
3. 0, 4, or 8 **4.** 47, 48, 49 **6. a)** 25 **b)** 51
7. a) 20 cm^2 **b)** 5 cm^2 **8.** 13 **9. b)** $33 + 34 + 35 + 36$
10. 12, considering both a.m. and p.m. **Data Bank**
1. 1241 km **2.** $-7°$C with the wind at 32 km/h
($-23°$C versus $-21°$C)

Chapter 2

Getting Started pp. 58–59

Activity 1: **1.** The third number in the column
is the sum of the first two numbers in the column,
while the fourth is their product. **2.** The second
number is twice the first; the third is twice the
second; the fourth is twice the third less the first.
3. The first number is the third less the fourth;
the second is the product of the third and fourth.
4. The first number is the product of the second and
third; the fourth number is the third less the second.

5. The second number is the product of the first
and fourth; the third is the sum of the other three.
6. The second number is three times the first; the
third is the second plus one; the fourth is the sum
of the second and third. **Activity 2:** **1.** 6 **2.** 4
3. 8 **4.** Count the number of factors. **Activity 3:**
1. a) 8 white, 1 yellow **b)** 13 white, 2 yellow
c) 21 white, 4 yellow **d)** 18 white, 3 yellow
e) 29 white, 6 yellow **f)** 40 white, 9 yellow **Mental
Math** **1.** 0 **2.** 10 **3.** -6 **4.** 6 **5.** -12 **6.** -30
7. -40 **8.** -25 **9.** -20 **10.** 10 **11.** 8 **12.** 9
13. -1 **14.** 1 **15.** -25 **16.** -1 **17.** 16 **18.** 4
19. -100 **20.** 27 **21.** -1 **22.** -1 **23.** 1 **24.** -27
25. -9 **26.** 30 **27.** -20 **28.** -50 **29.** -60 **30.** -24
31. 60 **32.** -1000 **33.** 200 **34.** -2 **35.** -3 **36.** -7
37. 2 **38.** 4 **39.** 4 **40.** 7 **41.** -7 **42.** 9 **43.** -3
44. -11 **45.** 10 **46.** 3^1 **47.** 2^3 **48.** 3^3 **49.** 6^2
50. 4^1 **51.** 5^2 **52.** 3^2 **53.** 4^2 **54.** 2^1 **55.** 2^3 **56.** 3^2
57. 4^2 **58.** 5^2 **59.** 6^1 **60.** 2^3

Section 2.1 p. 61

Problems and Applications **1.** 17, 20 **2.** 6, 4
3. 9, 6 **4.** 80, 160 **5.** 16, 8 **6. a)** 16 **b)** 19 **c)** 151
7. a) 9 **b)** 36 **c)** 100 **d)** The sum of the first cube is
1^2. To find the sum of the first 2 cubes, add 2 to the
base of the previous result: 3^2. To find the sum of the
first 3 cubes, add 3 to the base of the previous result:
6^2. etc. **e)** $1 + 2 + 3 + 4 + 5 + 6 + 7 + 8 + 9 = 45$, thus
the sum of the first 9 cubes is $45^2 = 2025$. **8.** 1,
121, 12321, 1234321, 123454321, 12345654321
9. $1\,900\,000 **10.** 5 **11.** 9 of the digit 0 and 19 of
each of the digits 1 to 9 **12.** 65 **13.** 45 **14.** 156
15. 28 **16.** 54

Section 2.2 p. 63

Practice **1.** a **2.** c **3.** q **4.** b **5.** k **6.** t **7.** c; 10
8. a, b; -6 **9.** x, y; -3 **10.** x, y, z; 0.5 **11.** 2; 2, 3
12. 3; 7, 9 **13.** 3; -5, $\frac{1}{4}$ **14.** 2; 6, 11 **15. a)** 10
b) -25 **c)** 0 **d)** -20 **16. a)** 1 **b)** 4 **c)** 16 **d)** -8
17. a) -3 **b)** 3 **c)** -11 **d)** 19 **18. a)** 1 **b)** -4
c) -10 **d)** 12 **19. a)** 1 **b)** -24 **c)** -6 **d)** 10
20. a) 7.5 **b)** 3 **c)** 0 **d)** 9.8 **e)** 1.9 **f)** 4.5 **g)** 0.25
h) -10.25 **Problems and Applications** **21. a)** A
b) 19 000 **22. a)** $290x + 360y + 210z$ **b)** 1975 kJ

Section 2.3 p. 65

Practice **1.** $8x$ **2.** $10t$ **3.** $-7b$ **4.** $-13y$ **5.** $21m$
6. $6p$ **7.** $9r$ **8.** $4t$ **9.** $2p$ **10.** $-4a$ **11.** $2y$ **12.** $-7q$
13. $t + 5$ **14.** $-3x - 7$ **15.** $5a - b$ **16.** $-10x + y$
17. $15y - 2z$ **18.** $-p - 10q$ **19.** $3c$ **20.** $8p - 3q$
21. $-2j - k$ **22.** $2a - 5b$ **23.** $r - s$ **24.** $4y$

25. $2x + 5y + 11$ **26.** $4a - 5b - 5$ **27.** $9x - 9z - 19$
28. $5p - 11q + 8r - 11$ **29.** $4c - 8x - 13w$ **30.** $2c$
$- 23d + 15j$ **31.** $2p + 4q + r + 1$ **32.** $-13x - y + 2z$
33. $13q - 15r + 4s$ **34.** $7a - 3c - d - 21$ **Problems
and Applications**   **35. a)** 20 **b)** 12 **c)** 28 **d)** 48
e) 13 **f)** 3 **36. a)** $m + m + n, 2m + n$ **b)** $z + z + z + z,$
$4z$ **c)** $f + f + f + q + q + q, 3f + 3q$ **d)** $x + x + y + y +$
$y + y, 2x + 4y$ **37. a)** $14c$ **b)** $2a + 2d + 4c$ **c)** $4e + 8f$
d) $2p + 6r + 2s$ **38.** The sum is meaningless. You are
not adding like terms.   **39.** $2p + 2q$

Learning Together pp. 66–67

Activity 1: $6t$ **Activity 2:**   **1.** $b + 5$ **2.** $n - 1$
3. $q \div 9$ **4.** $m - 2$ **5.** $w + 3$ **6.** $5x$ **7.** $6 - t$
8. $2 + y$ **9.** $3n$ **10.** $n + 1$ **11.** $n - 5$ **12.** $6n$ **13.** $\frac{n}{5}$
14. $2n + 3$ **15.** $10 - n$ **16.** $\frac{7}{n}$ **17.** $x + 4$ **18.** $7x$
19. $5x$ **20.** $\frac{3}{x}$ **21.** $x + 7$ **22.** $\frac{1}{2}x$ **23.** $x - 8$ **24.** $2x$
Activity 3:   **1.** $22, 33, 41, x - 23, y + 23, 3m - 23,$
$4t - 2, 6r + 18$ **2.** $12, 23, x - 4, m + 4, 5y - 4,$
$4t + 4, 3w + 4$ **3.** $78, 12, 6x, \frac{y}{6}, 6(m + 7), 6(3t + 8)$
Activity 4:   **1. a)** width   **b)** $x + 5$ **d)** $2(2x + 5)$
2. $x(x + 4)$ **3.** $4x$ **4.** $13, 18, x + 3, 10x + 3, 4x + 4$
b) 46 m, 130 m^2 ; 66 m, 270 m^2; $2(2x + 3), x(x + 3);$
$2(20x + 3), 10x(10x + 3); 2(8x + 5), (4x + 1)(4x + 4)$
5. a) $17, 17, x + 7, y - 7, 3t + 7, 4n - 7, 5z + 11$
b) 54 m, 170 m^2 ; 82 m, 408 m^2; $2(2x + 7), x(x + 7);$
$2(2y - 7), y(y - 7); 2(6t + 7), 3t(3t + 7); 2(8n - 7),$
$4n(4n - 7); 2(10z + 15), (5z + 4)(5z + 11)$

Section 2.4 p. 69

Practice   **1.** $3x = 18$ **2.** $y - 6 = 4$ **3.** $x + 4 = 18$
4. $x - 4 = 10$ **5.** $\frac{m}{4} = 18$ **6.** $4x = 20$ **7.** $\frac{x}{2} = 5$
8. $x + 6 = 15$ **9.** $x + 5 = 12$ **10.** $x - 6 = 10$
11. $x - 4 = 7$ **12.** $x^2 = 25$ **13.** $10 - x = 2$
14. $3x = 9$ **15.** $\frac{x}{5} = 10$ **16.** $x - 6 = -8$ **Problems
and Applications**   **17.** $2b + 16 = 88$ **18.** $2p + 12 = 84$
19. $2c + 7 = 29$ **20.** $3a = 250\,000\,000$
21. $5.5c = 150\,000\,000$ **23. a)** $2(2x + 6) = 36$
b) $2(3x + 3) = 36$ **24.** \$90.00; \$180.00; \$30.00 +
($\$15.00 \times x$)   **25.** $n = \$15.00 + \$14.00(m - 1)$

Section 2.5 p. 71

Practice   **1.** 4 **2.** -1 **3.** 0 **4.** -2 **5.** 7 **6.** 5
7. -7 **8.** -3 **9.** -4 **10.** 4 **11.** -2 **12.** 10 **13.** 14
14. -8.   **15.** 7 **16.** 22 **17.** -7 **18.** 4 **19.** -3
20. -5 **21.** yes   **22.** no   **23.** yes   **24.** no   **25.** yes
26. yes   **27.** no   **28.** yes   **29.** 8 **30.** 4 **31.** 8
32. 6 **33.** 12 **34.** 7 **35.** 5 **36.** 2 **37.** 22 **38.** -2
Problems and Applications   **39.** 1.0 **40.** 6.0

41. 4.0 **42.** 2.4 **43.** 32 **44.** 3.1 **45.** 8.7 **46.** 7.4
47. 0.8 **48.** -6.5 **49.** 4 cm   **50.** 22 km^2 **51.** 3
52. a) $2x = 6$ **b)** $x + 6 = 2$ **c)** $x + 2 = 6$ **d)** $x - 2 = 6$
e) $\frac{x}{2} = 6$ **f)** $6x = 2$ **53. a)** $-4, 4$ **b)** $-5, 5$

Learning Together pp. 72–73

Activity 1:   **1. a)** $-2x; -4, 6$ **b)** $3x; 6, -9$ **c)** $2x^2 + 2x;$
$12, 12$ **d)** $-2x^2 + 3x; -2, -27$ **e)** $-3x + 4; -2, 13$
f) $x^2 - 2x - 4; -4, 11$ **g)** $-x^2 + 3x + 3; 5, -15$ **h)** $2x^2 - 4x - 2;$
$-2, 28$ **Activity 2:**   **1.** $-x + 1, -2, 3; -x^2 + 2x, -3, -8;$
$x^2 - 2, 7, 2; -2x^2 + 4, -14, -4$ **2. a)** 2 long white   **b)** 3
square green   **c)** 2 long green, 2 white   **d)** 3 square green,
1 long green   **e)** 1 square white, 3 long green, 4 white
f) 1 square green, 2 long white, 1 red
g) 1 long green, 2 white   **h)** 2 square white, 5 red

Section 2.6 p. 76

Practice   **1.** $x - 2 = 1, 3$ **2.** $x - 4 = 2, 6$
3. $x + 2 = 4, 2$ **4.** $x + 4 = 4, 0$ **5.** 3 **6.** 1 **7.** 7
8. -4 **9.** 10 **10.** 5 **11.** 6 **12.** 1 **13.** 2 **14.** 5
15. 3 **16.** 7 **17.** 1 **18.** 5 **19.** 4 **20.** -16 **21.** -8
22. 18 **23.** -6 **24.** 12 **25.** -12 **26.** -10 **27.** 15
28. -3 **29.** -2 **Problems and Applications**   **30.** 0
31. 2.0 **32.** 8.0 **33.** 6.0 **34.** 2.1 **35.** -3.0 **36.** 1.0
37. 0.8 **38.** 2.7 **39.** 5.8 **40.** 15.7 **41.** -7.7
42. -33.8 **43.** $c, 5$ **44.** $a, 123$ **45.** $d, 2.0$ **46.** 10
47. 7.1 km   **48.** no effect   **49. a)** $-3, 3$ **b)** $-8, 8$

Section 2.7 p. 79

Practice   **1.** $2x = 4, 2$ **2.** $\frac{x}{2} = 3, 6$ **3.** 6 **4.** 2
5. 7 **6.** 11 **7.** 6 **8.** 8 **9.** 3 **10.** 2 **11.** 7
12. 5 **13.** 4 **14.** 6 **15.** 5 **16.** -6 **17.** -2
18. -3 **19.** 4 **20.** 4 **21.** 12 **22.** -5 **23.** 3
24. 4 **25.** -8 **26.** 21 **27.** -12 **28.** 2 **29.** -2
30. 2 **31.** -6 **32.** 4 **33.** 4.2 **34.** -2.1 **35.** 12
36. -2 **37.** 0.7 **38.** 3 **39.** 6 **40.** -42 **Problems
and Applications**   **41.** $a, \$2$ **42.** $b, 12.6$ cm
43. 360 cm   **44.** 70 kg   **45.** reduces the equation to
$0 = 0$ **46. a)** 0 **b)** no solution   **47. a)** $-6, 6$ **b)** $-2, 2$

Section 2.8 p. 81

Problems and Applications   **1.** Maria–grade 11,
Paula–grade 9, Shelly–grade 10   **2.** Al–golf,
Bjorn–swimming, Carl–running, Don–bowling
3. Susan–pilot, Irina–writer, Traci–doctor,
Debbie–dentist   **4.** 25 m   **5.** 3 quarters, 4 dimes,
4 pennies   **6.** 110 km   **7.** 20 **8.** 24 **9.** 23:59
10. Evans–artist, Thompson–plumber,
Smith–banker, DiMaggio–teacher

Learning Together pp. 82–83

Activity 1: 3; 2, 6; 4, 5; 7, 1   **Activity 2:** 3; 7, 8; 1, 9; 4, 5   **Activity 3:** 4; 3, 5; 1, 7; 6, 8
Activity 4: 6; 5, 4; 8, 9; 3, 1, 0

Section 2.9 p. 85

Problems and Applications   **1.** 06:10   **2.** $48.00
3. $100.00   **4.** 06:15   **5.** $40.00   **6.** 10:15   **7.** 80 h
8. 15 years   **9.** 264   **10. a)** $32 000 **b)** $243 000
11. 3 500 000

Section 2.10 pp. 90–91

Practice   **1.** Left side: Start, $5x + 2$, subtract 2, divide by 5, x, stop; Right side: Start, 22, subtract 2, divide by 5, 4, stop   **2.** Left side: Start, $2x + 5$, subtract 5, divide by 2, x, stop; Right side: Start, 25, subtract 5, divide by 2, 10, stop   **3.** 4   **4.** 7
5. −2   **6.** 4   **7.** −3   **8.** −7   **9.** 5   **10.** −2   **11.** −2
12. −3   **13.** −4   **14.** 4   **15.** 3   **16.** −20   **17.** −10
18. 16   **19.** 18   **20.** 6   **21.** 6   **22.** −20   **23.** −33
24. −4   **25.** −2   **26.** 1   **27.** 2   **28.** −6   **29.** 1   **30.** 2
31. −4   **32.** −1   **33.** −4   **34.** −7   **35.** 4   **36.** −2
37. 1   **38.** −4   **39.** 7   **40.** −3   **41.** 3.2   **42.** 2.2
43. 5   **44.** 5   **45.** −2   **46.** −3.2   **47.** −5   **48.** 7.8
49. −1.1   **50.** 2.0   **51.** −1.7   **52.** 1.7   **Problems and Applications**   **53.** 17, 15, 8   **54.** 6 years
55. a) 3 **b)** yes

Section 2.11 p. 93

Practice   **1.** $3x = 2x + 4$, 4   **2.** $4x + 1 = 2x − 5$, −3
3. 6   **4.** 6   **5.** 3   **6.** −4   **7.** −3   **8.** 6   **9.** −1   **10.** 5
11. 10   **12.** 5   **13.** 3   **14.** −6   **15.** 0.05   **16.** 0.6
17. 1   **18.** 3   **19.** −4   **20.** 2   **21.** 4   **22.** 3   **23.** 2
24. −5   **25.** 1   **26.** 3   **27.** −2   **28.** 3   **29.** −5
30. −3   **31.** 4   **32.** 7   **33.** −4   **34.** 5   **35.** −3
36. −10   **37.** −2   **38.** 1   **39.** 4   **40.** 2   **41.** 6
42. −2   **Problems and Applications**   **43.** 20   **44.** 6
45. a) $b + c + y − a$ **b)** $c − y − a + b$ **c)** $(c − y − b) ÷ a$
d) $(c − y) ÷ a + b$ **e)** $(a + b + y) ÷ c$ **f)** $a(y − b − c)$
46. 14 km/h   **47.** 6

Section 2.12 p. 95

Practice   **1.** $5x + 5$ **2.** $3x − 6$ **3.** $4x + 8$ **4.** $2x − 6$
5. $7x − 7$ **6.** $5x + 15$ **7.** $2x + 12$ **8.** $4x − 20$
9. $7x + 21$ **10.** $3x − 12$ **11.** $10x + 20$ **12.** $9x − 27$
13. $6x + 4$ **14.** $9x + 3$ **15.** $10x + 5$ **16.** $8x + 12$
17. $12x − 6$ **18.** $15x − 10$ **19.** $14x + 7$ **20.** $18x + 12$
21. $−3x − 6$ **22.** $−8x − 4$ **23.** $−10x + 6$ **24.** $−9x + 6$
25. $−10x + 5$ **26.** $−10x + 6$ **27.** $−4x − 20$ **28.** $−2x + 1$
29. $−6x + 4y$ **30.** $−15x − 9y$ **31.** $−20x − 8y$ **32.** $−2x − y$

33. $5x − 5y$ **34.** $−7x + 21y$ **35.** $−6x − 14$ **36.** $−8x + 4y$
37. $−8x − 12y − 4z$ **38.** $15x − 6y + 6$ **39.** $−6x + 18y + 24$
40. $−2x + 3y − 5$ **41.** $6y − 4$ **42.** $7x − 4$ **43.** $x + 26$
44. 6   **45.** $12x − 12$ **46.** $−10x + 10$ **47.** $−5x + 12y − 4$
Problems and Applications   **48.** $5x^2 + 12x + 1$
49. $6x^2 + 18x − 18$ **50.** $7y^2 + 7y − 18$ **51.** $8x − 18y + 35$
52. $−3x + 2$ **53.** 11   **54.** $14x − 17y + 12$ **55.** $x + 6y − 15$
56. $−x^2 + 6y^2 + 7$ **57.** $2x^2 + 8x − 8y − 10$
58. $8y^2 + 23y − 12$ **59. a)** $x + 3$, x **b)** $x^2 + 3x$
60. a) $2 + y$, y **b)** $2y + y^2$ **61.** $3x − x^2$ **62.** $15x − 3x^2$
63. a) $P + Prt$ **b)** $330

Section 2.13 p. 98

Practice   **1.** 1   **2.** 4   **3.** 1   **4.** −6   **5.** −5   **6.** −7
7. 1   **8.** 3   **9.** 1   **10.** −2   **11.** −9   **12.** −3   **13.** 1
14. −1   **15.** 2   **16.** −2   **17.** 1   **18.** 2   **19.** −1   **20.** −2
21. 10   **22.** −1   **23.** 4   **24.** 5   **25.** 2   **26.** 2   **27.** −3
28. 1   **29.** −15   **30.** 2   **31.** 2   **Problems and Applications**   **32. a)** 3 **b)** 4   **33. a)** 3 **b)** 11 by 7
34. 24%

Learning Together pp. 99–100

Activity 1:   **1. a)** 2, 5 and 10 **b)** $5x + 10 = 15$, $2x + 4 = 6$, $x + 2 = 3$ **c)** the last one **d)** multiplying the equation by whole numbers   **2. a)** $2x + 5 = 1$, $12x + 30 = 6$, $18x + 45 = 9$ **b)** $2x + 5 = 1$ **c)** −2
d) −2   **3. a)** $2x − 1 = 3$ **b)** $x + 3 = 10$ **c)** $2x − 5 = 23$
d) $7x − 25 = 70$ **Activity 2:**   **1. a)** $15x + 7 = 37$
b) whole-number equation **c)** 2   **2. a)** 100
b) $p − 20 = 25$ **c)** 5   **Activity 3:**   **1. a)** $\frac{1}{2}$ **b)** $\frac{3}{2}$
c) $\frac{1}{7}$ **d)** $\frac{5}{4}$ **2. a)** $\frac{2}{5}$ **b)** common denominator is 5
c) multiplying both sides of the equation by 5
3. $4x + 2 = 10$, $6x + 3 = 15$ **4.** yes   **5.** the second one is 5 times the first, the third is 14 times the first   **Activity 4:**   **1.** yes   **2.** $\frac{x}{3} + \frac{1}{3}$ **3.** b   **4.** the second is 3 times the first, the third is 4 times the first   **5. a)** the third **b)** 9.6

Section 2.14 pp. 102–103

Practice   **1.** 0.6   **2.** 1.7   **3.** 0.3   **4.** −7.5   **5.** −3
6. −6.9   **7.** 1   **8.** −10   **9.** −3   **10.** 4   **11.** 2.4
12. −4   **13.** 0.4   **14.** −0.53   **15.** 1.09   **16.** −6
17. −11.8   **18.** 1   **19.** 2   **20.** 4   **21.** 4   **22.** −2
23. −3   **24.** −2   **25.** −6   **26.** 20   **27.** −1   **28.** 1
29. 15   **30.** −4   **31.** −2   **32.** 1   **33.** −9   **34.** 14
35. 4   **36.** −9   **37.** −2   **38.** 5   **39.** 2   **40.** 2
Problems and Applications   **41.** 34 kg
42. 0.04 or 4%

Connecting Math and Logic pp. 104–105

Activity 1: **2. a)** TL **b)** TL **c)** TL **d)** TR **e)** LR
f) TL **3. a)** 5 by 6 **b)** 3 by 3 **4.** 5 by 6 **5.** no
Activity 2: **2.** odd number **3.** even number
4. LR **Activity 3:** **2.** even number **3.** odd
number **4.** TL **Activity 4:** **2.** odd number
3. odd number **4.** TR **Activity 5:** **1. a)** The
ball will always stop in the lower right corner.
b) The ball will always stop in the top left corner.
c) The ball will always stop in the top right corner.
2. a) TL **b)** TR **c)** LR **d)** TR **e)** TL **f)** LR

Review pp. 106–107

1. 9 **2.** 16 **3.** 23 **4.** 15 **5.** −12 **6.** −8 **7.** −1
8. −9 **9.** −21 **10.** 30.5 **11.** $3x + 7y + 11$
12. $3a − 4b − 5$ **13.** $3q − 7r − a + 1$ **14.** $8 + x = 20$
15. $6x = 72$ **16.** $2c + 8 = 24$ **17.** $2p − 10 = 90$
18. $4t = 2400$ **19. a)** $3x + 4 = 64$ **b)** $4x + 4 = 64$
20. 4 **21.** 5 **22.** 6 **23.** 4 **24.** −3 **25.** 8 **26.** −7
27. −2 **28.** 0.6 **29.** −0.4 **30.** 10 **31.** −10 **32.** −9
33. 24 **34.** 6 **35.** 10 **36.** −15 **37.** 12 **38.** 6
39. 5 **40.** 2 **41.** −2 **42.** −5 **43.** −9 **44.** 9
45. −0.3 **46.** 10 **47.** 9 **48.** −1.0 **49.** −18 **50.** 24
51. 6 **52.** −16 **53.** −6 **54.** −4 **55.** 2 **56.** 3
57. −3 **58.** −7 **59.** 2 **60.** 2 **61.** −2 **62.** 2 **63.** 4
64. 13 **65.** −3 **66.** −8 **67.** −25 **68.** 3 **69.** −5
70. −3 **71.** −2 **72.** −3.2 **73.** 2 **74.** −0.8 **75.** 3
76. 1 **77.** −1 **78.** −8 **79.** −4 **80.** 4 **81.** −3
82. −10 **83.** −5 **84.** 16 **85.** 26

Chapter Check p. 108

1. 10 **2.** $y + 2$ **3.** $6a − b − 10c − 5$ **4.** $2a + 4 = 36$
5. 8 **6.** −3 **7.** 6 **8.** −9 **9.** 8 **10.** 20 **11.** −9
12. 11 **13.** 35 **14.** 12 **15.** −3 **16.** −2 **17.** 5
18. −2 **19.** −5 **20.** −1 **21.** −0.4 **22.** −2.9 **23.** −9
24. −3 **25.** 1 **26.** 3 **27.** −4 **28.** 2 **29.** 0.06

Using the Strategies p. 109

1. Each entry is the sum of at most the 3 entries
immediately above and to the left, that is $1 + 1 = 2$,
$1 + 2 + 3 = 6$, $3 + 6 + 7 = 16$, etc. **2.** 2 cm
3. two 14 years, three 15 years **4.** 15, 21, 28
5. 8 **6.** 06:35 **7.** 163 216, 255 025
8. a) $13 + 15 + 17 + 19 = 64$
b) $21 + 23 + 25 + 27 + 29 = 125$
c) $31 + 33 + 35 + 37 + 39 + 41 = 216$
d) It is the mean or median.
e) $43 + 45 + 47 + 49 + 51 + 53 + 55 = 343$
Data Bank **1.** 1264 m **2.** 12.5%

Chapter 3

Getting Started p. 112

Activity 1: **1.** prescription, Yin and Yang, no left
turn, poison, copyright, lane ends, male or Mars,
explosive, peace, Aquarius, thunderstorm, new
paragraph, hurricane, registered trademark, Gemini,
female or Venus, hospital, Pisces. **Activity 2:**
1. −2 **2.** −3 **3.** 5 **4.** 3 **5.** 14 **6.** 0 **7.** 6 **8.** −6
9. −10 **10.** 4 **11.** −4 **12.** −6 **13.** 3 **14.** 3
15. −5 **16.** 15 **17.** 4 **18.** −6 **19.** −10 **20.** 2
21. −4 **22.** 3 **23.** 4 **24.** 1 **25.** 12 **Activity 3:**
1. 12.4 cm **2.** 20.8 cm **3.** 24.6 cm **4.** 21.5 cm
5. 45.8 m **6.** 38 cm **7.** 18.7 cm^2 **8.** 22.09 cm^2
9. 37 cm^2 **10.** 21 cm^2 **11.** 81 cm^2 **12.** 60 cm^2
Mental Math **1.** 20 **2.** 30 **3.** 30 **4.** 50 **5.** 51
6. 61 **7.** 60 **8.** 70 **9.** 80 **10.** 30 **11.** 20 **12.** 50
13. 30 **14.** 59 **15.** 49 **16.** 69 **17.** 59 **18.** 49
19. 100 **20.** 1000 **21.** 20 **22.** 2000 **23.** 40
24. 4000 **25.** 36 **26.** 360 **27.** 3600 **28.** 7 **29.** 70
30. 5 **31.** 500 **32.** 400 **33.** 40 **34.** 11 **35.** 14
36. 40 **37.** 20 **38.** 12 **39.** 18 **40.** 15 **41.** 15
42. 22 **43.** 3 **44.** 13 **45.** 10 **46.** 16 **47.** 3
48. 20 **49.** 9 **50.** $\frac{5}{8}$ **51.** $\frac{4}{9}$ **52.** $\frac{7}{10}$ **53.** $\frac{3}{10}$ **54.** $\frac{2}{3}$
55. $\frac{1}{10}$

Section 3.1 pp. 116–117

Practice **1.** $x, 35 − x$ **2.** $x, 50 − x$ **3.** $x, 125 − x$
4. $x, 36 − x$ **5.** $x, 32 − x$ **6.** $x, 758 − x$
7. $x, 468 − x$ **8.** $x, 246 − x$ **9.** 10 m, 12 m, 13 m
10. 4 m, 5 m, 5 m **11.** 3 m, 6 m **12.** 5 m, 7 m
13. 2 m, 6 m **14.** 5 m, 7 m **Problems and
Applications** **15.** 17, 29 **16.** 3058 km, 4241 km
17. 25 m by 20 m **18.** 34, 35, 36 **19.** 155
20. 3 years **21. a)** 3 **b)** 38 **22.** 20 **23.** 10 m,
17 m, 17 m **24.** $0.75 **25.** 14 **26.** 7 nickels,
5 dimes **27.** 57 nickels, 83 dimes **28. a)** 20 cm
b) 37 cm by 32 cm **29.** 16, 23 **30.** 8, 3 **31.** 50
32. 67 $2 bills, 78 $5 bills **33.** 17 small, 21 large
34. 350 **35.** 3 m **36. a)** 2 cm **b)** 296 cm^2

Section 3.2 p. 119

Problems and Applications **1. a)** 10.5 h
b) No; requires 12.5 h **2.** B3, C2, or D2
3. a) 365 050 km **b)** 403 790 km **4. a)** −28.3°C
b) −5°C **5.** Eiffel Tower: 319.9 m; CN Tower:
553.7 m; Washington Monument: 169.4 m
6. a) 1.25 m, 0 m **b)** 2.3 m, 4.2 m, 7.8 m, 1.2 m
c) 5.25 s

Section 3.3 p. 121

Practice **1. a)** 40 cm² **b)** 4 m **c)** 17 m
2. a) 62.8 cm **b)** 100 cm **3. a)** 24 cm² **b)** 20 cm
c) 6 m **4. a)** 30 m **b)** 14 m **c)** 37 m **5.** $w = \frac{A}{l}$
6. $b = \frac{2A}{h}$ **7.** $P = \frac{I}{rt}$ **8.** $r = \frac{C}{2\pi}$ **9.** $m = \frac{E}{c^2}$
10. $b = \frac{2A}{h} - a$ **Problems and Applications**
11. a) 200, 193, 181, 176, 159 **b)** 22 years, 49 years, 37 years **12. a)** 480 000 km, 700 000 km **b)** 3.25 h
13. 10 250, 12 375, 15 250, 16 500, 20 875 **14.** Paul

Learning Together pp. 122–123

Activity 1: **2.** 3, $\frac{1}{2}$; 4, 1; 6, 2; 8, 3; 6, 2; 5, $1\frac{1}{2}$;
7, $2\frac{1}{2}$; 8, 3; 4, 1; 5, $1\frac{1}{2}$; 9, $3\frac{1}{2}$ **3.** equal **4.** 3, 0.5;
4, 1; 5, 1.5; 6, 2; 7, 2.5; 8, 3; 9, 3.5 **5.** 4 square
units **6.** $A = \frac{1}{2}(P - 2)$ **8.** 48.5 square units
Activity 2: **2.** 10, 0, 4; 10, 1, 5; 10, 2, 6; 10, 3, 7;
10, 4, 8; 10, 5, 9; 10, 6, 10 **3.** The area increases by
1 square unit. **4.** 11 square units, 123 square units
5. $A = \frac{1}{2}(P - 2) + I$ **7. a)** 17.5 square units
b) 29 square units **c)** 23 square units

Section 3.4 p. 125

Practice **1.** 15, 18, 21; $b = 3a$ **2.** 10, 12, 14;
$m = n - 3$ **3.** 21, 20, 19; $t = \frac{a}{4}$ **4.** 16, $c = 4n$
5. 150, $w = 7.5n$ **6.** 120, $p = 0.2s$ **Problems and
Applications** **7.** $C = 100 + 3d$ **8.** $C = 3 + 1.5d$
9. a) Regions = Roads – Towns + 1 **b)** Towns =
Roads – Regions + 1 **c)** Roads = Regions + Towns – 1

Section 3.5 p. 127

Practice **1.** 180 km **2.** 170 km **3.** 45 km
4. 45 km **5.** 0.5 h **6.** 8 h **7.** 0.2 h **8.** 4.5 h
9. 100 km/h **10.** 80 km/h **11.** 90 km/h
12. 80 km/h **13.** 4.5 **14.** 195 **15.** 75 **16.** 80x
17. 90(x + 1) **18.** 85(x − 1) **19.** $\frac{200}{x}$ **20.** $\frac{400}{x}$
21. rt **22.** $\frac{D}{r}$ **23.** $\frac{D}{t}$ **Problems and Applications**
24. 5 h **25. a)** 3.75 h **b)** 20:15 **26. a)** 8 h **b)** 16:00
c) uniform motion **27. a)** 1.5 h **b)** 10:15 **28.** 1.25 h

Section 3.6 p. 129

Practice **1.** $\frac{1}{2}$, $\frac{1}{4}$ **2.** $\frac{1}{6}$, $\frac{1}{8}$ **Problems and
Applications** **3.** $2\frac{2}{5}$ min **4.** $1\frac{1}{5}$ h **5.** $\frac{1}{3}$ h
6. 12 min **7. a)** $4\frac{4}{9}$ h **b)** $80, $80, $80 **8.** 4 h
9. 6 h **10. a)** 20 min **b)** Each is occupied by a
separate task.

Section 3.7 p. 131

Problems and Applications **1.** driving from 08:00
until 09:00; at destination from 09:00 until 10:00;
driving from 10:00 until 11:00; at destination from
11:00 until 12:00; driving from 12:00 until 12:15;
stop for gas at 12:15; driving from 12:15 until 12:30;
at destination from 12:30 until 13:30; driving from
13:30 until 14:00; at destination from 14:00 until
16:00; driving from 16:00 until 17:00 **2.** Boat A
is not as old as boat B and costs more than boat B.
Boat B is faster than boat A and both boats have the
same length. **3.** Between A and B; car is travelling
at 100 km/h Between B and C: car is at rest Between
C and D: car is travelling at 50 km/h Between D
and E: car is travelling at 25 km/h

Section 3.8 pp. 134–135

Practice **1. a)** true **b)** true **c)** false **d)** true **e)** false
f) true **g)** false **h)** true **i)** true **j)** true **k)** false
l) true **2. a)** 3 **b)** −5 **c)** 1 **d)** 8 **e)** −1 **f)** 1 **g)** 7
h) −4 **3.** $x > 2$ **4.** $x < 5$ **5.** $x < 4$ **6.** $x > 7$
7. $y > 1$ **8.** $y < 1$ **9.** $z > 3$ **10.** $z < 3$ **11.** $x < 2$
12. $y > -4$ **13.** $m < 5$ **14.** $n < -4$ **15.** $s > 0$
16. $y \le 3$ **17.** $p \le -2$ **18.** $t \le -3$ **19.** $b \le 3$
20. $m > -3$ **21.** $n < -3$ **22.** $x > 3$ **23.** $y > 3$
24. $t \le 6$ **25.** $y \ge 5$ **26.** $x \ge -3$ **27.** $x \ge -3$
28. $x < 5$ **29.** $y > -4$ **30.** $m < -2$ **31.** $n > 3$
32. $t \ge -3$ **33.** $s \ge 1$ **34.** $y \le -2$ **35.** $x \le 5$
36. $x \ge -1$ **37.** $x < 3$ **38.** $x > 6$ **39.** $y \ge 7$
40. $y \le -9$ **41.** $t < -8$ **42.** $a > -2$ **43.** $n < -2$
44. $n > -3$ **45.** $x > 13$ **46.** $y < 3$ **47.** $m \ge 1$
48. $x > 1$ **49.** $y \le -1$ **50.** $m < -2$ **51.** $x > -5$
52. $m < 5$ **53.** $b \ge -8$ **54.** $w \le 4$ **55.** $p \ge 6$
56. $x \le 5$ **57.** $x \ge -3$ **58.** $x < 2$ **59.** $y \le 3$
60. $m < 3$ **61.** $x < -2$ **62.** $y \le 3$ **63.** $t \ge -4$
64. $y > -2$ **65.** $x \le 1$ **66.** $y < 10$ **67.** $t > -6$
68. $x > 2$ **69.** $x > -9$ **70.** $x \le -2$ **71.** $x \le -2$
72. $x \le 5$ **73.** $x > -24$ **74.** $t \le 23$ **75.** $m > 2$
76. $y \ge 2$ **77.** $x \ge 11$ **Problems and Applications**
78. 89 **79.** 59 **80.** $90 **81.** 20 min
82. a) $s \le 100$ **b)** 0 km/h; standstill **83. a)** $x \le 17$
b) $x > 3$; otherwise no triangle is possible
84. a) $x < 4$ **b)** $x > -1$; otherwise there is no rectangle

Connecting Math and Criminology
pp. 138–139

Activity 2: **3.** 1024 **Activity 3:** **3.** 25
Activity 4: **3.** 25 600

Review pp. 140–141

1. 6, 30   **2.** 8 m by 5 m   **3.** 60, 61, 62   **4.** 633 m
by 211 m   **5.** 41 m, 42 m, 43 m   **6.** 12, 48   **7.** 17 g
8. a) 17 m, 18 m, 20 m   **b)** 9 m, 12 m   **9.** 38, 13
10. 11, 16   **11.** 75   **12.** 29   **13.** $x < 5$ **14.** $y > -5$
15. $x > 4$ **16.** $x < 2$ **17.** $x \geq 4$ **18.** $x \geq -1$
19. $x > -3$ **20.** $x < 1$ **21.** $x \geq -2$ **22.** $x \leq 3$
23. $x \leq 2$ **24.** $t \geq -3$ **25.** $x \leq -2$ **26.** $x < 3$
27. $t \geq 7$ **28.** $t > 1$ **29.** $s \leq -9$ **30.** $y \leq 5$ **31.** $x > -10$
32. $x \leq -7$ **33.** $x < 8$ **34.** $x < 3$ **35.** $m \leq 21$
36. a) 95 L, 131 L   **b)** 14 min   **37. a)** 125 L, 50 L
b) 13 min   **38. a)** $\frac{3}{4}$ h   **b)** 09:30   **39.** 5 h
40. a) 9 h   **b)** 19:00   **41.** 6 h   **42.** $1\frac{1}{5}$ h   **43.** $1\frac{5}{7}$ h

Chapter Check p. 142

1. 81   **2.** 26 m, 11 m   **3.** 33 m, 34 m, 35 m
4. $x < -7$ **5.** $x > -2$ **6.** $r > -1$ **7.** $x \geq -5$
8. $x > -10$ **9.** $x \leq 7$ **10.** 44 m   **11.** $b = \frac{2A}{b}$
12. 3 h   **13.** 2.5 h   **14.** $d = 330t$ **15.** $2\frac{2}{5}$ h

Using the Strategies p. 143

1. $\frac{1}{24}$ **2.** 126 cm   **3.** 15:55   **4.** 1125 m   **5.** 343
four cylinder, 142 six cylinder   **6.** 34   **7. a)** 14
b) 28 years   **Data Bank**   **1.** 01:00

Chapter 4

Getting Started p. 146

Activity 1:   **1. a)** from left to right: x^2, x, -1, x^2,
x, x^2 **b)** 3 of the x^2 type, 2 of the x type and 1 of
the 1 type   **2. b)** $3x^2 + 2x - 1$ **c)** 20   **Activity 2:**
3. a) $2x^2 + x + 2$; $-x^2 - x$ **b)** 12; -6 **Mental Math**
1. -664 **2.** 765   **3.** 868   **4.** -690 **5.** 787   **6.** 777
7. -313 **8.** 999   **9.** 434   **10.** -890 **11.** 213
12. 121   **13.** -883 **14.** 400   **15.** 111   **16.** 310
17. 12   **18.** 12   **19.** 6   **20.** 5   **21.** 23   **22.** 51   **23.** 11
24. 22   **25.** 306   **26.** 777   **27.** -8008 **28.** -6060
29. -6868 **30.** 4848   **31.** -9009 **32.** 176
33. 1111   **34.** 202   **35.** -2020 **36.** -321 **37.** 4321
38. 21   **39.** -103 **40.** -41 **41.** 15   **42.** 60
43. -4 **44.** 8   **45.** 0   **46.** 15   **47.** -7 **48.** -72

Section 4.1 p. 149

Practice   **1.** monomial   **2.** binomial   **3.** trinomial
4. binomial   **5.** monomial   **6.** trinomial   **7.** 1   **8.** 4
9. 0   **10.** 5   **11.** 7   **12.** 6   **13.** 4   **14.** 1   **15.** 4
16. 8   **17.** 2   **18.** 6   **19.** 7   **20.** $x^5 + x^3 + x^2 + 1$

21. $-3x^3 + 2x + 5$ **22.** $-x^2 + 2xy + 5y^2$
23. $-4x^4 - 5x^2y + 25xy^2 + 3xy^3$
24. $7b^2x^4 - 3x^3 + 4abx^2 + 5ax$
25. $-2 + x + 3x^2 - 2x^3 + 5x^5$ **26.** $5 - x + x^2 - 3x^3 + 4x^4$
27. $4xy^2 - 2x^2y^2 + 2x^3y - 3x^4$
28. $-3 + 2xy^4z + 5x^2yz^2 + 3x^3y^4z^2$
29. $z - xy + x^2$ **30.** $16 - 2xy + x^2 - 3x^3$
31. $3xy + 2x^3y - x^3$ **32.** $-1 + xy + 3x^3y^2 + x^4y$
Problems and Applications   **33. a)** monomial
b) binomial   **c)** monomial   **34. a)** binomial
b) binomial   **c)** trinomial   **d)** monomial   **35. a)** 2
of 50 cm², 2 of 100 cm², 2 of 200 cm²   **b)** 700 cm²
c) $2lw + 2lh + 2wh$ **36.** 3822 cm³

Section 4.2 pp. 151–152

Practice   **1.** $3x^2 + 6x + 3$ **2.** $-2x^2 - 2x - 3$
3. $x - 1$ **4.** $-x^2 - 2x + 1$ **5.** $2x$, $5x$; $3y$, $-2y$;
$-4xy$, $6xy$ **6.** $2a$, $5a$; $-6b$, $8b$; $-2c$, $3c$ **7.** $3s^2$, $7s^2$;
$5s$, s; -2, -3 **8.** $7x - 1$ **9.** $4x^2 - 2x - 2$
10. $y^2 + 14y - 9$ **11.** $-2y^3 - 8y^2 + 2$ **12.** $6x + 9$
13. $7y^2 + 9y + 19$ **14.** $8x - 8y + 15$ **15.** $7x^2 - 8x - 5$
16. $9x^2 - x + 2$ **17.** $5y^2 - 6$ **18.** $-z^2 - 2z + 10$
19. $7x^2 + 5y^2 - 16$ **20.** $2x^4 + 2x^3 - 5x^2 + 7x - 4$
21. $9x^2 - x + 5$ **22.** $5y^2 - 6$ **23.** $m^3 + 9m^2 + 10$
24. $3x^2 - x - 6$ **25.** $3x^2 - 2xy + 5y^2$ **26.** $3y^2 - 2y + 1$
27. $4x^2y - 2xy + 5y^2$ **Problems and Applications**
29. a) $12x + 12$ **b)** 60 cm   **30. a)** $10x + 4$ **b)** 74 cm
31. a) triangle   **b)** 786 m   **32.** $4x^2 - 2x - 3$ **33. a)** $8x$
b) $20x$

Section 4.3 p. 155

Practice   **1.** $-x^2 - 4x - 1$ **2.** $-x^2 + 2x + 3$
3. $-2x^2 - x + 5$ **4.** $3x^2 + 7x - 2$ **5.** $2x - 7$
6. $-2x + 6$ **7.** $2x + 7$ **8.** $2x - 9$ **9.** $3x^2 + 8x - 1$
10. $-5x^2 + 2x - 4$ **11.** $-x^2 - 8x + 11$ **12.** -5
13. $3x - 2$ **14.** $3x^3 - x^2 - x$ **15.** $-y - 11$ **16.** $7s^2 + 3$
17. $3y^2 - 12y - 2$ **18.** $-x^2 - 9x + 6$ **19.** $-7y^2 - 4y + 3$
20. $3t^2 - 2t + 7$ **21.** $-3n^2 - 8n - 5$ **22.** $1 - 3x + 6x^2$
23. $-4t^2 - 5$ **24.** $2x^2 + 12x - 8$ **25.** $4m^2 + 6m - 7$
26. $-2y^2 + 3y - 10$ **Problems and Applications**
28. $5x + 2$ **29. a)** $3x^2 - y^2$ **b)** $2t^2 + 5t + 8$
30. $2x^2 + x - 3$ **31.** 0   **32. a)** No   **b)** Yes; the results
are opposite.

Section 4.4 p. 157

Problems and Applications   **1.** 4   **2.** 1   **3.** 19
4. 16   **5.** 9, assuming each width in times of 15 s
and 12 s respectively.   **6.** 6, assuming we consider
only who sits next to whom is of importance.   **7.** 6
8. 16   **9.** The farmer must make 7 trips across
the river. He begins by taking the goat across and

returns. He then takes the wolf across and returns with the goat. He then takes the cabbages across and returns for the goat. **10.** 4

Learning Together pp. 158–159

Activity 1: **2. b)** 6 **c)** 3, 2 **Activity 2:** **3. a)** 2 x-tiles **b)** 2 and x **Activity 3:** **2. a)** length = x, width = x **b)** a square **4. a)** x^2 **b)** x, x **Activity 4:** **1.** $34x^2$ **2.** x, $3x$ **Activity 5:** **1. a)** no **b)** the x-tile

Section 4.5 p. 161

Practice **1.** $15xy$ **2.** $6mn$ **3.** $35st$ **4.** $24ab$ **5.** $6x^2y$ **6.** $20ab^2$ **7.** $12bc$ **8.** $6ab^2$ **9.** $18st$ **10.** $6xy$ **11.** $12ab$ **12.** $10x^2y^2$ **13.** $15abc$ **14.** $12xy$ **15.** $30xyz$ **16.** $6a^2b^2$ **17.** $9ab$ **18.** $35ab$ **19.** $-15x^2y^2$ **20.** $8at^3$ **21.** $-12abc^2$ **22.** $-24a^2y^2$ **23.** $25xyz$ **24.** $-48x^2y^2$ **25.** $14x^2y^2$ **26.** $10m^3n$ **27.** $-12s^3t^4$ **28.** $6a^3b^5xy$ **29.** $10s^6t^5$ **30.** $-20c^2x^5y^{10}$ **31.** $-15x^2y^2z^2$ **32.** $6cx^2y^2z^3$ **33.** $4x^2y^2z$ **34.** $-70x^2yz$ **35.** $-70xyz$ **36.** $90xyz^2t^2$ **37.** $-8a^2x^6y^2z^3$ **38.** $-6b^2x^2y^5z^3$ **39.** $10a^4b^5$ **40.** $-24a^3b^3c^3$ **41.** $4x^4y^4z^4$ **42.** $-24j^3k^3l^3$ **Problems and Applications** **43. a)** $41x^2$ **b)** $28y^2$ **c)** $68c^2$ **d)** $16x^2$ **e)** $33x^2$ **f)** $20x^2$ **44. a)** the cost of making 24 hats **b)** $36 **45. a)** $27a^3$ **b)** $42y^3$ **46.** $6x$

Section 4.6 p. 163

Problems and Applications **1.** Multiply the number of listings on a typical page by the number of pages. **2.** Measure the thickness of 100 pages and divide by 100. **3.** Time yourself for 5 pages (say) and multiply by 50. **4.** 100 **5.** 10 000 **6.** 10 100 **7.** 40 **8.** 15 **9.** 324 **10.** 81 **11.** Time yourself for 1 min and multiply by 525 600. **12.** 2^{12} or 4096

Section 4.7 p. 165

Practice **1.** $2x$ **2.** $-3a$ **3.** $3y$ **4.** $4m$ **5.** $-5x$ **6.** $-5y$ **7.** 3 **8.** -6 **9.** 24 **10.** 32 **11.** $-x$ **12.** $4m$ **13.** $3z$ **14.** $-3b$ **15.** 3 **16.** $-9bc$ **17.** $4x$ **18.** $-5s$ **19.** 5 **20.** 2 **21.** 7 **22.** 9 **23.** $12t$ **24.** $3j$ **25.** $4qr$ **26.** $17df$ **27.** $5xy$ **28.** $-3a^2b^3$ **29.** $-2j^3k^7$ **30.** $-5x^3y^{14}$ **31.** $-a^2bc$ **32.** $4xy$ **33.** $2a^2b$ **34.** $3xy$ **35.** $-3m^3$ **36.** $2xyz^2$ **37.** $\frac{4}{3}$ **38.** $-\frac{3}{2}x^2y^2$ **39.** $\frac{2}{x^2y^2}$ **40.** $-4a^2b^2$ **41.** $\frac{-4}{mn^3}$ **42.** $3x^9y$ **43.** $-\frac{4x}{3y^4}$ **44.** $\frac{9p^3q^{12}}{r^2}$ **Problems and Applications** **45. a)** x **b)** p **c)** $2x^2$ **d)** $3b^4$ **46. a)** 16 cm by 10 cm **b)** 20 cm by 8 cm **47.** $\frac{x}{6}$ **48.** 1

Section 4.8 p. 167

Problems and Applications **1.** 3285 **2.** 18 750 **3.** $372 757.50 **4. a)** 315 km **b)** 280 km **c)** 90 km **5.** $15.50 **6.** $514.80 **7.** 9 397 728 000 000 km **9.** $78.05 **10.** 450 000 000

Connecting Math and Astronomy pp. 168–169

Activity 1: **5.** Mercury, 4847 km; Venus, 12 118 km; Mars, 6761 km; Jupiter, 142 867 km; Saturn, 119 906 km; Uranus, 51 024 km; Neptune, 48 473; Pluto, 2551 km **Activity 2:** (in millions of kilometres) **3.** Mercury, 58.3; Venus, 107.7; Mars, 227.4; Jupiter, 777.9; Saturn, 1421.2; Uranus, 2872.3; Neptune, 4503.0; Pluto, 5924.2

Review pp. 170–171

1. monomial, 3 **2.** monomial, 5 **3.** binomial, 3 **4.** binomial, 2 **5.** trinomial, 4 **6.** binomial, 5 **7.** trinomial, 4 **8.** trinomial, 3 **9.** binomial, 4 **10.** trinomial, 5 **11.** $-5x^3 + x^2 + 3x$ **12.** $y^4 + 2y^2 - 3y + 5$ **13.** $-m^4 + 6m^3 - 3m^2 + 2m + 6$ **14.** $x^4 + x^3 + x^2 + x + 3$ **15.** $-2y^7 + 5y^6 + y^5 - 4y^2 + 3y$ **16. a)** monomial **b)** trinomial **c)** binomial **d)** binomial **17. a)** 30 cm^2, 50 cm^2, 15 cm^2 **b)** 190 cm^2 **c)** $2(lh + hw + lw)$ **18.** $3m^2 - 2m + 2$ **19.** $4a^2 + 8a + 2$ **20.** $-b^2 - b + 6$ **21.** $2x^3 - 4x^2 + 8x$ **22.** $2x^2 - 8x + 2$ **23.** $a^2 + 2a - 4$ **24.** $9t^2 - 2t - 14$ **25.** $3a^2 - 6a - 1$ **26.** $-2m^2 + 3m + 2$ **27.** $2x^2 + x - 6$ **28.** $6x^2 - x - 2$ **29.** $-3x^2 + 2x + 2$ **30.** $5x^2 - 5x + 7$ **31.** $5x^2 - 3x - 8$ **32.** $-n^2 - 9n - 3$ **33.** $1 - 3x + 6x^2$ **34.** $-3p^2 + 2p - 7$ **35.** $5x^2 + 14x - 8$ **36.** $3m^2 + 6m - 6$ **37.** $y^2 + 2y - 13$ **38. a)** $4x - 8y - 3$ **b)** $2x^2 + 6x - 10$ **39.** $40xy$ **40.** $-150xy^2$ **41.** $12abx^2$ **42.** $10a^2bp$ **43.** $-15x^2y^2$ **44.** $4a^3b$ **45.** $-8x^3y^2z$ **46.** $-3s^5t^5$ **47. a)** $32x^2$ **b)** $60y^2$ **c)** $146c^2$ **d)** $33x^2$ **48.** $4xy^2$ **49.** $9xy$ **50.** $5a^2b^2$ **51.** $-2ab^7c^{-2}$ **52. a)** $4x^2y^2$ **b)** $5a^3b$

Chapter Check p. 172

1. trinomial, 2 **2.** binomial, 3 **3.** monomial, 3 **4.** monomial, 0 **5.** $x^5 + x^4 + x^3 + 1$ **6.** $-yx^4 + 5x^3 + 2xy$ **7.** $-3x^4 + x^3y - 2x^2y + 10xy^2$ **8.** $-5b^2x^3 + 5abx^2 + 3ax - 1$ **9.** $6a^2 - 4$ **10.** $b^3 - b^2 + y - 1$ **11.** $5y^2 - 12x + 6$ **12.** $-t^2 - t - 5$ **13.** $-x^2 - 7x + 6$ **14.** $5y^2 + 14y + 1$ **15.** $8x^2 - 9x - 12$ **16.** $-2x^2 + 10x + 1$ **17.** $10x^2 - 2x - 4$ **18.** $-4x^2 + 3x + 1$ **19.** $3x^2 - 8x + 8$ **20.** $8x^2 + 4x - 11$ **21.** $-50xy$ **22.** $45x^3y^3$ **23.** $-6b^2x^5yz$ **24.** $-15x^4y^2z^3$ **25. a)** $34x^2$ **b)** $26x^2$ **c)** $6y^2$ **26.** $\frac{-2}{a^3b^2}$ **27.** $\frac{3l^2}{j^2k}$

Using the Strategies p. 173

1. $\frac{5}{18}$ or approximately 0.3 h   **2. a)** 81 **b)** 961
3. 36, 37, 38   **4.** 20   **5.** 84   **6.** 34   **7.** Sue: 16
years, Alex: 12 years   **8. a)** more than 20 **b)** less
than 20 **c)** 20   **9.** 16   **10.** 5   **11.** 1681   **12. a)** 4
boxes of 6, 1 box of 20 **b)** 1 box of 9, 2 boxes of 6,
1 box of 20 **c)** 4 boxes of 9, 1 box of 6 or 2 boxes
of 9, 4 boxes of 6 or 7 boxes of 6 **d)** no   **Data
Bank** **1.** Saturday about 12:40   **2.** 484 m

Cumulative Review, Chapters 1–4
pp. 174–175

Chapter 1:   **1.** 9   **2.** 17   **3.** 9   **4.** 7   **5.** 163   **6.** 4
7. 27   **8.** 16   **9.** 25   **10.** 10 000   **11.** 82   **12.** $\frac{1}{2}$
13. $\frac{2}{9}$ **14.** 64   **15.** 1   **16.** −1   **17.** −125   **18.** 1
19. 3.73×10^7 **20.** 1.54×10^{-11} **21.** 340 000 000
22. 4 000 000   **23.** 8880   **24.** 30 100 000 000
25. $\frac{36}{49}$ **26.** $-\frac{s^5}{t^5}$ **27.** $\frac{27p^3}{64q^3}$ **28. a)** 10.0 cm **b)** 35.7 m
Chapter 2:   **1. a)** 1 **b)** −16 **c)** 1 **d)** −1   **2.** $3n = 15$
3. $n + 5 = 6$ **4.** $2n = n + 10$ **5.** $5(n + 2) = 20$ **6.** 12
7. 12   **8.** 1   **9.** 4   **10.** 3   **11.** 4   **12.** 16   **13.** 15
14. 6   **15.** 1   **16.** 20   **17.** 55   **18.** −4   **19.** 1   **20.** 5
21. 9   **22.** 3   **23.** 4   **24.** 9   **25.** 3   **Chapter 3:**
1. 17 cm, 18 cm, 19 cm   **2. a)** 20, 30, 40, 50
b) $A = 5b$ **c)** 75 cm^2 **3.** 40 min   **4.** 2000 km
5. 9, 17   **6.** $x \geq 1$ **7.** $x < -2$ **8.** $x < 1$ **9.** $x \geq -3$
10. 2.01 s, 2.84 s, 3.48 s   **Chapter 4:**   **1.** $4x^2 + 3x - 2$
2. $5y^2 - 4y$ **3.** $-x^2 - 2x - 9$ **4.** $-x^2 - 3$ **5.** $15xy$
6. $-12st$ **7.** $4x^2 - 3x + 3$ **8.** $7x^2 + 5x - 6$
9. $-4x^2 + 2x - 9$ **10.** $-3x^2 - 5x - 9$ **11.** $12x^2 - 2x - 5$
12. $-x^2 + 6x + 6$ **13.** $-9x^2 - 2x + 4$ **14.** $-x^2 - 6x - 17$
15. $20abx^2$ **16.** $12p^2wb$ **17.** $-35x^2y^2$ **18.** $25b^3a$
19. $-12x^4yz^2$ **20.** $-2p^6q^4$ **21.** $\frac{3}{x^3y}$ **22.** $-7a^2b^0$ **23.** $-\frac{2}{pq^4}$
24. $6x^{11}y^7$ **25.** $\frac{3}{2xy^5}$ **26.** $-\frac{5t^5}{7rs^3}$ **27.** $12x^2$ **28.** $13y^2$

Chapter 5

Getting Started pp. 178–179

Activity 1:   **1.** 1, 2, 3, 4, 6, 12   **2.** 1, 3, 5, 15
3. 1, 3, 7, 21   **4.** 1, 2, 4, 8   **5.** 1, 3, 5, 9, 15, 45
6. 1, 2, 3, 4, 6, 9, 12, 18, 36   **7.** 1, 2, 4, 13, 26, 52
8. 1, 17   **9.** 1, 2, 4, 5, 10, 20, 25, 50, 100   **10.** 1,
2, 3, 4, 6, 8, 12, 24   **11.** 1, 2, 4, 5, 8, 10, 16, 20,
40, 80   **12.** 1, 3, 13, 39   **13.** $2 \times 2 \times 2$ **14.** 3×5
15. $2 \times 2 \times 2 \times 3$ **16.** $2 \times 2 \times 5$ **17.** $2 \times 2 \times 3 \times 3$
18. $2 \times 3 \times 7$ **19.** $2 \times 2 \times 7$ **20.** 19   **21.** 2×13

22. −5, 6; 2, −35; −7, −18; −4, 20; 3, −3; −1, 9; 4, −12;
4, 5; −3, −4; 2, 10; −5, −6   **23.** 2   **24.** b **25.** 2
26. $-2x$ **27.** $3a$ **28.** $-2x$ **29.** $4y$ **30.** $-4x$ **31.** 2
32. $-6xy^2$ **33.** 1   **34.** $-4a$ **Activity 2:**   **1.** x^3 **2.** p
3. a^6 **4.** x^4 **5.** $-5t^3$ **6.** a^2 **7.** $-3x^3$ **8.** $-4a^3$ **9.** $5x^2$
10. $6mn$ **11.** $5ab$ **12.** $a + 2$ **13.** $3x - 2y$ **14.** $t - 3$
15. $3x - 2$ **16.** $3m - 2n + 1$ **17.** $2x^2 - 5x + 3$ **18.** $3a + 2b$
19. $4y^3 - 3x^2$ **Activity 3:**   **1.** 5   **2.** 11   **3.** 6   **4.** x
5. $2a$ **6.** $7x$ **7.** 4   **8.** 25   **9.** 81   **10.** $4x^2$ **11.** $9a^2$
12. $25x^6$ **Activity 4:**   **1.** $48x^3y^3$ **2.** $9x^2$ **3.** $6x^2$
4. $20x^2$ **5.** $x^2 + 3x + 2$ **6.** $x^2 + 3x$ **7.** $a^2 + 5a + 4$
8. $y^2 + 9y + 20$ **9.** $y^2 + 2y$ **10.** $a^2 + 11a + 30$
11. $x^2 + 5x + 10$ **12.** $y^2 + 5y + 9$ **Mental Math**
1. 15   **2.** 14   **3.** 16   **4.** 9   **5.** 34   **6.** 0   **7.** 9
8. 90   **9.** 25   **10.** 100   **11.** 25   **12.** 33   **13.** 6
14. 3   **15.** 54   **16.** 36   **17.** 26   **18.** 31   **19.** 13
20. 41   **21.** 6   **22.** $\frac{1}{6}$ **23.** $\frac{1}{20}$ **24.** 3   **25.** 2   **26.** $\frac{2}{3}$
27. $\frac{3}{4}$ **28.** 1   **29.** 2   **30.** $\frac{1}{3}$ **31.** $\frac{1}{2}$ **32.** $\frac{3}{2}$ **33.** $\frac{7}{5}$
34. $\frac{1}{12}$ **35.** $\frac{1}{4}$ **36.** 8   **37.** $\frac{3}{4}$ **38.** $\frac{1}{4}$ **39.** $\frac{1}{8}$ **40.** $\frac{2}{15}$
41. $\frac{1}{8}$ **42.** $\frac{3}{10}$ **43.** 9   **44.** $\frac{1}{3}$ **45.** $\frac{1}{2}$

Learning Together pp. 180–181

Activity 1:   **3.** 45   **4.** 45   **5.** equal   **6.** Multiply
the middle number by 3.   **8.** 11   **9.** 11
10. a) $x + 8$, $x + 9$; $x + 14$, $x + 15$, $x + 16$
b) $x - 8$, $x - 7$, $x - 6$; $x - 1$, $x + 1$; $x + 6$, $x + 7$, $x + 8$
c) $x - 14$, $x - 13$, $x - 12$; $x - 7$, $x - 6$, $x - 5$; $x + 1$, $x + 2$
Activity 2:   **1.** 5, 7, 9, 11; 7, 9, 11, 13; 9, 11, 13,
15; 11, 13, 15, 17   **3.** 44   **4.** yes   **5.** the sum always
equals $a + b + c + d + e + f + g + h$

Section 5.1 p. 184

Practice   **1.** 2, 2, 3   **2.** 2, 2, 2, 2   **3.** 2, 2, 7   **4.** 3,
3, 7   **5.** 2, 2, 2, 2, 3, 3   **6.** 3, 3, 5, 5   **7.** $2 \times 2 \times x \times$
$y \times y$ **8.** $2 \times 3 \times 3 \times a \times a \times b \times b \times b$ **9.** $2 \times 2 \times 3 \times 3 \times$
$x \times x \times x \times y \times z \times z$ **10.** $2 \times 5 \times x \times x \times y$ **11.** $2 \times 3 \times 3 \times 3 \times$
$x \times x \times x \times x \times x \times x$ **12.** $5 \times 5 \times 5 \times a \times a \times a \times a \times b \times b$
13. 5   **14.** 8   **15.** 9   **16.** 14   **17.** 24   **18.** 32   **19.** $2a$
20. x **21.** $2m^2$ **22.** $3abc$ **23.** 2   **24.** 7   **25.** $5x$ **26.** xy
27. mn **28.** $2a^2$ **29.** $5bc$ **30.** $3xy$ **31.** 5   **32.** $2x$
33. $6a$ **34.** $5xy$ **35.** $7ab$ **36.** $4xy$ **37.** $4ab$ **38.** x^2y^2
39. $2x^2y$ **40.** $3xy^2$ **41.** $4ab^3$ **42.** $5s^3t^4$ **Problems
and Applications**   **43.** 6   **44.** x **45. a)** A–Shirley,
B–Gustav, C–Bob, D–Collete, E–Karin

Section 5.2 p. 186

Practice   **1.** 6   **2.** x **3.** a **4.** $5x$ **5.** $4ab$ **6.** 6
7. $7a$ **8.** a **9.** x, 3   **10.** $3a$, 2   **11.** $2a^2$, $5a$, 3
12. $3a^2b$, $2a$, 1   **13.** $3x$, $2y$ **14.** $3a^2$, $4b^3$ **15.** $5(2x + 3)$

16. $14(2y - 1)$ **17.** $n(2m - 1)$ **18.** $5x(x + 2)$
19. $4x^2(2 + x)$ **20.** $3a^2b(3ab - 2)$ **21.** $2xy^2(2x - 3z^2)$
22. $7b^2(2a^2b^2 - 3c^2)$ **23.** $6xy^2z(xy + 2)$ **24.** $3b^4(5a^2b - 3c^2)$
Problems and Applications   **25.** $3(3a - 2b + 1)$
26. $4(a - 2b + 4)$ **27.** $6x(2x^2 - x + 4)$ **28.** $5x(2x^2 - x + 3)$
29. $6x^2y(4x^2 - 3x + 2y)$ **30.** $8a(ab + 2b - 3)$
31. $5mn(5m^2 - 3mn + n^2)$ **32. a)** $2x + 2y, 2(x + y)$
b) $2(x + y)$ **33.** 12 cm by 11 cm   **34. a)** $(a + b)(x + y)$
b) $(x - 2)(x + 3)$ **c)** $(2x - 3)(x - 5)$ **d)** $(a - b)(2a + b)$
35. a) $5t(1 - t)$ **b)** 1.2 m

Section 5.3 p. 189

Practice   **1.** $x^2 + 2x$ **2.** $x^2 - 3x$ **3.** $a^2 + a$ **4.** $t^2 - t$
5. $y^2 + 4y$ **6.** $m^2 + 5m$ **7.** $x^2 - 5x$ **8.** $y^2 - 7y$
9. $a^2 - 10a$ **10.** $3x^2 + 6x$ **11.** $4b^2 - 44b$ **12.** $5t^2 + 15t$
13. $6x + 2x^2$ **14.** $7y^2 - 35y$ **15.** $-2x^2 - 8x$ **16.** $-x^2 - 2x$
17. $-y^2 + 3y$ **18.** $5x$ **19.** $2y^2 + y$ **20.** $2m^2 - 2m$
21. $x^2 + 2$ **22.** $3y^2 - 7y$ **23.** $3a^2$ **24.** $-3x$
25. $5x^2 + 16x$ **26.** $x^2 - x$ **27.** $9x^2 + 5x$ **28.** $-3y^2 + 5y$
29. $5a^2$ **30.** $-x^2 + 2x$ **31.** $22x$ **32.** $x^3 + 2x^2 + 3x$
33. $3x^2 + 6x - 15$ **34.** $5x^3 + 10x^2 - 35x$
35. $-x^2 + 3x + 1$ **36.** $4m^2 - 20m^2 + 24m$
37. $6y^3 - 12y^2 + 9y$ **38.** $-9b^3 + 15b^2 - 3b$
39. $-5z^3 + 10z^2 + 25z$ **Problems and Applications**
40. $2x^2 + 5x - 15$ **41.** $8x^3 + 13x - 35$ **42.** $2x^2 + 5x + 1$
43. $3x^3 - 3x^2 + 17x + 12$ **44.** $7m^2 - 26m + 24$
45. $y^2 - 7y + 9$ **46.** $x^2 - 8x$ **47. a)** $35y^2 - 20y$
b) $14x + 14xy + 9y$ **c)** $38x^2$ **d)** $7x^2 + 6x$

Section 5.4 p. 191

Practice   **1.** 3   **2.** -6 **3.** $-4n$ **4.** 6   **5.** 11   **6.** y
7. $4x$ **8.** $-3b^2$ **9.** $-6x$ **10.** $4x - 5y + 8$ **11.** $x^2 + 2x - 3$
12. $-y^3 - y^2 + 3$ **13.** $m^2 + 2m - 3$ **14.** $-3x^2 + 8x + 5$
15. $-j^4 - 2j^3 - 3j^2$ **16.** $-2x^2 - x + 3$ **17.** $3 - 2m + 3m^2$
18. $-2p + 3q - 5p^2q^2$ **19.** $-4a + 3b + 8a^2b^2$ **20.** $2x^2 -$
$3xy + 4y^2$ **21.** $2ac^3 - 3c^2 + 4bc$ **22.** $3y^2 + 4xy + 6x^2$
23. $5n^2 - 6mn - 5m^2$ **24.** $-5abc^3 + 8a^2bc^2 - 7a^4b^2c$
Problems and Applications   **25. a)** $4x + 1$
b) $4x^3 - 5x + 3$ **c)** $3xy - 6 + 7x$ **d)** $2x^2 + 3xy - 6y^3$

Connecting Math and Logic p. 192

Activity 2:   **2.** Two sides; not a Möbius strip.
Activity 3:   **3.** One two-sided, one one-sided; only one Möbius strip

Section 5.5 p. 194

Practice   **1.** $(x + 4)(x + 1)$, $x^2 + 5x + 4$ **2.** $(x + 2)(x + 2)$,
$x^2 + 4x + 4$ **3.** $(x + 5)(x + 1)$, $x^2 + 6x + 5$ **4.** $(x + 1)(x + 1)$,
$x^2 + 2x + 1$ **5.** $3x - 15$ **6.** $2x^2 + 3x$ **7.** $-14x + 42$
8. $12x^2 - 4x$ **9.** $15a^3 - 20a^2b$ **10.** $-6x^2 - 10xy$

11. $x^2 + 3x + 2$ **12.** $x^2 + 7x + 12$ **13.** $a^2 + 8a + 16$
14. $y^2 + 11y + 30$ **15.** $x^2 - 7x + 12$ **16.** $a^2 - 6a + 8$
17. $b^2 - 6b + 5$ **18.** $y^2 - 18y + 81$ **19.** $x^2 - 3x - 18$
20. $c^2 - 6c - 16$ **21.** $t^2 - 100$ **22.** $q^2 + 3q - 10$
23. $c^2 - c - 12$ **24.** $x^2 - 3x - 10$ **25.** $y^2 + 4y - 12$
26. $a^2 + 4a - 45$ **27.** $x^2 - 9$ **28.** $b^2 + 3b - 70$
29. $y^2 - 9y - 36$ **30.** $x^2 - 6x - 7$ **31.** $2x^2 + 11x + 5$
32. $3y^2 + 7y + 2$ **33.** $2x^2 - 3x + 1$ **34.** $-2a^2 + a + 15$
35. $5y^2 + 8y - 21$ **36.** $4x^2 - 17x - 15$ **37.** $-4x^2 + 4x + 3$
38. $15y^2 - 26y + 8$ **39.** $12x^2 - 17x - 5$ **40.** $10y^2 - 41y - 18$
41. $14y^2 - 55y + 21$ **42.** $-24x^2 - 31x - 10$ **Problems
and Applications**   **43.** $x^2 + 2.5x + 1$ **44.** $x^2 + 1.8x - 3.6$
45. $x^2 - 12.5x + 25$ **46.** $x^2 - 0.9x - 6.3$ **47.** $2x^2 + 16x + 30$
48. $4x^2 - 16x - 180$ **49.** $-a^2 - a + 6$ **50.** $10x^2 + 20x - 350$
51. $18x^2 - 21x + 6$ **52.** $2x^3 - 6x^2 - 140x$ **53.** $0.5x^2 + x - 1.5$
54. $1.8x^2 + 3.6x + 1.8$ **55. a)** 21 cm²   **b)** 14 cm²   **c)** 7 cm²
56. a) $21 \neq 13$ **b)** $x^2 + 8x + 12$ **57. a)** $(x + 10)(x + 5)$
b) 750 m²   **58.** $1000 + 2000r + 1000r^2$ **b)** \$1166.40

Section 5.6 p. 197

Practice   **3. a)** 3, 4   **b)** 3, 5   **c)** 1, 12   **d)** 7, 11
e) $-3, -5$ **f)** $-5, -5$ **g)** $-3, -4$ **4. a)** $-4, 3$ **b)** $-3, 4$
c) $-8, 5$ **d)** 10, 15   **e)** $-1, 5$ **f)** $-7, 6$ **g)** $-12, 5$
5. $(x + 2)(x + 5)$ **6.** $(y - 3)(y - 5)$ **7.** $(w - 8)(w + 7)$
8. $(z - 5)(z + 8)$ **9.** $(x - 6)(x + 5)$ **10.** $(a - 1)(a - 16)$
11. $(x - 10)(x + 1)$ **12.** $(x + 2)(x + 10)$ **13.** $(x + 5)(x + 5)$
14. $(m - 3)(m - 6)$ **15.** $(a - 3)(a - 3)$ **16.** $(y + 5)(y + 6)$
17. $(x + 1)(x + 9)$ **18.** $(x - 16)(x + 1)$ **19.** $(a - 2)(a + 8)$
20. $(x + 4)(x + 5)$ **21.** $(a - 1)(a - 24)$ **22.** $(y - 2)(y - 7)$
23. $(y - 9)(y + 2)$ **24.** $(x - 9)(x + 8)$ **25.** $(s - 10)(s + 8)$
26. $(a - 9)(a - 9)$ **27.** $3(x - 4)(x - 3)$ **28.** $5(x - 2)(x + 1)$
29. $7(x + 2)(x + 3)$ **30.** not possible   **31.** $b(x - 3)(x - 25)$
32. not possible   **33.** $5j(x - 3)(x - 5)$ **34.** $3t(x + 2)(x + 2)$
35. $t(t - 3)(t + 4)$ **36.** $3k(k - 1)(k + 6)$ **Problems
and Applications**   **37.** not possible   **38.** $(a - 8)(a + 1)$
39. $(b + 6)(b + 8)$ **40.** not possible   **41.** $(z - 10)(z - 10)$
42. not possible   **43.** not possible   **44.** $(y - 2)(y + 10)$
45. a) $(x + 4)(x + 5)$ **b)** $(x + 3)(x + 4)$ **c)** $x^2 + 7x + 12$
46. $x^2 + 12x + 20$, $x^2 + 12x + 36$, $x^2 + 12x + 27$, $x^2 + 12x + 32$

Section 5.7 p. 199

Practice   **1.** $a + 7$ **2.** $x - 2$ **3.** $3m + 7$ **4.** $9x - 8$
5. $x + y$ **6.** $2a - 3b$ **7.** $x^2 - 1$ **8.** $a^2 - 25$ **9.** $p^2 - 36$
10. $x^2 - 81$ **11.** $y^2 - 64$ **12.** $t^2 - 100$ **13.** $4x^2 - 1$
14. $9y^2 - 1$ **15.** $16a^2 - 9$ **16.** $36t^2 - 25$ **17.** $x^2 - y^2$
18. $100t^2 - 9$ **19.** $p^2 - q^2$ **20.** $9a^2 - b^2$ **21.** $x^2 - 36y^2$
22. $j^2 - 100r^2$ **23.** $x^4 - 9$ **24.** $k^4 - 81$ **Problems
and Applications**   **25.** $(20 + 4)(20 - 4)$, 384;
$(50 - 3)(50 + 3)$, 2491; $(60 + 2)(60 - 2)$, 3596   **26.** 96
27. 216   **28.** 396   **29.** $(10 + 4)(10 - 4)$, 84
30. $(20 - 3)(20 + 3)$, 391   **31.** $(30 + 2)(30 - 2)$, 896
32. $x^4 - 1$ **33.** $a^4 - 16$ **34.** $x^4 - 6561$ **35.** $81x^4 - 16$

36. $x^8 - 1$ **37.** the new field has 2500 m^2 less area
38. 1 term, 5 terms

Section 5.8 p. 201

Practice   1. $x + 5$ **2.** $w - 10$ **3.** $k + 9$ **4.** $2a + 11$
5. $3 - 4x$ **6.** $x^2 - 6$ **7.** $(t - 2)(t + 2)$ **8.** $(x - 4)(x + 4)$
9. $(b - 3)(b + 3)$ **10.** $(m - 7)(m + 7)$ **11.** $(p - 5)(p + 5)$
12. $(w - 6)(w + 6)$ **13.** $(a - 9)(a + 9)$ **14.** $(q - 10)(q + 10)$
15. not possible   **16.** $(1 - c)(1 + c)$ **17.** $(8 - x)(8 + x)$
18. not possible   **19.** $(s - t)(s + t)$ **20.** $(z - x)(z + x)$
21. $(h - g)(h + g)$ **22.** $(p - q)(p + q)$ **23.** $(2a - 3b)$
$(2a + 3b)$ **24.** $(4p - 9)(4p + 9)$ **25.** $(5a - 7)(5a + 7)$
26. $(3b - 5)(3b + 5)$ **27.** $(4 - x)(4 + x)$ **28.** $(5 - 6b)$
$(5 + 6b)$ **29.** $(4 - 7x)(4 + 7x)$ **30.** $(9 - 2a)(9 + 2a)$
31. $(4x - 1)(4x + 1)$ **32.** $(12 - 11x)(12 + 11x)$
33. $(13 - 10t)(13 + 10t)$ **34.** $(15 - 7w)(15 + 7w)$
35. not possible   **36.** $(4y - 7)(4y + 7)$ **37.** $(3 - 2z)$
$(3 + 2z)$ **38.** $(5a - 6)(5a + 6)$ **39.** $(xy - 2)(xy + 2)$
40. not possible   **41.** $((a + b) - (a - b))((a + b) + (a - b))$
42. $(5 - 9pq)(5 + 9pq)$ **43.** $2(m - 5)(m + 5)$
44. $9(x - 2)(x + 2)$ **45.** $5(2r - 3)(2r + 3)$
46. $a(2a - 5)(2a + 5)$ **47.** $10(y - 10)(y + 10)$
48. $x(x - 1)(x + 1)$ **49.** $2(5y - 6)(5y + 6)$
50. $x(x - 3)(x + 3)$ **51.** $8(y - 1)(y + 1)$
52. $4(p - 2)(p + 2)$ **53.** $3(3k - 2)(3k + 2)$
54. $16(t - 1)(t + 1)$ **55.** $(8 - x)(8 + x)$
56. $2(5 - 3x)(5 + 3x)$ **57.** $3(2x - 5y)(2x + 5y)$
58. $2(5x - 7y)(5x + 7y)$ **Problems and Applications**
59. a) 91   **b)** 13 by 7   **c)** equal   **d)** 32, 8 by 4
e) $x^2 - y^2$, $x + y$ by $x - y$ **60. a)** $(x - 1)(x + 1)(x^2 + 1)$
b) $(x - 1)(x + 1)(x^2 + 1)(x^4 + 1)$ **c)** $(x - 5)(x + 5)(x^2 + 25)$

Section 5.9 p. 203

Practice   1. 49   **2.** 81   **3.** 36   **4.** 144   **5.** $4x^2$
6. $9a^2$ **7.** $121y^2$ **8.** x^2 **9.** $16y^2$ **10.** x^2 **11.** a^2
12. $4x^2$ **13.** $81t^2$ **14.** $100b^2$ **15.** $9y^2$ **16.** $49p^2$
17. $16j^2$ **18.** $36q^2$ **19.** $-6x$ **20.** $+16y$ **21.** $+2xy$
22. $-2ab$ **23.** $+12x$ **24.** $-40a$ **25.** $+12xy$ **26.** $-84p$
27. $y^2 - 20y + 100$ **28.** $9a^2 - 6a + 1$ **29.** $25x^2 + 20x + 4$
30. $9 - 6x + x^2$ **31.** $25 - 10y + y^2$ **32.** $25a^2 + 10ab + b^2$
33. $9x^2 + 6xy + y^2$ **34.** $16x^2 - 24xy + 9y^2$
35. $49a^2 - 28ab + 4b^2$ **36.** $16m^2 + 40mn + 25n^2$
Problems and Applications   37. $(x + 7)^2$
38. $(x - 8)^2$ **39.** $(2a + 3)^2$ **40.** $(3b - 4)^2$ **41.** $(8m - 2)^2$
42. $(9n + 5)^2$ **43.** $x^2 + 12x + 36$ **44.** $a^2 + 8a + 16$
45. $y^2 - 6y + 9$ **46.** $m^2 - 8m + 16$ or $m^2 - 4m + 4$
47. $2x^2 - 4x + 2$ or $4x^2 - 4x + 1$ **48.** $9y^2 + 12y + 4$
49. $16 \neq 10$ **50.** $a^2 + b^2 + c^2 + 2ab + 2ac + 2bc$

Section 5.10 p. 205

Practice   1. $3x^2 + 9x - 15$ **2.** $6a^2 - 10a + 14$

3. $2x^2 + 14x + 24$ **4.** $3a^2 + 21a + 30$ **5.** $5y^2 + 20y + 50$
6. $x^3 - 10x^2 + 25x$ **7.** $x^3 + 11x^2 + 28x$ **8.** $2a^3 + 8a^2 + 15a$
9. $4x^3 - 3x^2 - 4x$ **10.** $6x^3 - 23x^2 + 20x$ **11.** $x^3 + 3x^2 +$
$5x + 3$ **12.** $x^3 - x^2 - 5x - 2$ **13.** $x^3 + 5x^2 + 3x - 9$
14. $x^3 + 3x^2 - 13x - 15$ **15.** $x^3 - 12x^2 + 25x + 28$
16. $x^3 - 7x^2 + 16x - 12$ **17.** $x^3 + 5x^2 - 61x + 55$ **18.** $3a^3$
$-2a^2 + 4a - 5$ **19.** $5b^3 - 36b^2 + 5b + 14$ **20.** $2x^3 - 19x^2$
$+27x - 24$ **21.** $4x^3 - 23x^2 + 8x + 35$ **22.** $3x^3 - 11x^2 + 6x + 8$
23. $7a^3 - 8a^2 + 2a - 1$ **24.** $2y^3 - 5y^2 - 23y - 10$
25. $2x^3 + 13x^2 + 13x - 10$ **26.** $3a^3 + 4a^2 - 21a - 18$
27. $5b^3 - 2b^2 + 3b + 10$ **28.** $7w^3 - 8w^2 + 1$ **29.** $2y^3$
$- y^2 - 4y - 4$ **30.** $4t^3 - 22t^2 + 9t + 5$ **31.** $x^3 + 2x^2y + x^2$
$+2xy + xy^2 + y^2$ **32.** $x^3 - 3x^2y - 2x^2 + 6xy + xy^2 - 2y^2$
33. $xb^2 + 3b^2 - 3bxy - 9by - xy^2 - 3y^2$ **Problems and**
Applications   34. $15x^3 - 6x^2y + 10x^2 - 4xy + 3xy^2 + 2y^2$
35. $4y^4 - 16y^3 + 15y^2 + 14y - 35$ **36.** $28x^3 + 67x^2 - 3x$
$- 27$ **37.** $6a^3 - 23a^2 + 36a - 35$ **38.** $6y^3 + 11y^2 + 8y + 2$
39. $9a^3 - 33a^2 + 9a + 35$ **40. a)** $6a^2 - a - 2$
b) $2x^3 + x^2 - 4x + 1$ **c)** $7a^2 + ab - 2b^2$
41. a) $x^3 + 3x^2$ **b)** $24x^2 - 12x$ **c)** $6x^2 + 30x + 36$

Section 5.11 p. 208

Practice   1. 8   **2.** 24   **3.** 6   **4.** $21x$ **5.** $15a$
6. $24x$ **7.** $\frac{3}{y}, x \neq 0, y \neq 0$ **8.** $\frac{2}{y}, y \neq 0$ **9.** $3x, x \neq 0$
10. $2c, a \neq 0, b \neq 0$ **11.** $-2xy^2, x \neq 0, y \neq 0$
12. $-4ab, a \neq 0, b \neq 0$ **13.** $\frac{3}{2}$ **14.** $\frac{1}{2}$ **15.** 1   **16.** $\frac{4}{3}$
17. $\frac{1}{2}$ **18.** 1   **19.** x^2y **20.** $\frac{5xy^3}{3}$ **21.** $\frac{2pq^2}{r}$ **22.** $\frac{7a^2b^2}{2}$
23. xy^2 **24.** x **25.** $\frac{x^3}{4}$ **26.** $\frac{x^2y}{2}$ **27.** $\frac{19}{y}$ **28.** $\frac{x - 11}{a}$
29. $\frac{1}{4x}$ **30.** $\frac{9xy}{z}$ **31.** $\frac{5 - x}{x}$ **32.** $\frac{7}{3x^2}$ **33.** $\frac{x - 4}{x^2}$
34. $\frac{1 - x}{5x^2}$ **35.** $\frac{3x + 1}{4}$ **36.** $\frac{x + 10}{12}$ **37.** $\frac{5x - 2}{6}$
38. $\frac{2x - 9}{15}$ **39.** $\frac{9 - x}{12}$ **40.** $\frac{9x - 3}{10}$ **Problems and**
Applications   41. a) $4x(x + 1)$ **b)** $x(x + 1)$ **c)** $\frac{1}{4}$
42. a) $6(x + 1)(x + 2)$ **b)** $(x + 1)(x + 2)$ **c)** $\frac{1}{6}$

Connecting Math and Design pp. 210–211

Activity 2:   1. 314 m, 320.28 m, 326.56 m,
332.84 m, 339.12 m   **Activity 3:   1.** The sides
of the track must be 43 m.   **2.** 400 m, 406.28 m,
412.56 m, 418.84 m, 425.12 m

Review p. 212–213

1. a) 5   **b)** 7   **c)** 17   **d)** 24   **e)** $5a$ **f)** $4x$ **g)** $2ab$ **h)** $5xy$
2. a) $3xy$ **b)** 8   **c)** $9xy$ **3.** $5(x - 3)$ **4.** $6x(x - 3)$
5. $5a(b + 2c)$ **6.** $7a^2(1 + 5a)$ **7.** $4bc(2a - 3)$
8. $3(x^2 + 3y^2)$ **9.** $a(3a - 6b + 1)$ **10.** $2(x + 3y - 5z)$

11. $9x + 14$ **12.** $7a + 14$ **13.** $6y^2 - 19y - 10$
14. $-m^2 + m + 2$ **15.** $-2z^2 - 4z + 5$ **16.** $x^2 - 20x$
17. $-2y^3 + 6y^2 - 14y$ **18.** $-3t + 6t^2 + 3t^3$
19. $4m^3 + 8m^2 - 12m$ **20.** $-6x^3 + 12x^2 - 6x$
21. $2b^2 - 4ab + a^2$ **22.** $-2abz^3 + 4abz^2$ **23.** $x^2 - x - 6$
24. $x^2 + 3x - 28$ **25.** $x^2 + 7x + 10$ **26.** $x^2 - 5x + 6$
27. $x^2 + 8x - 20$ **28.** $6x^2 - 19x + 10$
29. $10a^2 - 11a - 6$ **30.** $12x^2 - 13x - 14$
31. $-21x^2 + 53x - 30$ **32.** $10a^2 + 13ab - 3b^2$
33. $(x + 1)(x + 7)$ **34.** $(x - 1)(x - 5)$ **35.** $(y + 3)(y + 5)$
36. $(a + 2)(a + 6)$ **37.** $(b + 4)(b + 6)$ **38.** $(x - 1)(x - 6)$
39. $(x - 4)(x - 7)$ **40.** $(a - 3)(a - 4)$ **41.** $(a - 5)(a + 4)$
42. $(x - 6)(x + 5)$ **43.** $(x - 7)(x + 2)$
44. $(m - 10)(m + 4)$ **45.** $(x - 3)(x + 7)$
46. $(x - 2)(x + 12)$ **47.** $(x - 5)(x + 7)$
48. $(x - 5)(x + 3)$ **49.** $2(x + 2)(x + 10)$
50. $5(a - 4)(a - 4)$ **51.** $4(w - 6)(w + 5)$
52. $3(r - 2)(r - 5)$ **53.** $2(j^2 - 3j + 4)$
54. $3(t - 1)(t + 7)$ **55.** $7(y - 4)(y + 5)$
56. $3(z - 6)(z - 7)$ **57.** $(x - 1)(x + 1)$
58. $(y - 2)(y + 2)$ **59.** $(2a - 3)(2a + 3)$
60. $(a - 2b)(a + 2b)$ **61.** $(2x - y)(2x + y)$
62. $(2a - 3b)(2a + 3b)$ **63.** $(3 - x)(3 + x)$
64. $(5 - 7x)(5 + 7x)$ **65.** $2(a - 5)(a + 5)$
66. $5(x - 2)(x + 2)$ **67.** $4(x - 3)(x + 3)$
68. $4(2a - 3)(2a + 3)$ **69.** yes   **70.** no   **71.** no
72. yes   **73.** $x^2 + 4x + 4$ **74.** $x^2 - 6x + 9$
75. $x^2 - 6x + 9$ **76.** $y^2 + 12y + 36$
77. $x^3 - 5x^2 + 8x - 4$ **78.** $x^3 - 8x^2 + 12x + 9$
79. $2x^3 - x + 1$ **80.** $3x^3 + 14x^2 - 6x - 5$
81. $x^3 + 1$ **82.** $x^3 + x^2 + x - 3$
83. $5x^3 - 25x^2 + 17x + 12$ **84.** $4x^3 + 5x^2 - 13x - 14$
85. $\frac{5x - 11}{6}$ **86.** $\frac{2x - 7}{15}$ **87.** $\frac{x}{6}$ **88.** $\frac{19x + 1}{42}$ **89.** $\frac{2 - x}{x^2}$
90. $\frac{2x + 3}{7x^2}$ **91.** $\frac{x - 17}{6}$ **92.** $\frac{x + 17}{12}$ **93.** $\frac{6x + 22}{7}$
94. $\frac{13x - 19}{42}$ **95.** $\frac{2x - 9}{35}$ **96.** $\frac{3x - 2}{28}$ **97.** $\frac{2 + x}{2x}$ **98.** $\frac{5}{x^2}$
99. a) $(x + 2)(x + 8)$ **b)** $(x + 4)(x + 10)$ **c)** $x^2 + 14x + 40$

Chapter Check p. 214

1. $3xy(y - 2a)$ **2.** $12xy(2y + x)$ **3.** $2x^2 - x + 9$
4. $-x^2 + 9x$ **5.** $-3x^3 + 6x^2 - 3x$ **6.** $4m^3 - 12m^2 - 20m$
7. $1 - 2y + 3y^2$ **8.** $3a^2 - 2a + 1$ **9.** $x^2 + 2x - 8$
10. $2x^2 + x - 21$ **11.** $8a^2 - 18ab + 9b^2$ **12.** $-2y^2 - 5y + 3$
13. $(x + 2)(x + 5)$ **14.** $(x - 3)(x - 6)$ **15.** $(x - 5)(x + 2)$
16. $(x - 5)(x + 7)$ **17.** $(x + 4)^2$ **18.** $(x - 17)(x - 1)$
19. $2(x - 2)^2$ **20.** $5(x - 5)(x + 4)$ **21.** $x^2 - 4x + 4$
22. $w^2 + 14w + 49$ **23.** $(a - 2)(a + 2)$ **24.** $(2x - 5)$
$(2x + 5)$ **25.** $(9 - x)(9 + x)$ **26.** $(1 - 2b)(1 + 2b)$
27. $2(t - 10)(t + 10)$ **28.** $3(x - 2)(x + 2)$
29. $4(5 - 2t)(5 + 2t)$ **30.** $2(1 - 3y)(1 + 3y)$
31. yes   **32.** no   **33.** yes   **34.** no   **35.** $5x^3y^2$

36. $5a^2$ **37.** $\frac{5x + 19}{6}$ **38.** $\frac{9x - 37}{35}$
39. a) $(x + 3)(x + 10)$ **b)** $(x + 2)(x + 12)$ **c)** $x^2 + 14x + 24$

Using the Strategies p. 215

1. Top Row: $\frac{8}{10}$, $\frac{1}{10}$, $\frac{6}{10}$, Middle Row: $\frac{3}{10}$, $\frac{5}{10}$, $\frac{7}{10}$,
Bottom Row: $\frac{4}{10}$, $\frac{9}{10}$, $\frac{2}{10}$ **3.** $a = 3$, $b = 4$
4. 14, 42, 126   **5.** Saturday   **6. a)** 14   **b)** $2(n + 1)$
Data Bank   **1.** 43%

Chapter 6

Getting Started pp. 218–219

Warm Up   **1.** 180°   **2.** 50°   **3.** 36°   **4.** 120°   **5.** 21°
6. 60°   **7.** 75°   **8.** 45°   **9.** 25°   **14.** 2   **15.** 0.5   **Mental
Math**   **1.** 40 m   **2.** 24 m   **3.** 44 m   **4.** 38 m
5. 150 m²   **6.** 100 m²   **7.** 96 m²   **8.** 150 m²   **9.** 90
10. 50   **11.** 80   **12.** 70   **13.** 30   **14.** 40   **15.** 40

Learning Together pp. 220–221

Activity 1:   **2.** No   **Activity 2:**   **2.** Yes, $\angle G$
and $\angle J$ could differ.   **Activity 3:**   **2.** Yes, the
side lengths could differ.   **Activity 4:**   **2.** No
Activity 5:   **2.** No   **Activity 6:**   **2.** Yes, the other
side lengths could differ.

Section 6.1 pp. 224–225

Practice   **1.** BI = CA, BG = CT, IG = AT, $\angle B$ =
$\angle C$, $\angle I = \angle A$, $\angle G = \angle T$ **2.** HO = CA, HT = CR,
OT = AR, $\angle H = \angle C$, $\angle O = \angle A$, $\angle T = \angle R$
3. No   **4.** ASA   **5.** No   **6.** SSS   **7.** No   **8.** No
9. SAS   **10.** JC = EK OR $\angle A = \angle I$ **11.** RK = PC
12. ASA; $\angle Q = \angle Y$, $\angle P = \angle X$, $\angle R = \angle Z$,
XY = PQ, XZ = PR, RQ = ZY   **13.** No   **14.** SSS;
$\angle A = \angle F$, $\angle B = \angle E$, $\angle C = \angle D$, AB = FE, AC = FD,
BC = ED   **15.** No   **16.** SAS; LU = LY, LJ = LJ,
JU = JY, $\angle U = \angle Y$, $\angle UJL = \angle YJL$, $\angle ULJ = \angle YLJ$
17. ASA; $\angle S = \angle Q$, $\angle SPR = \angle QRP$, $\angle SRP = \angle QPR$,
PS = RQ, PR = RP, SR = QP   **18.** No   **19.** No
20. SAS; $\angle P = \angle B$, $\angle PAT = \angle BTA$, $\angle PTA = \angle BAT$,
PT = BA, PA = BT, AT = TA   **Problems and
Applications**   **23.** No   **24. a)** otherwise SSS
guarantees congruence   **b)** may change just the
angles   **25. a)** sometimes congruent   **b)** sometimes
congruent   **c)** always congruent   **d)** sometimes
congruent

Learning Together p. 227

Activity 2:   **1.** The length of the hypotenuse

squared is equal to the sum of the squares of the other two sides. **2.** $c^2 = a^2 + b^2$ **3. a)** 13 **b)** 5 **c)** 24 **d)** 6 **4. a)** 5.8 **b)** 13.6 **c)** 9.6 **d)** 8.3

Section 6.2 pp. 230–231

Practice **5.** $f = 8$ cm, $d = 14$ cm **6.** $r = 30$ cm, $s = 6$ cm **7.** $w = 6$ cm, $b = 7.5$ cm **8.** $p = 6.75$ cm, $r = 7.5$ cm **9.** $d = 12.5$ cm, $e = 15$ cm **10.** 8 cm **11.** 9 cm **Problems and Applications** **12.** 37.5 m **13.** 260 m **14.** 233 m **16.** 19 m **17. a)** false **b)** true

Connecting Math and Design pp. 234–235

Activity 1: **1. a)** complementary angles **2.** △FBD is isosceles. **Activity 2:** Maple Leaf Gardens: 39°, 42°, 45°; B.C. Place: 40°, 45°, 55°; O'Keefe Centre: 27°, 33°, 37°; Lansdowne Park: 44°, 50°, 58°

Section 6.3 p. 238

Practice **1.** 0.268 **2.** 1.881 **3.** 0.087 **4.** 0.577 **5.** 7.115 **6.** 1.000 **7.** 31° **8.** 40° **9.** 72° **10.** 79° **11.** 39° **12.** 41° **13.** 60° **14.** 59° **15.** 0.4 **16.** 1.0 **17.** 1.333, 53°, 0.75, 37° **18.** 1.875, 62°, 0.533, 28° **19.** 11.0 cm **20.** 6.0 cm **21.** 11.2 m **22.** 11.3 m **23.** 5.1 cm **24.** 13.1 cm **Problems and Applications** **25.** 5.1 cm **26.** 3.0 cm **27.** 2.1 m **28.** 93 m **29.** 12 m **30.** 35° **31.** 27°

Section 6.4 p. 241

Practice **1.** 0.707 **2.** 0.866 **3.** 0.602 **4.** 0.423 **5.** 0.000 **6.** 1.000 **7.** 30° **8.** 72° **9.** 45° **10.** 18° **11.** 86° **12.** 6° **13.** 42° **14.** 49° **15.** 30° **16.** 24° **17.** 7° **18.** 51° **19.** 0.455, 27° **20.** 0.2, 12° **21.** 13.1 cm **22.** 29.0 cm **23.** 48.1 cm **24.** 15.7 cm **25.** 18.3 cm **26.** 27.4 cm **27.** 13.1 cm **28.** 56° **29.** 16.2 cm **30.** 1.4 m **31.** 3.6 cm **32.** 4.1 m **33. a)** 0.629 **b)** $0.629 = \frac{a}{c}$ **c)** $a = 0.629 \times c$ **d)** $c = \frac{a}{0.629}$

Section 6.5 p. 244

Practice **1.** 0.866 **2.** 0.707 **3.** 0.5 **4.** 0.017 **5.** 1.000 **6.** 0.996 **7.** 0.946 **8.** 0.122 **9.** 70° **10.** 28° **11.** 52° **12.** 89° **13.** 43° **14.** 58° **15.** 80° **16.** 63° **17.** 56° **18.** 29° **19.** 20° **20.** 78° **21.** 0.5, 60° **22.** 0.3, 73° **23.** 7.6 cm **24.** 13.1 cm **25.** 8.2 cm **26.** 11.7 cm **27.** 12.2 cm **28.** 19.8 cm **29.** 10.4 cm **30.** 6.3 cm **Problems and Applications** **31.** 21.8 cm **32.** 9.3 cm **33.** 225.0 m **34.** 17.1 m **35.** ∠X = 37°= ∠Y, ∠W = 106°

Section 6.6 p. 247

Practice **1.** ∠A = 30°, ∠C = 60°, 7.5 cm **2.** ∠H = 52°, ∠I = 38°, 11.4 cm **3.** ∠J = 56°, ∠L = 34°, 3.3 cm **4.** ∠R = 42°, ∠P = 48°, 14.9 cm **5.** ∠T = 42°, ∠R = 48°, 24.1 m **6.** ∠W = 28°, ∠Y = 62°, 47.9 cm **7.** 57°, CD = 12.0 m, ED = 18.5 m **8.** 25°, BG = 32 cm, FG = 13.5 cm **9.** 29°, RP = 58.3 m, PM = 28.2 m **10.** 60°, XZ = 12 cm, YZ = 10.4 cm **11.** 36°, OS = 13.8 km, NO = 10.0 km **12.** 77°, XY = 2.9 m, MX = 12.7 m **13.** 51 m **14.** 23 m **15.** 76° **17. a)** 0.577, 0.5, 0.866, 0.577; 0.810, 0.629, 0.777, 0.810; 1.000, 0.707, 0.707, 1.000; 1.327, 0.799, 0.602, 1.327; 1.732, 0.866, 0.500, 1.732; 2.246, 0.914, 0.407, 2.246 **b)** the same

Review pp. 252–253

1. SAS; ∠N = ∠S, NP = RS, NM = QS, △NPM ≅ △RSQ **2.** SSS **3.** SAS **4.** SAS **5.** ASA **6.** $e = 10$ cm, $f = 6$ cm **7.** $q = 4$ cm, $w = 18$ cm **8.** $q = 6$ cm, $y = 10$ cm **9.** 44 m **10.** 10.5 cm **11.** 50.8 cm **12.** 14.8 m **13.** 53.9 m **14.** 18 mm **15.** 11 km **16.** ∠A = 31°, ∠C = 59°, 5.8 m **17.** ∠E = 67°, ∠D = 23°, 12 cm **18.** 40°, JH = 3.1 m, GJ = 2.5 m **19.** ∠K = 58°, ∠M = 32°, 39 mm **20.** ∠Q = 58°, NQ = 30 cm, PQ = 56.6 cm **21.** 35°, RT = 24.2 km, ST = 29.6 km **22.** 6° **23.** 47.3 m **24.** 58°

Chapter Check p. 254

1. SAS **2.** ASA **3.** SSS **4.** SSS **5.** $a = 10$ cm, $b = 8$ cm **6.** $r = 10$ cm, $w = 10.5$ cm **7.** congruent, ASA **8.** similar **9.** 14.5 cm **10.** 45.7 cm **11.** 19 km **12.** 58.7 m **13.** 16.0 cm **14.** 11.2 m **15.** ST = 24.2 m, PT = 7.5 m, ∠S = 18° **16.** RX = 9.8 cm, WR = 13.9 cm, ∠W = 35°

Using the Strategies p. 255

1. 6 **2.** 35, 12, 23 **3.** 15:00 **4.** $2 × \$5$, $1 × \$2$, $1 × \$0.25$, $1 × \$0.10$, $1 × \$0.05$, $3 × \$0.01$ **6.** 78 **7.** The 35 cm pizza costs less per square centimetre. **8.** Take the middle full glass and empty it into the middle empty glass. **9.** 4 **Data Bank** **1.** Approximately 19 000 000 000 000 **2.** Manitoba and Saskatchewan; Saskatchewan is larger by 2380 km².

Chapter 7

Getting Started pp. 258–259

Activity 4: Small triangle, 1; square, parallelogram, medium triangle, 2; large triangle, 4 **Mental Math**
1. 31.4 **2.** 314 **3.** 3140 **4.** 31 400 **5.** 0.314
6. 0.0314 **7.** 0.003 14 **8.** 0.000 314 **9.** 0.125
10. 96 **11.** 98 **12.** 15 **13.** 120 **14.** 630 **15.** 52
16. 3.1 **17.** 3 **18.** 6 **19.** 18 **20.** 3 **21.** 5.5, 5.5
22. 4, 4 **23.** 6, 6 **24.** 10, 10 **25.** 12 **26.** 27
27. 75 **28.** 75 **29.** 18 **30.** 30 **31.** 90 **32.** 210
33. 24 **34.** 192 **35.** 3000 **36.** 375

Section 7.1 p. 261

1. 39.69 m^2 **2.** 36.12 cm^2 **3.** 113 cm^2 **4.** 88 cm^2
Problems and Applications 5. 44 m^2 **6.** 22.94 m^2
7. a) 32 cm^2 **b)** 6 m^2 **8. a)** 1.5 m^2 **b)** $29.99
9. 708 m^2 **10.** square **11.** 25 m^2

Section 7.2 p. 264

Practice 1. 54 cm^2 **2.** 64 cm^2 **3.** 42 cm^2
4. 137.5 m^2 **5.** 93 m^2 **6.** 192 cm^2 **7.** 39 cm^2
8. 3 cm^2 **Problems and Applications**
9. a) 60 cm^2 **b)** 40 cm^2 **10.** 140 cm **11.** Front or Back: 1120 cm^2, Side: 1504 cm^2 **12.** 4.5 cm
13. Area of each triangle is half the area of parallelogram or trapezoid. **14.** 5 cm

Section 7.3 pp. 270–271

Practice 1. rectangular prism **2.** triangular prism
3. square prism **4.** triangular prism **5.** square
prism **6.** triangular prism **7.** 346 m^2 **8.** 43.6 cm^2
9. 150 cm^2 **10.** 958 m^2 **11.** 24 m^3 **12.** 180 cm^3
13. 1716 cm^3 **14.** 108 m^3 **15.** 278 m^2, 198 m^3
16. 685 m^2, 850 m^3 **17.** 12 000 cm^2, 60 000 cm^3
18. 150 cm^2, 112 cm^3 **19.** 132 200 m^2, 3 036 000 m^3
20. 1637 m^2, 3300 m^3 **Problems and Applications**
21. a) 9 m^2 **b)** 1.8 m^3 **22. a)** 94 m^2 **b)** 5
23. a) 4.6 m^2 **b)** $45.91 **c)** 27 227 **24.** 6 cm by 6 cm by 6 cm **25. a)** 232 cm^2 **c)** rectangular prism
26. 5.44 m^3 **27.** 662 m^2, 841 m^3 **28. a)** 115 m^3
b) approximately 6 h 23 min

Section 7.4 p. 274

Practice 1. 161 cm^2 **2.** 72 m^2 **3.** 64 cm^2
4. 175 m^2 **5.** 50 cm^3 **6.** 15 m^3 **7.** 240 m^3
8. 900 cm^3 **Problems and Applications**
9. 360 cm^3 **10.** 2 574 467 m^3 **11. a)** doubles
b) triples **c)** doubles **12.** 76 000 m^2 including the base

Section 7.5 p. 278

Practice 1. 641 cm^2 **2.** 144 cm^2 **3.** 283 cm^2
4. 703 cm^2 **5.** 157 m^3 **6.** 7598.8 cm^3 **7.** 1570 cm^3
8. 37.68 m^3 **9.** 100.48 m^2, 75.36 m^3 **10.** 75.36 cm^2,
37.68 cm^3 **Problems and Applications**
11. a) 6.7 cm **b)** 91 cm^2 **12.** 16.4 m^2 **13.** 2 L
14. 8 m^3

Learning Together pp. 288–289

Activity 3: 5. 78.5 m^2 **6. b)** 743 m^2

Review pp. 292–293

1–11. Estimates may vary. **1.** 39.69 cm^2
2. 30.66 m^2 **3.** 26.32 cm^2 **4.** 66.03 m^2 **5.** 1385 m^2
6. 77 cm^2 **7.** 4.8 m^3 **8.** 3.52 cm^2 **9.** 125.12 m^2
10. 78 m^2 **11. a)** 76 m^2 **b)** $54.45 **12.** 288 cm^2
13. 21.4 m^2 **14.** 1734 m^2 **15.** 95.5 cm^2
16. 648 cm^3 **17.** 29 335.5 cm^3 **18.** 24.87 cm^2
19. 3014.4 m^2 **20.** 99 m^2 **21.** 1055.04 cm^2
22. 864 cm^3 **23.** 192 m^3 **24.** 707 m^3 **25.** 270 cm^3
26. 390 cm^3 **27. a)** 900 cm^2 **b)** 1220 cm^2
c) 1056 cm^3 **28.** 434 m^2 **29.** 334 cm^2 **30.** 62 m^2

Chapter Check p. 294

1. 900 cm^2 **2.** 100 cm^2 **3.** 27 cm^2 **4.** 314.16 m^2
5. 220 cm^2 **6.** 2512 cm^2 **7.** 3.84 m^2
8. 628 cm^2 **9.** 117 m^3 **10.** 1099 m^3 **11.** 22 m^3
12. 6 510 000 cm^3 **13.** 23 m^2 **14.** 88 m^2 **15. a)** 16
b) 1.78 m^2 **16. a)** 216 cm^2 **b)** 180 cm^3 **17.** 3 cm
18. 266.25 cm^3

Using the Strategies p. 493

1. a) 9 **b)** 16 **c)** 25 **d)** 36 **e)** 625 **f)** 11 025
2. February, March **3.** 1 cm^2 **4.** 47 **5.** 4624
6. 27 **7. a)** 6 **b)** 4 **c)** 2 **8.** 4 quarters; 3 quarters, 5 nickels; 2 quarters, 10 nickels; 1 quarter, 15 nickels; 20 nickels **9.** 6 **10.** 32 cm **11.** 05:55 **Data Bank 1.** approximately 50 times

Chapter 8

Getting Started pp. 298–299

Activity 2: 1. a) flip **b)** turn **c)** slide **Activity 3:**
1. $\frac{1}{4}$ turn clockwise **2.** vertical flip **3.** horizontal
flip **4.** $\frac{1}{4}$ turn clockwise, horizontal flip **5.** $\frac{1}{2}$ turn
6. slide **7.** $\frac{1}{4}$ turn clockwise, vertical flip **8.** $\frac{1}{4}$
turn counterclockwise **Activity 4: 1. a)** flip

b) turn **c)** slide **d)** turn **2. a)** turn **b)** turn
c) flip **d)** slide **3. a)** slide **b)** turn **c)** turn **d)** flip
4. a) flip **b)** slide **c)** turn **d)** turn **5. a)** turn **b)** flip
c) turn **d)** slide **Mental Math 1.** 22 **2.** 20 **3.** 3
4. 4.5 **5.** 0.02 **6.** 60 000 **7.** 3 **8.** 1 **9.** $8.98
10. $7.75 **11.** $8.96 **12.** $10.94 **13.** $8.85
14. $3.44 **15.** $4.90 **16.** $8.20 **17.** −4 **18.** 2
19. 20 **20.** −12 **21.** −11 **22.** −4 **23.** −6 **24.** 10
25. $5.98 **26.** $11.92 **27.** $4.95 **28.** $59.94
29. $15.80 **30.** $29.88 **31.** $8.85 **32.** $9.90
33. $\frac{1}{6}$ **34.** $\frac{7}{8}$ **35.** $\frac{3}{5}$ **36.** $\frac{3}{10}$ **37.** 24 **38.** 21
39. 15 **40.** 0 **41.** 97 **42.** 56 **43.** 77 **44.** 29
45. 222 **46.** 69 **47.** 947 **48.** 87 **49.** 53 **50.** 145

Section 8.1 pp. 301−302

Practice 1. A, B, D, F **3. a)** [2, 0] **b)** [4, 4]
c) [1, −3] **4.** 3 units to the right and 2 units up
5. 1 unit to the left and 4 units up **6.** 2 units to the
left and 3 units down **7.** 5 units to the right and
1 unit down **8.** 6 units up **9.** 3 units to the left
10. 2 units to the right and 3 units down
11. 3 units to the left and 5 units up **12.** 4 units to
the left and 2 units up **13.** 1 unit to the right and
6 units down **22.** [4, −5] **23.** [−4, −3] **24.** (5, 7)
25. (−1, −3) **26.** (4, 3) **27.** (−7, 1) **28.** [4, 4]
29. [1, −1] **30.** [−1, −1] **31.** [4, −5] **32.** [−5, 8]
33. [−1, −6] **Problems and Applications**
37. A(1, 1), B(−2, 4), C(−4, −4) **38. b)** R′(7, 2),
S′(3, 7), T′(1, 3) **c)** R″(8, −3), S″(4, 2), T″(2, −2)
d) [5, −3] **40.** [0, −1], [−3, 0], [0, −4], [5, 0], [0, −3]

Section 8.2 pp. 304−305

Practice 1. A, B **16. a)** (1, −4), (−1, 4) **b)** (2, −3),
(−2, 3) **c)** (−1, 2), (1, −2) **d)** (−3, 2), (3, 2)
e) (−3, −2), (3, 2) **f)** (4, 0), (−4, 0) **17.** A′(−1, 1),
B′(−5, 2), C′(−3, 6) **18.** R′(2, −5), S′(−2, −4), T′(−1, 2)
Problems and Applications 19. a) A, H, I, O, T,
V, W, X, Y **b)** B, C, D, E, H, I, O, X **c)** H, I, O, X
d) 0, 3, 8 **26. a)** x-coordinate **b)** y-coordinate

Section 8.3 pp. 307−308

Practice 1. 90° ccw **2.** 180° cw **3.** 270° ccw
4. 90° cw, 270° ccw **5.** 180° cw, 180° ccw **6.** 90°
cw, 270° ccw **24.** (−6, 0), (0, −6), (6, 0) **25.** (0, −4),
(4, 0), (0, 4) **26.** (3, 0), (0, 3), (−3, 0) **27.** (−4, 3),
(−3, −4), (4, −3) **28.** (−3, −4), (4, −3), (3, 4)
Problems and Applications 32. parallelogram
33. a, b, and d **34. a)** T **b)** S, P, Q, R, T **35.** 90°
36. a) parallel **b)** equal **c)** The line $y = x$ passes
through the turn centre. **37. a)** 450° cw **b)** 270° ccw
38. the North Star

Section 8.4 pp. 310−311

Practice 1. 2 **2.** $\frac{1}{3}$ **9.** R′(6, 9), S′(−3, 12),
T′(−9, −6) **10.** D′(3, 2), E′(−1, 3), F′(−2, −2),
G′(2, −3) **Problems and Applications 13. b)** 8
c) P′(−6, 6), Q′(−6, −6), R′(6, −6) **d)** 72 **e)** P″(−1, 1),
Q″(−1, −1), R″(1, −1) **f)** 2 **g)** 72:8 or 9:1; 2:8 or 1:4
h) the square of the scale factor **15.** $\frac{1}{2}$ **16.** 2 **17.** 3
18. identical **19. b)** A′(4, 6), B′(−5, −6), C′(16, −9)

Section 8.5 p. 315

Practice 1. 2 **2.** 1 **3.** 4 **4.** 5 **5.** 3 **6.** 4 **7.** 2
8. 5 **Problems and Applications 9. a)** A, H, I,
M, O, T, U, V, W, X, Y **b)** B, C, D, E, H, I, K, O,
X **c)** H, I, O, X **d)** H, I, X, N, S, Z **10.** BOOK
11. CHEEK **14. a)** 2 **b)** 0 **c)** 5 **d)** 7

Learning Together pp. 316−317

Activity 1: 1. a) horizontal stretch **b)** vertical
stretch **2.** always a kite **3.** no; may be rectangular
Activity 2: a) vertical stretch and a reflection in
the y-axis **b)** horizontal stretch and a reflection in
the x-axis **Activity 3: a)** horizontal contraction
and vertical stretch **b)** horizontal stretch and vertical
contraction

Review pp. 320−321

1. [4, 2] **2.** [−4, 1] **3.** [−4, −2] **4.** [2, −4] **5.** 2
units to the right and 3 units up **6.** 3 units to the
left and 1 unit down **7.** 4 units to the left and 5
units up **8.** 6 units up **9.** [1, −2] **10.** [−4, 6]
11. [2, −3] **12.** A′(7, 5), B′(8, 2), C′(2, 4) **13.** R′(−5, 1),
I′(0, −2), K′(−1, −5) **14.** (4, 5), (−4, 5) **15.** (5, 2),
(−5, −2) **16.** (−3, −6), (3, 6) **17.** (−3, 2), (3, −2)
22. D′(2, −3), E′(5, −1), F′(4, −6) **23.** R′(−3, −1), S′(3, 2),
T′(4, −3) **30. a)** P″(0, 4), Q″(0, 2), R″(−3, 2) **b)** [−2, 3]
31. a) X″(2, −2), Y″(−1, −4), Z″(−2, −1) **32.** A′(4, 6),
B′(10, 0) **33.** C′(−3, 6), D′(9, −9) **34.** E′(2, 3),
F′(−3, −1) **35.** G′(−2, 0), H′(0, 2) **36.** P′(6, 4),
Q′(6, −2), R′(4, −4) **37.** A′(−3, 1), B′(−2, −3), C′(1, −4),
D′(3, 5) **38.** 4 **39.** 3 **40.** 2 **41.** 3 **42.** 2 **43.** 5

Chapter Check p. 322

1. A′(3, 4), B′(5, 1), C′(8, 2) **2.** P′(−2, 2), Q′(−4, 5),
R′(−7, 1) **3.** R′(−1, −1), S′(−3, −4), T′(−6, −3)
4. D′(−2, 4), E′(4, 1), F′(1, −3) **5.** J′(4, 0), K′(3, −5),
L′(0, 3) **6.** G′(0, 4), H′(3, 4), I′(2, 0) **7.** S′(0, 2),
T′(−6, 6), U′(8, −6) **8. b)** P′(6, 6), Q′(6, 12), R′(9, 3),
S′(3, −3) **9.** X″(−2, −1), Y″(2, −1), Z″(1, −3) **10.** 2
11. 4 **12.** 2 **13.** 5

Using the Strategies p. 323

1. 7　**2.** 221, 442　**3.** 11, 12, 13　**4.** forty
5. 112 cm　**6.** 52 (53 in a leap year)　**7.** 7 others
8. 1, 3, 5, 7, 19, 39, 199, $2n - 1$　**9.** $0.95, $9.05;
$1.85, $8.15; $3.65, $6.35; $4.55, $5.45

Cumulative Review, Chapters 5–8
pp. 324–325

Chapter 5:　**1.** 7　**2.** $2t$　**3.** $7xy$　**4.** $3(x - 7)$
5. $5xy(x + y)$　**6.** $20xy$　**7.** $-6x + 2x^2$　**8.** $6x^2 - 9x$
9. $5x$　**10.** $-4x$　**11.** $1 - 2x + 3x^2$　**12.** $x^2 - 2x - 3$
13. $6x^2 - 7x + 2$　**14.** $(x - 8)(x + 1)$　**15.** $(a + 11)(a - 1)$
16. $(b - 1)(b - 1)$　**17.** $(y - 14)(y + 4)$
18. $2(x - 5)(x - 5)$　**19.** $3(x + 4)(x - 3)$
20. $4(a - 5)(a + 4)$　**21.** $5(a - 3)(a - 2)$　**22.** $x^2 - 49$
23. $9 - t^2$　**24.** $25p^2 - 1$　**25.** $36 - 81y^2$
26. $(x + 2)(x - 2)$　**27.** $(2p - 7)(2p + 7)$
28. $8(x + 3)(x - 3)$　**29.** x^3　**30.** $\frac{20 + 3x}{10}$
31. $4x^2 - 4x + 1$　**32.** $9 - 12y + 4y^2$
33. $p^2 - 6pq + 9q^2$　**34.** $(m + 5)(m + 5)$
35. $(2w - 3)(2w - 3)$　**36.** $2y^3 + 9y^2 + 9y$　**Chapter 6:**
1. SSS　**2.** SAS　**3.** SAS　**4.** ASA　**5.** $f = 10.5$ cm,
$d = 13.5$ cm　**6.** 8.2 m　**7.** 4.9 m　**8.** 6.5 cm
9. 52°, AC = 10.2 cm, AB = 16.6 cm　**10.** 65°,
XZ = 19.9 cm, YZ = 9.3 cm　**11.** 1885 m
Chapter 7:　**1–7.** Estimates may vary.
1. 169.75 cm²　**2.** 38.44 cm²　**3.** 962.11 cm²
4. 64.6 cm²　**5.** 97.83 cm²　**6.** 56.1 cm²
7. 72.96 cm²　**8.** 240 m³, 248 m²　**9.** 720 cm³,
332.8 cm²　**10.** 563 cm², 804 cm³　**11.** 1627 m²,
4617 m³　**12.** 13.5 m³　**13.** 240　**Chapter 8:**
2. K(5, –1), L(5, –5), M(10, –1)　**8. b)** 1　**9. b)** 6

Chapter 9

Getting Started pp. 328–329

Activity 1:　**1.** Vancouver, Halifax, and St. John's;
Toronto and Montreal　**2.** Regina　**3.** Edmonton
4. Toronto　**5.** Halifax and St. John's　**6. a)** 2
b) 46　**c)** 28　**Warm Up**　**3.** $\frac{3}{8}$　**4.** $\frac{1}{12}$　**5.** $\frac{1}{8}$　**6.** $\frac{5}{24}$
7. $\frac{1}{8}$　**8.** $\frac{9}{40}$　**9.** $\frac{27}{1000}$　**10.** $\frac{5}{18}$　**11.** 25%　**12.** 80%
13. 33.3%　**14.** 37.5%　**15.** 66.7%　**16.** 16.7%
Mental Math　**1.** 80　**2.** 700　**3.** 70　**4.** 1200
5. 600　**6.** 180　**7.** $21.00　**8.** $7.75　**9.** $7.25
10. $11.00　**11.** $14.50　**12.** $15.00　**13.** 90
14. 95　**15.** 98　**16.** $5.00　**17.** $7.00　**18.** $14.00
19. $10.00　**20.** 24　**21.** 39　**22.** 400　**23.** 1500
24. 7　**25.** 25　**26.** 8　**27.** 16

Section 9.1 pp. 330–331

Problems and Applications　**1–2.** Answers may
vary.　**1. a)** 43.5 s　**b)** 10 times　**c)** about 120 s
d) 1400 m　**2. a)** about 2.5 m　**b)** 0.9 m　**c)** about
2.5 m　**3. a)** Temperature decreases as latitude
increases.　**b)** about 12°C　**4. a)** No　**b)** not necessarily

Section 9.2 p. 333

Problems and Applications　**4. b)** The average age
of Canadians has been increasing.

Section 9.3 p. 335

Problems and Applications　**1. b)** 14.6 s　**d)** 12.6 s
2. c) 0　**3. c)** 20 cm, 37 cm　**d)** 3 m, less than 0

Learning Together pp. 340–341

Activity 1:　**1. a)** primary　**b)** primary　**c)** primary
d) secondary　**e)** secondary　**f)** primary　**Activity 2:**
1. representative　**Activity 3:**　**4. a)** stratified
b) random

Section 9.4 p. 349

Practice　**1. a)** $\frac{1}{5}$　**b)** $\frac{3}{5}$　**c)** $\frac{4}{5}$　**d)** 0　**2. a)** none　**b)** all
c) none　**3. a)** $16\frac{2}{3}$%　**b)** 50%　**c)** 50%　**d)** 100%
4. a) $\frac{1}{2}$　**b)** $\frac{1}{4}$　**c)** 2　**5. a)** $\frac{1}{2}$　**b)** $\frac{1}{6}$　**c)** 0　**d)** 1　**6. a)** 0.2
b) 0　**c)** 0.2　**d)** 0.1　**7. a)** $\frac{1}{52}$　**b)** $\frac{1}{2}$　**c)** $\frac{1}{4}$　**d)** $\frac{1}{26}$　**8.** 1;
one of the possible outcomes must occur　**9.** 0.8
10. a) 20　**b)** 0.80

Section 9.5 pp. 351–352

Problems and Applications　**1. a)** $\frac{1}{4}$　**b)** $\frac{1}{6}$　**c)** $\frac{1}{24}$
d) $\frac{1}{8}$　**2. a)** $\frac{1}{36}$　**b)** $\frac{1}{36}$　**c)** $\frac{1}{4}$　**3. a)** $\frac{6}{25}$　**b)** $\frac{9}{25}$　**4.** same
chance of winning either game　**6. a)** $\frac{1}{8}$　**b)** $\frac{1}{216}$
7. a) $\frac{1}{4}$　**b)** $\frac{1}{2}$　**c)** 0　**8. a)** $\frac{1}{2197}$　**b)** $\frac{1}{64}$　**c)** $\frac{1}{64}$　**d)** $\frac{1}{140\,608}$
e) $\frac{1}{140\,608}$　**9. a)** $\frac{1}{27}$　**b)** $\frac{1}{9}$　**c)** $\frac{1}{27}$　**d)** $\frac{1}{81}$　**10. a)** $\frac{1}{6}$　**b)** $\frac{1}{9}$
c) $\frac{1}{12}$　**d)** $\frac{1}{36}$　**e)** $\frac{1}{36}$　**f)** $\frac{1}{243}$　**g)** 0　**12. a)** $\frac{1}{2}$　**b)** $\frac{1}{4}$　**c)** $\frac{1}{8}$
13. a) $\frac{1}{10}$　**b)** $\frac{1}{20}$　**c)** $\frac{1}{40}$　**d)** $\frac{1}{15}$　**e)** $\frac{1}{60}$　**f)** $\frac{1}{120}$　**14.** $\frac{1}{2}$;
The events are independent.

Technology p. 353

Activity 1:　**1. a)** HHH, HHT, HTH, HTT, THH,
THT, TTH, TTT　**b)** $\frac{1}{8}$　**Activity 2:**　**1.** 1000
2. $\frac{1}{1000}$

Review pp. 356–357

1–3. Answers may vary. **1. b)** about 22 s **c)** 1968
d) about 2.5 s **2. c)** about 5 million, about 8.6
million **3. c)** 13 m **d)** 21 m **4. a)** $\frac{1}{6}$ **b)** $\frac{1}{3}$ **c)** $\frac{1}{3}$
d) 0 **e)** $\frac{1}{2}$ **f)** $\frac{1}{2}$ **g)** 1 **5. a)** $\frac{9}{100}$ **b)** 0 **c)** $\frac{3}{100}$ **6. a)** 60
b) $\frac{1}{60}$ **c)** $\frac{3}{20}$ **d)** $\frac{1}{10}$ **7. a)** $\frac{1}{2197}$ **b)** $\frac{1}{64}$ **c)** $\frac{1}{2197}$ **d)** $\frac{1}{64}$
e) $\frac{1}{5408}$ **f)** $\frac{1}{140\,608}$ **g)** $\frac{1}{140\,608}$

Chapter Check p. 358

1. Answers may vary. **a)** 1000 km³, 2000 km³,
3000 km³, 4500 km³ **b)** 1975 **c)** about 3 times
d) about 5500 km³ **2. c)** Asia and Europe
d) Antarctica and Australia **3.** 48 possible outcomes
4. a) $\frac{1}{6}$ **b)** $\frac{1}{2}$ **c)** $\frac{1}{3}$ **d)** 0 **e)** $\frac{1}{3}$ **f)** 1 **g)** 1 **h)** $\frac{1}{2}$ **5. a)** $\frac{1}{3}$
b) $\frac{5}{48}$ **c)** $\frac{1}{64}$ **d)** $\frac{5}{144}$

Using the Strategies p. 359

1. Beginning at the 5, place the numbers in
the following order: 5, 6, 3, 10, 1, 9, 4, 8, 2, 7
2. a) 180 **b)** 8 **c)** 44 **d)** 48 **3.** Move two sheep into
the top right pen, one from each of its neighbouring
pens; move two sheep into the bottom left pen, one
from each of its neighbouring pens. **4.** 14 **5.** 1,
4, 9, 16, 25, 36, 49 **6.** 6 **7. a)** remove any corner
square **b)** remove any two corner squares **c)** remove
any side square **d)** remove any corner square and
nonadjacent side square **e)** remove two side squares
9. February and March **Data Bank** **1.** 22:18
2. gain

Cumulative Review, Chapters 1–9
pp. 360–363

1. 7.1 **2.** 17.0 **3.** 8.6 **4.** 11 cm **5.** 7 **6.** 11
7. 73 **8.** 16 **9.** 400 **10.** b^9 **11.** 3^3 **12.** n^{10} **13.** 5
14. 3 **15.** 6 **16.** 2 **17.** 9.88×10^6 **18.** 1.9×10^{-2} **19.** 11.2×10^{-5} **20.** 2.0×10^{-2} **21.** 244.14
22. 36 **23.** 82 **24.** 0.5 **25.** $\frac{2}{9}$ **26.** $\frac{1}{16}$ **27.** 64
28. -1 **29.** m **30.** x **31.** $16m^8$ **32.** $\frac{-8x^3}{y^3}$ **33.** w^2
34. $-9x^5y^5$ **35.** 15 **36.** 10 **37.** m **38.** $-w + 6z$
39. a) 8.7 cm **b)** 17.3 m **c)** 5.4 cm **40.** $4x = 12$
41. $x + 2 = 8$ **42.** $4(x - 5) = 8$ **43.** 7 **44.** 7 **45.** 3
46. 4 **47.** 5 **48.** 2 **49.** 1.2 **50.** 12 **51.** 20
52. -33 **53.** 1 **54.** 0.5 **55.** 4 **56.** -3.2 **57.** -11
58. -3 **59.** 3.1 **60.** $12m + 15n - 21$ **61.** $2x + 21$
62. 5 **63.** 7.5 **64.** 3.7 **65.** 49 **66.** 25 **67.** 2
68. $21, $22, $23 **69. a)** 74, 92.5 **b)** $d = 18.5 \times t$

70. Vancouver: 27 mm, Edmonton: 80 mm
71. 1.2 h **72.** $x \geq 1$ **73.** $x < -3$ **74.** $x > 3$
75. $x \geq -2$ **76.** 2 **77.** 3 **78.** $7x^4 - 2x^3 + 3x + 5$
79. $-x^4y^5 + 2x^3 + 3xy + y^2$ **80.** $4x^2 + 4x - 2$
81. $2x^2 - x - 6$ **82.** $5x^2 + 2x - 1$ **83.** $6x^2 - 5x - 5$
84. $3x^2 - 11x + 3$ **85.** $9x^2 + 3x - 10$ **86.** $15xy$
87. $-12st$ **88.** $6m^3y^2$ **89.** $15y^7x^2$ **90.** $3.5x^2y^2$
91. $-2ab^3c^2$ **92.** 6 **93.** 5 **94.** $4y^2$ **95.** $6mn^3$
96. $7(y + 2)$ **97.** $3p^2q(1 - 4q)$ **98.** $5ab(2a + 7b)$
99. $7xy(2x - y + 4x^2y^2)$ **100.** $2y^2 - 6y$
101. $2m^2 + m + 6$ **102.** $-2x^3 - 4x^2 - 10x$
103. $-2q + 3p - p^2q^2$ **104.** $-y + 3y^3z^2 - \frac{1}{2}y^2$
105. $a^2 - 2a - 8$ **106.** $6m^2 + 19m + 10$
107. $y^2 - 0.5y - 1.5$ **108.** $1.5n^2 - 1.5n - 3$
109. $(x + 16)(x + 2)$ **110.** $(x - 7)(x + 5)$
111. $2(x^2 - 2x - 6)$ **112.** $4(x + 5)(x + 2)$ **113.** $m^2 - 25$
114. $9y^2 - 4$ **115.** $(y + 4)(y - 4)$
116. $(10w - 2z)(10 + 2z)$ **117.** $w^2 - 6w + 9$
118. $4x^2 + 20x + 25$ **119.** $3z^2 + 6za + a^2$
120. $4p^2 - 12pq + 9q^2$ **121.** $x^3 + x^2 - 5x - 2$
122. $6w^3 - 5w^2 + 2$ **123.** $6x^2 + x - 15$ **124.** x^2
125. $\frac{5}{3}w^3z$ **126.** $\frac{8 + x}{x}$ **127.** $\frac{5y + 19}{12}$ **128.** SSS
129. ASA **130.** ASA **131.** No **132.** 6 cm
133. 5.5 cm **134.** 7.5 m **135.** 64° **136.** 56°
137. $XY = 6.8$ cm, $\angle Z = 34°$, $\angle X = 56°$
138. $FD = 6.5$ m, $DE = 5.5$ m, $\angle E = 50°$
139. 63.7 m² **140.** 51.8 cm² **141.** 181.4 cm²
142. 429 mm² **143.** 869.8 cm² **144.** 115 m²
145. 141.4 cm² **146.** 379.7 cm² **147.** 245 m², 247 m³
148. 269 cm², 189 cm³ **149.** 384 cm², 384 cm³
150. 263 cm², 253 cm³ **151.** 2281 cm², 8209 cm³
152. 2 units to the left, 5 units up **153.** 4 units to
the left, 4 units down **154.** 7 units to the right,
3 units up **155.** 3 units to the right, 5 units down
156. $[4, -1]$ **163.** 7 **165.** 4 **167. a)** $\frac{1}{4}$ **b)** $\frac{1}{13}$ **c)** $\frac{1}{52}$
168. a) $\frac{1}{12}$ **b)** $\frac{1}{4}$ **169. a)** $\frac{1}{18}$ **b)** $\frac{1}{8}$ **c)** $\frac{1}{36}$

Glossary

A

Acute Angle An angle whose measure is less than 90°.

Algebraic Expression An expression which includes numbers and variables.

Angle The figure formed by 2 rays or 2 line segments with a common endpoint called the vertex.

Angle of Depression The line of sight made with the horizontal as you look down towards an object.

Angle of Elevation The line of sight made with the horizontal as you look up towards an object.

Area The number of square units required to cover a surface.

Average The mean of a set of numbers, found by dividing the sum of the numbers by the number of numbers.

Axes The intersecting number lines on a graph.

B

Base (of a power) The number used as a factor for repeated multiplication. In 6^3, the base is 6.

BEDMAS An acronym which stands for Brackets, Exponents, Division, Multiplication, Addition, Subtraction.

Binary System The number system that consists of the two digits 0 and 1.

Binomial A polynomial with 2 terms.

Bit A short form for binary digit.

Broken-line Graph A graph that represents data, using line segments joined end to end.

Byte A group of 8 bits.

C

Capacity The greatest volume that a container can hold, usually measured in litres or millilitres.

Centre of Rotation The point around which an object can be rotated.

Chord A line segment that joins 2 points on the circumference of a circle.

Circumference The perimeter of a circle: $C = 2 \times \pi \times r$ and $C = \pi \times d$.

Clockwise The same direction as the movement of a clock.

Coefficient A number that multiplies a variable.

Common Denominator A number that is a common multiple of the denominators of a set of fractions. The common denominator of $\frac{1}{2}$ and $\frac{1}{3}$ is 6.

Complementary Angles Two angles whose sum is 90°.

Composite Solid A solid made up of 2 or more prisms joined together.

Computer Spreadsheet A computer application that stores information in cells and allows a variety of computations to be performed using formulas.

Congruent Figures Figures with the same size and shape.

Coordinates An ordered pair, (x, y), that locates a point on a coordinate plane.

Corresponding Angles Angles that have the same relative positions in geometric figures.

Corresponding Sides Sides that have the same relative positions in geometric figures.

Cosine Ratio In a right triangle, the ratio of the length of the leg adjacent to the angle whose cosine is being calculated divided by the length of the hypotenuse: $\cos = \dfrac{\text{adjacent}}{\text{hypotenuse}}$.

Counterclockwise The opposite direction as the movement of a clock.

Cube A polyhedron with 6 congruent square faces.

D

Data Facts or information.

Database An organized and sorted list of information.

Degree (measure of an angle) The unit for measuring angles: $1° = \dfrac{1}{360}$ of a complete turn.

Degree of a Monomial The sum of the exponents of the variables.

Degree of a Polynomial The largest sum of the exponents of the variables in any one term of the polynomial.

Denominator The number of equal parts in the whole or the group: $\dfrac{3}{4}$ has denominator 4.

Diagonal A line segment joining 2 nonadjacent vertices in a polygon.

Diameter A chord that passes through the centre of a circle.

Dilatation A transformation that changes the size of an object.

Distortion A transformation in which a figure has been stretched, shrunk, or turned in many directions.

Distributive Property A rule for expanding an expression with brackets by multiplying each term inside brackets by the term outside the brackets.

E

Enlargement A dilatation for which the image is larger than the original figure.

Equation A number sentence that contains the symbol =.

Equilateral Triangle A triangle with all sides equal.

Equally Likely Outcomes Outcomes of an experiment that have an equal chance of occurring.

Equivalent Fractions Fractions such as $\dfrac{1}{3}$, $\dfrac{2}{6}$, and $\dfrac{3}{9}$ that represent the same part of a whole or group.

Estimate An approximate answer.

Experimental Probability The probability of an outcome occurring, determined by conducting an experiment.

Exponent The raised number used in a power to show the number of repeated multiplications of the base. In 4^2, the exponent is 2.

Exponential Form A shorthand method for writing numbers expressed as repeated multiplications. $81 = 3 \times 3 \times 3 \times 3 = 3^4$

Expression A mathematical phrase made up of numbers and variables, connected by operators.

Extrapolation The process of extending a line to estimate points that lie outside a given range of values.

(F)

Face A plane surface of a polyhedron.

Factors The numbers multiplied to give a specific product.

Flow Chart An organized diagram that displays the steps in a problem's solution.

FOIL A rule used for multiplying two binomials. The acronym stands for <u>F</u>irst terms, <u>O</u>utside terms, <u>I</u>nside terms, and <u>L</u>ast terms.

Fraction A number that describes part of a whole or part of a group.

Frequency The number of times an item or event occurs.

Frequency Table A table that uses tallies to count data.

(G)

Greatest Common Factor (GCF) The largest factor that two or more numbers have in common. The GCF of 8, 12, and 24 is 4.

(H)

Hexagon A polygon with 6 sides.

Hypotenuse The side opposite the right angle in a right triangle.

(I)

Image The figure produced by a transformation.

Independent Events Events whose outcomes do not influence each other.

Inequality The statement that one expression is greater than, less than, or not equal to another expression.

Integers Numbers in the sequence ... , -3, -2, -1, 0, 1, 2, 3, ...

Interpolation The process of estimating values that lie within a given range of values.

Irrational Number A real number that cannot be expressed in the form $\frac{a}{b}$ where a and b are integers and $b \neq 0$.

Isosceles Triangle A triangle with 2 equal sides.

(L)

Like Terms Terms, such as x and $4x$, with the same variable raised to the same exponent.

Line of Best Fit A line on a graph that lies as close as possible to all the points on the graph. There are about as many points above the line as there are below the line.

Locus The set of all points in a plane that satisfy a given condition.

Lowest Common Denominator (LCD) The lowest multiple shared by two or more denominators. The LCD of $\frac{1}{8}$ and $\frac{1}{6}$ is 24.

(M)

Mapping A correspondence of points between an object and its image.

Mass The amount of matter in an object, usually measured in grams or kilograms.

Midpoint The point that divides a line segment into 2 equal parts.

Monomial A number, a variable, or a product of numbers and variables.

(N)

Natural Numbers Numbers in the sequence 1, 2, 3, ...

Net A pattern used to construct a polyhedron.

Non-repeating Decimal A decimal that does not repeat, such as 0.123 223 333 444 234 … .

Non-terminating Decimal A decimal that continues without end, such as 0.333 333 333 … .

Numerator The number of equal parts being considered in a whole or group: $\frac{5}{7}$ has numerator 5.

O

Open Sentence A statement or equation for which it is not possible to say whether it is true or false.

Order of Magnitude The approximate size of a quantity expressed as a power of 10.

Order of Operations The rules to be followed when simplifying expressions: 1. brackets 2. exponents 3. division and multiplication 4. addition and subtraction.

Ordered Pair A pair of numbers, (x, y), indicating the x and y coordinates of a point on a graph.

Origin The intersection of the horizontal and vertical axes on a graph. The origin has the coordinates (0, 0).

Outcome The result of an experiment.

P

Palindrome A number which reads the same forward or backwards.

Parallel Lines Lines in the same plane that never meet.

Parallelogram A quadrilateral with opposite sides parallel and equal in length.

Percent A fraction or ratio in which the denominator is 100.

Perimeter The distance around a polygon.

Perpendicular Lines Two lines that intersect at a 90° angle.

Perspective The different views of an object—top, bottom, side, front.

Pi (π) The quotient that results when the circumference of a circle is divided by its diameter.

Point Symmetry Rotational symmetry of order 2.

Polygon A closed figure formed by 3 or more line segments.

Polynomial A monomial or the sum of monomials.

Population The entire set of items from which data can be taken.

Power A number, such as 3^4, written in exponential form.

Primary Data Data that you collect yourself.

Prime Triplet Three consecutive odd numbers that are also prime.

Prism A polyhedron with 2 parallel and congruent bases in the shape of polygons. The other faces are parallelograms.

Probability The ratio of the number of ways an outcome can occur to the total number of possible outcomes.

Program A set of instructions that a computer carries out in order.

Protractor An instrument used to measure angles.

Pyramid A polyhedron with 1 base and the same number of triangular faces as there are sides on the base.

Pythagorean Theorem The area of the square drawn on the hypotenuse of a right triangle is equal to the sum of the areas of the squares drawn on the other 2 sides.

Q

Quadrant One of the 4 regions formed in the coordinate plane by the intersection of the *x*-axis and the *y*-axis.

Quadrilateral A polygon with 4 sides.

Quotient The result of dividing one number by the another number.

R

Radius The length of the line segment that joins the centre of a circle and a point on the circumference.

Random Sample A sample in which each member of the population has an equal chance of being selected.

Range The difference between the highest and lowest numbers in a set.

Rate A comparison of two measurements with different units: $\frac{9 \text{ m}}{2 \text{ s}}$.

Ratio A comparison of two numbers: 4:5 or $\frac{4}{5}$.

Rational Expression An expression that can be written as the quotient of 2 polynomials.

Rational Number A number that can be expressed as the ratio of 2 integers.

Real Numbers All the rational and irrational numbers.

Rectangle A quadrilateral with opposite sides parallel and equal in length, and four 90° angles.

Rectangular Prism A prism whose bases are congruent rectangles.

Reduction A dilatation for which the image is smaller than the original figure.

Reflection A flip transformation of an object in a mirror line or reflection line.

Restriction A condition or set of conditions placed on variables.

Right Angle An angle whose measure is 90°.

Right Triangle A triangle with 1 right angle.

Rotation A turn transformation of an object about a fixed point or turn centre.

Rotational Symmetry A figure has rotational symmetry if it maps onto itself more than once in a complete turn.

S

Sample A selection from a population.

Sample Size The number of items selected from the total population.

Scale Drawing An accurate drawing that is either an enlargement or a reduction of an actual object.

Scalene Triangle A triangle with no sides equal.

Scatter Plot A graph used to show the relationship between two variables.

Secondary Data Data that is gathered from another source.

Similar Figures Figures that have the same shape but not always the same size.

Simplest Form The form of a fraction whose numerator and denominator have no common factors other than 1.

Sine Ratio In a right triangle, the ratio of the length of the leg opposite the angle whose sine is being calculated divided by the length of the hypotenuse: $\sin = \frac{\text{opposite}}{\text{hypotenuse}}$.

Square Root of a Number The number that when multiplied by itself gives the number.

Stratified Sample A population is subdivided into distinct groups.

Stylometry The science of measuring written words.

Substitution A specific value is assigned to a variable in an algebraic expression.

T

Tangent Ratio In a right triangle, the ratio of the length of the leg opposite to the angle whose tangent is being calculated divided by the length of the leg adjacent to the angle: $\tan = \dfrac{\text{opposite}}{\text{adjacent}}$

Terminating Decimal A decimal, such as 3.154, whose digits terminate.

Tessellation Another name for tiling pattern.

Theoretical Probability To determine the probability of an outcome mathematically without doing the experiment.

Tiling Pattern A repeated pattern of geometric figures that will completely cover a surface.

Translation A slide transformation of an object.

Trapezoid A quadrilateral with exactly 2 parallel sides.

Triangle A polygon with 3 sides.

Trigonometry The study of the relationships among the sides and angles of triangles.

Trinomial A polynomial with 3 terms.

Twin Primes Consecutive odd numbers that are also prime.

U

Unbiased Sample A sample in which all groups in a population are fairly represented.

Uniform Motion Movement at a constant speed.

Unlike Terms Terms, such as $2x$, $3y$, and $2z$, with different variables or with the same variable raised to different exponents.

V

Variable A letter or symbol used to represent a number.

Vertex The common endpoint of 2 rays or line segments.

Volume The number of cubic units contained in a space.

W

Whole Numbers Numbers in the sequence 0, 1, 2, 3, 4, 5, … .

X

x-axis The horizontal number line in the Cartesian coordinate plane.

Y

y-axis The vertical number line in the Cartesian coordinate plane.

Index